Prentice Hall Brief Review
for New Jersey

HSPA
Mathematics

A. Rose Primiani, Ed.D. / William Caroscio

Order Information

Send orders to:
PEARSON CUSTOMER SERVICE
P.O. BOX 2500
LEBANON, IN 46052-3009

or

CALL TOLL FREE 1-800-848-9500
(8:00 A.M.-6:00 P.M. EST)

• Orders can be placed via phone

Authors

A. Rose Primiani, Ed.D., is a former Director of Mathematics and Computer Education for District 10, Bronx, NYC and a Supervisor of Mathematics K–12 for the Yonkers Public Schools, NY. She has also been an adjunct professor at Manhattan College, Mercy College, CUNY, and Fordham University. Presently she is a Curriculum and Instructional Materials Consultant for Prentice Hall Publishers, School Division. She has consulted extensively on mathematics curriculum development and effective instructional practices and has been involved in correlating other states' curriculum to Prentice Hall middle school and high school mathematics texts; including New Jersey, Ohio, Maryland, and New York.

William Caroscio has over 35 years of experience in mathematics education. This experience includes middle school, high school, and college teaching experience. Bill is past president of the Association of Mathematics Teachers of New York State and the New York State Mathematics Supervisor Association. He is a member of AMTNYS, NYSAMS, NCTM, MAA, NCSM, NYSMATYC, and AMATYC. Bill is a National Instructor in the T3 (Teachers Teaching with Technology) program. He has conducted sessions and workshops at the local, state, and national levels. Bill has served as an item writer for the NYS Education Department assessment committees, as a member of the Commissioner's Committee on the New Mathematics Standards, and the Geometry Committee writing sample tasks for the new standards.

Reviewers

Carmen B. Archetto
Director of Mathematics K–12
Bergenfield School District
Bergenfield, NJ

Ron Mezzadri
Mathematics Supervisor K–12
Fair Lawn School District
Fair Lawn, NJ

Joan C. Lamborne
Supervisor of Mathematics
Egg Harbor Township Schools
Egg Harbor Township, NJ

Dr. Emine Kayaalp
Lecturer in Statistics
Lehman College,
City University of New York
Bronx, New York

Barbara VanDenBerg
Mathematics Training Workshop
Math Consultant
Hawthorne, NJ

Acknowledgements appear on p. 451, which constitutes an extension of this copyright page.

13-digit ISBN 978-0-13-363040-4
ISBN 0-13-363040-4
3 4 5 6 7 8 9 10   11 10 09 08

TABLE OF CONTENTS

Chapter 1   Real Numbers and Algebraic Expressions

New Jersey Performance Indicators

Chapter 2   Linear Equations and Inequalities in One Variable

New Jersey Performance Indicators

Chapter 3   Linear Equations and Inequalities in Two Variables

Chapter 4 More About Exponents and Exponential Functions

Chapter 5 Polynomials and Factoring

Chapter 6 Quadratic Equations and Functions

Chapter 7   Rational and Radical Expressions and Equations

New Jersey Performance Indicators

Chapter 8 Probability

Chapter 9 Data Analysis

Chapter 10   Basic Geometry in the Plane

New Jersey Performance Indicators

Chapter 11   Geometry and Measurement

New Jersey Performance Indicators

Chapter 12   Surface Area and Volume

New Jersey Performance Indicators

Chapter 13 Transformational Geometry

If you wish to receive a New Jersey State Endorsed High School Diploma when you graduate from high school you must pass the New Jersey High School Proficiency Assessment (HSPA). To help your teachers prepare you for this exam, the New Jersey State Education Department has outlined Core Curriculum Content Standards for Mathematics. This curriculum revolves around four Content Clusters: Number and Numerical Applications; Geometry and Measurement; Patterns and Algebra; and Data Analysis, Probability, and Discrete Mathematics. The intent of the Core Curriculum Content Standards is to ensure that your mathematics education provides you with the knowledge and skills you will need to be successful in your future endeavors.

This book has been written for you, a high school student in the State of New Jersey. You can use it as a tool for understanding and applying the Mathematics Core Curriculum.

Structure of the Comprehensive Review

Included in the front of the book are brief diagnostic tests for each chapter. These tests will allow you to measure your level of understanding of the content and concentrate on the specific concepts according to your needs.

Each lesson in this book
- addresses specific performance indicators of the Core Curriculum Content Standards.
- includes definitions, formulas, and model examples with complete explanations.
- provides practice exercises at the end of every lesson to check for understanding.

At the end of each chapter, review exercises entitled *Preparing for the HSPA,* address the entire content of the chapter and include both multiple choice and open-ended questions in the HSPA format.

Calculator Solutions

Both scientific and graphing calculator solutions are offered throughout the text as an alternative method in solving problems. Scientific calculators will be provided for the HSPA.

Glossary

A complete glossary of definitions used throughout the text with examples to illustrate the definitions is included.

HSPA Practice Test

A practice test based on previous HSPA tests and the material in this book is provided to further prepare you for the HSPA.

Reference Table

A reference table is provided for quick reference to standard mathematical formulas commonly used in problem-solving.

FACTS AND STRATEGIES

The High School Proficiency Assessment

The High School Proficiency Assessment (HSPA) is a graduation requirement for all students in the state of New Jersey. The test measures your level of mastery of the skills outlined in the New Jersey Core Curriculum Content Standards. The HSPA covers the four major content areas and addresses 16 subtopics.

New Jersey Core Curriculum Clusters	
Number and Numerical Operations	**Patterns and Algebra**
• Number Sense • Numerical Operations • Estimation	• Patterns and Relationships • Functions • Modeling • Procedures
Geometry and Measurement	**Data Analysis, Probability, and Discrete Mathematics**
• Geometric Properties • Transforming Shapes • Coordinate Geometry • Units of Measure • Measuring Geometric Objects	• Data Analysis (Statistics) • Probability • Discrete Mathematics—Systematic Listing and Counting • Discrete Mathematics—Vertex-Edge Graphs and Algorithms

Structure of the HSPA

Each of the four parts contains 10 multiple-choice questions and 2 open-ended questions for a total of 40 multiple-choice and 8 open-ended questions. You should anticipate spending an average of between one and two minutes to answer each multiple-choice question. The answers are computer scored and are worth one point each.

The open-ended questions require you to develop an independent response. It will take you approximately ten minutes to thoroughly answer each question. Each answer will be awarded between 0 to 3 points based on a question-specific scoring rubric that is based on the general scoring rubric.

General Scoring Rubric
3-Point Response
The answer demonstrates a thorough understanding of the essential mathematical concepts.
The procedures demonstrated are complete and relevant, addressing all components of the question.
The explanation is clear and details how the problem was solved.
2-Point Response
The answer demonstrates an almost complete understanding of the essential mathematical concepts.
The procedures demonstrated are generally complete and relevant, addressing most components of the question.
There are minor errors in computation and/or reasoning.
The explanation requires the reader to infer some reasoning.
1-Point Response
The answer demonstrates a limited understanding of the essential mathematical concepts.
The procedures demonstrated may be incomplete.
There may be major errors in computation and/or reasoning.
The explanation is incomplete and requires the reader to make inferences about some of the student's reasoning.
0-Point Response
The answer demonstrates insufficient understanding of the essential mathematical concepts.
The procedures contain major errors.
The explanation of the solution may be missing or unclear.
The reader must make inferences about the student's reasoning.

Test-Taking Facts and Tips

- You will have approximately two hours to complete the exam.

- You should answer all 48 exam questions. If you skip a question, you will receive zero credits for it.

- Bring several pencils and a good eraser to the exam room. All work must be done in pencil.

- You must record all your work in the answer booklet directly under the corresponding question. Your work should include tables, diagrams, and graphs where necessary. You can receive partial credit on these items.

- Scrap paper is not permitted. A sheet of graph paper will be provided for any exam questions for which graphing may be helpful but not required.

- You will be provided with a scientific calculator, a straightedge, and a compass.

FACTS AND STRATEGIES

Facts and Strategies for Multiple-Choice Questions

General Facts and Strategies

- Budget your time. Wear a watch, if possible, because a wall clock may not be in sight during the exam.

- Do *not* leave any blanks, because even by guessing, you have a 25% chance of getting an answer correct.

- Carefully read each question *twice* before answering to be sure you know what is being asked.

- If you are somewhat unsure of an answer, skip the question and move on to the next one. However, place a mark in your exam booklet next to the question you skipped as a reminder to return to it later. Remember to skip the corresponding location on your answer sheet.

- You can do all your computations right in the exam booklet, but be sure you write your answers in the correct space on the answer sheet provided.

- Before writing an answer, check to see if your answer is reasonable.

Strategies for Multiple-Choice Questions

- Immediately cross out choices that you know cannot be correct.

- Try to estimate the answer when appropriate. This may help you eliminate some choices.

- Use your calculator for square roots, decimals, percents, and so on.

- Check each choice against the wording of the question itself, just as you would check the solution to a problem.

- Use the problem solving strategies you have studied. These include the following:
  - drawing a diagram when the question describes a figure;
  - looking for a pattern when you suspect a relationship;
  - making a table when data is given;
  - working backward from the choices given;
  - using guess-and-test or trial-and-error; and
  - writing an equation.

On the following page, you will have an opportunity to examine four multiple-choice questions of the type that might appear on the HSPA. As you solve the questions, the directions will guide you through a few of the strategies listed above. These are only a few examples of the numerous multiple-choice questions you will find throughout this book. Additional multiple-choice practice test questions can be found in the Diagnostic Tests Section, the HSPA Test Preps at the end of each chapter, and the HSPA Practice Tests in the back of this book.

Multiple-Choice Items (1 point each)

 Given the table at the right, which equation describes the relationship between x and y?

x	0	1	2	3	4
y	-1	1	3	5	7

A. $y = 2x$ B. $y = x - 1$ C. $y = 2x - 1$ D. $y = 2x + 1$

Problem solving strategies: trial-and-error; elimination; looking for a pattern

Try choice A: $y = 2x$. When $x = 0$, it is clear that $y = 2x$ will not produce the given table.

x	0	1	2	3	4
y	$2(0) = 0$				

Try choice B: $y = x - 1$. When $x = 1$, it is clear that $y = x - 1$ will not produce the given table.

x	0	1	2	3	4
y	$0 - 1 = -1$	$1 - 1 = 0$			

Now you complete the work to determine the correct answer.

Try choice C: $y = 2x - 1$. Fill in the table at the right.

x	0	1	2	3	4
y					

Do you need to try choice D: $y = 2x + 1$? If so, fill in the table at the right.

x	0	1	2	3	4
y					

My answer is _____.   *[See page xxiii for the answer.]*

 The solution set for the equation $x^2 - 4x + 3 = 0$ is

A. $\{-1, -3\}$ B. $\{1, 3\}$ C. $\{-1, 3\}$ D. $\{1, -3\}$

Problem-solving strategies: Working Backwards; Elimination

Take each choice and substitute it in the equation $x^2 - 4x + 3 = 0$.

Choice A.
Does $(-1)^2 - 4(-1) + 3 = 0$?
$1 + 4 + 3 \neq 0$
Since $x = -1$ is not a solution should you continue with this choice?

Choice B.
Does $(1)^2 - 4(1) + 3 = 0$?
$1 - 4 + 3 = 0$
Yes, $x = 1$ is a solution.
Should you continue?
Does $(3)2 - 4(3) + 3 = 0$?
        $x^2 - 4x + 3 = 0$
Do you have to continue?

My answer is _____.   *[See page xxiii for the answer.]*

FACTS AND STRATEGIES

● Trey has 7 pairs of unmatched socks in his drawer. Each pair is a different color and today Trey wants to wear his blue socks. If he pulls one sock at a time out of the drawer without replacement, what is the probability that the first two socks he picks will be a matching pair?

A. $\frac{1}{7}$ B. $\frac{2}{7}$ C. $\frac{1}{91}$ D. $\frac{2}{91}$

Problem-solving strategy: Draw a picture

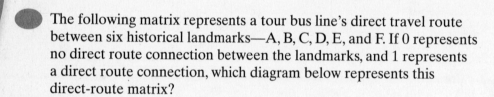 Let the circles represent the 14 socks in the drawer. Let the shaded circles represent the two blue socks Trey wants to wear. There is a $\frac{2}{14}$ or $\frac{1}{7}$ chance that the first sock will be blue.

Assuming Trey draws a blue sock the first time, what is the probability that the second sock will also be blue?

The probability of two events without replacement happening is the product of the individual probabilities.

My answer is _____.   *[See page xxiii for the answer.]*

● The following matrix represents a tour bus line's direct travel route between six historical landmarks—A, B, C, D, E, and F. If 0 represents no direct route connection between the landmarks, and 1 represents a direct route connection, which diagram below represents this direct-route matrix?

$$\begin{bmatrix} 0 & 1 & 1 & 1 & 0 & 1 \\ 1 & 0 & 1 & 0 & 0 & 0 \\ 1 & 1 & 0 & 1 & 0 & 0 \\ 1 & 0 & 1 & 0 & 1 & 1 \\ 0 & 0 & 0 & 1 & 0 & 1 \\ 1 & 0 & 0 & 1 & 1 & 0 \end{bmatrix}$$

A. 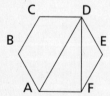   C.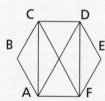

B. 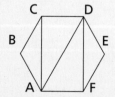   D.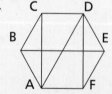

My answer is _____.   *[See page xxiii for the answer.]*

Facts and Strategies for Open-Ended Questions

General Facts and Strategies

- Budget your time on each selection. Try to spend as much as, but no more than, 10 minutes on each open-ended question.

- Be sure to write your answer(s) clearly. You must show all of your work in the exam booklet, directly under the question.

- Do all your computations in pencil.

- If you are using a calculator, estimate your answer to make sure your calculator answer is reasonable. Be sure to explain your work in detail, including those steps you performed on the calculator.

- The open-ended questions will be scored by trained readers using scoring rubrics. These rubrics explain the number of points that should be awarded for different types of answers.

- To receive full credit for these questions, you must answer each part completely. If you are unable to answer part of the question, you will still be able to receive some points for the parts you are able to answer.

- Label all answers that are measurements with the proper units of measure, such as inches, feet, square inches, and so on. Items involving measurements might not *require* you to name the unit of measure in the answer, but it is better to be cautious to be sure you receive the maximum number of points.

Strategies for Open-Ended Questions

- Use your calculator for square roots, decimals, percents, and so on.

- Use the problem-solving strategies you have studied. These include the following:
  - drawing a diagram when the question describes a figure;
  - looking for a pattern when you suspect a relationship;
  - making a table when data is given;
  - working backward;
  - using guess-and-test or trial-and-error; and
  - writing an equation.

On the following pages are examples of the types of questions that might appear in the open-ended section of the HSPA. The sample scoring keys provide some insight into how the readers score solutions to these questions.

FACTS AND STRATEGIES

Open-Ended Questions (3 points each)

Below is a sample question you might see on the exam.

Jane sees a $48 dress whose cost is to be reduced by 25%. The state sales tax is 8%.

- What is the sale price of the dress?
- How much sales tax will Jane pay?
- What will be the total cost of the dress?

Four sample solutions to this question and the points awarded are shown below.

0 points	1 point	2 points	3 points
No work shown *or* 48 − 25 = $23 (incorrect procedure)	25% × $48 = 0.25 × $48 = $12 (no other work shown)	$48 × 25% = $12 $36 × 8% = $2.88 $38.88	25% × $48 = 0.25 × $48 = $12 Then $48 − $12 = $36. Sales tax: $36 × 8% = $36 × 0.08 = $2.88 Total cost: $36 + $2.88 = $38.88

Here is another sample question you might see on the exam.

A circular garden has circumference 75 feet. A landscaper suggests enclosing it in a square fence.

- To the nearest foot, what is the length of the side of the smallest square that will enclose the garden?
- How much total fencing is needed to enclose the garden?

In the table below are four sample solutions written by four different students.

0 points	1 point	2 points	3 points
No work shown	$C = \pi d$ $d \approx \dfrac{75}{3.14} \approx 24$	$C = \pi d$ $d \approx \dfrac{75}{3.14} \approx 24$ length of one side of the fence = 24 perimeter: 2(24) = 48	fence / garden $C = \pi d$ $d \approx \dfrac{75}{3.14} \approx 24$ length of one side of the fence = 24 perimeter: 4(24) = 96

Now it is your turn to read three open-ended questions and the scoring keys for them. Then, you will be asked to analyze various student solutions. Think about the accuracy and completeness of the answers and score them yourself.

 Mary and Amy had 20 yards of material with which to make costumes. Mary used three times the amount of material that Amy used. Two yards of material were not used.

- How many yards of material did Amy use for her costume?
- How many yards of material did Mary use for her costume?

Student 1's solution

> Let x represent the amount Amy used.
> Then 3x represents the amount Mary used.
> $$3x + x + 2 = 20$$
> $$4x = 22$$
> $$x = 5.5$$

Student 2's solution

> Let x represent the amount Amy used.
> Then 3x represents the amount Mary used.
> $$3x + x + 2 = 20$$
> $$4x = 18$$
> $$x = 4.5$$

Imagine you are the scorer. Study the scoring key, award appropriate points to each student, and give reasons for the score you gave.

Scoring Key

3 points	correct answer is given, (4.5 and 13.5); appropriate method shown, such as solving $3x + x + 2 = 20$, using trial-and-error, or some arithmetic process
2 points	correct answer is given, (4.5 and 13.5); but some errors in mathematical process or reasoning
1 point	answer given is incorrect; but appropriate method shown *or* 4.5 and 13.5 with no work shown *or* solves $x + 3x - 2 = 20$ and reports 5.5 as the answer
0 points	completely incorrect, irrelevant, or incoherent *or* a correct response obtained by an obviously incorrect procedure

My score for student 1 _____

My reason(s) _____

_____

_____

My score for student 2 _____

My reason(s) _____

_____

_____

[See page xxiii for the answers.]

FACTS AND STRATEGIES

This Venn diagram shows the numbers of students who take various courses. Circle A represents all students studying math. Circle B represents all students studying science. Finally, Circle C represents all students studying technology.

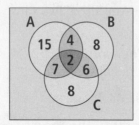

- How many students study math or technology?
- What percentage of the students study math or technology?

Scoring Key

3 points answer given is correct (42 and 84%); appropriate work shown; such as math or technology = 42, the total equal to 50, and the percentage equal to 84%

2 points correct numbers of students shown, but incorrect percentage *or* one error made in computing the numbers of students, but appropriate percentage found using those numbers

1 point only one correct number, such as 28 taking math *or* appropriate percentage shown for two incorrect values *or* correct percentage, 84%, but no work shown

0 points completely incorrect, irrelevant, or incoherent *or* correct response obtained by an obviously incorrect procedure

---

Shown below are four solutions to the Venn diagram problem on the preceding page. Imagine you are the scorer. Study the scoring key, award appropriate points to each student, and give reasons for the score you gave.

Student 1's solution

> 50 students in all
> math or technology: $15 + 4 + 2 + 7 + 8 + 6 = 42$
> $\frac{42}{50} = 84\%$

My score for student 1 _____

My reason(s) _____

_____

_____

Student 2's solution

> Total = 42
> math: 19 and tech: 14
> math or tech: 19 + 14 = 33
> $\frac{33}{42}$ = 79%

My score for student 2 _____

My reason(s) _____

_____

_____

Student 3's solution

> Total = 48
> math or tech: 15 + 4 + 2 + 7 + 8 + 6 = 42
> $\frac{42}{48}$ = 88%

My score for student 3 _____

My reason(s) _____

_____

_____

Student 4's solution

> The only overlaps are 7, 2, 4, and 6 for 19

My score for student 4 _____

My reason(s) _____

_____

_____

[See page xxiii for the answers.]

FACTS AND STRATEGIES

 The General Organization (G.O.) announces the Spring Dance. The price of a ticket for G.O. members is $8.00. The price of a ticket for nonmembers is $11.00. There are 50 more G.O. member tickets sold than nonmember tickets. The G.O. collected a total of $1,312.

- Write an equation or system of equations that describes the problem situation and define the variables.
- Find the number of each kind of ticket sold.

0 points	1 point	2 points	3 points
no work is shown or incorrect procedure	Partial correct answers are given but variables are not defined or an error is made in the set-up or calculations or no work is shown.	Correct answers are given with variables defined. Work is shown but slight errors in set-up or calculations	Complete solution with variables defined. Let x = non-Members then $y = x + 50$ Members $8(x + 50) + 11x = 1,312$ $8x + 400 + 11x = 1,312$ $19x = 912;$ $x = 48$ and $y = 98$ 48 non-G.O.; 98 G.O.

Imagine that you are the scorer. Study the scoring key, award appropriate points to each student, and give reasons for the score you gave. Shown below are two solutions to the Spring Dance problem.

Student 1's solution

- $x + y = 50$
  $8x + 11y = 1,312$

- $8x + 8y = 400$
  $8x + 11y = 1,312$
  $3y = 912$
  $y = 304$

My score for student 1 _____

My reason(s) _____

Student 2's solution

- Let x = nonmembers
  then $y = x + 50$ members
  $8(x + 50) + 11x = 1,312$

- $8(x + 50) + 11x = 1,312$
  $8x + 400 + 11x = 1,312$
  $19x = 912$
  $x = 48$ nonmembers
  and $y = 98$ members

My score for student 2 _____

My reason(s) _____

[See page xxiii for the answers.]

ANSWERS

Multiple-Choice Questions

Table Problem	C.
Loci Problem	B.
Sock Problem	C.
Matrix Problem	B.

Your scores for the open-ended questions should be the same as those shown below. However, the exact words that you used in writing the reasons for your scores might be a little different than the words used in the reasons below.

Open-Ended Questions

Costume Problem
Score for Student 1: 1 point
Reason(s) for Score: appropriate method shown but incorrect answer found

Score for Student 2: 3 points
Reason(s) for Score: correct answer and appropriate method shown

Venn Diagram Problem
Score for Student 1: 3 points
Reason(s) for Score: correct answer and appropriate work shown

Score for Student 2: 1 point
Reason(s) for Score: an appropriate percent shown for two incorrect values

Score for Student 3: 2 points
Reason(s) for Score: one error in computing total number of students, but percent is correct

Score for Student 4: 0 points
Reason(s) for Score: completely incorrect, irrelevant, or incoherent

Spring Dance Problem
Score for Student 1: 1 point
Reason(s) for Score: Error in the set up
No definition of variables
Partial correct answers

Score for Student 2: 3 points
Reason(s) for Score: Correct set up
Defined variables
Showed substitution and calculations are correct with answers defined.

Graphing Calculators and Their Potential

The graphing calculator is a great tool for solving problems and for learning mathematics. This section gives you a concise overview of some of the ways the graphing calculator can be used to solve problems. Use this section as a quick review of some of the calculator functions learned throughout the year. If you have not learned about some of the functions, you can read about them here.

Because calculators vary, these discussions do not show all of the calculator keystrokes. If you need help, consult your manual, in which the steps are shown in detail. What is important is that you get to know what your graphing calculator can do to help you explore mathematical concepts more easily.

The use of a graphing calculator in mathematics instruction provides you with a new set of algorithms and procedures for solving problems. It takes practice to learn a new set of procedures. Sometimes you may get a solution that seems odd or even incorrect. Be sure to follow the steps correctly and use sound reasoning skills in all of your work.

Note

Consider solution methods you can implement on a graphing calculator throughout the text. Often these solutions will lead to an insight that would otherwise be overlooked.

Numeration

The large screen on a graphing calculator is helpful. You can see both the expression and the answer displayed on the screen at the same time.

```
1+4*5
              21
2*3+6
              12
5-2*3
              -1
■
```

```
-2²+5
               1
(-2)²+5
               9
2³-2²
               4
■
```

```
12+4/2-3*5
              -1
5+3/4
            5.75
Ans►Frac
            23/4
■
```

Note

When you enter an operation without first entering a value, the calculator will perform the operation on the previous answer.

In the display at the right above, the result is shown as a fraction by using MATH 1: ▷ Frac. In this case, 5.75 is displayed as a fraction.

Your calculator can display results in scientific notation. The product of two large numbers is shown at the right. This result is the same as $6.050760407 \times 10^{12}$. The symbol **E** represents multiplying by 10 and the number following the symbol is the exponent. Numbers can also be entered into the calculator in scientific notation by typing 2nd ⟩ which is **EE**. If you want the result displayed in scientific notation, choose Sci in the MODE menu. From the display at the right below, you can read that $(2.5 \times 10^4)(3.7 \times 10^2) = 9.25 \times 10^6$.

```
1555999*3888666
    6.050760407E12
```

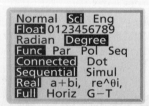

```
Normal Sci Eng
Float 0123456789
Radian Degree
Func Par Pol Seq
Connected Dot
Sequential Simul
Real a+bi, re^θi,
Full Horiz G-T
```

```
2.5E4*3.7E2
            9250000
2.5E4*3.7E2
            9.25E6
```

Evaluating algebraic expressions

Using $\boxed{\text{STO} \blacktriangleright}$, you can evaluate an expression like $a^2 - ab$, given $a = 2$ and $b = -3$. In the figure below, you can see how to combine these instructions onto one line by using a colon between the statements.

```
2→A
                    2
-3→B
                   -3
A²−AB
                   10
■
```

```
2→A:-3→B:A²−AB
                    10
■
```

Informal logic

Logical statements such as those below can be investigated by using the $\boxed{\text{2nd}}$ 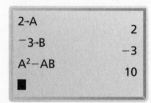 , or **TEST**, feature of the calculator. Consider these statements.

$$5 = 3 + 2 \text{ and } 5 = 10 \div 2 \quad 5 = 3 \times 2 \text{ and } 5 = 10 \div 2$$

```
5=3+2  and  5=10/2
                  1
5=3*2  and  5=10/2
                  0
```

The screen at the right shows the results of testing the truth of these statements. The display shows the following as truth values.

True: 1 *False*: 0

Testing equality of radical expressions

When simplifying a radical expression such as $\sqrt{24}$, you can check to see if $\sqrt{24} = 2\sqrt{6}$ by using **TEST**. You can also check the validity of an equation. The statement below is false.

```
√(24)=2√(6)
                  1
√(48)=4√(3)
                  1
√(18)=6√(3)
                  0
■
```

$$2\sqrt{5} + 3\sqrt{5} = 5\sqrt{10}$$

The calculator confirms this by displaying 0. However, the following statement is true.

$$2\sqrt{5} + 3\sqrt{5} = 5\sqrt{5}$$

```
2√(5)+3√(5)=5√(1
0)
                  0
2√(5)+3√(5)=5√(5
)
                  1
■
```

The calculator confirms this by displaying 1.

Used in this way, the calculator enables you to verify answers worked out with paper and pencil.

Logical tests can also be performed to check for the correct factorization of algebraic expressions. This checking procedure can often help you identify errors before you proceed with the remainder of a problem. Notice that in the second example below, a result of zero would indicate that the result is incorrect, allowing the opportunity to correct the answer.

```
X²+5X+6=(X+2)(X+
3)
                  1
```

```
X²−9=(x−3)(X−3)
                  0
■
```

USING A CALCULATOR

Linear functions and equations

Suppose that you want to graph $4x + 2y = 12$. First solve for y.

$$y = -2x + 6$$

Enter $-2x + 6$ into the function list $\boxed{Y=}$. Press the $\boxed{\text{GRAPH}}$ button, and you will see a display like the one at the right.

If you want to solve $-2x + 6 = 0$, you can use the graph of $y = -2x + 6$ and a solving routine to find where the graph intersects the x-axis. Press $\boxed{\text{2nd}}$ $\boxed{\text{TRACE}}$ **CALC.** You will see the menu below. From it, select **2: zero.** Enter a *left bound*, *right bound*, and *guess*. The exact solution will be displayed.

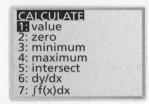
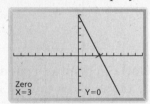

This equation could also be solved by using the Solver feature of the calculator. In the $\boxed{\text{MATH}}$ menu, choose item **0: Solver.** Notice that the equation you wish to solve must be set equal to zero. Enter the equation as shown in the figure below. Press $\boxed{\text{ENTER}}$ to see the Solver screen. To solve for the variable, press $\boxed{\text{ALPHA}}$ $\boxed{\text{ENTER}}$, which is the SOLVE command. It is important to note that the Solver has not determined the solution until the black square (■) appears in front of the variable you are solving for and the check sum **left − rt = 0** appears.

```
EQUATION SOLVER
eqn:0=-2X+6■
```

```
-2X+6=0
X=10
   bound=(-1E99, 1...
```

```
-2X+6=0
■X=3
   bound=(-1E99, 1...
■left-rt=0
```

Friendly window

When using a graphing calculator, it is important to have graphical representations displayed accurately. Perpendicular lines should look perpendicular, circles should look like circles, and so on. With most graphing calculators, graphic accuracy can be accomplished by setting a "friendly window." One such window is shown at the right. This window establishes a "nice" value for Δx and also takes the screen aspect ratio into account. When the calculator graphs a function, it creates a table of values beginning with x-min and ending with x-max. These values are incremented by $\Delta x = \frac{x_{\max} - x_{\min}}{94}$. Therefore, when the numerator is a multiple of 94, the increment in x will be "nice." In the case shown, $\Delta x = 0.2$. By maintaining a ratio of approximately $\frac{3}{2}$ for x to y, the screen is "squared," meaning that perpendicular lines will look perpendicular, and so on.

```
WINDOW
  Xmin=-9.4
  Xmax=9.4
  Xscl=1
  Ymin=-6.2
  Ymax=6.2
  Yscl=1
  Xres=■
```

Note

The display may be 188 units across and 124 units down.

$$\frac{-94}{10} \leq x \leq \frac{-94}{10}$$

$$-9.4 \leq x \leq 9.4$$

$$\frac{-62}{10} \leq y \leq \frac{-62}{10}$$

$$-6.2 \leq y \leq 6.2$$

If you are to interpret graphical information visually, it is important that you can set windows that take into account these two important ideas, "nice" Δx and square window. These two features are shown in the following graphs. Notice that the two lines look perpendicular. You can also trace the graph of one of these lines by hitting the TRACE key. Notice that the points reflect the "nice" increment of $\Delta x = 0.2$.

Enter the expressions.	Draw the graphs.	Use tracing.
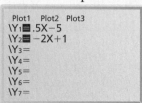	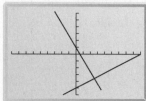	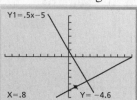

The calculator features under the ZOOM menu, namely **4: ZDecimal** and **5: ZSquare,** can accomplish the same results. However, by setting the window manually, you will better understand the numerical features of the calculator you are using. Whichever graphing calculator you choose to use, you will find it helpful to determine the appropriate settings for establishing a "friendly window."

Solving systems of equations and inequalities

Suppose that you are given the system of equations at the right. You can find a solution to such a system in a variety of ways. You can use a graphing approach, or you can use a matrix approach.

$$\begin{cases} x - y = -1 \\ x + 2y = 6 \end{cases}$$

Use the **CALC** feature by pressing 2nd TRACE. Selecting menu option **5: intersect** requires three inputs; *first curve, second curve,* and *guess.* After you enter a guess, the solution is displayed. In the **HOME** screen at the right below, the results can be displayed as fractions.

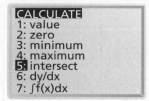	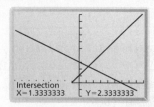	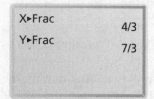

The solution to the system is $x = \frac{4}{3}$ and $y = \frac{7}{3}$, or $\left(\frac{4}{3}, \frac{7}{3}\right)$.

The system $\begin{cases} x - y = -1 \\ x + 2y = 6 \end{cases}$, or $\begin{cases} y = x + 1 \\ y = -\frac{1}{2}x + 3 \end{cases}$, is related to $x + 1 = -\frac{1}{2}x + 3$.

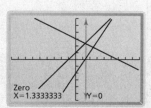

With technology, the solution $\left(\frac{4}{3}, \frac{7}{3}\right)$ can be compared to the result of solving the equation $x + 1 = -\frac{1}{2}x + 3$, which you can write as $\frac{3}{2}x - 2 = 0$. Graphing this line with the system provides a visualization that allows for the comparison of these graphs. The point of intersection for the system occurs at the same x-value at which the single equation has a solution.

USING A CALCULATOR

You can also use the matrix capabilities of the calculator to solve
$\begin{cases} x - y = -1 \\ x + 2y = 6 \end{cases}$. These are the matrices you need.

$$\text{coefficient matrix } A: \begin{bmatrix} 1 & -1 \\ 1 & 2 \end{bmatrix} \qquad \text{constant matrix } B: \begin{bmatrix} -1 \\ 6 \end{bmatrix}$$

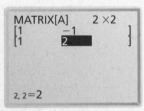 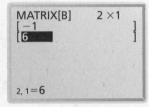 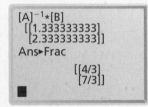

Solving a system of inequalities using the calculator is similar to solving the system of equations graphically. The system $y < -\frac{1}{2}x + 3$ and $y \geq x + 1$ is entered in the $\boxed{Y=}$ menu as shown below, and then the style icon in front of **Y1** and **Y2** is changed to the appropriate *shade above* or *shade below* icon. As seen in the second figure below, the region in which the shaded areas intersect is the solution set.

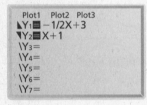 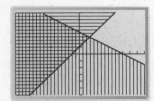

It is important to state whether or not the line is part of the solution. As shown here, some calculators do not allow the line **Y1** to be drawn as a "dashed" line.

Quadratic functions and equations

When you are solving a quadratic equation such as $2x^2 - 7x - 15 = 0$, a graphical solution is easily implemented by using the calculator. Use the graphing calculator to display the graph of $y = 2x^2 - 7x - 15$. The equation is entered in $\boxed{Y=}$ and the **CALC** menu is accessed by pressing $\boxed{\text{2nd}}$ $\boxed{\text{TRACE}}$. Each root is found separately by entering a *left bound*, *right bound*, and *guess*. Shown below are the window settings, the graph, and the solutions for this quadratic equation.

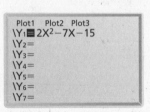

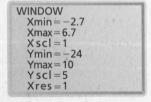 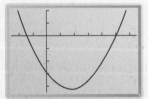 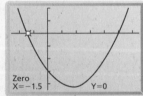 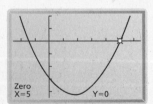

The graph of a quadratic function can also be helpful when trying to factor a quadratic expression. For example, when factoring $3x^2 + x - 24$, it is helpful to know the roots. The roots can be found from the graph. Now, knowing the roots, the factors can be determined as shown below.

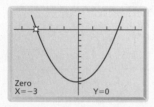 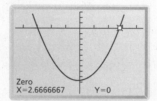

$$x = -3 \quad \text{or} \quad x = 2\tfrac{2}{3} \quad \leftarrow \textbf{Identify the } x\textbf{-intercepts.}$$
$$x + 3 = 0 \quad \text{or} \quad 3x - 8 = 0 \quad \leftarrow \begin{array}{l}\textbf{Write linear equations with integer} \\ \textbf{coefficients and with 0 on one side.}\end{array}$$

Write the product of the linear expressions, $(x + 3)(3x - 8)$. Therefore, $3x^2 + x - 24 = (x + 3)(3x - 8)$.

The calculator can help create a table of values for an expression like $x^2 - x - 6$. This is helpful when you are graphing by traditional methods using paper and pencil. Enter the equation in the **Y=** menu. Then the values are entered into **2nd** **WINDOW**, **TBLSET**. Finally, press **2nd** **GRAPH**, **TABLE**, to display the table of values. By using the calculator in this way, you can often eliminate careless mistakes in creating a table of values.

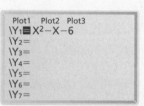

Enter $x^2 - x - 6$.   Set the lowest value for x.   Display the table.

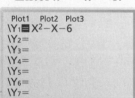 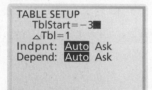

You can also determine the nature of the roots of a quadratic equation by looking at its graph.

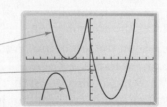

The graph touches the x-axis once: double root.
The graph crosses the x-axis twice: two real roots.
The graph never touches the x-axis: no real roots.

Permutations and Combinations

Like a scientific calculator, the graphing calculator can evaluate an expression involving permutations and combinations.

permutations: $_nP_r$ combinations: $_nC_r$

These features are located in the **MATH** menu under **PRB**. When evaluating an expression like $_{10}P_6$, enter 10 on the home screen first, and then press and select MATH **PRB 2: nPr**, enter 6, and finally press ENTER. The result can be verified by entering the factorial form of the expression, $\frac{10!}{(10-6)!}$, or $\frac{10!}{4!}$.

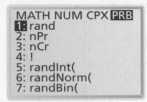

Statistics

Statistical data can be entered from the home screen by using the STO▶ key and listing the data as a set. The screen at the left below shows a set of test scores entered into list one, **L1**. Enter **{** and **}** by typing 2nd (and 2nd). Press the ENTER key to store this list. When this is done, the set of scores is echoed back as shown in the display at the right below.

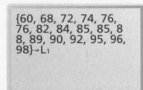 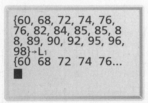

Now these data can be examined by performing one-variable statistical analysis. Pressing STAT will access the statistics menu shown below. Selecting **1: Edit** ... displays the data as a list **L1**. Pressing STAT again and ▶ shows the **CALC** menu for statistics.

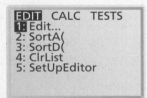 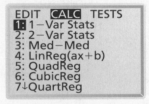

Selecting **1** now places the command on the home screen. Press 2nd **1**. You will see the screen at the left below. Press ENTER to view the middle display below. The arrow to the left of $n = 17$ tells you that there is more information to be shown. Holding down the ▼ key, you can scroll through the other items resulting in the screen at the right below. The mean, $\bar{x}$; median, Med; the first quartile, Q_1; and third quartile, Q_3, are easily identified. (Some information shown here is beyond the scope of this book.)

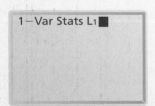

A graphical representation of a data set that includes the Min, Q_1, Med, Q_3, and Max is called a box plot. The box plot for the set of test scores is shown at the right below, and the window settings are also shown. You graph the box plot by typing **2nd** **Y=** to display the **STAT PLOTS** screen. Select plot **1**, turn on box plot ⊞ , use **L1** as the **Xlist**, and **Freq = 1**.

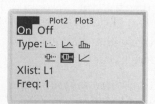
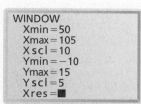
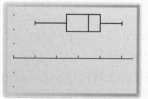

These data can also be graphed in a histogram in a similar fashion. From the **STAT PLOTS** screen, select plot **2**, select ⟂⟂⟂ , use **L1** as the **Xlist**, and **Freq = 1**. Using the same window settings as shown above, you can make the histogram. If the two plots are left on together, both will be displayed at the same time. This is shown in the screen at the far right.

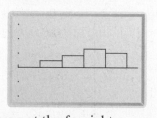
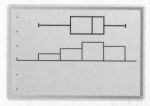

If you want to compare scores already analyzed to a second set of scores, perhaps in science, a scatter plot can be used to visualize these two sets of data. The second set of data, 58, 70, 75, 68, 75, 72, 80, 88, 85, 89, 84, 90, 85, 96, 96, 92, 95, is entered in **L2**. In the **STAT PLOTS** screen, select plot **1** and scatter plot ⟋ .

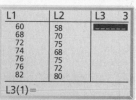

The **Xlist** is **L1** and the **Ylist** is **L2**. The displays are shown below.

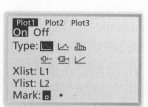
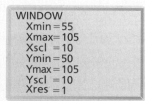
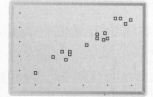

To get an estimate for trend line, press **STAT** ▶ **CALC** and arrow down to item **D: Manual-Fit**. The cursor appears on the graph with the coordinates showing. Move the cursor to the first point on your estimated line and press **ENTER** . Then move to a second point and press **ENTER** again. Now you can change the values of the slope and y-intercept until you have the best estimate for the trend line.

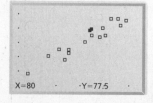
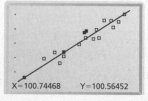
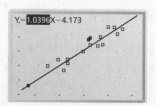
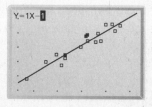

USING A CALCULATOR

To determine the Least Squares Line of Best Fit, press and select STAT ▶ **CALC** and arrow down to item **4: LinReg(ax + b)**. These choices result in the screen display shown at the right.

In order to see the screen including the values of r^2 and r, the correlation coefficient, you must press 2nd 0, which displays the **CATALOG**, and toggle down ▼ until you come to **DiagnosticOn**. From the display, you can read the slope of the line of best fit as approximately 0.99 and the y-intercept of the line as approximately -0.12. The correlation coefficient is approximately 0.95, indicating a very high positive correlation.

The equation of the line can be placed in a Y= location when making the selection from the home screen by indicating the desired location after the **4: LinReg(ax+b)** menu choice. This is shown at the right. Now when the graph is displayed by pressing GRAPH, both the scatter plot and the least-square regression (line of best fit) line are displayed.

```
EDIT  CALC  TESTS
1: 1–Var Stats
2: 2–Var Stats
3: Med–Med
4: LinReg(ax+b)
5: QuadReg
6: CubicReg
7↓QuartReg
```

```
LinReg
  y=ax+b
  a=.9929133858
  b=−.1181102362
  r²=.9069092385
  r=.9523178243
```

```
LinReg(ax+b)    Y₁■
```

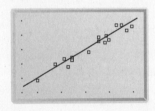

This line is referred to as the line of best fit and can be used to extrapolate and interpolate the data.

Solver and formula evaluation

In the MATH menu, **0: Solver** is the Solver. This feature can be used to solve an equation that has 0 on one side for any one of the variables in the equation if the values of the other variables are known.

For example, the volume of a right circular cylinder is given by $V = \pi r^2 h$. This formula can be set equal to zero by subtracting V from each side, resulting in $0 = \pi r^2 h - V$. You can see this below.

$$V = \pi r^2 h$$
$$V - V = \pi r^2 h - V$$
$$0 = \pi r^2 h - V$$

```
MATH  NUM CPX PRB
4↑³√(
5: ×√
6: fMin
7: fMax(
8: nDeriv(
9: fnInt(
0: Solver...
```

```
EQUATION SOLVER
eqn:0=πR²H−V
```

This is the format for entering the formula into the solver after selecting **0: Solver** from the **MATH** menu.

Given a value for the volume and the radius, you can use the solver to determine the height of the cylinder. Suppose that the volume of a certain cylinder is 100 cm³ and that the radius of the base is 5 cm. What would the height of the cylinder be? Enter V and R. Move the cursor to H as shown. Press ALPHA ENTER for **SOLVE**. The ■ to the left of H indicates that H has been found.

```
πR²H−V=0
  R=5
  H=0
  V=100
  bound={−1ᴇ99, 1...
```

```
πR²H−V=0
  R=5
 ■H=1.2732395447...
  V=100
  bound={−1ᴇ99, 1...
 ■left−rt=0
```

The solver can be used to find V, given R and H. Enter R and H as shown. Press and select ALPHA ENTER for **SOLVE** when the cursor is at the desired variable. One display shows the volume of a cylinder with radius 5 and height 5. The other display shows the volume of a cylinder with radius 2 and height 4.

```
πR²H−V=θ
  R=5
  H=5
■V=392.69908169...
  bound={−1E99, 1...
■left−rt=0
```

```
πR²H−V=θ
  R=2
  H=4
■V=50.265482457...
  bound={−1E99, 1...
■left−rt=0
```

Trigonometry

To evaluate trigonometric functions, use SIN , COS , and TAN . Press 2nd APPS . The **ANGLE** menu is displayed and the degree symbol can be found as the first menu item. To evaluate sin 30°, press and select SIN **30** 2nd APPS **1** :° **)** ENTER .

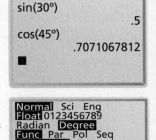

Using the degree symbol calculates the correct trigonometric function value, regardless of the MODE setting of the calculator.

The degree measure of an angle for a given trigonometric function value can be found by using the inverse trigonometric function keys. **In this case, the MODE of the calculator must be changed to degree mode.**

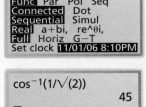

These keys are 2nd SIN for $\sin^{-1}$, 2nd COS for $\cos^{-1}$, and 2nd TAN for $\tan^{-1}$. Now, to determine the angle whose cosine is $\frac{1}{\sqrt{2}}$, press 2nd COS **(1** ÷ 2nd x^2 **2))** ENTER . This procedure shows that 45° is the measure of an angle whose cosine is $\frac{1}{\sqrt{2}}$. Using the trigonometric features of the calculator, you can solve a right triangle for unknown lengths and angle measures.

$$\cos 75° = \frac{15}{AB}$$

$$AB = \frac{15}{\cos 75°}$$

$$AB \approx 57.96 \approx 58$$

$$\sin B = \frac{15}{58}$$

$$m\angle B = \sin^{-1}\left(\frac{15}{58}\right) \approx 14.988° \approx 15°$$

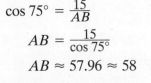

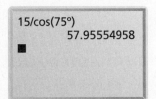

Transformations

Many transformations can be visualized on the graphing calculator. A reflection in the x-axis maps the point (x, y) to the point $(x, -y)$. Therefore, if the triangle whose vertices are $A(1, 2)$, $B(3, 4)$, and $C(6, 1)$ is to be reflected in the x-axis, the result could be displayed by using a graphing calculator. The x-coordinates of the vertices are entered into **L1**, and the y-coordinates are entered into **L2**.

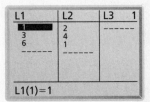

By drawing a scatter plot of these points, the vertices of the triangle can be displayed. Using **DRAW 2: Line(**, the vertices can be connected to make $\triangle ABC$.

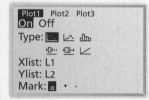 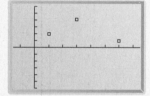  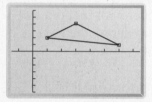

In **L3** enter the opposites of the y-coordinates by moving the cursor over **L3** and pressing [(-)] **L2**. A second scatter plot is drawn, this time using **L1** and **L3**.

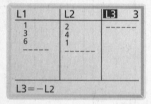 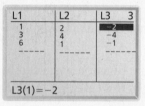 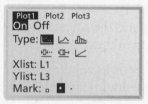 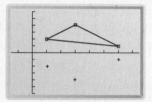

When the cursor is over **L3** and you press [(-)] **L2**, it appears in the prompt line at the bottom of the screen. Press [ENTER] to see the values appear in the list as shown in the second screen above. The scatter plot is the reflection of the vertices over the x-axis. Complete the image by using **DRAW 2: Line(** as before. You can see the triangle and its image on the display.

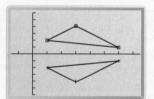

Another way of determining the vertices of the reflection of a figure in the x-axis is by using matrix multiplication.

matrix for $\triangle ABC$: $A = \begin{bmatrix} 1 & 3 & 6 \\ 2 & 4 & 1 \end{bmatrix}$ reflection matrix $B = \begin{bmatrix} 1 & 0 \\ 0 & -1 \end{bmatrix}$

The coordinates of the vertices are entered into a matrix A by typing [2nd] [x^{-1}] **MATRX** and selecting **EDIT**. Enter a 2×3 matrix in **[A]** with the x-coordinates of the vertices in the top row and the y-coordinates of the vertices in the second row. Now a second matrix B, the reflection matrix, is entered into **[B]**. On the home screen, the multiplication of matrix B by matrix A is performed. The resulting matrix contains the vertices of the image of the original triangle.

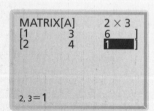 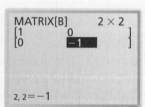 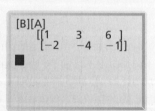

Name _____ Date _____

Diagnostic Test 1: Chapter 1

Real Numbers and Algebraic Expressions

Choose the letter preceding the word or expression that best completes the statement or answers the question.

1 Given $X = \{2, 4, 6, 8, 10\}$ and set $Y = \{4, 6\}$, find the complement of Y in X.

A. $\{2, 8, 10\}$ C. $\{2, 4, 6, 8, 10\}$

B. $\{6\}$ D. $\{4, 6\}$

2 Let $P = \{x \mid x \text{ is a multiple of 2}\}$ and $Q = \{x \mid x \text{ is a multiple of 3}\}$. What is $P \cap Q$?

A. $\{x \mid x \text{ is a multiple of 2}\}$

B. $\{x \mid x \text{ is an integer}\}$

C. $\{x \mid x \text{ is a multiple of 6}\}$

D. $\{x \mid x \text{ is a multiple of 3}\}$

3 If n is a number, translate the phrase "6 less than n."

A. $6 < n$ C. $n - 6$

B. $n < 6$ D. $6 - n$

4 Which expression names an integer?

A. $\frac{2}{6}$ C. $0.\overline{3}$

B. $\frac{-6}{2}$ D. 0.333

5 Which point on the number line has the greatest absolute value?

```
      A      B    C      D
  ←─┼─┼─┼─┼─┼─┼─┼─┼─┼─┼─┼─┼─→
   -7-6-5-4-3-2-1 0 1 2 3 4 5
```

A. A   C. C

B. B   D. D

6 Change 0.00125 to a percent.

A. 12.5%   C. 125%

B. $\frac{1}{8}$%   D. 1.25%

7 The number $\sqrt{107}$ is between

A. 26 and 28.   C. 100 and 110.

B. 53 and 54.   D. 10 and 11.

8 Which of the following is an example of the Associative Property of Multiplication?

A. $a(bc) = (ab)c$

B. $a(bc) = (bc)a$

C. $a(bc) = (ab) + (ac)$

D. $a(bc) = (ab)(ac)$

9 If $a = -2$, then $2a^2 - 5a + 6$ equals

A. 4.   C. -12.

B. 8.   D. 24.

10 Rewrite 4.5×10^6 in standard form.

A. 45,000,000   C. 0.0000045

B. 4,500,000   D. 0.00000045

11 How many significant digits are in 10,590?

A. 2   C. 4

B. 3   D. 5

Name _____ Date _____

Go Online
PHSchool.com

Visit: PHSchool.com
Web Code: bhk-0802

Diagnostic Test 2: Chapter 2

Linear Equations and Inequalities in One Variable

Choose the letter preceding the word or expression that best completes the statement or answers the question.

1 If $a = b$, then $b = a$ illustrates which property?

   A. the reflexive property

   B. the symmetric property

   C. the transitive property

   D. the addition property

2 Find a if $8a - 23 = 4a + 45$.

   A. 68   C. 22

   B. 17   D. 6.75

3 Which number is not a solution of $2(k - 6) \leq -2$?

   A. -1 C. 5

   B. 0   D. 6

4 Solve $|2p + 4| = 10$.

   A. $p = 3$ C. $p = -7$

   B. $p = 3$ and -7 D. $p = -3$ and 7

5 Find the solution set of the following inequality: $42 > -3x$

   A. $x < -14$ C. $x > 14$

   B. $x > -14$ D. $x < 14$

6 $C = \frac{5}{9}(F - 32)$, where C is the temperature in degrees Celsius and F is the temperature in degrees Fahrenheit. Solve the formula for F.

   A. $F = \frac{9}{5}C + 32$ C. $F - 32 = \frac{5}{9}C$

   B. $F = \frac{9}{5}(C + 32)$ D. $F + 32 = \frac{5}{9}C$

7 Solve for c.

$$\frac{c + 4}{12} = \frac{c + 2}{10}$$

   A. $c = 1$ C. $c = 8$

   B. $c = -1$ D. $c = -8$

8 Jim and Susan mow lawns. The ratio that compares the amount of time each works is 8:5. They were paid $65 for their work. How much did Susan earn if she worked more than Jim?

   A. $25   C. $30

   B. $45   D. $40

In Exercises 9–10, use the following problem situation.

Students raised $800 for a ski trip. The cost of the bus for the trip will be $350. The bus holds 40 students. The cost for each student's lift ticket is $25.

9 If 40 students wish to attend, how much more money must be collected to pay for the entire trip?

   A. $550   C. $1,000

   B. $800   D. $1,350

10 If no additional money is collected, what is the maximum number of students who can go on the trip?

   A. 23 students   C. 18 students

   B. 20 students   D. 15 students

Name _____ Date _____

Diagnostic Test 3: Chapter 3

Linear Equations and Inequalities in Two Variables

Choose the letter preceding the word or expression that best completes the statement or answers the question.

1 The slope of the line passing through the points $(3, -2)$ and $(7, 2)$ is

A. 0.　　　　　　　C. undefined.

B. 1.　　　　　　　D. -1.

2 If the slope of a line is *zero*, then the line is

A. rising left to right.

B. falling left to right.

C. horizontal.

D. vertical.

3 Which of the following is not the graph of a function?

A. 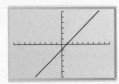　　C.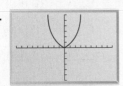

B. 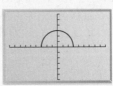　　D.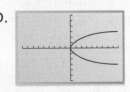

4 Determine the range value of the function $f(x) = \frac{3}{4}x - 11$ when $x = 8$.

A. $\frac{9}{4}$　　B. -5　　C. $-\frac{9}{4}$　　D. $\frac{3}{4}$

5 Which equation does not represent a function?

A. $x = 4$　　　　　C. $y = 4$

B. $y = x$　　　　　D. $-4 = y$

6 What is the slope of a line perpendicular to $y = 4x + 3$?

A. 4　　B. -4　　C. $\frac{1}{4}$　　D. $-\frac{1}{4}$

7 The equation of a line with a slope of 3 and a y-intercept of -8 is which of the following?

A. $y = -8x + 3$　　C. $y = 3x + 8$

B. $y = 3x - 8$　　D. $y = 3x - (-8)$

8 The equation $y = |x - 2| + 5$ is which translation of the absolute value function?

A. left two up five

B. right two down five

C. left two down five

D. right two up five

9 The solution to the system of equations $3x + 2y = 12$ and $x - 2y = 12$ is

A. $(6, -3)$.　　　C. $(3, 6)$.

B. $(-3, 6)$.　　　D. $(6, 3)$.

10 Which function does not demonstrate inverse variation?

A. $xy = 240$

B. $y = x^2$

C. $y = \frac{4}{x}$

D. $x = \frac{10}{y}$

11 Given the matrices $A = \begin{bmatrix} 3 & -7 \\ x & 4.5 \end{bmatrix}$ and $B = \begin{bmatrix} 11 & -3 \\ 0.13 & 2 \end{bmatrix}$ what is $B - A$?

A. $\begin{bmatrix} -33 & 21 \\ -0.13x & -9 \end{bmatrix}$　　C. $\begin{bmatrix} 8 & 4 \\ -x + 0.13 & -2.5 \end{bmatrix}$

B. $\begin{bmatrix} 8 & 4 \\ -x + 0.13 & 9 \end{bmatrix}$　　D. $\begin{bmatrix} -33 & -21 \\ -0.13x & -9 \end{bmatrix}$

Diagnostic Test

Name _____   Date _____

Go Online
PHSchool.com
Visit: PHSchool.com
Web Code: bhk-0802

Diagnostic Test 4: Chapter 4

More About Exponents and Exponential Functions

Choose the letter preceding the word or expression that best completes the statement or answers the question.

1 Which of the following is equivalent to $(3a^2b^3)^3$?

A. $3a^6b^9$ C. $3a^5b^6$

B. $27a^6b^9$ D. $27a^5b^6$

2 The product of 5.4×10^3 and 6.2×10^5 written in scientific notation is

A. 11.6×10^8.   C. 33.48×10^8.

B. 33.48×10^{15}.   D. 3.348×10^9.

3 Which of the following is equivalent to $\left(\dfrac{a^2}{b^{-2}}\right)^3\left(\dfrac{ab^{-3}}{a^2}\right)$ when written in simplest form with all positive exponents?

A. a^5b^3 B. $\dfrac{a^5}{b^3}$ C. $\dfrac{1}{a^5b^3}$ D. $\dfrac{a}{b}$

4 Which of the following is not an exponential function?

A. $y = 3^x$ C. $y = x^3$

B. $y = 2(5^x)$ D. $y = \left(\dfrac{1}{4}\right)^x$

5 If $a \neq 0$ and $y = a^x$, what value of x will result in a value of 1 for y?

A. $x = 1$ C. $x = 0$

B. $x = -1$ D. $x = a$

6 The function $y = a(b^x)$ will represent exponential growth when

A. $a < 0$ and $b > 1$.

B. $a < 0$ and $b < 1$.

C. $a > 0$ and $b > 1$.

D. $a > 0$ and $b < 1$.

7 The graphs of every exponential function of the form $y = k^x$ have a point in common. What is that point?

A. $(1, 1)$ C. $(1, 0)$

B. $(0, 1)$ D. $(0, 0)$

8 If $10,000 is invested at 6% interest compounded annually, the value of the investment can be represented by which of the following functions?

A. $y = 10{,}000(1.06)^x$

B. $y = 10{,}600^x$

C. $y = 10{,}000(6)^x$

D. $y = 10{,}000(0.94)^x$

9 The half-life of a certain substance is two days. If you have 200 grams of the substance, how much is left after 10 days?

A. 200 g

B. 100 g

C. 6.25 g

D. 0 g

10 What are the first four terms of the explicit sequence $a_n = \dfrac{3}{2}(a_{n-1}) + 1$ when $a_1 = 4$?

A. $4, 7, 11.5, 18.25$

B. $4, 6, 9, 13.5$

C. $1, 2.5, 4.75, 8.125$

D. $1, 1.5, 2.25, 3.375$

Name _____   Date _____

Diagnostic Test 5: Chapter 5

Polynomials and Factoring

Choose the letter preceding the word or expression that best completes the statement or answers the question.

1 Simplify the expression $\dfrac{5y^3 + 35y^2 - 25y}{5y}$.

   A. $5y^3 + 35y - 30y$

   B. $y^3 - 7y - 5y$

   C. $5y^2 + 35y - 30$

   D. $y^2 + 7y - 5$

2 Factor the expression $4x^2 - 36$.

   A. $4(x - 3)(x + 3)$

   B. $(4x - 9)(4x + 9)$

   C. $(x - 6)(x + 6)$

   D. $(4x - 9)(x + 4)$

3 Factor $a^2 + 7a + 12$.

   A. $(a + 2)(a + 6)$

   B. $(a - 2)(a + 6)$

   C. $(a + 3)(a + 4)$

   D. $(a - 3)(a - 4)$

4 Simplify the expression.

$(-10n^5 - 30n^4 + 10n^3 - 20n^2) \div 10n^2$

   A. $n^3 + 3n^2 - n + 2$

   B. $-n^3 - 3n^2 + n - 2$

   C. $-n^4 - 3n^3 + n^2 - 2n$

   D. $n^4 + 3n^3 - n^2 + 2n$

5 Find the product of $(y + 8)(y - 1)$.

   A. $y^2 + 9y - 9$ C. $y^2 - 7y - 8$

   B. $y^2 + 7y - 8$ D. $y^2 + 9y - 8$

6 Factor completely. $3x^2 - 12x + 9$

   A. $3(x + 1)(x + 3)$

   B. $(3x - 9)(x - 1)$

   C. $(3x - 3)(x - 3)$

   D. $3(x - 1)(x - 3)$

7 Combine the following.

$(4b^2 - 6b + 9) - (5b^2 + 8b + 6)$

   A. $-b^2 - 14b + 3$

   B. $-b^2 + 2b + 15$

   C. $9b^2 + 2b + 15$

   D. $b^2 + 14b - 3$

In Exercises 8–9, find the product of the algebraic expressions.

8 $(2x^3y^2)(-2x^2y)(-x^4)$

   A. $4x^{10}y^4$ C. $4x^9y^3$

   B. $-2x^9y^3$ D. $-4x^{10}y^4$

9 $5m^2n\,(3mn^2 - mn + n)$

   A. $8m^2n^3 + 6m^2n^2 + 6n$

   B. $15m^3n^3 + 5m^3n^2 + 5m^2n^2$

   C. $8m^2n^2 + 4mn + 6n^2$

   D. $15m^3n^3 - 5m^3n^2 + 5m^2n^2$

10 Simplify $(c - d)^2$.

   A. $c^2 - d^2$ C. $c^2 - d^2$

   B. $c^2 - 2cd + d^2$ D. $c^2 + 2cd + d^2$

Name _____ Date _____

Go Online
PHSchool.com
Visit: PHSchool.com
Web Code: bhk-0802

Diagnostic Test 6: Chapter 6

Quadratic Equations and Functions

Choose the letter preceding the word or expression that best completes the statement or answers the question.

1 Which of the following is the solution(s) to the equation $k^2 = 36$?

   A. $k = 6$ C. $k = \pm 6$

   B. $k = 18$ D. $k = 4$ and $k = 9$

2 For which value of b will the equation $x^2 = b$ have irrational roots?

   A. $b = 25$ C. $b = 10$

   B. $b = -9$ D. $b = 0$

3 The product of two consecutive positive integers is 240. What is the sum of the two integers?

   A. 15   C. 240

   B. 31   D. 16

4 Which of the following does not have a maximum?

   A. $y = x^2 + 3x + 5$

   B. $y = -4x^2 - 3x - 7$

   C. $y = 5x + 7 - 3x^2$

   D. $y = -x^2$

5 Which of the following are the coordinates of the vertex of the parabola whose equation is $y = x^2 - 4x + 5$?

   A. $(0, 0)$ C. $(2, 1)$

   B. $(1, 2)$ D. $(-4, 5)$

6 If the value of the discriminant is a perfect square, then the quadratic will have

   A. one real root.

   B. two rational roots.

   C. two irrational roots.

   D. no real roots.

7 For which equation will the graph of $y = -x^2 + 2$ and the line intersect in two points?

   A. $y = -2x + 3$ C. $y = 5$

   B. $y = 2$ D. $y = 0$

8 If the roots of a quadratic equation are $x = 2$ and $x = 5$, which of the following are possible factors of the quadratic?

   A. $(x + 2)$ and $(x + 5)$

   B. $(x - 2)$ and $(x - 5)$

   C. $(x + 2)$ and $(x - 5)$

   D. $(x - 2)$ and $(x + 5)$

9 If the point $(5, 2)$ is on the graph of $f(x)$, which point is on the graph of $f(-x) + 3$?

   A. $(-5, -1)$

   B. $(-5, 5)$

   C. $(5, -5)$

   D. $(-2, 8)$

Name _____ Date _____

Diagnostic Test 7: Chapter 7

Rational and Radical Expressions and Equations

Choose the letter preceding the word or expression that best completes the statement or answers the question.

1 For what value(s) of n will the rational expression $\frac{4}{n+3}$ be undefined?

A. 3   C. 0

B. -3 D. 4

2 Simplify $\frac{x^2 - y^2}{x^2 - 2xy + y^2}$.

A. $\frac{x-y}{x+y}$ C. $\frac{x+y}{x-y}$

B. -1 D. 0

3 Multiply $\frac{a-2}{3a+9} \cdot \frac{2a+6}{2a-4}$.

A. $\frac{1}{3}$ C. $\frac{4}{6}$

B. $\frac{a-2}{a+3}$ D. $\frac{a+3}{a-2}$

4 Divide $\frac{4}{m^2 - 25} \div \frac{8}{m^2 + 10m + 25}$.

A. $\frac{2}{m-5}$

B. $\frac{2(m+5)}{m-5}$

C. $\frac{m+5}{2(m-5)}$

D. $\frac{10m-1}{2}$

5 For what value(s) of m in Exercise 4 is the expression undefined?

A. $25, -25$ C. 0

B. -5 D. $5, -5$

6 What is the least common denominator of $\frac{q}{q^2 - 1}$ and $\frac{-2}{q-1}$?

A. $(q-1)(q^2-1)$

B. $(q-1)$

C. (q^2-1)

D. $(q+1)$

7 Simplify $\frac{3p}{2p-8} - \frac{12}{p-4}$.

A. $\frac{3p-24}{2p-8}$ C. $\frac{3p}{p-4}$

B. $\frac{3}{2}$ D. $\frac{6}{p-4}$

8 Solve $\frac{2}{3x} + \frac{3}{4} = 1$.

A. $\frac{8}{3}$ C. $\frac{5}{12}$

B. 8   D. 1

9 Simplify $3\sqrt{3} + \sqrt{45} + \sqrt{12}$.

A. $8\sqrt{3}$ C. $8\sqrt{15}$

B. $8\sqrt{5}$ D. $5\sqrt{3} + 3\sqrt{5}$

10 Solve $\sqrt{2-y} = y$.

A. $\{-1, 2\}$

B. no solution

C. $\{1\}$

D. $\{-1, -2\}$

Name _____ Date _____

Go Online
PHSchool.com
Visit: PHSchool.com
Web Code: bhk-0802

Diagnostic Test 8: Chapter 8

Probability

Choose the letter preceding the word or expression that best completes the statement or answers the question.

1 A die is rolled. Which has the same probability as $P(\text{prime})$?

   A. $P(\text{greater than 4})$

   B. $P(1 \text{ or } 6)$

   C. $P(\text{odd})$

   D. $P(\text{multiple of 3})$

2 $_5P_3 = ?$

   A. 10   C. 60

   B. 1   D. 20

3 A bag contains 3 red and 5 blue marbles. What is the probability that if two marbles are selected *without replacement* they will both be blue?

   A. $\frac{5}{8} + \frac{4}{8}$ C. $\frac{5}{8} + \frac{4}{7}$

   B. $\frac{5}{8} \cdot \frac{4}{8}$ D. $\frac{5}{8} \cdot \frac{4}{7}$

4 If $P(A \text{ and } B) = 0$, then the events A and B are

   A. impossible.   C. mutually exclusive.

   B. dependent.   D. random.

5 $\frac{9!}{5!} = ?$

   A. $\frac{9 \cdot 8 \cdot 7 \cdot 6 \cdot 5}{5 \cdot 4 \cdot 3 \cdot 2 \cdot 1}$

   B. $\frac{9 \cdot 8 \cdot 7 \cdot 6 \cdot 5 \cdot 4 \cdot 3 \cdot 2 \cdot 1}{5}$

   C. $9 \cdot 8 \cdot 7 \cdot 6$

   D. $\frac{9}{5}$

6 How many six letter "words" can be made by using the letters in *butter*?

   A. 360   C. 720

   B. 120   D. 36

7 The $P(E) = \frac{5}{8}$. What is the probability that event E does not occur?

   A. $\frac{5}{8}$ C. $\frac{8}{8}$

   B. $\frac{3}{8}$ D. $\frac{0}{8}$

8 If A and B are independent, then

   A. $P(A \text{ and } B) = P(A) + P(B)$.

   B. $P(A \text{ and } B) = P(A) + P(B) - P(A \text{ or } B)$.

   C. $P(A \text{ and } B) = P(A) - P(B)$.

   D. $P(A \text{ and } B) = P(A) \cdot P(B)$.

9 Jacob is choosing 3 CDs out of his collection of 100 CDs to take on a trip. How many combinations are possible?

   A. 300

   B. 161,700

   C. 970,200

   D. $3 \times 100!$

10 Enrique wants to decide if a number cube is fair. It has eight sides labeled from 1 to 8. Based on the law of large numbers, if he rolls it 160 times, how many times should it land on 5?

   A. 5   B. 20   C. 100   D. 155

Name _____ Date _____

Diagnostic Test 9: Chapter 9

Data Analysis

Choose the letter preceding the word or expression that best completes the statement or answers the question.

1 In the graph shown, the value of K is which of the following?

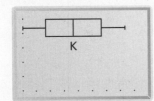

A. mean   C. mode

B. median   D. average

2 When gathering data for a survey, you should make every attempt to avoid which of the following?

A. random samples

B. long questions

C. measures of central tendency

D. bias

3 What is the median of the set {50, 55, 62, 66, 78, 82, 82}?

A. 67.857   B. 66   C. 82   D. 78

4 A set of data has a mean of 70. If 5 is added to each value in the set, what will the new mean will be?

A. less then 70

B. 75

C. 70

D. The new mean cannot be determined.

5 Another name for the mean is

A. average.   C. Q_1.

B. 2nd Quartile.   D. most.

6 The best graphical representation for bivariate data would be a

A. histogram.   C. bar graph.

B. box plot.   D. scatter plot.

7 What type of correlation is shown in the graph below?

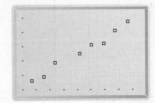

A. negative   C. positive

B. no correlation D. scatter plot

8 When making a prediction from a scatter plot, which of the following would be used?

A. trend line

B. correlation coefficient

C. guess

D. statistics line

9 If you receive the result of a standardized test and find that you are in the 88th percentile, which statement is true?

A. 88% of the students scored higher than you did.

B. You answered 88% of the questions correctly.

C. 88% of the students had the same score or a lower score than you did.

D. 88 out of 100 students earned the same score as you did.

Name _____ Date _____

Diagnostic Test 10: Chapter 10

Basic Geometry in the Plane

Choose the letter preceding the word or expression that best completes the statement or answers the question.

1 Which best describes skew lines?

   A. Lines that never meet.

   B. Lines that do not lie in the same plane.

   C. Lines that are coplanar.

   D. Lines that are parallel.

2 If two angles are supplementary and congruent, then they are

   A. acute angles.

   B. obtuse angles.

   C. right angles.

   D. complementary.

3 If two lines cut by a transversal are parallel what is true of the corresponding angles?

   A. The angles are supplementary.

   B. The angles are complementary.

   C. The angles are congruent.

   D. The angles are right angles.

4 An exterior angle of a triangle is equal to

   A. the sum of the 3 interior angles.

   B. the vertex angle.

   C. its supplement.

   D. the sum of the 2 remote interior angles.

5 Use the trapezoid below to find x.

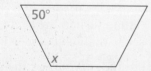

   A. 50°   B. 130°   C. 120°   D. 100°

6 Which formula can be used to find the sum of the measures of the interior angles of a polygon with n sides?

   A. $180n$

   B. $180(n - 2)$

   C. $\dfrac{180(n - 2)}{n}$

   D. 360

7 What is the measure of an interior angle of a regular decagon?

   A. 180°

   B. 144°

   C. 36°

   D. 60°

8 In the diagram below, find the $m\angle 1$.

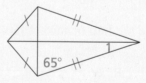

   A. 90°

   B. 65°

   C. 25°

   D. 35°

9 Which of the following statements is not true?

   A. All equilateral triangles are similar.

   B. All isosceles triangles are congruent.

   C. All congruent triangles are similar.

   D. All similar right angles are congruent.

Name _____ Date _____

Diagnostic Test 11: Chapter 11

Geometry and Measurement

Choose the letter preceding the word or expression that best completes the statement or answers the question.

1 Which is the most precise unit of measure?

A. cm   C. mm

B. dm   D. m

2 What is the greatest possible error for a measurement of 28.5 ft?

A. 1 ft   C. 0.5 ft

B. 0.25 ft   D. 5 ft

3 The circumference of a circle is 110 in. What is the radius?

A. 17.5 in.   C. 3.14 in.

B. 35 in.   D. 6.28 in.

4 The perimeter of a regular pentagon is 45 cm. Find the length of each side.

A. 7.5 cm   C. 11.25 cm

B. 15 cm   D. 9 cm

5 Which of the following is the correct formula for calculating the area of a circle with a diameter of 12 in.?

A. $(12)(12)(\pi)$ C. $(\pi)(12)$

B. $(6)(6)(\pi)$ D. $(\pi)(6)$

6 Find the area of an equilateral triangle whose side is 8 in. Give an exact answer.

A. $32\sqrt{3}$ in.²   C. $16\sqrt{3}$ in.²

B. $8\sqrt{3}$ in.²   D. $64\sqrt{3}$ in.²

7 Find the area of the sector of the circle below.

A. 144π cm²

B. 36π cm²

C. 72π cm²

D. 18π cm²

8 The length of the leg opposite the 60° angle of a right triangle with hypotenuse 34 is

A. 17.   C. $17\sqrt{3}$.

B. $17\sqrt{2}$.   D. $34\sqrt{3}$.

9 What is the length of $\overline{DE}$, given that $\overline{AB} = 14$, $\overline{BC} = 11$?

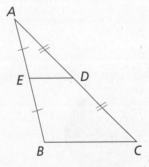

A. 3   B. 5.5   C. 12.5   D. 17.8

10 What is $m\angle x$ if $m\widehat{AB} = 60$ and $m\widehat{CD} = 45$?

A. 105°

B. 52.5°

C. 15°

D. 7.5°

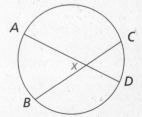

Diagnostic Test

Name _____ Date _____

Go Online
PHSchool.com
Visit: PHSchool.com
Web Code: bhk-0802

Diagnostic Test 12: Chapter 12

Surface Area and Volume

Choose the letter preceding the word or expression that best completes the statement or answers the question.

1 Find the surface area of a rectangular prism with dimensions $l = 6$ in., $w = 4$ in., and $h = 2$ in.

   A. 48 cu in.   C. 120 sq in.

   B. 88 sq in.   D. 112 cu in.

2 If the volume of a cylinder is 252π ft^3, what is the volume of a cone with the same base and height?

   A. 36π cu ft^3 C. 84π cu ft^3

   B. 126π cu ft^3 D. 252π ft^3

3 Two pyramids are similar, and the ratio of their corresponding sides is 5:8. What is the ratio of their surface areas?

   A. 25:64   C. 125:512

   B. 5:8   D. 20:32

In Exercises 4–5, use the diagram below.

.10 in.

4 Find the surface area of the sphere.

   A. 80π in.^{2} C. 100π in.^{2}

   B. 200π in.^{2} D. 400π in.^{2}

5 Find the volume of the sphere above.

   A. $1,333.3\pi$ in.^{3} C. 133.3π in.^{3}

   B. 400π in.^{3} D. $4,000\pi$ in.^{3}

6 Find the volume of the prism below.

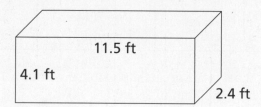

11.5 ft

4.1 ft

2.4 ft

   A. 124.8 ft^3 C. 62.4 ft^3

   B. 113.16 ft^3 D. 162 ft^3

7 Find the lateral area of a cylinder whose base has a radius of 7 m and whose height is 14 m.

   A. 196π m^2 C. 686π m^2

   B. 63π m^2 D. $1,372\pi$ m^2

8 Find the volume of a square pyramid with base area of 36 cm^2 and height of 8 cm.

   A. 144 cm^3

   B. 44 cm^3

   C. 96 cm^3

   D. 288 cm^3

9 A rectangle has a perimeter of 100 in. Which equation could be used to find the maximum possible area of the rectangle?

   A. $A = x(100 - x)$

   B. $A = x(50 - x)$

   C. $A = 2x + 2(50 - x)$

   D. $A = 2x + 2(100 - x)$

Name _____ Date _____

Diagnostic Test 13: Chapter 13

Transformational Geometry

Choose the letter preceding the word or expression that best completes the statement or answers the question.

1 Which of the following transformations is not isometric?

  A. translation   C. rotation

  B. reflection   D. dilation

2 A rotation about the origin of 180° is also known as a

  A. translation.

  B. line reflection.

  C. half turn.

  D. full turn.

3 Which of the following represent a reflection of $y = f(x)$ over the x-axis?

  A. $y = -f(x)$ C. $y = f(-x)$

  B. $y = f(x)$ D. $x = f(y)$

4 The image of the point $(3, -5)$ in the transformation $T_{(-2,3)}$ is

  A. $(5, 8)$ C. $(1, 2)$

  B. $(1, -2)$ D. $(-1, -2)$

5 Which of the following transformations result in the point $(1, 2)$ having the image $(2, 1)$?

  A. half turn   C. $R_{y=x}$

  B. $R_{y=0}$ D. $R_{x=0}$

6 When $\triangle ABC$ is reflected over the y-axis and then dilated by a factor of two the image will be

  A. smaller than $\triangle ABC$.

  B. coincide with $\triangle ABC$ $16\sqrt{3}$.

  C. congruent to $\triangle ABC$.

  D. larger than $\triangle ABC$.

7 The graph shown is an example of which transformation?

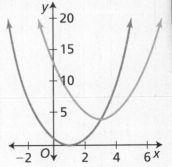

  A. translation

  B. rotation

  C. reflection

  D. dilation

8 What is the sum of the interior angles of a polygon that tessellates the plane?

  A. 90°   B. 270°   C. 180°   D. 360°

9 A triangle with a perimeter of 20 cm is dilated about the origin by a factor of 2. What is the perimeter of the image triangle?

  A. 20 cm   B. 40 cm   C. 10 cm   D. 400 cm

10 If the coordinates of a point remain unchanged in a transformation, it is called a(n)

  A. center point.   C. origin.

  B. fixed point.   D. constant point.

NOTES:

1 Real Numbers and Algebraic Expressions

Discovering New Jersey

Thomas Edison

One of the most prolific inventors in American history was Thomas Edison. Thomas Alva Edison was born in 1847 in Ohio and grew up in Michigan. He became a scientist and an inventor, patenting his first invention at the age of 22.

In 1876, Edison moved into his research shop and laboratories in Menlo Park, New Jersey. It is here where he developed his three greatest inventions: the transmitter, the phonograph, and the incandescent light bulb. It was the invention of the phonograph that gave Edison the nickname "The Wizard of Menlo Park."

During his lifetime, Thomas Edison patented 1093 inventions. He is recognized as the man who said, "Genius is one percent inspiration and 99 percent perspiration." Edison died in 1931.

The set of **natural numbers,** or **counting numbers,** consists of the numbers that you use when you count.

$$N = \{1, 2, 3, 4, 5, 6 \ldots\} \text{ or } N = \{x \mid x \text{ is a counting number}\}$$

When 0 is an element, the new set is the set of **whole numbers.**

$$W = \{0, 1, 2, 3, 4, 5, 6 \ldots\} \text{ or } W = \{x \mid x \text{ is a whole number}\}$$

The set of whole numbers and their **opposites** is called the set of **integers.**

$$Z = \{\ldots, -3, -2, -1, 0, 1, 2, 3 \ldots\} \text{ or } Z = \{x \mid x \text{ is an integer}\}$$

A natural number is a **factor** of a whole number if it divides the whole number with a remainder of 0. The first number is **divisible** by the second.

$18 \div 6 = 3R0 \quad \rightarrow \quad$ 6 is a factor of 18. $\quad \rightarrow \quad$ 18 is divisible by 6.

$18 \div 7 = 2R4 \quad \rightarrow \quad$ 7 is *not* a factor of 18. $\quad \rightarrow \quad$ 18 is not divisible by 7.

The following are some commonly used *divisibility tests*.

Divisibility Tests

A number is divisible by

2 if its last digit is 0, 2, 4, 6, or 8;
3 if the sum of its digits is divisible by 3;
4 if the number formed by the last two digits is divisible by 4;
5 if the last digit is 0 or 5;
8 if the number formed by the last three digits is divisible by 8;
9 if the sum of its digits is divisible by 9;
10 if the last digit is 0.

Note

The number 246 is divisible by

2 since its last digit is 6 and
3 since $2 + 4 + 6 = 12$, and 12 is divisible by 3.

The number 246 is not divisible by

4 since 46 is not divisible by 4;
5 since its last digit is not 0 or 5;
8 since 246 is not divisible by 8;
9 since $2 + 4 + 6 = 12$ and 12 is not divisible by 9;
10 since its last digit is not 0.

A **prime number** is a natural number greater than 1 that has exactly two factors, 1 and the number itself. The first eight prime numbers are 2, 3, 5, 7, 11, 13, 17, and 19.

A **composite number** is a natural number greater than 1 that has more than two factors. For example, the number 18 has six factors in all: 1, 2, 3, 6, 9, and 18. So the number 18 is composite.

When you write a natural number as a product of prime numbers, you are writing the **prime factorization** of the number. Every natural number has exactly one prime factorization.

  Writing the prime factorization of a number

 Write the prime factorization of 350.

■ **SOLUTION 1**

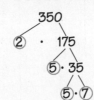

← Start with the least prime factor.

← Continue to factor until all factors are prime.

■ **SOLUTION 2**

350
35 · 10 ← Start with any pair of factors.
⑤·⑦ ②·⑤ ← Continue to factor until all factors are prime.

Using either method, *the prime factorization of 350 is 2 · 5 · 5 · 7.*

The greatest factor of two or more natural numbers is called their **greatest common factor,** or **GCF.** If the GCF of two numbers is 1, the numbers are called **relatively prime.**

EXAMPLE 2   **Finding the GCF**

 Find the GCF of 24 and 84.

■ **SOLUTION**

Step 1

Write the prime factorization of each number. Circle the prime factors common to both numbers.

$$24 = ②\cdot②\cdot 2 \cdot ③$$
$$84 = ②\cdot②\cdot③\cdot 7$$

Step 2

Multiply the circled factors.

$$2 \cdot 2 \cdot 3 = 12$$

The GCF of 24 and 84 is 12.

When a number is multiplied by a whole number, the result is a **multiple** of the first number. The least multiple of two or more numbers is called their **least common multiple,** or **LCM.**

EXAMPLE 3   **Finding the LCM**

Find the LCM of 6, 8, and 30.

■ **SOLUTION**

Step 1

Write the prime factorization of each number. Circle each prime factor only once and where it appears most often.

$$6 = 2 \cdot ③$$
$$8 = ②\cdot②\cdot②$$ (circled together)
$$30 = 2 \cdot 3 \cdot ⑤$$

Step 2

Multiply the circled factors.

$$2 \cdot 2 \cdot 2 \cdot 3 \cdot 5 = 120$$

The LCM of 6, 8, and 30 is 120.

3

The LCM can also be found by examining the multiples of a group of numbers.

EXAMPLE 4   **Examining multiples to find LCM**

4   Find the LCM of 5, 12, and 20.

■ SOLUTION

Begin by finding the multiples of the largest number in the group. Check whether each of those multiples is also a multiple of the smaller numbers. Continue this process until you find the first number that is a multiple of all of three.

Begin checking multiples of 20.   ←   20 is not a multiple of 12.
Check 20(2) or 40.   ←   40 is not a multiple of 12.
Check 20(3) or 60.   ←   60 is a multiple of both 5 and 12.

Therefore, **the LCM of 5, 12, and 20 is 60.**

The set of **rational numbers** consists of all numbers that can be expressed in the form $\frac{a}{b}$, where a and b are integers and $b \neq 0$. The following are examples of rational numbers.

$$\frac{9}{14} \qquad -5 = \frac{-5}{1} \qquad 2\frac{1}{7} = \frac{15}{7} \qquad 0.71 = \frac{71}{100} \qquad 0.\overline{83} = \frac{83}{99}$$

Expressions that name the same number are **equivalent expressions**. To write a fraction that is equivalent to a given fraction, you can multiply or divide the fraction by 1. That is, a fraction with the same numerator and denominator.

Note

Recall these symbols.
= is equal to
≠ is not equal to

EXAMPLES 5 and 6   **Writing equivalent fractions**

Replace each ___?___ with the number that makes the fractions equivalent.

5   $\frac{5}{6} = \frac{?}{54}$

■ SOLUTION

$\frac{5}{6} = \frac{5 \times 9}{6 \times 9}$ ←   Because 6 × 9 = 54, multiply both the numerator and the denominator by 9.

$\quad = \frac{45}{54}$

6   $\frac{24}{40} = \frac{?}{10}$

■ SOLUTION

$\frac{24}{40} = \frac{24 \div 4}{40 \div 4}$ ←   Because 40 ÷ 4 = 10, divide both the numerator and the denominator by 4.

$\quad = \frac{6}{10}$

The expression $0.\overline{83}$ is an example of a *repeating decimal*. The bar over 83 shows that this block of digits repeats without end. That is, $0.\overline{83} = 0.838383.\ldots$ Any rational number can be expressed in equivalent form either as a repeating decimal or as a *terminating decimal*.

Note

The fraction bar is a division symbol.

$\frac{a}{b} = a \div b \rightarrow b\overline{)a}$

EXAMPLES 7 and 8   **Writing a fraction as a decimal**

7   Write $\frac{5}{8}$ as a terminating decimal.

■ SOLUTION

```
      0.625      ←  The division
  8)5.000           terminates.
   -4 8
     20
    -16
     40
    -40
      0
```

Therefore, $\frac{5}{8} = 0.625$.

8   Write $\frac{2}{3}$ as a repeating decimal.

■ SOLUTION

```
      0.666...   ←  The 6
  3)2.000           repeats.
   -18
     20
    -18
     20
    -18
      2 ...
```

Therefore, $\frac{2}{3} = 0.666\ldots = 0.\overline{6}$.

4

Any repeating or terminating decimal can be written as a fraction. A fraction is in **lowest terms** if the GCF of its numerator and denominator is 1.

$\dfrac{a}{b}$ ← numerator
← denominator

9 Write 0.28 as a fraction in lowest terms.

■ SOLUTION $0.28 = \dfrac{28}{100} = \dfrac{28 \div 4}{100 \div 4} = \dfrac{7}{25}$ ← The GCF of 28 and 100 is 4.

10 Write $0.\overline{45}$ as a fraction in lowest terms.

■ SOLUTION

$\begin{aligned} 100 \times 0.\overline{45} &= 45.454545\ldots \quad \leftarrow \text{Multiply by 100.} \\ - \quad 1 \times 0.\overline{45} &= - \;\; 0.454545\ldots \quad \leftarrow \text{Subtract the original number.} \\ \hline 99 \times 0.\overline{45} &= 45 \end{aligned}$

$\dfrac{99 \times 0.\overline{45}}{99} = \dfrac{45}{99}$ ← Divide by 99.

$0.\overline{45} = \dfrac{45 \div 9}{99 \div 9} = \dfrac{5}{11}$ ← Write in lowest terms.

Therefore, $0.\overline{45} = \dfrac{5}{11}$.

Note

If only one digit repeats, multiply by 10, then subtract, and then divide by 9.

If three digits repeat, multiply by 1000, then subtract, and then divide by 999.

Some decimals do not terminate or repeat. If we try to find the square root of a nonperfect square, we will get only an approximation. Square roots of numbers that are not perfect squares are **irrational**.

The resulting root will be a **nonterminating, nonrepeating decimal**. These decimals make up the set of **irrational numbers**.

Some examples of irrational numbers are:

a) 0.01010011101111 …
b) $\pi = 3.14159\ldots$
c) $\sqrt{3} = 1.732\ldots$

The **rational numbers** and the **irrational numbers** together make up the set of **real numbers**. The diagram at the right shows how the real numbers and its subsets are related.

Real Numbers

Rational Numbers

Integers

Whole Numbers

Natural Numbers

Irrational Numbers

11 Which of the following is an irrational number?

A. 5.209   **B.** $5.2\overline{09}$ **C.** 5.209090909…   **D.** 5.2090090009…

■ SOLUTION

Choice **A** is a terminating decimal; therefore, it is rational.
Choice **B** and **C** are nonterminating but are repeating; therefore, they are rational.
Choice **D** is a nonterminating, nonrepeating decimal; therefore, it is irrational.

The correct choice is **D**.

Choose the letter preceding the word or expression that best completes the statement or answers the question.

1 Which is the set of all factors of 36?

   A. $\{12, 24, 36\}$

   B. $\{2, 3, 4, 6, 9, 12, 18\}$

   C. $\{1, 2, 3, 4, 6, 9, 12, 18, 36\}$

   D. $\{36, 72, 108, 144, 180, \ldots\}$

2 Which number is *not* divisible by 13?

   A. 1   **B.** 13   **C.** 26   **D.** 130

3 What is the prime factorization of 100?

   A. $1 \cdot 100$

   B. $10 \cdot 10$

   C. $1 \cdot 2 \cdot 5 \cdot 10 \cdot 20 \cdot 50 \cdot 100$

   D. $2 \cdot 2 \cdot 5 \cdot 5$

4 Which expression does *not* name an integer?

   A. -9 **B.** 0   **C.** $\frac{3}{15}$ **D.** $\frac{8}{2}$

5 Which expression does *not* represent the quotient when a is divided by b?

   A. $\frac{a}{b}$ **C.** $b\sqrt{a}$

   B. $b \div a$ **D.** $a \div b$

6 Which expression is *not* equivalent to $\frac{42}{50}$?

   A. 0.42   **B.** 0.84   **C.** 84%   **D.** $\frac{21}{25}$

7 Which expression represents an irrational number?

   A. $0.040404\ldots$ **C.** $0.7070070007\ldots$

   B. $1.\overline{01001}$ **D.** $\sqrt{2} - \sqrt{2}$

8 Which number is *not* a whole number?

   A. 3   **B.** 0   **C.** -5 **D.** $\frac{12}{2}$

9 Which of the following statements is *not* true?

   A. 33 is divisible by 3.

   B. 11 is a factor of 33.

   C. 66 is a multiple of 33.

   D. 33 is a prime number.

10 Which set of numbers has a GCF of 18?

   A. $\{18, 36\}$ **C.** $\{3, 6, 9\}$

   B. $\{6, 9\}$ **D.** $\{9, 18\}$

11 Which number is the LCM of 12 and 20?

   A. 4   **B.** 60   **C.** 2   **D.** 120

12 Which fraction is equivalent to $\frac{9}{15}$?

   A. $\frac{1}{6}$ **B.** $\frac{6}{12}$ **C.** $\frac{3}{5}$ **D.** $\frac{12}{18}$

13 $0.\overline{381}$ can be written as which fraction?

   A. $\frac{127}{333}$ **B.** $\frac{381}{10,000}$ **C.** $\frac{19}{15}$ **D.** $\frac{3}{10}$

14 Which of the following is a true statement?

   A. -3 is a whole number.

   B. $\sqrt{9}$ is an irrational number.

   C. 0 is a natural number.

   D. $\frac{1}{3}$ is a rational number.

15 Which of the following statements is false?

    A. All real numbers are rational numbers.

    B. Every integer is a rational number.

    C. All natural numbers are integers.

    D. Every whole number is a real number.

In Exercises 16–18, list all of the factors of the given number.

16 49   **17** 31   **18** 120

In Exercises 19–22, is the first number divisible by the second? Write *Yes* or *No*.

19 624; 3   **20** 114; 4

21 2670; 5   **22** 84; 6

In Exercises 23–24, write the prime factorization of each number.

23 32   **24** 120

In Exercises 25–28, find the GCF.

25 8, 12   **26** 15, 45

27 12, 35   **28** 4, 14, 22

In Exercises 29–32, find the LCM.

29 6, 16   **30** 15, 25

31 7, 8   **32** 6, 8, 12

In Exercises 33–34, replace each _?_ with the number that makes the fractions equivalent.

33 $\frac{9}{27} = \frac{?}{3}$ **34** $\frac{48}{60} = \frac{?}{15}$

In Exercises 35–36, write three fractions that are equivalent to the given fraction.

35 $\frac{3}{5}$ **36** $\frac{12}{36}$

In Exercises 37–40, write each fraction as a decimal.

37 $\frac{94}{100}$ **38** $\frac{17}{20}$

39 $\frac{1}{3}$ **40** $\frac{2}{9}$

In Exercises 41–44, write each decimal as a fraction in lowest terms.

41 0.72   **42** 0.102

43 $0.4\overline{3}$ **44** $0.\overline{43}$

In Exercises 45–48, show that each expression represents a rational number.

45 $4\frac{1}{8}$ **46** 0.42

47 0.222 ...   **48** 0

In Exercises 49–54, give an example to illustrate the type of number described and explain your answer.

49 a whole number that is not a natural number

50 a real number that is not rational

51 a rational number that is not an integer

52 two whole numbers that are neither prime nor composite

53 two composite numbers that are relatively prime

54 two nonequivalent expressions that use the same numbers; like $\frac{1}{4}$ and 1.4

1.2 The Real Number Line

Recall that the set of rational numbers and the set of irrational numbers make up the set of real numbers.

There is a *one-to-one correspondence* between the set of real numbers and the points on a **number line.**

The point that corresponds to a real number is called the **graph of the number.** The number line below shows the graphs of $-2\frac{3}{4}, -1.6, \sqrt{2}, 2,$ and π.

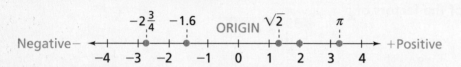

You can use a number line to *compare* numbers. Given real numbers a and b, exactly one of the following is true.

a is less than b		a is equal to b		a is greater than b
$a < b$	or	$a = b$	or	$a > b$

Note

If $a < b$ or $a > b$, then $a \ne b$ (a is not equal to b). Also, if $a < b$ or $a = b$, then $a \le b$ (a is less than or equal to b) and if $a > b$ or $a = b$, then $a \ge b$ (a is greater than or equal to b).

EXAMPLE 1   **Using a number line to compare**

1 Replace __?__ with $<, >,$ or $=$ to make a true statement: 1 __?__ -3

■ **SOLUTION**

Draw a number line like the one at the right.
The graph of 1 is to the right of the graph of -3.
Therefore, $1 > -3$.

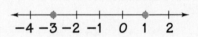

To place a set of three or more decimals in increasing or decreasing *order,* you can use the method in Example 2.

EXAMPLE 2   **Ordering a set of decimals**

2 Write these decimals in order from least to greatest: $1.04, -14, -1.4, 0.104$

■ **SOLUTION**

Step 1	**Step 2**	**Step 3**
Write the numbers with the decimal points lined up.	Annex zeros so that each has the same number of decimal places.	Order the numbers as if they were integers.
1.04	1.040	−14.000
−14.	−14.000	−1.400
−1.4	−1.400	0.104
0.104	0.104	1.040

From least to greatest, the numbers are **$-14, -1.4, 0.104, 1.04$.**

To order a set of fractions, you may need to write equivalent fractions using the least common denominator. The **least common denominator,** or **LCD,** of a set of fractions is the LCM of all the denominators.

EXAMPLE 3 **Ordering a set of fractions**

 Write these fractions in order from least to greatest: $\frac{3}{4}, \frac{5}{6}, \frac{11}{15}$

■ **SOLUTION**

Step 1
Find the least common denominator (LCD).

$$\frac{3}{4}, \frac{5}{6}, \frac{11}{15}$$

The LCM of 4, 6, and 15 is 60.

Step 2
Write equivalent fractions, using the LCD.

$$\frac{3}{4} = \frac{3 \times 15}{4 \times 15} = \frac{45}{60}$$

$$\frac{5}{6} = \frac{5 \times 10}{6 \times 10} = \frac{50}{60}$$

$$\frac{11}{15} = \frac{11 \times 4}{15 \times 4} = \frac{44}{60}$$

Step 3
Use the numerators to order the fractions.

$$44 < 45 < 50$$

$$\frac{44}{60} < \frac{45}{60} < \frac{50}{60}$$

$$\frac{11}{15} < \frac{3}{4} < \frac{5}{6}$$

Written in order from least to greatest, the fractions are $\frac{11}{15}, \frac{3}{4}, \frac{5}{6}$.

> **Note**
> $a < b < c$ means that "a is less than b and b is less than c"
> or
> "b is between a and c."

You can use a calculator to order a set of numbers that includes both fractions and decimals.

EXAMPLE 4 **Ordering a set of decimals and fractions**

 Write these numbers in order from least to greatest:
$-\frac{7}{15}, -\frac{11}{24}, -\frac{9}{20}, -0.4512$

■ **SOLUTION**

The fraction $\frac{a}{b}$ means $a \div b$. Use a calculator to perform the divisions.

$-\frac{7}{15} \rightarrow$ [(-)] 7 [÷] 15 [ENTER] $-.4666666667 \rightarrow -0.4666666667$

$-\frac{11}{24} \rightarrow$ [(-)] 11 [÷] 24 [ENTER] $-.4583333333 \rightarrow -0.4583333333$

$-\frac{9}{20} \rightarrow$ [(-)] 9 [÷] 20 [ENTER] $-.45 \rightarrow -0.4500000000$

$-0.4512 \rightarrow \qquad\qquad\qquad\qquad\qquad\qquad -0.4512000000$

Written in order from least to greatest, the numbers are $-\frac{7}{15}, -\frac{11}{24}, -0.4512, -\frac{9}{20}$.

Rational numbers are often written as *percents*. The word **percent** means "per 100," "out of 100," or "divided by 100." The symbol for percent is %.

$$37\% = 37 \text{ per } 100 = 37 \text{ divided by } 100 = \frac{37}{100} = 0.37$$

Visit: PHSchool.com
Web Code: ayp-0044

EXAMPLES 5 and 6 **Converting between percents and decimals**

 Write 0.581 as a percent.

■ **SOLUTION**

To write a decimal as a percent, multiply by 100.

$0.581 = 58.1\%$ ← Move the decimal point two places *to the right.*

 Write 3% as a decimal.

■ **SOLUTION**

To write a percent as a decimal, divide by 100.

$3\% = 0.03$ ← Move the decimal point two places *to the left.*

It is sometimes helpful to convert a percent to a fraction or a fraction to a percent. These conversions are illustrated in the following examples.

Converting between percents and fractions

 Write $\frac{7}{20}$ as a percent.

■ SOLUTION

To write a fraction as a percent, find an equivalent fraction with denominator 100.

$$\frac{7}{20} = \frac{7 \times 5}{20 \times 5}$$
$$= \frac{35}{100} = 35\%$$

8 Write 4.4% as a fraction in lowest terms.

■ SOLUTION

To write a percent as a fraction, write the percent as a number divided by 100.

$$4.4\% = \frac{4.4}{100} = \frac{4.4 \times 10}{100 \times 10}$$
$$= \frac{44}{1000} = \frac{44 \div 4}{1000 \div 4} = \frac{11}{250}$$

We can order a set of numbers consisting of percents, fractions, and decimals by converting them all to decimals.

EXAMPLE 9 **Ordering a set of fractions, decimals, and percents**

 Write these numbers in order from least to greatest: $13\%, \frac{3}{8}, 0.003, \frac{1}{4}$.

■ SOLUTION

Step 1		Step 2
13% = 13 divided by 100 = 0.13		0.003
$\frac{3}{8}$ = 3 ÷ 8	= 0.375	0.130 ← **Annex zeros to make**
0.003	= 0.003	0.250 **it easier to arrange.**
$\frac{1}{4}$ = 1 ÷ 4	= 0.25	0.375

Written in order from least to greatest, *the numbers are 0.003, 13%, $\frac{1}{4}$, and $\frac{3}{8}$.*

Recall that when adding, subtracting, multiplying, and dividing with percents, we first change the percent to a fraction or decimal to perform the operations.

EXAMPLES 10 and 11 **Rewriting percents greater than 100% or less than 1%**

 Write 125% as a decimal and as a fraction in lowest terms.

■ SOLUTION

125% = 1.25   ← **Move the decimal point 2 places to the left.**

$= \frac{125}{100} = 1\frac{25}{100} = 1\frac{1}{4}$ ← **Simplify the fraction after dividing by 100.**

11 Write 0.3% as a decimal and as a fraction in lowest terms.

■ SOLUTION

0.3% = 0.003   ← **Move the decimal point 2 places to the left.**

$= \frac{0.3 \times 10}{100 \times 10}$ ← **Multiply the numerator and denominator by 10 to get a whole number in the numerator.**

$= \frac{3}{1000}$

You should memorize certain percents and their decimal and fraction equivalents. The table below shows some of these.

Percent	$12\frac{1}{2}\%$	20%	25%	$33\frac{1}{3}\%$	$37\frac{1}{2}\%$	40%	50%	60%	$62\frac{1}{2}\%$	$66\frac{2}{3}\%$	75%	80%	$87\frac{1}{2}\%$	100%
Decimal	0.125	0.2	0.25	$0.\overline{3}$	0.375	0.4	0.5	0.6	0.625	$0.\overline{6}$	0.75	0.8	0.875	1
Fraction	$\frac{1}{8}$	$\frac{1}{5}$	$\frac{1}{4}$	$\frac{1}{3}$	$\frac{3}{8}$	$\frac{2}{5}$	$\frac{1}{2}$	$\frac{3}{5}$	$\frac{5}{8}$	$\frac{2}{3}$	$\frac{3}{4}$	$\frac{4}{5}$	$\frac{7}{8}$	$\frac{1}{1}$

Practice

Choose the letter preceding the word or expression that best completes the statement or answers the question.

1 Which number is not greater than -5?

A. $-5\frac{1}{2}$ **B.** $-\frac{5}{2}$ **C.** 0 **D.** $5\frac{1}{2}$

2 Which statement is true?

A. $\frac{1}{4} < \frac{1}{3}$ **C.** $-\frac{1}{4} > \frac{1}{3}$

B. $-\frac{1}{2} > -\frac{1}{4}$ **D.** $\frac{1}{2} < -\frac{1}{3}$

3 Which number is between -2.5 and $-2\frac{3}{5}$?

A. $-2\frac{2}{5}$ **C.** $-2.\overline{5}$

B. $-2.\overline{3}$ **D.** 0

4 Which decimal is equivalent to $\frac{1}{4}\%$?

A. 0.0025 **C.** 0.25

B. 0.025 **D.** 2.5

5 Which of the following fractions is equivalent to 0.875?

A. $\frac{875}{100}$ **C.** $\frac{7}{8}$

B. $\frac{15}{16}$ **D.** $8\frac{75}{100}$

In Exercises 6–15, replace each __?__ with <, >, or = to make a true statement.

6 -100 __?__ 4 **7** -2 __?__ -35

8 6.01 __?__ -6.1 **9** -8.98 __?__ -8.94

10 $\frac{7}{12}$ __?__ $\frac{11}{18}$ **11** $1\frac{1}{5}$ __?__ $1\frac{1}{6}$

12 $-2\frac{3}{4}$ __?__ $-2\frac{7}{8}$ **13** $2\frac{5}{11}$ __?__ 2.45

14 -0.23 __?__ $-\frac{2}{9}$ **15** $\frac{14}{25}$ __?__ $0.5\overline{6}$

In Exercises 16–21, write each set of numbers in order from least to greatest.

16 $\frac{9}{5}, \frac{5}{3}, \frac{17}{10}$ **17** $-\frac{5}{6}, -\frac{13}{15}, -\frac{8}{9}$

18 $-3, 7, -10, 0, -5, 1, -2$

19 $-1.1, -1.01, -1.101, -0.1001$

20 $\frac{1}{20}, 0.5, \frac{2}{5}, \frac{5}{9}, 0.505$

21 $-\frac{9}{2}, -4.3, -4\frac{1}{3}, 4.\overline{3}, -4\frac{3}{100}$

In Exercises 22–25, write each fraction as a decimal.

22 $\frac{94}{100}$ **23** $\frac{17}{20}$ **24** $\frac{7}{4}$ **25** $\frac{3}{16}$

In Exercises 26–28, write each decimal as a fraction in lowest terms.

26 0.8 **27** 0.72 **28** 0.102

In Exercises 29–31, write each fraction as a percent.

29 $\frac{23}{25}$ **30** $\frac{87}{1000}$ **31** $\frac{9}{16}$

In Exercises 32–34, write each percent as a fraction in lowest terms and as a decimal.

32 3% **33** 1.08% **34** $2\frac{1}{2}\%$

1.3 Real Number Operations

The **absolute value** of a number is its distance from zero on a number line. The symbol for the absolute value of a number n is $|n|$.

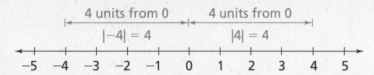

Opposites are two numbers that are the same distance from zero on a number line, but on opposite sides of zero. The opposite of a number n is written as $-n$.

-4 is the opposite of 4.   4 is the opposite of -4.

The concept of absolute value is used in establishing rules for basic operations with signed numbers.

The absolute value of 0 is 0.
$$|0| = 0$$
The opposite of 0 is 0.
$$-0 = 0$$

Note

Recall that in addition, the numbers you are adding are called **addends** and the result of the addition is called the **sum**.

Adding Integers

- To add two numbers with like signs, add their absolute values. The sum has the same sign as both addends.

- To add two numbers with unlike signs, subtract the lesser absolute value from the greater absolute value. The sum has the same sign as the addend with the greater absolute value.

EXAMPLES 1 through 4   **Adding integers**

1 $7 + 9$

- **SOLUTION**

$$
\begin{array}{ll}
|7| \rightarrow & 7 \\
|9| \rightarrow & \underline{+\ 9} \\
& 16
\end{array}
$$
← Both addends are *positive*.

$7 + 9 = 16$ ← The sum is *positive*.

2 $-8 + (-6)$

- **SOLUTION**

$$
\begin{array}{ll}
|-8| \rightarrow & 8 \\
|-6| \rightarrow & \underline{+\ 6} \\
& 14
\end{array}
$$
← Both addends are *negative*.

$-8 + (-6) = -14$ ← The sum is *negative*.

3 $-12 + 5$

- **SOLUTION**

$$
\begin{array}{ll}
|-12| \rightarrow & 12 \\
|5| \rightarrow & 5
\end{array}
$$
← *Negative* addend has the greater absolute value.

$12 - 5 = 7$

$-12 + 5 = -7$ ← The sum is *negative*.

4 $-6 + 15$

- **SOLUTION**

$$
\begin{array}{ll}
|15| \rightarrow & 15 \\
|-6| \rightarrow & 6
\end{array}
$$
← *Positive* addend has the greater absolute value.

$15 - 6 = 9$

$-6 + 15 = 9$ ← The sum is *positive*.

Subtracting Integers

- To subtract a signed number, add its opposite.

Note

When you subtract two numbers, the result is called the **difference**.

Using this rule, you can rewrite any subtraction $a - b$ as $a + (-b)$. Then you proceed by following the rules for adding signed numbers.

EXAMPLES 5 through 7   Subtracting integers

5 $-7 - (-21)$

- **SOLUTION**

$$-7 - (-21)$$
$$-7 + 21$$
$$14$$

6 $-9 - 18$

- **SOLUTION**

$$-9 - 18$$
$$-9 + (-18)$$
$$-27$$

7 $2 - 14$

- **SOLUTION**

$$2 - 14$$
$$2 + (-14)$$
$$-12$$

The rules for adding and subtracting signed numbers can also be applied to decimals.

EXAMPLES 8 and 9   Adding and subtracting decimals

8 $-0.23 + (-0.083) + (-9.5)$

- **SOLUTION**

$$-0.230$$
$$-0.083$$
$$-9.500$$
$$-9.813$$

← Line up the decimal points. Annex zeros so that each addend has the same number of decimal places.

9 $34 - 2.75$

- **SOLUTION**

$$34.00$$
$$- \ 2.75$$
$$31.25$$

← In a whole number, the decimal point follows the ones' place.

You must also use the rules for adding and subtracting signed numbers with fractions.

Go Online
PHSchool.com

Visit: PHSchool.com
Web Code: ayp-0046

EXAMPLES 10 and 11   Adding and subtracting fractions

10 $-2\frac{2}{3} + \left(-4\frac{2}{3}\right)$

- **SOLUTION**

$$-2\frac{2}{3} + \left(-4\frac{2}{3}\right)$$

$$-\frac{8}{3} + \left(-\frac{14}{3}\right)$$ ← Rewrite the mixed numbers as fractions.

$$\frac{-8 + (-14)}{3}$$ ← Write the sum of the numerators over the common denominator.

$$\frac{-22}{3}$$

$$-7\frac{1}{3}$$

11 $\frac{1}{5} - \frac{5}{8}$

- **SOLUTION**

$$\frac{1}{5} - \frac{5}{8}$$

$$\frac{1}{5} + \left(-\frac{5}{8}\right)$$ ← Rewrite the subtraction as an addition.

$$\frac{8}{40} + \left(-\frac{25}{40}\right)$$ ← The LCD is 40.

$$\frac{8 + (-25)}{40}$$

$$\frac{-17}{40} = -\frac{17}{40}$$

The procedure for multiplication of signed numbers is related to the procedure for division. The rules for both operations can be summarized as follows.

Multiplying and Dividing Integers

- To multiply or divide two numbers with like signs, multiply or divide their absolute values. The product or quotient is positive.
- To multiply or divide two numbers with unlike signs, multiply or divide their absolute values. The product or quotient is negative.

EXAMPLES 12 and 13   **Multiplying and dividing integers**

12 $(-12) \times (-6)$ ▪ SOLUTION

$(-12) \times (-6)$ ← The numbers have like signs.
$12 \times 6 = 72$ ← $|-12| = 12$ and $|-6| = 6$
$(-12) \times (-6) = 72$ ← The product is *positive.*

13 $-72 \div 9$ ▪ SOLUTION

$-72 \div 9$ ← The numbers have unlike signs.
$72 \div 9 = 8$ ← $|-72| = 72$ and $|9| = 9$
$-72 \div 9 = -8$ ← The quotient is *negative.*

Although you do not need to align the decimals before multiplying, you must be careful to place the decimal in the answer correctly.

EXAMPLES 14 and 15   **Multiplying decimals**

14 3.42×0.026

▪ SOLUTION

- Multiply as with whole numbers.
- Count the *total* decimal places in the factors.
- Give the product that number of decimal places.
- Insert zeros as placeholders where necessary.

$$
\begin{array}{r}
3.42 \\
\times\ 0.026 \\
\hline
2\,052 \\
684 \\
\hline
0.08892
\end{array}
$$

← 2 decimal places
← + 3 decimal places
← 5 decimal places

15 $(-0.32)(12.5)$

▪ SOLUTION

- The decimals have unlike signs.
- Multiply the absolute values of the decimals.
- Count the *total* decimal places in the factors.
- Place the decimal in the product accordingly.

$$
\begin{array}{r}
(-0.32)(12.5) \\
0.32 \\
\times\ 12.5 \\
\hline
160 \\
64 \\
32 \\
\hline
4.000
\end{array}
$$

- The product is *negative.* Therefore, $(-0.32)(12.5) = -4.$

Remember that to divide by a decimal, you change the divisor into a whole number by moving the decimal all the way to the right. To keep the value of the original division problem, you need to move the decimal in the dividend the same number of places to the right. The remaining steps are reviewed in the following example.

EXAMPLES 16 and 17   **Dividing decimals**

 $1.452 \div 0.24$

- **SOLUTION**
  - In the *divisor*, move the decimal point right to make it a whole number.
  - In the *dividend*, move the decimal point the same number of places to the right.
  - Divide as with whole numbers.
  - Place the decimal point in the quotient above the decimal point in the dividend.
  - Insert zeros as placeholders where necessary.

$$
\begin{array}{r}
6.05 \\
0.24\overline{)1.4520} \\
-144 \\
\hline
120 \\
-120 \\
\hline
0
\end{array}
$$

 $12.35 \div -0.125$

- **SOLUTION**
  - The decimals have unlike signs.
  - Divide the absolute values of the decimals.
  - Insert zeros as placeholders where necessary.
  - The quotient is *negative*. Therefore, $12.35 \div -0.125 = 98.8$.

$$
\begin{array}{r}
98.8 \\
0.125\overline{)12.3500} \\
-1125 \\
\hline
1100 \\
-1000 \\
\hline
1000 \\
-1000 \\
\hline
0
\end{array}
$$

Again, you must apply the rules for multiplying and dividing signed numbers when finding the products and quotients of fractions.

Go Online PHSchool.com
Visit: PHSchool.com
Web Codes: ayp-0810
ayp-0812

EXAMPLES 18 and 19   **Multiplying and dividing fractions**

 $\left(-1\frac{1}{2}\right)\left(1\frac{7}{9}\right)$

- **SOLUTION**
  - Multiply the numerators.
  - Multiply the denominators.
  - Simplify the result.

$$\left(-1\tfrac{1}{2}\right)\left(1\tfrac{7}{9}\right)$$
$$\tfrac{-3}{2} \times \tfrac{16}{9} \quad \leftarrow$$
Rewrite the mixed numbers as fractions.
$$\tfrac{-3 \times 16}{2 \times 9}$$
$$\tfrac{-48}{18} = \tfrac{-8}{3} = -2\tfrac{2}{3}$$

 $-\frac{3}{4} \div (-3)$

- **SOLUTION**
  - Multiply the dividend by the reciprocal of the divisor.
  - Simplify the result.

$$-\tfrac{3}{4} \div (-3)$$
$$\tfrac{-3}{4} \times \tfrac{-1}{3} \quad \leftarrow$$
The reciprocal of -3 is $-\tfrac{1}{3}$.
$$\tfrac{3}{12} = \tfrac{1}{4}$$

The following are *field properties* of real numbers. These properties govern the operations of addition and multiplication.

Field Properties of Real Numbers
Let a, b, and c represent real numbers.

Property	Addition	Multiplication
Closure	$a + b$ is a unique real number.	$a \cdot b$ is a unique real number.
Commutative	$a + b = b + a$	$a \cdot b = b \cdot a$
Associative	$a + b + c = (a + b) + c$ $= a + (b + c)$	$a \cdot b \cdot c = (a \cdot b) \cdot c$ $= a \cdot (b \cdot c)$
Identity	$a + 0 = a$ and $0 + a = a$ The **additive identity** is 0.	$a \cdot 1 = a$ and $1 \cdot a = a$ The **multiplicative identity** is 1.
Inverse	For every real number a, there is a unique real number $-a$ such that $a + (-a) = 0$ and $-a + a = 0$; $-a$ is the **additive inverse** of a, or the **opposite** of a.	For every nonzero real number a, there is a unique real number $\frac{1}{a}$ such that $a \cdot \frac{1}{a} = 1$ and $\frac{1}{a} \cdot a = 1$; $\frac{1}{a}$ is the **multiplicative inverse** of a, or the **reciprocal** of a.
Distributive	$a \cdot (b + c) = a \cdot b + a \cdot c$ and $(b + c) \cdot a = b \cdot a + c \cdot a$	

EXAMPLES 20 through 22   **Using properties of real numbers**

Simplify each expression.

20 $-19 + 24 + (-11)$

■ SOLUTION

$$
\begin{aligned}
-19 + 24 + (-11) &= 24 + (-19) + (-11) \\
&= 24 + [(-19) + (-11)] \\
&= 24 + (-30) \\
&= -6
\end{aligned}
$$

← Use the Associative and Commutative Properties of Addition to change the order and group the negative numbers.

21 $12 \times 25 \times \frac{1}{12}$

■ SOLUTION

$$
\begin{aligned}
12 \times 25 \times \frac{1}{12} &= \left[12 \times \frac{1}{12}\right] \times 25 \\
&= 1 \times 25 \\
&= 25
\end{aligned}
$$

← Use the Associative and Commutative Properties of Multiplication.
← Use the Multiplicative Inverse Property.
← Use the Multiplicative Identity Property.

22 $36 \cdot \left(0.01 + \frac{1}{3}\right)$

■ SOLUTION

$$
\begin{aligned}
36 \cdot \left(0.01 + \frac{1}{3}\right) &= 36 \cdot 0.01 + 36 \cdot \frac{1}{3} \\
&= 0.36 + 12 \\
&= 12.36
\end{aligned}
$$

← Use the Distributive Property.
← Find the products.
← Find the sum.

Practice

Choose the letter preceding the word or expression that best completes the statement or answers the question.

1 Which sum is a negative number?

A. $\frac{1}{2} + \left(-\frac{3}{4}\right) + \frac{3}{4}$ **C.** $-\frac{1}{2} + \left(-\frac{3}{4}\right) + \frac{1}{2}$

B. $\frac{1}{2} + \frac{3}{4} + \left(-\frac{1}{2}\right)$ **D.** $-\frac{1}{2} + \frac{3}{4} + \frac{1}{2}$

2 Which is true of $\left(-1\frac{1}{2}\right)\left(-3\frac{1}{3}\right)$?

A. The product is negative.

B. The product is positive and less than 1.

C. The product is positive and greater than 6.

D. The product is a whole number.

3 Which expression is *not* equivalent to $-6.25 \div 2.5$?

A. $-62.5 \div 25$ **C.** $-625 \div 25$

B. $-0.625 \div 0.25$ **D.** $-6250 \div 2500$

4 Which statement about inverses is false?

A. Every real number has a reciprocal.

B. Every real number has an additive inverse.

C. The sum of a number and its additive inverse is 0.

D. The product of a number and its reciprocal is 1.

5 Which statement is true?

A. $|-8| = -|8|$ **C.** $-|-8| = -(-8)$

B. $|-8| = -(-8)$ **D.** $-|-8| = |-(-8)|$

In Exercises 6–18, simplify each expression.

6 $-9 + (-5)$ **7** $-0.15 + 0.75$

8 $\frac{7}{8} + \left(-\frac{1}{6}\right)$ **9** $12 - 19$

10 $124.7 - 56.79$ **11** $\left(-\frac{3}{5}\right) - \frac{9}{10}$

12 $15 \times (-8)$ **13** $(-1.3)(5.6)$

14 $\frac{1}{9} \times \frac{3}{8}$ **15** $14 \div (-7)$

16 $-57 \div 2.4$ **17** $-\frac{7}{20} \div \left(-\frac{3}{7}\right)$

18 $|22.7 - 173|$

In Exercises 19–24, write the name of the property that is illustrated by each statement.

19 $8(5) = 5(8)$

20 $-3.008 + 3.008 = 0$

21 $6(10 + 5) = 6(10) + 6(5)$

22 $1 \cdot (6 - 0.02) = (6 - 0.02)$

23 $(8 + 3) + 4 = 4 + (8 + 3)$

24 $(6 \cdot 5) \cdot 4 = 6 \cdot (5 \cdot 4)$

In Exercises 25–27, simplify each expression.

25 $|-9|$ **26** $-|-4|$ **27** $-(-2)$

In Exercises 28–29, replace each ___?___ with <, >, or = to make a true statement.

28 $|-5|$ ___?___ $|5|$ **29** $-|1|$ ___?___ $|-1|$

In Exercises 30–33, $T = \{x \mid x$ is an odd whole number$\}$ and $T \subset W$.

30 Is T closed under addition? Explain.

31 What is the additive identity of T?

32 What is T'?

33 Is T commutative under addition? Explain your reasoning.

1.4 Significant Digits

Significant digits are the digits of a number that are known for certain. Any nonzero digit, the numbers from 1–9, is *always* significant. The number of significant digits in any number depends on the value of zero in the number.

For example, all of the following numbers have 3 significant digits.

256
2.56
25.6
0.256
0.00256

Note

Significant digits refers most often to the reliability and accuracy of a measurement.

 EXAMPLE 1   **Recognizing significant digits in positive integers**

1 How many significant digits are in 120,580?

■ **SOLUTION**

The zero between the 2 and the 5 is significant because the following digits indicate an accuracy to at least the tens place. The final zero is not significant because there is no decimal place to verify the certainty of the zero in this number. So, the digits 1, 2, 0, 5, and 8 are all significant digits.

Therefore, there are **5** significant digits in 120,580.

As with whole numbers, when a number is a decimal less than 1, not all zeros are considered significant. The *leading zero* in a decimal less than 1 is not significant but the zeros at the end, or the *trailing zeros,* are significant.

 EXAMPLE 2   **Recognizing significant digits in decimals less than 1**

2 How many significant digits are in 0.03850?

■ **SOLUTION**

The digits 3, 8, 5, and 0 are significant. The zeros in front of the 3 are not significant.

Therefore, there are **4** significant digits in 0.03850.

When a decimal is greater than 1, all zeros in the number become significant.

 EXAMPLE 3   **Recognizing significant digits in decimals ≥ 1**

3 How many significant digits are in 23.00340?

■ **SOLUTION**

All the zeros are significant, along with the digits 2, 3, 3, and 4.

Therefore, there are **7** significant digits in 23.00340.

When you find the sum, difference, product, or quotient of numbers and measurements, you should round your answers to the *least number* of significant digits in any of the numbers involved.

18

Significant digits in a sum, difference, product, or quotient

Find the sum, difference, product, or quotient. Round your answers to the appropriate number of significant digits.

4 12.04 ft + 4.60 ft

■ SOLUTION

12.04 ft + 4.60 ft = 16.64 ft = 16.6 ft
4 significant digits + 3 significant digits = 3 significant digits

5 1,200 − 452.50

■ SOLUTION

1,200 − 452.50 = 747.50 = 750
2 significant digits − 5 significant digits = 2 significant digits

6 23.45 km × 0.0031 km

■ SOLUTION

23.45 km × 0.0031 km = 0.072695 km = 0.073 km
4 significant digits × 2 significant digits = 2 significant digits

7 2,166,789 ÷ 5,230

■ SOLUTION

2,166,789 ÷ 5230 = 414.3 = 414
7 significant digits ÷ 3 significant digits = 3 significant digits

Practice

In Exercises 1–4, determine the number of significant digits in each measurement.

1 2,050 cm

   A. 1   **B.** 3   **C.** 2   **D.** 4

2 0.00025 km

   A. 2   **B.** 4   **C.** 3   **D.** 5

3 58.0790 mm

   A. 6   **B.** 3   **C.** 5   **D.** 2

4 0.064308 ft

   A. 4   **B.** 6   **C.** 5   **D.** 7

In Exercises 5–16, perform the operation indicated; use significant digits.

5 1,803 mi + 450 mi   **6** 0.2083 + 0.0756

7 11 ft × 825 ft   **8** 1,370 ÷ 31.7

9 6.45 + 4.140   **10** 665 m ÷ 0.0505 m

11 5.2 × 6.44   **12** 2,002 − 345

13 0.123 + 0.001   **14** 457 in. × 0.038 in.

15 754.90 yd − 2.06 yd   **16** 12,039 ÷ 0.0306

1.5 Exponents, Square Roots, and the Order of Operations

New Jersey Standards
4.1.B.1 Use operations on real numbers

You can write $3 \cdot 3 \cdot 3 \cdot 3 \cdot 3 \cdot 3$ in **exponential form** as 3^6. In this expression, 3 is the **base** and 6 is the **exponent**. It is read as "three to the sixth power." Because $3^6 = 729$, the number 729 is called *the sixth power of three.*

$$\underbrace{3 \cdot 3 \cdot 3 \cdot 3 \cdot 3 \cdot 3}_{6 \text{ factors}} = \overset{\text{exponent}}{\underset{\text{base}}{3^6}} = 729 \leftarrow \text{6th power of 3}$$

It is also possible for an exponent to be 0 or a negative integer.

- For any nonzero number a, $a^0 = 1$.
- For any nonzero number a and any integer n, $a^{-n} = \frac{1}{a^n}$.

Go Online
PHSchool.com
Visit: PHSchool.com
Web Code: ayp-0242

EXAMPLES 1 through 3 — Simplifying exponential expressions

Simplify each expression.

1 5^4

■ SOLUTION

$5^4 = 5 \cdot 5 \cdot 5 \cdot 5 = 625$

2 372^0

■ SOLUTION

$372^0 = 1$

3 2^{-3}

■ SOLUTION

$2^{-3} = \frac{1}{2^3} = \frac{1}{2 \cdot 2 \cdot 2} = \frac{1}{8}$

Exponents are used to write very large and very small positive numbers in *scientific notation*. A number written in **scientific notation** has two factors.

The first factor is a number that is at least 1, but is less than 10. $\rightarrow$ $a \times 10^n$ $\leftarrow$ The second factor is an integer power of 10, expressed in exponential form.

Go Online
PHSchool.com
Visit: PHSchool.com
Web Code: ayp-0243

You can use what you know about scientific notation to convert a number in standard form to scientific notation.

EXAMPLES 4 through 7 — Converting numbers in standard form and scientific notation

Write each number in standard form.

4 7.4×10^5 ■ SOLUTION The exponent is 5. Move the decimal point 5 places *to the right.*

$7.4 \times 10^5 = 7.4 \times 100,000 = 740,000$

5 4.43×10^{-6} ■ SOLUTION The exponent is -6. Move the decimal point 6 places *to the left.*

$4.43 \times 10^{-6} = 4.43 \times 0.000001 = 0.00000443$

Write each number in scientific notation.

6 32,500,000 ■ SOLUTION $32,500,000 = 3.25 \times 10,000,000 = 3.25 \times 10^7$
7 places

7 0.0068 ■ SOLUTION $0.0068 = 6.8 \times 0.001 = 6.8 \times 10^{-3}$
3 places

For any real number a, finding the value of a^2 is called **squaring** the number.

$$4^2 = 16 \quad \rightarrow \quad \text{4 squared is equal to 16.} \quad \rightarrow \quad \text{The square of 4 is 16.}$$
$$(-4)^2 = 16 \quad \rightarrow \quad \text{−4 squared is equal to 16.} \quad \rightarrow \quad \text{The square of –4 is 16.}$$

If $a^2 = b$, then a is called a **square root** of b. The *radical sign* $\sqrt{}$ indicates a square root. The expression under the radical sign is called the **radicand.** An expression that contains a radical sign is called a **radical expression.**

Every positive real number b has two square roots. The expression $\sqrt{b}$ indicates its positive square root, called the **principal square root.** The expression $-\sqrt{b}$ indicates its negative square root.

Rational numbers such as 25 and 0.01 are called **perfect squares** because their square roots are rational numbers.

$$\sqrt{25} = 5 \text{ and } -\sqrt{25} = -5 \qquad \sqrt{0.01} = 0.1 \text{ and } -\sqrt{0.01} = -0.1$$

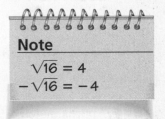

Note

$\sqrt{16} = 4$

$-\sqrt{16} = -4$

If a rational number is not a perfect square, then its square roots are irrational numbers. This means that their decimal representations are nonterminating, nonrepeating decimals. Therefore, you cannot write exact decimal values. However, it is possible to find an *approximation.*

EXAMPLE 8   **Locating square roots between consecutive integers**

8 Between which two consecutive integers is $\sqrt{42}$?

■ **SOLUTION 1**

$\sqrt{36} < \sqrt{42} < \sqrt{49}$ ← 42 is between the

$\quad 6 \;\; < \sqrt{42} < \;\; 7$ perfect-square

integers 36 and 49.

Therefore, $\sqrt{42}$ is between 6 and 7.

■ **SOLUTION 2**

You can also use a calculator to find an approximation of a radical expression.

√(42)

6.480740698

■

Therefore, $\sqrt{42}$ is between 6 and 7.

Sometimes your approximation needs to be more precise. You may be asked to determine which whole number is closest to a root.

EXAMPLE 9   **Approximating square roots to the nearest whole number**

9 What is $\sqrt{132}$ to the nearest whole number?

■ **SOLUTION**

$11 < \sqrt{132} < 12$ ← $\sqrt{132}$ is between 11 and 12.

Is it closer to 11 or 12?

$11^2 = 121; \, 132 - 121 = 11$

$12^2 = 144; \, 144 - 132 = 12$

Therefore, $\sqrt{132} \approx 11$.

Note

The symbol $\approx$ is read "is approximately equal to."

You can also use a calculator to find a more exact approximation of a square root. A calculator gives an estimate of the square root of a nonsquare, rational number.

EXAMPLES 10 and 11   **Approximating irrational square roots**

10 Approximate $\sqrt{4.3}$ to the nearest hundredth.

■ SOLUTION

$\sqrt{4.3} \rightarrow$ ⌐√⌐ 4.3 ENTER

$\rightarrow 2.073644135$ ← 3 is less than 5, so round down. Drop the digits to the right of 7.

Therefore, $\sqrt{4.3} \approx 2.07$.

11 Approximate $-\sqrt{10.8}$ to the nearest hundredth.

■ SOLUTION

$-\sqrt{10.8} \rightarrow$ (−) ⌐√⌐ 10.8 ENTER

$\rightarrow -3.286335345$ ← 6 is greater than 5, so round up. Add 1 to 8. Drop the digits to the right of 8.

Therefore, $-\sqrt{10.8} \approx -3.29$.

Note

To round a decimal:

Look at the digit to the right of the place to which you are rounding.

■ If it is less than 5, round down.
■ If it is greater than or equal to 5, round up.

Many expressions involve two or more operations. When simplifying such expressions, it is important to perform the operations in the following order.

Order of Operations

1. Perform any operation(s) within grouping symbols.
2. Simplify all powers.
3. Multiply and divide in order from left to right.
4. Add and subtract in order from left to right.

Note

Grouping symbols

parentheses ( )
brackets [ ]
braces { }
fraction bar —
absolute-value bars | |
radical sign $\sqrt{}$

EXAMPLES 12 and 13   **Applying the order of operations**

Simplify each expression.

12 $11 - 3 \cdot 8$

■ SOLUTION

$11 - 3 \cdot 8$ ← Multiply first.
$11 - 24$ ← Then subtract.
$ -13$

13 $3(5 + 4^2) \div 7 - 7$

■ SOLUTION

$3(5 + 4^2) \div 7 - 7$ ← Simplify 4^2.
$3(5 + 16) \div 7 - 7$ ← Add within the parentheses.
$3(21) \div 7 - 7$ ← Multiply $3(21)$.
$63 \div 7 - 7$ ← Divide $63 \div 7$.
$9 - 7$ ← Subtract.
2

Practice

Choose the letter preceding the word or expression that best completes the statement or answers the question.

1 Which expression is equivalent to 3^{-4}?

A. $3(-4)$ **B.** $\frac{1}{3^4}$ **C.** $|3^4|$ **D.** $\frac{1}{3 \cdot 4}$

2 Which number is equivalent to 8.72×10^{-4}?

A. 0.000872   **C.** 0.0872

B. 0.00872   **D.** 87,200

3 Which expression represents 32.45 in scientific notation?

A. $3 \times 10^1 + 2 \times 10^0 + 4 \times 10^{-1} + 5 \times 10^{-2}$

B. 3.245×10^1

C. 3.245×10^{-1}

D. 3245×10^{-2}

4 Which symbol makes a true statement when placed in the blank below?

$$0.38 \times 10^{-2} \underline{\quad ? \quad} 0.38 \times 10^{-3}$$

A. $<$ **B.** $>$ **C.** $=$ **D.** $\leq$

5 Which is not a perfect square?

A. $\frac{1}{4}$ **B.** $\frac{28}{63}$ **C.** $\frac{18}{2}$ **D.** $\frac{32}{48}$

6 Between which two consecutive integers does $-\sqrt{20}$ lie?

A. 4 and 5   **C.** -5 and -3

B. -5 and -4 **D.** -21 and -19

7 To simplify $15 + 5(12 \div 4)$, first calculate

A. $15 + 5$.   **C.** $12 \div 4$.

B. $5(12)$.   **D.** $5 \div 4$.

8 Which set of numbers has been placed in order from least to greatest?

A. $-\sqrt{7.2}, -2.\overline{7}, -2\frac{1}{7}$

B. $-2\frac{1}{7}, -2.\overline{7}, -\sqrt{7.2}$

C. $-2.\overline{7}, -\sqrt{7.2}, -2\frac{1}{7}$

D. $-2.\overline{7}, -2\frac{1}{7}, -\sqrt{7.2}$

In Exercises 9–12, simplify each expression.

9 11^2 **10** 2^7 **11** 5^0 **12** 9^1

In Exercises 13–16, write each number in standard form.

13 8×10^3 **14** 8×10^{-3}

15 3.1×10^{-5} **16** 9.2×10^7

In Exercises 17–22, write each number in scientific notation.

17 4,000,000   **18** 0.000004

19 34.09   **20** 0.205

21 65,000,000   **22** 0.0099

In Exercises 23–26, simplify each expression.

23 $\sqrt{64}$ **24** $-\sqrt{400}$

25 $-\sqrt{1.44}$ **26** $\sqrt{0.09}$

In Exercises 27–30, name the two consecutive integers between which each number lies.

27 $\sqrt{30}$ **28** $-\sqrt{75}$

29 $\sqrt{14.9}$ **30** $-\sqrt{32.2}$

In Exercises 31–36, use a calculator to approximate to the nearest hundredth.

31 $\sqrt{3}$ **32** $-\sqrt{24}$ **33** $-\sqrt{4.9}$

34 $\sqrt{85.2}$ **35** $\sqrt{0.95}$ **36** $\sqrt{0.2}$

In Exercises 37–42, simplify each expression.

37 $15 - 8 \times 4$ **38** $-4 + 32 \div 4 - 2$

39 $(-2 + 6)^2 \div 2$ **40** $16 - 2^2 \times 8 + 16$

41 $[2(6 - 5) + 8] - 2^3$ **42** $2^2 \cdot 3^1 \cdot 5^2 \cdot 11^1$

In Exercises 43–44, write the prime factorization of each number, using exponents to indicate repeated factors.

43 675   **44** 192

In Exercises 45–46, solve the following problems. Clearly explain your reasoning and show all necessary work.

45 Insert one pair of grouping symbols into $4 \times 3 + 12 \div 3$ to create an expression that is equivalent to 8.

46 Write $3 \times 10^0, 3 \times 10^2, 3 \times 10^{-2}$, and 3×10^{-5} from least to greatest.

1.6 Arithmetic and Geometric Sequences

A number pattern is called an **arithmetic sequence** when each **term** of the sequence differs by a fixed number, called the **common difference**.

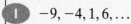

Finding the common difference of a sequence

Find the common difference and determine the next three terms of the sequence.

1 $-9, -4, 1, 6, \ldots$

- SOLUTION

To find the common difference, find the difference between consecutive terms.

$$-4 - (-9) = 5$$
$$1 - (-4) = 5$$
$$6 - 1 = 5$$

The common difference is 5.

Add 5 to the fourth term to find the fifth term, add 5 to the fifth term to find the sixth, and so on. So the next three terms of the sequence are 11, 16, 21.

2 $11, 4, -3, -10$

- SOLUTION

To find the common difference, find the difference between consecutive terms.

$$4 - 11 = -7$$
$$-3 - 4 = -7$$
$$-10 - (-3) = -7$$

The common difference is -7.

Add -7 to the fourth term to find the fifth term, add -7 to the fifth term to find the sixth, and so on. So the next three terms of the sequence are $-17, -24, -31$.

a_1 represents the first term of a sequence, a_2 the second term, a_3 the third, and so on to the nth term a_n. You can find any term of an arithmetic sequence by using the common difference d and the first term a_1 of the sequence.

In the sequence $6, 10, 14, 18, \ldots$, the 1st term a_1 is 6 and each consecutive term is found by the formula $a_n = 6 + (n-1)4$ where n represents the number of the term in the sequence.

The nth Term of an Arithmetic Sequence

The nth term in an arithmetic sequence a_n, where a_1 is the first term and d is the common difference is

$$a_n = a_1 + (n-1)d$$

EXAMPLES 3 and 4 Finding the terms of an arithmetic sequence

3 Find the 9th term of the sequence $29, 26, 23, \ldots$.

- SOLUTION

$a_n = a_1 + (n-1)d$
$a_9 = 29 + (9-1)(-3)$ ← $a_1 = 29$ and $d = -3$.
$a_9 = 29 + (-24)$
$a_9 = 5$

4 A sequence is given by $a_n = 8 + (n-1)3$. Find a_4.

- SOLUTION

$a_n = 8 + (n-1)3$
$a_4 = 8 + (4-1)3$
$a_4 = 8 + 9$
$a_4 = 17$

You can also find the equation that represents the nth term of an arithmetic sequence. Once you have found this equation you can find the value of any term of the sequence.

EXAMPLE 5   Finding the equation for the nth term of an arithmetic sequence

5   Write the equation that represents the nth term of the sequence $12, 17, 22, 27, \ldots$

■ SOLUTION

Step 1
Identify a_1.
$a_1 = 12$

Step 2
Find d.
$17 - 12 = 5, 22 - 17 = 5, 27 - 22 = 5$
$d = 5$

Step 3
Use the formula $a_n = a_1 + (n - 1)d$ to write the equation for the nth term.
$a_n = 12 + (n - 1)5$

Another type of number sequence is a **geometric sequence**. This quotient is constant between consecutive terms of a geometric sequence and is called the **common ratio r**. You can find the common ratio by dividing any term of the sequence by the preceding term.

EXAMPLES 6 and 7   Finding the common ratio of a geometric sequence

Find the common ratio and the next two terms of each of the following geometric sequences.

6   $4, 12, 36, \ldots$

■ SOLUTION
Find the common ratio

$$\frac{12}{4} = 3$$

The common ratio is 3.
The next two terms are $36(3) = 108$ and $108(3) = 324$.

7   $9, 3, 1, \ldots$

■ SOLUTION
Find the common ratio

$$\frac{3}{9} = \frac{1}{3}$$

The common ratio is $\frac{1}{3}$.

The next 2 terms are $1\left(\frac{1}{3}\right) = \frac{1}{3}$ and $\frac{1}{3}\left(\frac{1}{3}\right) = \frac{1}{9}$.

The *n*th Term of a Geometric Sequence

The *n*th term in a geometric sequence a_n where a_1 is the first term and r is the common ratio is

$$a_n = a_1 r^{n-1}$$

Go Online
PHSchool.com
Visit: PHSchool.com
Web Code: ayp-0255

EXAMPLES 8 and 9   Finding the terms of a geometric sequence

8 Find the 6th term of the sequence 7, 14, 28, . . .

■ SOLUTION

$a_n = a_1 r^{n-1}$ ← $n = 6$.

$a_6 = a_1 r^{6-1}$ ← $a_1 = 7$ and $r = 2$.

$\quad = 7(2)^{6-1}$

$\quad = 7(2)^5$

$\quad = 224$

The 6th term of the sequence is **224**.

9 Find the 8th term of the sequence 4, 20, 100, . . .

■ SOLUTION

$a_n = a_1 r^{n-1}$

$a_8 = a_1 r^{8-1}$

$\quad = 4(5)^{8-1}$

$\quad = 4(5)^7$

$\quad = 312{,}500$

The 8th term of the sequence is **312,500**.

Likewise, you can write an equation for the *n*th term of a given geometric sequence by determining the value of the common ratio, *r*.

EXAMPLE 10   Finding the equation for the *n*th term of a geometric sequence

10 Write an equation for the *n*th term of the sequence 10, 7.5, 5.625, . . .

■ SOLUTION

Step 1
Identify a_1.
$a_1 = 10$

Step 2
Find the common ratio, *r*.
$\dfrac{7.5}{10} = \dfrac{5.625}{7.5} = \dfrac{3}{4}$

Step 3
Use the equation $a_n = a_1 r^{n-1}$ to write the equation for the *n*th term.

$$a_n = 10\left(\tfrac{3}{4}\right)^{n-1}$$

You can also use geometric sequences to solve real-world problems.

EXAMPLE 11   Using geometric sequences to solve real-world problems

11 In February 2006, about 65 thousand homes were sold in northeastern United States. If the number of home sales increases by about 3.5% each year, write an equation for the total number of homes sold a_n in terms of the year.

■ SOLUTION

Let $a_1 = 65$, then $a_n = 65(1.035)^{n-1}$

Practice

Choose the letter preceding the word or expression that best completes the statement or answers the question

1 Which set of numbers extends the pattern $27, 9, 3, 1, \ldots$

   A. $3, 9, 27$ C. $3, \frac{1}{3}, \frac{1}{27}$

   B. $\frac{1}{3}, \frac{1}{9}, \frac{1}{27}$ D. $\frac{1}{3}, \frac{1}{12}, \frac{1}{36}$

2 Which equation can be used to find the next number in the pattern $4, 8, 16, 32, 64, \ldots$

   A. $a_n = 4^{n-1}$ C. $a_n = 4(2)^{n-1}$

   B. $a_n = 4(2n)$ D. $a_n = 4(n^2)$

3 What is the 8th term of the sequence $48, 24, 12, 6, \ldots$?

   A. 0.375 C. 0.25

   B. 0.75 D. 1.5

4 What is 7th term of the sequence $a_n = -9 + (n-1)0.5$?

   A. -6.5 C. -7

   B. -6 D. -5.5

In Exercises 5–8, determine whether each sequence is arithmetic or geometric.

5 $-6, 0, 6, 12, \ldots$ 6 $2, 6, 18, 54, \ldots$

7 $4, 2, 1, \frac{1}{2}, \ldots$ 8 $13, 6, -1, -8, \ldots$

In Exercises 9–12, find the 7th and 10th term of each sequence.

9 $a_n = 2 + (n-1)3$

10 $a_n = -5 + (n-1)7$

11 $a_n = 9 + (n-1)(-6)$

12 $a_n = 0.5 + (n-1)3$

In Exercises 13–16, find the 3rd and 5th term of each sequence.

13 $5(3)^{n-1}$

14 $-2(5)^{n-1}$

15 $5(-3)^{n-1}$

16 $-5(3)^{n-1}$

In Exercises 17–20, find the common difference in each sequence and then find the next two terms in each sequence.

17 $-5, -10, -15, \ldots$ 18 $0.7, 1.4, 2.1, \ldots$

19 $12, 8, 4, 0, \ldots$ 20 $0.5, 0.25, 0, \ldots$

In Exercises 21–24, find the common ratio in each sequence and then find the next two terms.

21 $18, 9, 4.5, \ldots$ 22 $2, 12, 72, \ldots$

23 $9, -36, 144, \ldots$ 24 $9, 12, 16, \ldots$

In Exercises 25–32, write an equation for the nth term of the sequence.

25 $7, 14, 21, 28, \ldots$

26 $3, 9, 27, 81, \ldots$

27 $-252, -42, -7, -\frac{7}{6}, \ldots$

28 $5, 2, -1, -4, \ldots$

29 $4, 9, 14, 19, \ldots$

30 $3, 12, 48, 192, \ldots$

31 $-8, -4, -2, -1, \ldots$

32 $10, 8, 6, 4, \ldots$

New Jersey Standards
4.3.D.1.1 Evaluate/simplify expressions
4.3.D.1.2 Multiply by a monomial

1.7 Variables and Variable Expressions

A **variable** is a letter that represents a number. An expression that contains at least one variable is called a **variable expression** or an **algebraic expression.** A variable expression has one or more *terms.* A **term** is a number, a variable, or a product of numbers and variables.

$$\text{variable expression} \rightarrow 7x^2y + \tfrac{1}{2}xy + x - 5$$

4 terms

When working with variable expressions, you often use the following basic principle.

Substitution Principle

If $a = b$, then a may be replaced by b in any expression.

The set of numbers that a variable may represent is called the **replacement set,** or **domain,** of the variable. Each number in the replacement set is a **value** of the variable. To **evaluate a variable expression,** you replace each variable with one of its values and simplify the numerical expression that results.

Note

A product involving a variable is often written without an operation symbol or parentheses.
$m \cdot n$ is written mn.
$3 \cdot x$ is written $3x$.

Go Online
PHSchool.com
Visit: PHSchool.com
Web Code: ayp-0002

EXAMPLES 1 through 3   Evaluating variable expressions

Evaluate each expression for $x = 10$ and $y = -7$.

1 $3x - 4y$ ■ SOLUTION

$3x - 4y$	
$3(10) - 4(-7)$	← Replace x with 10 and y with -7.
$30 - (-28)$	← Multiply first.
$30 + 28$	← Rewrite the subtraction as an addition.
58	← Add.

2 $(x + y)^2$ ■ SOLUTION

$(x + y)^2$	
$(10 + [-7])^2$	← Replace x with 10 and y with -7.
3^2	← Add inside the parentheses first.
9	← Simplify the power.

3 $5xy^2$ ■ SOLUTION

$5xy^2$	
$5(10)(-7)^2$	← Replace x with 10 and y with -7.
$5(10)(49)$	← Simplify the power first.
$2,450$	← Multiply.

To **simplify a variable expression,** you must perform as many of the indicated operations as possible. The Distributive Property is frequently used to do this.

Go Online
PHSchool.com
Visit: PHSchool.com
Web Code: ayp-0795

| EXAMPLE 4 | **Simplifying an indicated multiplication** |

4 Simplify $-4(k - 6)$.

■ SOLUTION

$$-4(k - 6)$$
$$-4(k + [-6]) \quad \leftarrow \textbf{Rewrite the subtraction as addition.}$$
$$(-4) \cdot k + (-4) \cdot (-6) \quad \leftarrow \textbf{Apply the Distributive Property.}$$
$$-4k + 24 \quad \leftarrow \textbf{Simplify each term.}$$

In a variable expression, **like terms** are terms that have exactly the same variable part. The numerical part of a term that contains variables is the **coefficient,** or **numerical coefficient,** of the term. The Distributive Property allows you to simplify an expression by adding the coefficients of like terms. This process is called *combining like terms.*

Note

Examples of Like Terms
$4n$ and $-6n$
pq and $2pq$
1 and -5

Examples of Unlike Terms
$4n$ and $-6n^2$
pq and $2pr$
x and -5

| EXAMPLES 5 and 6 | **Combining like terms** |

5 Simplify $-5w - 9 + w$.

■ SOLUTION

$$-5w - 9 + w$$
$$[-5w + w] - 9 \quad \leftarrow \textbf{Change the order. Group like terms.}$$
$$[-5w + 1w] - 9 \quad \leftarrow \textbf{Rewrite } w \textbf{ as } 1w.$$
$$-4w - 9 \quad \leftarrow \textbf{Combine like terms by adding the}$$
$$\textbf{coefficients of } w.$$

6 Simplify $6c^2 - 8c - 4c^2 - 2c$.

■ SOLUTION

$$6c^2 - 8c - 4c^2 - 2c$$
$$6c^2 + (-8c) + (-4c^2) + (-2c) \quad \leftarrow \textbf{Write the subtractions as additions.}$$
$$[6c^2 + (-4c^2)] + [(-8c) + (-2c)] \quad \leftarrow \textbf{Change the order. Group like terms.}$$
$$2c^2 + -10c \quad \leftarrow \textbf{Add the coefficients of } c^2 \textbf{ and of } c.$$
$$2c^2 - 10c$$

It often is helpful to use a numerical or variable expression to represent a real-life situation. To do this, you must be able to translate words and phrases into symbols. The following table shows some common translations.

English Phrase	Mathematical Expression
m plus n, the sum of m and n, m increased by n, n more than m	$m + n$
m minus n, the difference when n is subtracted from m, m decreased by n, n less than m, n fewer than m	$m - n$
m times n, the product of m and n	$mn, m \times n, m \cdot n, (m)(n)$
m divided by n, the quotient when m is divided by n	$m \div n, \frac{m}{n}$

EXAMPLES 7 through 10   Translating phrases into variable expressions

Write each phrase as a variable expression.

7 five less than a number s ■ SOLUTION $s - 5$

8 three times a number z, increased by 4   ■ SOLUTION $3z + 4$

9 seven times the sum of a number p and 25   ■ SOLUTION $7(p + 25)$

10 the square of a number a, divided by nine   ■ SOLUTION $a^2 \div 9$, or $\frac{a^2}{9}$

You may also be asked to translate an algebraic expression into words.

EXAMPLES 11 through 13   Translating algebraic expressions into English phrases

> **Note**
> Translations may vary.

Translate the algebraic expressions into English phrases.

11 $2x + 3y$

12 $-4(a + b)$

13 $\frac{a}{b} - c$

■ SOLUTION

the sum of twice a number and 3 times a different number

■ SOLUTION

-4 times the sum of a and b

■ SOLUTION

c subtracted from the quotient of a and b

Translating word phrases into arithmetic and algebraic expressions can be helpful when setting up and solving application problems.

EXAMPLES 14 and 15   Using variable expressions in problems

> **Note**
> even numbers:
> $\ldots, -4, -2, 0, 2, 4, \ldots$
> odd numbers:
> $\ldots, -5, -3, -1, 1, 3, \ldots$
> Both differ by 2.

14 Let y represent an odd number. What are the next two odd numbers?

■ SOLUTION

$y + 2$ and $y + 4$

15 Sam started hiking on a trail at 6:00 A.M. His sister Lisa began hiking the same trail at 8:00 A.M. Sam has now been hiking for h hours. Which expression represents the number of hours that Lisa has been hiking?

A. $h + 2$ **B.** $h - 2$ **C.** $h + 8$ **D.** $h - 6$

■ SOLUTION

Lisa started two hours after Sam, so she has been hiking two fewer hours. *Two fewer than a number h is translated into symbols as $h - 2$.*

The correct choice is **B.**

Choose the letter preceding the word or expression that best completes the statement or answers the question.

1 Which expression results from substituting 5 for m and -6 for n in $-3m - 9n$?

A. $3(-6) - 9(5)$ C. $-3(-6) - 9(-6)$

B. $-3(5) - 9(5)$ D. $-3(5) - 9(-6)$

2 Which number is the value of $\frac{k - p}{p - k}$ for $k = -6$ and $p = 6$?

A. -12 B. -1 C. 0 D. 1

3 If $a = -2$, then $3a^2 - 4a + 6$ equals

A. 2 B. 5 C. 10 D. 26

4 Which are a pair of like terms?

A. $5x$ and $7y$ C. $5x$ and $7x$

B. $5x$ and $7x^2$ D. $-5x$ and $-5y$

5 Which expression is not equivalent to $-5n + 9 - 2n$?

A. $-5n - 2n + 9$ C. $-5n + 2n - 9$

B. $9 - 5n - 2n$ D. $9 + (-5n - 2n)$

6 Which expression represents the phrase "a number x less a number y"?

A. $x < y$ C. $x - y$

B. $y - x$ D. $y < x$

7 If $d + 2$ is an even integer, which is the next greater even integer?

A. d B. $d + 3$ C. $d + 4$ D. $2d$

8 For which value of z is the following true?

$$z < \sqrt{z + 1} < 1$$

A. -1 B. 1 C. 2 D. 3

In Exercises 9–13, evaluate each expression for the given value(s) of the variable(s).

9 $3s - 5$; $s = -5$

10 $q^2 + 9q$; $q = -3$

11 $\frac{j + k}{2}$; $j = 5$ and $k = 6$

12 $rs - r$; $r = 2$ and $s = -3$

13 $3a^2 - 4b$; $a = -2$ and $b = 0$

In Exercises 14–21, simplify each expression.

14 $2(a + b)$ **15** $-5(r - s)$

16 $8(6 - p)$ **17** $-3(x + 12)$

18 $(c + 5)(6)$ **19** $(v - 7)(-11)$

20 $-6n + 20n$ **21** $3t - (-15t)$

In Exercises 22–27, write each phrase as a variable expression.

22 eight more than a number t

23 a number c decreased by seventeen

24 the quotient when the square root of a number n is divided by two

25 twice the sum of a number y and nine

26 twelve less than the product of a number m and its opposite

27 the quotient when the sum of a number a and a number b is divided by their product

In Exercises 28–30, translate the algebraic expressions into English phrases.

28 $(abc)^3$ **29** $\sqrt{\dfrac{3a^2}{5b^4}}$ **30** $(7 - 2x)(-3y)$

In Exercises 31–33, solve the following problems. Clearly show all necessary work.

31 If $-2n - 4$ represents an even integer, write an expression to represent the next lesser even integer.

32 If n is an integer, which of the following expressions represents an odd integer? Show your work.

$$n - 2, n - 1, n, n + 1, n + 2$$

33 Mel began studying at 6:45 P.M., and Tim began at 6:15 P.M. Let m represent the number of minutes Mel has been studying. Write an expression to represent the number of minutes Tim has been studying.

DIRECTIONS FOR QUESTIONS 1–28: For each of the questions below, select the answer choice that is best for each case.

1 Which statement represents the relationship between the set of integers and the set of rational numbers?

　A. All integers are rational numbers.

　B. All rational numbers are integers.

　C. Some integers are rational numbers and others are not.

　D. No numbers are in both sets.

2 Which of the following equations is an example of the Distributive Property of Multiplication over Addition?

　A. $7 + ab = ab + 7$

　B. $5(x + y) = 5x + 5y$

　C. $ax + b = b + ax$

　D. $(a)0 = 0(a) = 0$

3 Which number has the greatest value?

　A. $1\frac{2}{3}$　　　　C. 1.7

　B. $\sqrt{2}$　　　　D. $\frac{3}{2}$

4 Evaluate the expression $-|x + y|$ for $x = 3$ and $y = -10$.

　A. 13　　　　C. 7

　B. -13　　　　D. -7

5 How many significant digits are in the measurement 12.025 km?

　A. 2　　B. 3　　C. 4　　D. 5

6 What is the value of $0.057 + 1.196$ with the appropriate number of significant digits?

　A. 1.3　　　　C. 1.2

　B. 1.253　　　　D. 1

7 Which statement illustrates the Associative Property of Multiplication?

　A. $2 \cdot (3 \cdot 4) = (3 \cdot 4) \cdot 2$

　B. $2 \cdot (3 \cdot 4) = (2 \cdot 3) \cdot 4$

　C. $2 \cdot (3 \cdot 4) = (2 \cdot 3) \cdot (2 \cdot 4)$

　D. $2 \cdot (3 \cdot 4) = (2 + 3) \cdot (2 + 4)$

8 If $a \neq 0$ and the product of x and $-a$ is 1, then

　A. $x = 1$.　　　　C. $x = 1 + a$.

　B. $x = a$.　　　　D. $x = -\frac{1}{a}$.

9 Which expression is equivalent to $6.4 - 8.2$?

　A. $|8.2 - 6.4|$　　　C. $-(8.2 - 6.4)$

　B. $8.2 - 6.4$　　　D. $6.4 - (-8.2)$

10 The number $\sqrt{83}$ is between

　A. 9 and 10.　　　　C. 10 and 20.

　B. 41 and 42.　　　　D. 80 and 90.

11 Which expression is not equivalent to $-\frac{1}{2}(3 + 2)$?

　A. $(3 + 2)(-0.5)$　　C. $-\frac{1}{2}(3) + 2$

　B. $-\frac{3 + 2}{2}$　　　D. $-\frac{5}{2}$

In Exercises 12–19, simplify each expression.

12 $(-4)^3$

　A. -12　　　　C. 64

　B. -64　　　　D. 12

13 7^0

　A. 1　　　　C. 7

　B. 0　　　　D. $\frac{1}{7}$

14 3^{-5}

A. 15   B. -243 C. $\frac{1}{243}$ D. $-\frac{1}{15}$

15 $-\sqrt{225}$

A. 15   B. -15 C. -225 D. 25

16 $\sqrt{1.21}$

A. 1   B. 11   C. 60.5   D. 1.1

17 $-\sqrt{\frac{1}{9}}$

A. $-\frac{1}{9}$ B. -3 C. $-\frac{1}{3}$ D. $\frac{1}{9}$

18 $0.32 \div (-8)$

A. 0.4   C. 0.24

B. -0.04 D. 8.32

19 $-12.8 + 17$

A. -29.8 C. 29.8

B. 4.2   D. -4.2

20 Ari bought twelve CDs that each cost d dollars. Write an expression to represent the total cost in dollars of the CDs.

A. $12 + d$ C. $12d$

B. $\frac{d}{12}$ D. $12 + d + 100$

21 Given that $a = 3b$, simplify $a - 3b$.

A. $6b$ C. $3 - ab$

B. $3ab$ D. 0

22 If $z = -2$, what is the value of the square of z divided by the sum of twice z and 3?

A. $-\frac{4}{3}$ C. $\frac{4}{7}$

B. -4 D. 4

23 If $2n - 1$ represents an odd integer, which of the following expressions represents the next greater odd integer?

A. $2n + 2$ C. $2n$

B. $2n - 3$ D. $2n + 1$

In Exercises 24–26, evaluate each expression for the given values of the variable.

24 $g(h + 9)^2$; $g = -10$ and $h = 8$

A. -2890

B. 5041

C. 8

D. -64

25 xy^2z; $x = -4, y = -1,$ and $z = 5$

A. 20   C. -20

B. -80 D. 100

26 $(a + b)(c - 4)$; $a = -2,$ $b = -1,$ and $c = 0$

A. 4   C. -4

B. 12   D. 0

27 Write 7.011×10^{-4} in standard notation.

A. 0.0007011   C. 0.7011

B. 70,110   D. 701.1

28 Write 5,134,000,000 in scientific notation.

A. 5.134×10^{-9}

B. 51.34×10^6

C. 5.134×10^8

D. 5.134×10^9

DIRECTIONS FOR 29–31: Solve each problem and show your work.

29 The employees of a company contribute d dollars to charity. The company matches the contribution with an equal amount, and the total is shared equally among c charities.

   • Write an expression to represent the dollar amount received by each charity.

   • How much does each charity receive if the employees contributed $280.75 and there are 3 charities?

30 The following table shows how many miles George ran each day during the week.

Mon.	Tues.	Wed.	Thurs.	Fri.
3	4.5	$3\frac{3}{4}$	2	$4\frac{1}{3}$

   • On what day did George run the farthest?

   • Write the distance he ran on Wednesday as a terminating decimal.

   • How many miles did he run in total for the week?

31 The distance from the sun to Earth is approximately 9.3×10^7 miles and the distance from the sun to Mars is approximately 1.4×10^8 miles.

   • Write the distance from Earth to the sun in standard form.

   • Write the distance from Mars to the sun in standard form.

   • Use these distances to approximate the distance from Earth to Mars.

2 Linear Equations and Inequalities in One Variable

Discovering New Jersey

The New Jersey State Seal

The state seal, created by Pierre Eugene du Simitiere in 1777, displays five symbols, each one representing a feature typically found in the state.

The blue shield in the center depicts three plows, symbolic of the rich agricultural history of New Jersey. On the left side of the shield, the goddesses Liberty holds a staff topped with a Phrygian cap, a symbol of freedom. On the right, Ceres, the goddess of grain, holds a full cornucopia, picturing the abundant produce of the state. Above the shield are a helmet signifying New Jersey's independence and sovereignty as a state and a horse's head representing strength and speed.

A scroll below the shield is inscribed with the state motto "Liberty and Prosperity" and 1776, the year that New Jersey became a state.

2.1 Solving Linear Equations in One Variable

New Jersey Standards

4.3.D.2.1 Solving equations

An **equation** is a statement that sets two mathematical expressions equal.

When both sides of an equation are numerical expressions, the equation is a closed statement. This means the equation can be assigned a truth value.

$$6 + 4 = 10 \quad true \qquad 7 - 2 = 6 \quad false$$

If an equation is neither true nor false, the equation is an **open sentence**. When variables are present in an equation, the **solution** is unknown. The set of numbers that you use to represent the variable(s) is called the **replacement set**. The **solution set** is found when any value(s) for the variable from the replacement set makes the equation a **true statement**.

Note

The equation $n + 4 = 12$ is an example of an open sentence.

EXAMPLES 1 and 2 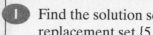 **Finding the solution of an equation from a replacement set**

1 Find the solution set of the equation $x + 4 = 13$, given the replacement set $\{5, 6, 7, 8, 9\}$.

- **SOLUTION**

Substitute the values from the replacement set for x into the equation.

Let $x = 5$; is $5 + 4 = 13$?   *No*

Let $x = 6$; is $6 + 4 = 13$?   *No*

Let $x = 7$; is $7 + 4 = 13$?   *No*

Let $x = 8$; is $8 + 4 = 13$?   *No*

Let $x = 9$; is $9 + 4 = 13$?   *Yes*

Therefore, {9} is the solution set or solution for $x + 4 = 13$.

2 Find the solution set of the equation $3x - 6 = 12$, given the replacement set $\{5, 6, 7, 11, 13\}$.

- **SOLUTION**

Substitute the values from the replacement set into the equation.

Let $x = 5$; is $3(5) - 6 = 12$?   *No*

Let $x = 6$; is $3(6) - 6 = 12$?   *Yes*

Let $x = 7$; is $3(7) - 6 = 12$?   *No*

Let $x = 11$; is $3(11) - 6 = 12$?   *No*

Let $x = 13$; is $3(13) - 6 = 12$?   *No*

Therefore, {6} is the solution set or solution for $3x - 6 = 12$.

If you multiply all of the terms of the above equation by 2, will $2x + 8 = 26$ still have a solution of $x = 9$?

Does $2(9) + 8 = 26$? Yes; $18 + 8 = 26$.

Equations that have the same solution set are called **equivalent equations**. In general, solving an equation is a process of writing a set of equivalent equations until you *isolate* the variable on one side. To find these equivalent equations, you must apply the following *properties of equality*.

Go Online
PHSchool.com
Visit: PHSchool.com
Web Code: ayp-0012

Properties of Equality

Let a, b, and c represent real numbers.

Reflexive Property	$a = a$
Symmetric Property	If $a = b$, then $b = a$.
Transitive Property	If $a = b$ and $b = c$, then $a = c$.
Addition Property	If $a = b$, then $a + c = b + c$.
Subtraction Property	If $a = b$, then $a - c = b - c$.
Multiplication Property	If $a = b$, then $ac = bc$.
Division Property	If $a = b$ and $c \neq 0$, then $\frac{a}{c} = \frac{b}{c}$.

To determine which property of equality to apply, you use *inverse operations*. Addition can "undo" subtraction, and subtraction can "undo" addition. Addition and subtraction are considered inverse operations. By similar reasoning, multiplication and division are inverse operations.

EXAMPLES 3 through 6 **Solving equations by using one property of equality**

Solve each equation.

3 $n - 6 = 9$

■ SOLUTION

Use the addition property of equality.

$$n - 6 = 9$$
$$n - 6 + 6 = 9 + 6 \quad \leftarrow \text{To isolate } n, \textit{ add } 6 \text{ to each side.}$$
$$n = 15$$

Check: $n - 6 = 9 \rightarrow 15 - 6 = 9$ ✔

4 $y + 12 = 5$

■ SOLUTION

Use the subtraction property of equality.

$$y + 12 = 5$$
$$y + 12 - 12 = 5 - 12 \quad \leftarrow \text{To isolate } y, \textit{ subtract } 12 \text{ from each side.}$$
$$y = -7$$

Check: $y + 12 = 5 \rightarrow -7 + 12 = 5$ ✔

5 $\frac{x}{-4} = 8$

■ SOLUTION

Use the multiplication property of equality.

$$\frac{x}{-4} = 8$$
$$-4\left(\frac{x}{-4}\right) = -4(8) \quad \leftarrow \text{To isolate } x, \textit{ multiply } \text{each side by } -4.$$
$$x = -32$$

Check: $\frac{x}{-4} = 8 \rightarrow \frac{-32}{-4} = 8$ ✔

6 $-35 = -5r$

■ SOLUTION

Use the division property of equality.

$$-35 = -5r$$
$$\frac{-35}{-5} = \frac{-5r}{-5} \quad \leftarrow \text{To isolate } r, \textit{ divide } \text{each side by } -5.$$
$$7 = r$$

Check: $-35 = -5r \rightarrow -35 = -5(7)$ ✔

You may need to apply more than one property of equality to solve an equation.

EXAMPLES 7 and 8 **Solving equations by using two properties of equality**

Solve each equation.

 $4z + 28 = 5$

■ SOLUTION

$$4z + 28 = 5$$
$$4z + 28 - 28 = 5 - 28$$
$$4z = -23$$
$$\frac{4z}{4} = \frac{-23}{4}$$
$$z = -5.75$$

Check: $4z + 28 = 5$
$\rightarrow 4(-5.75) + 28 = 5$ ✔

⑧ $6 = -4 - k$

■ SOLUTION

$$6 = -4 - k$$
$$6 + 4 = -4 - k + 4$$
$$10 = -k$$
$$(-1)10 = (-1)(-k) \leftarrow$$ **Recall that** $-k = -1k.$
$$-10 = k$$

Check: $6 = -4 - k$
$\rightarrow 6 = -4 - (-10)$ ✔

Note

If the variable is negative, such as $-x$, $-y$ . . . , then you can multiply both sides of the equation by -1 to make the variable positive. The variable in the solution of an equation must always be positive.

Sometimes the first step in solving an equation is using the distributive property to simplify one or both sides.

EXAMPLE 9 **Using the distributive property before solving**

 Solve $-3(m + 3) = 16$.

■ SOLUTION

$$-3(m + 3) = 16$$
$$-3m - 9 = 16 \leftarrow$$ **Use the distributive property to simplify the left side.**
$$-3m - 9 + 9 = 16 + 9$$
$$-3m = 25$$
$$\frac{-3m}{-3} = \frac{25}{-3}$$
$$m = -\frac{25}{3}$$

Check: $-3(m + 3) = 16 \rightarrow -3\left(-\frac{25}{3} + 3\right) = 16$ ✔

Note

To check a solution, substitute it for the variable in the original equation. If the resulting statement is true, you have found a solution.

You must combine all like terms on one or both sides of an equation before solving an equation.

EXAMPLE 10 **Combining like terms before solving**

 Solve $99 - 4s - 6s = -1$.

■ SOLUTION

$$99 - 4s - 6s = -1 \leftarrow -4s \text{ and } -6s \text{ are like terms.}$$
$$99 - 10s = -1$$
$$99 - 10s - 99 = -1 - 99 \leftarrow \text{Subtract 99 from both sides.}$$
$$-10s = -100$$
$$\frac{-10s}{-10} = \frac{-100}{-10} \leftarrow \text{Divide by } -10 \text{ on both sides.}$$
$$s = 10$$

Check: $99 - 4s - 6s = -1 \rightarrow 99 - 4(10) - 6(10) = -1$ ✔

Sometimes there are variable terms on both sides of an equation.

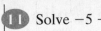

Solving equations with variable terms on both sides

11 Solve $-5 - \frac{1}{2}g = 4 + \frac{1}{4}g$.

- SOLUTION

$$-5 - \frac{1}{2}g = 4 + \frac{1}{4}g$$

$$-5 - \frac{1}{2}g + \frac{1}{2}g = 4 + \frac{1}{4}g + \frac{1}{2}g \quad \leftarrow \text{ Add } \frac{1}{2}g \text{ to each side.}$$

$$-5 = 4 + \frac{3}{4}g$$

$$-5 - 4 = 4 + \frac{3}{4}g - 4 \quad \leftarrow \text{ Subtract 4 from both sides.}$$

$$-9 = \frac{3}{4}g$$

$$\frac{4}{3}(-9) = \frac{4}{3}\left(\frac{3}{4}g\right) \quad \leftarrow \text{ Multiply each side by } \frac{4}{3}.$$

$$-12 = g$$

Check: $-5 - \frac{1}{2}g = 4 + \frac{1}{4}g \rightarrow -5 - \frac{1}{2}(-12) = 4 + \frac{1}{4}(-12)$ ✔

> **Note**
> If the variable term is isolated and the coefficient is a fraction, multiply both sides of the equation by the reciprocal of the fraction.

Some equations are true for all values of the variable. An equation like this is called an **identity**, and its solution set is the set of all real numbers. Other equations are true for no value of the variable, and they have no solution.

EXAMPLES 12 and 13   **Solving equations that are identities or that have no solution**

Solve each equation.

12 $-7t + 9 = 1 - 7t$

- SOLUTION

$$-7t + 9 = 1 - 7t$$
$$-7t + 9 + 7t = 1 - 7t + 7t$$
$$9 = 1$$

The equation $9 = 1$ is a false statement.
The equation has no solution.

13 $3(q + 5) = 3q + 15$

- SOLUTION

$$3(q + 5) = 3q + 15$$
$$3q + 15 = 3q + 15$$

The equation $3q + 15 = 3q + 15$ is true for any value of q, so it is an identity. The solution set is the set of all real numbers.

A **literal equation** is an equation that contains two or more variables. You can use the properties of equality to solve for one variable *in terms of* the others.

EXAMPLE 14   **Solving a literal equation for one of its variables**

14 Given that $2a + b = c$, which equation expresses a in terms of b and c?

A. $a = -\frac{1}{2}b + c$ **B.** $a = -\frac{1}{2}b - c$ **C.** $a = -\frac{1}{2}(b + c)$ **D.** $a = \frac{1}{2}(c - b)$

- SOLUTION

$$2a + b = c$$
$$2a = c - b \quad \leftarrow \text{ Subtract } b \text{ from each side.}$$
$$a = \frac{c - b}{2} = \frac{1}{2}(c - b) \quad \leftarrow \text{ Divide each side by 2.}$$

The correct choice is D.

A **formula** is a literal equation in which each variable represents a specific quantity. The formula describes the relationship between the quantities. Often a formula is given in one form and you need to *transform* it to an equivalent form.

EXAMPLE 15   **Transforming formulas**

 The formula $F = \frac{9}{5}C + 32$ gives the temperature F in degrees Fahrenheit in terms of a given temperature C in degrees Celsius. Write a formula for C in terms of F.

■ SOLUTION

$$F = \frac{9}{5}C + 32$$

$$F - 32 = \frac{9}{5}C \qquad \leftarrow \textbf{Subtract 32 from each side.}$$

$$\frac{5}{9}(F - 32) = C, \ \ or \ \ C = \frac{5}{9}(F - 32) \leftarrow \textbf{Multiply each side by } \frac{5}{9}.$$

When an equation involves absolute value, you can use a number line and the definition of absolute value to solve. If $|x| = 3$, then the value of x can be any integer exactly 3 units from zero on the number line. You can count these units to the left or to the right of zero. Therefore, $x = 3$ or $x = -3$.

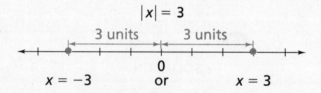

$$|x| = 3$$

3 units   3 units

0
$x = -3$ or $x = 3$

Note

The absolute value of a number is its distance from 0 on a number line.

The absolute value of zero is zero.

This example leads to the following algebraic generalization.

Absolute Value Equations

Let $|x| = a$.

If $a > 0$,	If $a = 0$,	If $a < 0$,
then $x = a$ or $x = -a$.	then $x = 0$.	then there is no solution.

EXAMPLES 16 through 18   **Solving absolute value equations**

Solve each equation.

16 $2|n| = 16$	17 $|b| - 7 = 3$	18 $|t - 2| = 5$
■ SOLUTION	■ SOLUTION	■ SOLUTION
$2|n| = 16$	$|b| - 7 = 3$	$|t - 2| = 5$
$|n| = 8$	$|b| = 10$	$t - 2 = 5$ or $t - 2 = -5$
$n = 8$ or $n = -8$	$b = 10$ or $b = -10$	$t = 7$ or $t = -3$

Practice

Choose the letter preceding the word or expression that best completes the statement or answers the question.

1 Which is a solution to $\frac{2a-1}{3} = 7$?

    A. $5\frac{1}{3}$ **B.** 11   **C.** 12   **D.** 21

2 In which equation is it possible to isolate the variable by first subtracting 3 from each side and then multiplying each side by 4?

    A. $4x + 3 = 7$ **C.** $4x - 3 = 7$

    B. $\frac{1}{4}x + 3 = 7$ **D.** $\frac{1}{4}x - 3 = 7$

3 If $2c - d = c - 2d$, then $c =$

    A. 0   **B.** 1   **C.** d **D.** $-d$

4 Which equations are equivalent?

    I. $6(m + 5) = -6$
    II. $4 + 2(m + 3) = 28$
    III. $\frac{m}{4} = -2.25$

    A. I and II   **C.** II and III

    B. I and III   **D.** none of these

5 Which is equivalent to $|2d + 6| = 18$?

    A. $2d = 12$

    B. $2d = 12$ or $2d = -12$

    C. $2d = 12$ or $2d = 24$

    D. $2d = 12$ or $2d = -24$

6 Which equation has no solution?

    A. $|p - 1| = 5$

    B. $7 = |p + 3|$

    C. $|p| - 3 = -8$

    D. $|8 - 2p| = 6$

In Exercises 7–23, solve each equation. Check your solution(s). If there is no solution, so state.

7 $b - 13 = 24$ **8** $j + 8 = 7$

9 $-x + 12 = -9$ **10** $10 = 3 - m$

11 $\frac{d}{5} = -20$ **12** $-45 = -3h$

13 $14 = -\frac{2}{3}k$ **14** $4z + 5 = -25$

15 $4(z + 5) = -25$ **16** $0.4(s + 4) = 4.8$

17 $\frac{1}{4}(p + 8) = 12$ **18** $n + 9n + 7 = -41$

19 $6g + 1 = -3g - 8$ **20** $1 + 2(y + 4) = 29$

21 $5 = 6h + 5(h - 5)$

22 $4(x - 1) - 2x = 2x - 4$

23 $6(q - 4) - 3(q - 2) = 12$

In Exercises 24–29, solve each equation for the given variable.

24 $a + b = c$; b **25** $2p - q = r$; p

26 $2(p - q) = r$; p **27** $xy = z$; y

28 $I = prt$; p **29** $r = \frac{d}{t}$; t

In Exercises 30–33, solve each equation. Check your solution(s).

30 $|z| = 11$ **31** $5|k| = 24$

32 $|n| - 3 = -6$ **33** $3|b - 2| = 4$

In Exercises 34–35, solve the problem. Clearly show all necessary work.

34 Sean says that the equation $s + 3 = s - 3$ has no solution. Is Sean's statement correct? Explain your answer.

35 Daneesha says that the equation $3t = -3t$ has no solution. Is Daneesha's statement correct? Explain your answer.

2.2 Problems Involving Linear Equations in One Variable

New Jersey Standards

4.3.D.2.1 Solving equations

4.3.C.1.2 Solving direct variation problems

4.3.C.1.4 Solving problems involving varying quantities

Just as you can translate verbal phrases into mathematical expressions, you can translate English sentences into mathematical statements. This means that you can use an equation to model and solve a problem.

In general, before solving a problem you should assign a variable to the unknown and translate the problem into a mathematical equation. After you have solved the equation for the variable, label the solution according to the question asked. To check whether the solution is correct, apply the problem statement to the solution.

Go Online
PHSchool.com

Visit: PHSchool.com
Web Code: ayp-0066

EXAMPLES 1 through 3 Using equations and formulas to model and solve problems

1 Wendy has 14 coins. Some are quarters and some are nickels. The total value of the coins is $1.70. How many quarters does Wendy have?

■ **SOLUTION**

Let q represent the number of quarters. Then $14 - q$ is the number of nickels.

Step 1 Translate the words into an equation.

value of quarters in cents	plus	value of nickels in cents	is	170 cents
↓	↓	↓	↓	↓
$25q$	+	$5(14 - q)$	=	170

Step 2 Solve the equation.

$$25q + 5(14 - q) = 170$$
$$20q + 70 = 170$$
$$20q = 100$$
$$q = 5$$

Wendy has five quarters.

2 The sum of three consecutive integers is 99. Find the three integers.

■ **SOLUTION**

Step 1 Assign the variable and write the equation.

x = 1st integer,
$x + 1$ = 2nd integer,
$x + 2$ = 3rd integer.

So, $x + (x + 1) + (x + 2) = 99$
or $3x + 3 = 99$

Step 2 Solve the equation.

$$3x + 3 = 99$$
$$3x = 96$$
$$x = 32$$

Therefore, the three integers are $x = 32$,
$x + 1 = 33$,
$x + 2 = 34$.

> **Note**
>
> *Consecutive integers always increase by 1, so if x represents an integer, then x + 1 represents the next consecutive integer.*

3 Mr. Redbird is driving at an average speed of 60 miles per hour. How far can he drive in 4.5 hours?

■ **SOLUTION**

Step 1 Apply the formula $d = rt$, where d represents distance, r represents rate, and t represents time.

d	=	r	×	t
↓		↓		↓
d	=	60	×	4.5

Step 2 Solve the equation.

$$d = 60 \times 4.5$$
$$d = 270$$

Mr. Redbird can drive 270 miles in 4.5 hours.

You can use formulas to solve problems that involve perimeter.

EXAMPLE 4   **Using formulas to solve problems**

 Ben builds a fence around a rectangular garden. The perimeter of the garden is 64 ft. The width is 12 ft less than the length. Find the dimensions of the garden.

■ SOLUTION

Step 1 Apply the formula for the perimeter of a rectangle.

$P = 2l + 2w$

$P = 64$

$w = l - 12$

Step 2 Substitute and solve.

$64 = 2l + 2(l - 12)$

$64 = 2l + 2l - 24$

$64 = 4l - 24$

$88 = 4l$

$22 = \text{length}$

Step 3 Find both dimensions.

If the **length is 22 ft,** and the width is 12 ft less than the length, then the **width is 10 ft.**

Practice

Choose the letter preceding the word or expression that best completes the statement or answers the question.

1 The total value of some nickels and dimes is $2.20. There are 36 coins in all. Which equation gives the number of dimes, d?

A. $10d + 5d = 220$

B. $10d + 5(d - 36) = 220$

C. $10d + 5(36 - d) = 220$

D. $10d + 5(36 - d) = 2.20$

2 The formula $A = lw$ gives the area A of a rectangle with length l and width w. What is the width in feet of a rectangle with length 8 feet and area 14 square feet?

A. 112   **B.** 22   **C.** 6   **D.** 1.75

3 If the number represented by $x - 5$ is an odd integer, which expression represents the next greatest odd integer?

A. $x - 7$ **B.** $x - 4$ **C.** $x - 3$ **D.** $x - 6$

4 Half of the money collected for a show was donated to charity. Tickets for a show cost $100 per pair. The charity collected $3500. How many tickets were sold?

A. 140   **B.** 700   **C.** 350   **D.** 70

5 Find four consecutive integers whose sum is 138.

A. 68, 69, 70, 71   **C.** 33, 34, 35, 36

B. 38, 39, 40, 41   **D.** 35, 36, 37, 38

6 A computer programmer charges $30 for an initial consultation and $35 per hour for programming. Write a formula for her total charge for h hours of work.

A. $(30 + 35)h$ **C.** $35 + 30h$

B. $30 + 35h$ **D.** $65h$

In Exercises 7–9, solve the problem.

7 Complementary angles have a sum of 90°. The sum of the measure of an angle and 5 times its complement is 298. What is the measure of the angle?

8 A train traveling at the rate of 90 miles per hour (mi/hr) leaves New York City. Two hours later, another train traveling at the rate of 120 mi/hr also leaves New York City on a parallel track. How long will it take the faster train to catch up to the slower train?

9 Five times a number n is three less than twice n. Find n.

2.3 Ratio and Rates

New Jersey Standards
4.1.B.1 Using operations of real numbers

A **ratio** is a comparison of two numbers. You can write a ratio in these ways: a to b, $a : b$, or $\frac{a}{b}$. A ratio that is expressed as a fraction is generally written in lowest terms. If the ratio involves units of measure, you must ensure that the units are the same.

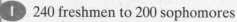

EXAMPLES 1 and 2   Writing ratios in lowest terms

Write each ratio as a fraction in lowest terms.

1 240 freshmen to 200 sophomores

■ SOLUTION

freshmen → $\dfrac{240}{200} = \dfrac{240 \div 40}{200 \div 40} = \dfrac{6}{5}$
sophomores →

2 40 inches to 6 feet

■ SOLUTION

inches → $\dfrac{40}{72} = \dfrac{40 \div 8}{72 \div 8} = \dfrac{5}{9}$ ← Rewrite 6 feet
inches →   as 72 inches.

A **continued ratio,** or **extended ratio,** relates more than two numbers.

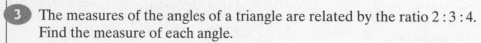

EXAMPLE 3   Using continued ratios to solve problems

3 The measures of the angles of a triangle are related by the ratio $2 : 3 : 4$. Find the measure of each angle.

■ SOLUTION

The ratio $2 : 3 : 4$ is equivalent to $2x : 3x : 4x$. Write an equation using $2x, 3x,$ and $4x$ to represent the measures of the angles.

$2x + 3x + 4x = 180$ ← The sum of the
$9x = 180$ measures of the
$x = 20$ angles is 180°.

The measures of the angles are $2(20)°, 3(20)°,$ and $4(20)°,$ or $40°, 60°,$ and $80°.$

A ratio that compares different types of measures is called a **rate.** A **unit rate** is a rate per one unit of a given measure.

Go Online
PHSchool.com
Visit: PHSchool.com
Web Code: ayp-0891

EXAMPLES 4 and 5   Using unit rates to solve problems

4 Three cans of peas cost \$2. Write the unit cost per can of peas.

■ SOLUTION

dollars → $\dfrac{2}{3} = \dfrac{2 \div 3}{3 \div 3} = \dfrac{0.6666\ldots}{1}$ ← Divide both numerator and denominator
cans →   by 3 to obtain a denominator equal to 1.

The exact unit cost is \$$.6\overline{6}$ per can.

5 A 13-ounce box of cereal costs \$3.99, and a 16-ounce box of cereal costs \$5.19. Which is the better buy? Round to the nearest cent.

■ SOLUTION

$\dfrac{3.99}{13} \approx 0.31/\text{oz}$ ← Cost per ounce of 13-ounce box of cereal

$\dfrac{5.19}{16} \approx 0.32/\text{oz}$ ← Cost per ounce of 16-ounce box of cereal

The better buy is the 13-ounce box because $0.31 < 0.32.$

You can use the simple interest formula to solve problems involving interest rates.

Go Online
PHSchool.com
Visit: PHSchool.com
Web Code: ayp-0070

EXAMPLE 6 **Solving interest rate problems**

6 Ariane has invested $500 in an account that earns simple interest at an annual rate of 4%. Assuming that Ariane makes no withdrawals or additional deposits, how long will it take for this money to earn $50 in interest?

■ **SOLUTION**

Step 1 Apply the simple interest formula $I = prt$, where I is the amount of interest, p is the amount invested, r is the annual interest rate, and t is the time in years.

$$I = p \times r \times t$$
$$\downarrow \quad \downarrow \quad \quad \downarrow \quad \quad \downarrow$$
$$50 = 500 \times 0.04 \times t$$

It will take 2.5 years to earn $50 in interest.

Step 2 Solve the equation.
$$50 = 500 \times 0.04 \times t$$
$$50 = 20t$$
$$2.5 = t$$

Practice

Choose the letter preceding the word or expression that best completes the statement or answers the question.

1 Which ratio is equivalent to $\frac{7}{9}$?

  A. $\frac{6}{8}$ **B.** $\frac{21}{27}$ **C.** $\frac{14}{20}$ **D.** $\frac{14}{16}$

2 A soccer team won 18 games and lost 6 games. What is the ratio of the team's wins to the total games played?

  A. 3 to 1   **C.** 4 to 3

  B. 1 to 4   **D.** 3 to 4

3 A small company made a $900 profit one year. The two partners split the profit, using a ratio of 2 to 3. What was each partner's share?

  A. $180 and $720   **C.** $360 and $540

  B. $450 and $450   **D.** $300 and $600

4 Which of the following jars of peanut butter represents the lowest unit cost?

  A. a 10-ounce jar for $2.36

  B. a 12-ounce jar for $2.52

  C. a 16-ounce jar for $2.64

  D. a 20-ounce jar for $3.50

5 175 people are on a jogging trail. 125 are running and 50 are walking. What is the ratio of runners to walkers?

  A. $\frac{2}{5}$ **C.** $\frac{5}{2}$

  B. $\frac{5}{7}$ **D.** $\frac{2}{7}$

6 Sammy rides his bike 14 miles in $3\frac{1}{2}$ hrs. What is his average speed?

  A. 4 mi/hr   **C.** 12 mi/hr

  B. $3\frac{1}{2}$ mi/3hr   **D.** 0.25 mi/hr

7 The lengths of the sides of a triangle are related by the ratio $3 : 4 : 5$. Which set of measures could be the lengths of the sides?

  A. 6 ft, 7 ft, 8 ft

  B. 6 ft, 8 ft, 10 ft

  C. 9 ft, 12 ft, 20 ft

  D. 9 ft, 16 ft, 25 ft

2.4 Proportion and Percents

New Jersey Standards

4.1.B.1 Understand and use operations of real numbers

A **proportion** is a statement that two ratios are equal. You can write a proportion in different ways, as shown in the note below. The numbers that form a proportion are called the **terms of the proportion**. There is a special relationship between the terms, called the *cross products property*. For example,

$$\frac{3}{7} = \frac{15}{35}$$
$$3 \cdot 35 = 7 \cdot 15$$
$$105 = 105$$

Cross Products Property of Proportions

For real numbers a, b, c, and d, where $b \neq 0$ and $d \neq 0$, if $\frac{a}{b} = \frac{c}{d}$, then $ad = bc$.

Note

Ways to Write a Proportion

a is to b as c is to d

$a : b = c : d$

$\frac{a}{b} = \frac{c}{d}$

In $\frac{a}{b} = \frac{c}{d}$, a and d are called the **extremes** of the proportion and b and c are called the **means**. So the cross products property is sometimes stated as follows.

In a proportion, the product of the means equals the product of the extremes.

 EXAMPLE 1   **Using cross products to solve a proportion**

1   Solve $\frac{r}{8.5} = \frac{3}{4}$.

■ **SOLUTION**

$\frac{r}{8.5} = \frac{3}{4}$

$r(4) = (8.5)(3)$ ← Write the cross products.

$4r = 25.5$ ← Simplify each side.

$r = 6.375$ ← Divide each side by 4.

You can use a proportion to solve problems involving ratios.

 EXAMPLE 2   **Using a proportion to solve problems**

2   The scale of a map is 1 inch : 24 miles. What map distance represents 75 miles?

■ **SOLUTION**

Step 1 Write a proportion.

map distance in inches → $\quad \frac{1}{24} = \frac{n}{75}$ ← **Let n represent** the unknown map distance.
actual distance in miles →

Step 2 Solve the proportion.

$\frac{1}{24} = \frac{n}{75}$

$1 \cdot 75 = 24 \cdot n$ ← Write the cross products.

$3.125 = n$ ← Divide each side by 24.

The map distance is 3.125 inches, or $3\frac{1}{8}$ inches.

If two triangles have angles of equal measure, then they are similar and their corresponding sides are proportional.

Go Online
PHSchool.com
Visit: PHSchool.com
Web Code: ayp-0830

EXAMPLE 3 Using proportions to solve similar-triangle problems

3 The triangles at the right are similar. Find *KM*.

■ **SOLUTION**

Write and solve a proportion.

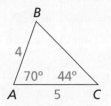
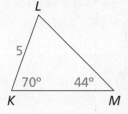

$$\frac{KL}{AB} = \frac{KM}{AC}$$

$$\frac{5}{4} = \frac{KM}{5}$$

$$4(KM) = 5(5) \quad \leftarrow \textbf{The cross products are equal.}$$

$$KM = 6.25$$

Therefore, *KM* = 6.25.

You can also use proportions to solve percent problems.

EXAMPLES 4 through 7 Solving percent problems

4 What is 16% of 23?

■ **SOLUTION**

$$\frac{16}{100} = \frac{x}{23}$$

$$23 \cdot 16 = 100x$$

$$\frac{368}{100} = x$$

$$x = 3.68$$

5 15 is what percent of 90?

■ **SOLUTION**

$$\frac{15}{90} = \frac{x}{100}$$

$$90x = 1500$$

$$x = \frac{1500}{90}$$

$$x = 16\frac{2}{3}\%$$

6 75 is 25% of what number?

■ **SOLUTION**

$$\frac{75}{x} = \frac{25}{100}$$

$$25x = 7500$$

$$x = 300$$

7 35% of 18 is what number?

■ **SOLUTION**

$$\frac{35}{100} = \frac{x}{18}$$

$$100x = 35 \cdot 18$$

$$x = 6.3$$

You can use equations to solve problems involving percent. The following are three basic types of percent problems and their solutions.

What is 25% of 10?
↓ ↓ ↓ ↓ ↓
n = 25% × 10
n = 0.25 × 10
n = 2.5
So 25% of 10 is 2.5.

80 is 40% of what number?
↓ ↓ ↓ ↓ ↓
80 = 0.4 × n
$\frac{80}{0.4}$ = n
$n = 80 \div 0.4 = 200$
So 80 is 40% of 200.

75 is what percent of 62.5?
↓ ↓ ↓ ↓ ↓
75 = n × 62.5
$\frac{75}{62.5}$ = n
$n = 1.2 = 120\%$
So 75 is 120% of 62.5.

You can use percent equations to solve real-life problems.

8 Carlos works at a computer store. He earns a 4% commission on all of his sales. What amount must he sell to earn a commission of $200?

■ **SOLUTION**

$200 is 4% of what amount? → $200 = 0.04n → n = $200 ÷ 0.04 = $5000

Carlos must sell $5000 worth of goods to earn a $200 commission.

9 Jane and Susan go to dinner. The cost of the dinner is $45.60 and they leave a 15% tip. What is the total cost of the dinner, including the tip?

■ **SOLUTION**

Step 1 What is 15% of $45.60? → n = 0.15($45.60) → n = $6.84

Step 2 Add the tip to the price of the dinner. $6.84 + $45.60 = $52.44

The total cost of the dinner is $52.44.

10 Carlos purchases a sweater on sale for 30% off. The original price of the sweater is $54. How much does Carlos spend on the sweater?

■ **SOLUTION**

Step 1 What is 30% of $54? → x = 0.30($54) → x = $16.20

Step 2 Subtract the savings from the original price. $54 − $16.20 = $37.80

The purchase price of the sweater is $37.80.

A **percent of change** is the percent something increases or decreases from an original amount.

$$\frac{\text{percent of}}{\text{increase}} = \frac{\text{new amount } - \text{ original amount}}{\text{original amount}} \qquad \frac{\text{percent of}}{\text{decrease}} = \frac{\text{original amount } - \text{ new amount}}{\text{original amount}}$$

11 There were 75 members of the Drama Club last year, but there are only 65 members this year. What is the percent of decrease?

■ **SOLUTION**

Let p represent the percent of decrease.

$$p = \frac{75 - 65}{75} \leftarrow \frac{\text{original } - \text{ new}}{\text{original}}$$

$$p = \frac{10}{75} = 0.13333\ldots = 13\tfrac{1}{3}\%$$

The percent of decrease is $13\tfrac{1}{3}\%$.

12 Sam's employer has promised him a 20% pay increase. He presently earns $5 per hour. What will be his new hourly pay after the increase?

■ **SOLUTION**

Let n represent the new hourly pay.

$$20\% = \frac{n-5}{5} \leftarrow \frac{\text{new } - \text{ original}}{\text{original}}$$

$$5(20\%) = n - 5$$

$$1 = n - 5$$

$$6 = n$$

Sam's new pay will be $6 per hour.

Choose the letter preceding the word or expression that best completes the statement or answers the question.

1 What percent of 42 is equal to 35% of 120?

   A. 50%   **B.** 75%   **C.** 100%   **D.** 120%

2 Which of these questions can be modeled by the equation $72 = 0.18n$?

   A. 72 is what percent of 18?

   B. 72 is 18 percent of what number?

   C. 18 is what percent of 72?

   D. What number is 18 percent of 72?

3 Which is a true statement?

   A. $\frac{16}{5} = \frac{12}{9}$ **C.** $\frac{16}{5} = \frac{28.8}{9}$

   B. $\frac{16}{5} = \frac{20}{9}$ **D.** $\frac{16}{5} = \frac{139}{9}$

4 There were 420 students in the senior class last year. This year's senior class has 378 students. Which statement is false?

   A. The percent of decrease in the size of the class is 10%.

   B. This year there are 10% fewer students in the senior class than there were last year.

   C. The size of the senior class increased by 10% from last year to this year.

   D. This year's class is 90% of the size of last year's class.

5 The scale of a map is 1 in. : 50 mi. How many miles correspond to a map distance of 3.25 in.?

   A. 150 mi   **C.** 62.5 mi

   B. 162.5 mi   **D.** 200 mi

6 Solve the proportion $\frac{54}{8} = \frac{r}{6}$.

   A. 72   **B.** 40.5   **C.** 324   **D.** 48

In Exercises 7–9, answer the question by solving a percent equation.

7 What percent of 50 is 36?

8 12% of what number is 15?

9 What is 150% of 8?

In Exercises 10–13, find the percent of change from the first quantity to the second. Describe it as a percent of *increase* or *decrease*.

10 16 pounds
    20 pounds

11 50 inches
    36 inches

12 $13.98
    $9.32

13 1.6 meters
    4 meters

In Exercises 14–15, solve each proportion.

14 $\frac{m}{2} = \frac{56}{16}$ **15** $\frac{51}{21} = \frac{z}{7}$

In Exercises 16–22, solve the problem. Clearly show all necessary work.

16 John plans to save 15% of his salary each week. His weekly salary is $700. What amount does he plan to save each week?

17 The marked price of a CD is $12.75. In addition, there is a state sales tax of 4% of the price. What is the total cost of the CD?

18 A retailer buys T-shirts from a supplier for $6 each and sells each T-shirt for $13.50. What is the percent of increase in the price?

19 A copy machine can print 125 pages in 3 minutes. How many minutes will it take for this machine to print 800 pages?

20 Tamara buys a $23 blouse on sale for 20% off. How much did Tamara spend on the blouse?

21 80% of the students at Rally High participate in a pep rally. If there are 1800 students in the school, how many participate in the pep rally?

22 A food inspector weighs 50 cans of soup taken at random from a shipment of 3,000 cans. She finds that 4 out of the 50 cans are underweight. Based on this sample, how many cans in the shipment can the inspector expect to be underweight?

2.5 Solving Linear Inequalities in One Variable

New Jersey Standards
4.3.D.2.1 Solving inequalities

An **inequality** is a statement that consists of two mathematical expressions joined by an inequality symbol. The expressions are called the **sides of the inequality.**

Just as with equations, both sides of an inequality may be numerical expressions. In such a case, the inequality is a closed statement and can be assigned a truth value.

$$5 + (-9) < 0 \quad true \qquad 5 + (-9) > 0 \quad false$$

When at least one side of an inequality is a variable expression, the inequality is an open statement. To solve the inequality, you must find its solution set. When the replacement set of the variable is the set of all real numbers, the inequality may have infinitely many solutions. For example, given the inequality $x < 3$, each of the following replacements for x results in a true statement.

$$-17 < 3 \qquad -5.4 < 3 \qquad 0 < 3 \qquad \tfrac{1}{2} < 3 \qquad 2.999 < 3$$

In fact, any number to the left of 3 on a number line is a solution to $x < 3$. Clearly it would be impossible to list all these solutions. For this reason, a number line is used to draw the *graph of the inequality*. The **graph of an inequality** consists of the graphs of all its solutions.

Note

Inequality Symbols

<	is less than
≤	is less than or equal to
>	is greater than
≥	is greater than or equal to
≠	is not equal to

EXAMPLES 1 through 5 Graphing an inequality

Graph each inequality on a number line.

1 $x < 3$ ▪ SOLUTION Graph all real numbers to the left of 3.

Use an open dot ← to indicate that 3 is *not* a solution.

2 $x > 3$ ▪ SOLUTION Graph all real numbers to the right of 3.

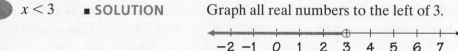 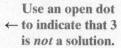

3 $x \le 3$ ▪ SOLUTION Graph 3 and all real numbers to its left.

 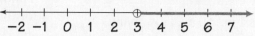

Use a closed dot ← to indicate that 3 *is* a solution.

4 $x \ge 3$ ▪ SOLUTION Graph 3 and all real numbers to its right.

 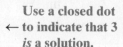

5 $x \ne 3$ ▪ SOLUTION Graph all real numbers except 3.

 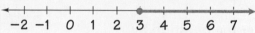

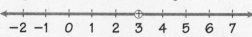

Inequalities that have the same solution set are called **equivalent inequalities.**
Solving an inequality is a process of writing equivalent inequalities until you
isolate the variable. To do this, you apply the following *properties of inequality*.

Properties of Inequality

Let a, b, and c represent real numbers.

Addition Property

If $a < b$, then $a + c < b + c$.
If $a > b$, then $a + c > b + c$.

Subtraction Property

If $a < b$, then $a - c < b - c$.
If $a > b$, then $a - c > b - c$.

Multiplication Property

If $a < b$ and $c > 0$, then $ac < bc$.
If $a < b$ and $c < 0$, then $ac > bc$.

If $a > b$ and $c > 0$, then $ac > bc$.
If $a > b$ and $c < 0$, then $ac < bc$.

Division Property

If $a < b$ and $c > 0$, then $\frac{a}{c} < \frac{b}{c}$.

If $a < b$ and $c < 0$, then $\frac{a}{c} > \frac{b}{c}$.

If $a > b$ and $c > 0$, then $\frac{a}{c} > \frac{b}{c}$.

If $a > b$ and $c < 0$, then $\frac{a}{c} < \frac{b}{c}$.

Transitive Property   If $a < b$ and $b < c$, then $a < c$.
If $a > b$ and $b > c$, then $a > c$.

Note

For each property of inequality, a true statement also results if $<$ is replaced by $\leq$ and if $>$ is replaced by $\geq$.

Adding or subtracting the same number from each side of an inequality
results in an equivalent inequality. To apply the addition and subtraction
properties, use inverse operations: addition and subtraction.

Note

If a is greater than b, it is also true that b is less than a. So $a > b$ is equivalent to $b < a$.

EXAMPLES 6 and 7   Solving inequalities by using addition or subtraction

Solve each inequality and graph it on a number line.

6 $b + 7 \leq 4$

■ SOLUTION

$b + 7 \leq 4$ Subtract 7
$b + 7 - 7 \leq 4 - 7$ ← from each side.
$b \leq -3$

All numbers less than or equal to -3
are solutions.

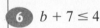
$$-6\ -5\ -4\ -3\ -2\ -1\ \ 0\ \ 1$$

7 $-5 < n - 3$

■ SOLUTION

$-5 < n - 3$ Add 3
$-5 + 3 < n - 3 + 3$ ← to each side.
$-2 < n$
$n > -2$

All numbers greater than -2 are solutions.

$$-5\ -4\ -3\ -2\ -1\ \ 0\ \ 1\ \ 2$$

It is impossible to check every solution to inequalities like those in
Examples 6 and 7. However, you can usually detect an error by checking one
number from each region of the graph. For example, here is how you might
verify that $n > -2$ is a reasonable solution to $-5 < n - 3$.

You should obtain a *true* statement when you
replace n with any number greater than -2.

You should obtain a *false* statement when you
replace n with any number less than -2.

Try -1: $-5 < n - 3$ → $-5 < -1 - 3$ *true*

Try -3: $-5 < n - 3$ → $-5 < -3 - 3$ *false*

If you multiply or divide each side of an inequality by the same positive number, the inequality symbol stays the same. If you multiply or divide each side by the same negative number, the inequality symbol is reversed.

EXAMPLES 8 and 9 Solving inequalities by using multiplication or division

Solve each inequality and graph it on a number line.

8 $\frac{a}{4} < -1$

■ SOLUTION

$$\frac{a}{4} < -1$$

$$4\left(\frac{a}{4}\right) < 4(-1) \quad \leftarrow \begin{array}{l}\textbf{Multiply each side by 4.}\\ \textbf{The order of the}\\ \textbf{inequality stays the same.}\end{array}$$

$$a < -4$$

All numbers less than −4 are solutions.

$$\leftarrow \; -7 \; -6 \; -5 \; -4 \; -3 \; -2 \; -1 \; \; 0 \;\rightarrow$$

9 $-4w \le 20$

■ SOLUTION

$$-4w \le 20$$

$$\frac{-4w}{-4} \ge \frac{20}{-4} \quad \begin{array}{l}\textbf{Divide each side by −4.}\\ \leftarrow \textbf{Reverse the order}\\ \textbf{of the inequality.}\end{array}$$

$$w \ge -5$$

All numbers greater than or equal to −5 are solutions.

$$\leftarrow \; -7 \; -6 \; -5 \; -4 \; -3 \; -2 \; -1 \; \; 0 \;\rightarrow$$

You may need to apply the properties of equality several times to isolate the variable and solve the inequality.

Go Online
PHSchool.com
Visit: PHSchool.com
Web Code: ayp-0180

EXAMPLE 10 Solving an inequality in multiple steps

10 Solve the inequality $-2(p - 5) \le -5$ and graph it on a number line.

■ SOLUTION 1

$$-2(p - 5) \le -5$$
$$-2p + 10 \le -5 \quad \leftarrow \textbf{Use the distributive property to simplify the left side.}$$
$$-2p \le -15 \quad \leftarrow \textbf{Subtract 10 from each side.}$$
$$p \ge 7.5 \quad \leftarrow \textbf{Divide each side by −2. Reverse the order of the inequality.}$$

All numbers greater than or equal to 7.5 are solutions. The graph is shown at the right.

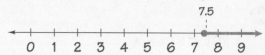
$$\begin{array}{c}7.5\\ \leftarrow \;\; 0 \; 1 \; 2 \; 3 \; 4 \; 5 \; 6 \; 7 \; 8 \; 9 \;\rightarrow\end{array}$$

■ SOLUTION 2

Another method for solving inequalities is to use a graphing calculator.

- In the Y= screen, enter −2(X−5) as Y1 and −5 as Y2.
- Choose WINDOW settings that will show where the lines intersect.
- Press GRAPH.
- Using intersect in the CALC menu, find the intersection of the lines.

The intersection is X = 7.5, Y = −5. So when $p = 7.5$, $-2(p - 5) = -5$. You also see that when $p > 7.5$, $-2(p - 5) < -5$. Therefore, $p \ge 7.5$ is correct.

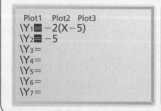
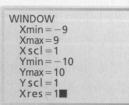
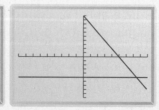
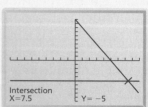

Plot1 Plot2 Plot3
\Y1■−2(X−5)
\Y2■−5
\Y3=
\Y4=
\Y5=
\Y6=
\Y7=

WINDOW
Xmin=−9
Xmax=9
Xscl=1
Ymin=−10
Ymax=10
Yscl=1
Xres=1■

Intersection
X=7.5   Y=−5

Two inequalities joined by the word *and* or the word *or* form a **compound inequality.**

$h > -2$ and $h < 4$

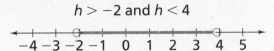

The word *and* signals a conjunction. The solutions are all numbers that are solutions of *both* inequalities.

$j < -2$ or $j > 4$

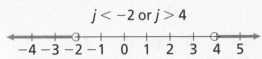

The word *or* signals a disjunction. The solutions are all numbers that are solutions of *either* inequality.

Go Online PHSchool.com
Visit: PHSchool.com
Web Code: ayp-0182

EXAMPLE 11   **Solving a compound inequality**

11 Solve $-3 < 2 - b \leq 1$ and graph it on a number line.

■ SOLUTION

Write two inequalities joined by *and*. Then solve each inequality.

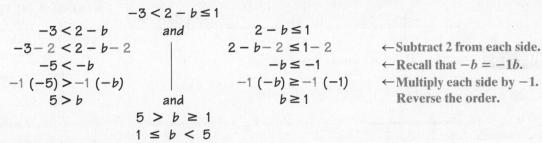

$$-3 < 2 - b \leq 1$$

$-3 < 2 - b$	and	$2 - b \leq 1$	
$-3 - 2 < 2 - b - 2$		$2 - b - 2 \leq 1 - 2$	← Subtract 2 from each side.
$-5 < -b$		$-b \leq -1$	← Recall that $-b = -1b$.
$-1(-5) > -1(-b)$		$-1(-b) \geq -1(-1)$	← Multiply each side by -1. Reverse the order.
$5 > b$	and	$b \geq 1$	

$$5 > b \geq 1$$
$$1 \leq b < 5$$

All numbers greater than or equal to 1 and less than 5 are solutions. The graph is at the right.

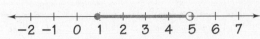

Just as with equations, some inequalities have no solution. For other inequalities, the solution set is the set of all real numbers.

$2(y - 3) > 2y + 8$
$2y - 6 > 2y + 8$
$-6 > 8$ *false*

The inequality has no solution.

$5t + 1 \geq 6t - 1 - t$
$5t + 1 \geq 5t - 1$
$1 \geq -1$ *true*

All real numbers are solutions.

Usually the replacement set for the variable in an inequality is the set of all real numbers. In some cases, however, the replacement set is restricted.

EXAMPLE 12   **Solving an inequality given a restricted replacement set**

Note

Three dots (…) on a graph indicate that the pattern continues without end.

12 Given the set of integers as the replacement set for z, solve the following inequality. $2z < -1$ or $z + 3 > 5$

■ SOLUTION

$2z < -1$	or	$z + 3 > 5$
$\frac{2z}{2} < \frac{-1}{2}$		$z + 3 - 3 > 5 - 3$
$z < -0.5$	or	$z > 2$

All *integers* less than -0.5 or greater than 2 are solutions. The graph is at the right.

When an inequality involves absolute value, you can use a number line and the definition of absolute value to locate its solutions.

$|x| < 3$

Graph all numbers whose distance from zero is less than 3 units.

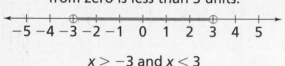

$x > -3$ and $x < 3$

$|x| > 3$

Graph all numbers whose distance from zero is greater than 3 units.

$x < -3$ or $x > 3$

These examples lead to the following algebraic generalization.

Absolute Value Inequalities

If $a > 0$ and $|x| < a$,

then $x > -a$ and $x < a$.

If $a > 0$ and $|x| > a$,

then $x < -a$ or $x > a$.

Go Online
PHSchool.com

Visit: PHSchool.com
Web Code: ayp-0185

EXAMPLE 13   Solving absolute value inequalities

13 Which is the graph of $|v + 3| + 1 < 2$?

A. (number line −4 to 4)

B. (number line −4 to 4)

C. (number line −5 to 3)

D. (number line −5 to 3)

■ SOLUTION

$$|v + 3| + 1 < 2 \qquad \leftarrow \text{Isolate the absolute value expression.}$$
$$|v + 3| < 1 \qquad \leftarrow \text{Write the equivalent compound inequality.}$$
$$v + 3 > -1 \qquad \text{and} \qquad v + 3 < 1$$
$$v + 3 - 3 > -1 - 3 \quad | \quad v + 3 - 3 < 1 - 3$$
$$v > -4 \qquad \text{and} \qquad v < -2$$

All numbers greater than −4 and less than −2 are solutions. The correct choice is C.

Practice

Choose the letter preceding the word or expression that best completes the statement or answers the question.

1 Given $-4t < 28$, which step can be used to obtain the equivalent inequality $t > -7$?

A. Divide each side by −4.

B. Multiply each side by 4.

C. Add 4 to each side.

D. Subtract −4 from each side.

2 Which is not equivalent to $-3x < 15$?

A. $-x < 5$ **C.** $x < -5$

B. $-5 < x$ **D.** $5 > -x$

3 Which inequality is graphed below?

(number line 2 to 11)

A. $4 < b \le 9$ **C.** $b \ge 4$ or $b < 9$

B. $4 \le b < 9$ **D.** $b \le 4$ or $b > 9$

4 Which inequality is not equivalent to $-3 \le k < 5$?

    A. $5 < k \le -3$ **C.** $-3 \le k$ and $k < 5$

    B. $5 > k \ge -3$ **D.** $k < 5$ and $k \ge -3$

5 Which inequality represents all of the solutions to $-3m + 8 \ge -13$?

    A. $m \le \frac{5}{3}$ **C.** $m \ge 7$

    B. $m \le 7$ **D.** $m \le -7$

6 Suppose that m, n, r, and s are positive numbers, with $\frac{m}{n} < 1$ and $\frac{r}{s} > 1$. Which statement is always true?

    A. $\frac{m}{n} \cdot \frac{r}{s} < 1$ **C.** $\frac{m}{n} + \frac{r}{s} < 1$

    B. $\frac{m}{n} \cdot \frac{r}{s} > 1$ **D.** $\frac{m}{n} + \frac{r}{s} > 1$

In Exercises 7–10, write an inequality that each graph could represent.

7
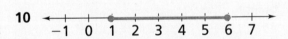

8

9

10

In Exercises 11–18, graph each inequality on a number line.

11 $c > 5$ **12** $-2 > k$

13 $r < -1$ or $r \ge 3$ **14** $-7 < m < -2.5$

15 $x < 5$ and $x > 3$ **16** $g \ge 8$ or $g \le -4$

17 $p \le 12$ and $p \ge 1$ **18** $-5 \le b \le 2$

In Exercises 19–29, solve each inequality and graph it on a number line.

19 $n - 3 > -11$ **20** $-8x \ge -16$

21 $\frac{a}{6} \le -3$ **22** $-y < 4$

23 $\frac{1}{3}w \ge 1$ **24** $3f - 12 \le 15$

25 $45 > 3(6 - z)$

26 $5n + 3 - 4n < -5 - 3n$

27 $5 - 2(4 - c) \le 9 - c$

28 $4d < -8$ or $6 < 2d$

29 $5 < x + 4 \le 8$

In Exercises 30–33, given the set of integers as the replacement set, solve each inequality and graph it on a number line.

30 $0 < a + 4 < 3$

31 $n - 6 \ge 4$

32 $s + 2 \le -2$ or $-2s \le -2$

33 $-2r \le 9$ and $7 > 3r$

In Exercises 34–37, solve each inequality and graph it on a number line.

34 $|w| \le 4.5$ **35** $|h| > 2$

36 $|3c - 6| \ge 3$ **37** $|4t + 2| + 1 < 7$

In Exercises 38–39, solve the problem. Clearly show all necessary work.

38 Are there any integers that satisfy the following inequality? If so, what are they?

    $0 \le 2c \le 9$ and $-4 < 3c - 5 < 13$

39 Is the statement below *true* or *false*? Explain your response.

    The inequalities $2q + 5 \le 3$ and $q > 0$ taken together have no solution.

2.6 Problems Involving Linear Inequalities in One Variable

New Jersey Standards

4.3.D.2.1 Solving inequalities

When a verbal problem includes a verb such as *is, are, will be, were,* or *equals,* you often can translate it into an equation. The table below summarizes some ways to tell when an appropriate translation of a problem is an *inequality.*

English Sentence	Mathematical Statement
p is greater than q, p is more than q	$p > q$
p is greater than or equal to q, p is no less than q, p is at least q	$p \geq q$
p is less than q, p is fewer than q	$p < q$
p is less than or equal to q, p is no more than q, p is at most q	$p \leq q$
q is greater than p and less than r, q is between p and r	$p < q < r$
q is greater than or equal to p and less than or equal to r, q is between p and r inclusive	$p \leq q \leq r$

Visit: PHSchool.com
Web Code: ayp-0507

EXAMPLES 1 and 2   **Translating and solving inequality problems**

1   Which inequality represents the following statement?

Five less than a number y is at most twenty.

A. $y - 5 < 20$ **B.** $y - 5 \leq 20$ **C.** $y - 5 \geq 20$ **D.** $5 < y < 20$

■ **SOLUTION**

Examine the choices and eliminate those that are inappropriate.

In **D**, $5 < y < 20$ describes a number y between 5 and 20. *Eliminate choice* **D.**

In **C**, the symbol $\geq$ means that $y - 5$ is 20 or more. *Eliminate choice* **C.**

In **A**, the symbol $<$ means that $y - 5$ cannot equal 20. *Eliminate choice* **A.**

The remaining choice is **B.** Work backward to verify the translation.

$$\underset{\substack{\downarrow \\ \text{five less than a number } y}}{y - 5} \quad \underset{\substack{\downarrow \\ \text{is at most}}}{\leq} \quad \underset{\substack{\downarrow \\ \text{twenty}}}{20}$$

The correct choice is **B.**

2   A real number c increased by six is more than four times c. Identify all possible values of c.

■ **SOLUTION**

Step 1   Translate the words into an inequality.

$$\underset{\substack{\downarrow \\ c + 6}}{\text{a number } c \text{ increased by six}} \quad \underset{\substack{\downarrow \\ >}}{\text{is more than}} \quad \underset{\substack{\downarrow \\ 4c}}{\text{four times } c}$$

Step 2   Solve the inequality.

$$c + 6 > 4c$$
$$6 > 3c$$
$$2 > c$$

All real numbers less than 2 can be values of c.

When you use an inequality to model a real-life problem, it is important to consider replacement sets. For instance, consider this situation.

The temperature t on Tuesday ranged from 25°F to 35°F, inclusive.

Temperature is a continuous measure. Therefore, the replacement set for t is the set of all real numbers, and the graph of the temperatures is the graph of all real-number solutions to $25 \leq t \leq 35$.

Number line from 24 to 36 with a solid segment from 25 to 35:
24 25 26 27 28 29 30 31 32 33 34 35 36

Now consider this situation.

The number n of students in a homeroom is between 25 and 35, inclusive.

The numbers of students in the homerooms form a discrete set of data. In this case, the replacement set for n is the set of whole numbers. So the graph is the graph of all whole-number solutions to $25 \leq n \leq 35$.

Number line from 24 to 36 with dots at 25 through 35:
24 25 26 27 28 29 30 31 32 33 34 35 36

EXAMPLES 3 and 4   **Using an inequality to solve a real-life problem**

3   Nancy earns $6.50 per hour. How many hours must she work to earn $130?

■ **SOLUTION**

Let h represent the number of hours Nancy must work. Then $6.50h$, or $6.5h$, represents the amount in dollars that she earns in h hours.

Step 1 Translate the words into an inequality.   **Step 2** Solve the inequality.

amount earned in dollars	is at least	130
↓	↓	↓
$6.5h$	$\geq$	130

$$6.5h \geq 130$$
$$h \geq 20$$

Nancy must work at least 20 hours.

4   Stan has $55. He wants to buy a belt that costs $14 and some T-shirts that cost $9 each. How many T-shirts can he buy?

■ **SOLUTION**

Let n represent the number of T-shirts. Then $9n$ represents the cost in dollars of the T-shirts.

Step 1 Translate the words into an inequality.   **Step 2** Solve the inequality.

cost of belt in dollars	plus	cost of T-shirts in dollars	is no more than	55
↓	↓	↓	↓	↓
14	$+$	$9n$	$\leq$	55

$$14 + 9n \leq 55$$
$$9n \leq 41$$
$$n \leq 4.\overline{5}$$

Stan can buy any whole number of T-shirts that is less than or equal to $4.\overline{5}$.
Stan can buy 0, 1, 2, 3, or 4 T-shirts.

You can use a combined inequality to find a range of possible values.

EXAMPLE 5 **Using a combined inequality to solve a real-life problem**

5 To get a grade of A for the semester, you must earn between 540 and 600 points inclusive. Before the last test, you have a total of 503 points. How many points must you earn on the last test in order to get a grade of A for the semester?

■ SOLUTION

Let p represent the number of points you must score on the last test.
Then $503 + p$ represents your total points for the semester.

$$540 \le 503 + p \le 600$$
$$540 \le 503 + p \quad \text{and} \quad 503 + p \le 600$$
$$37 \le p \qquad\qquad \text{and} \qquad\qquad p \le 97$$
$$37 \le p \le 97$$

Your number of points on the last test must be between 37 and 97 inclusive.

Although formulas are equations, you may need to use a formula when solving a problem involving inequality.

EXAMPLE 6 **Using formulas when solving inequality problems**

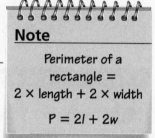

Note

Perimeter of a rectangle =
2 × length + 2 × width

$P = 2l + 2w$

6 Rosalita has 68 feet of fencing. She wants to use it to fence the perimeter of a rectangular garden so that it is 5 feet longer than it is wide. What is the greatest possible width for her garden?

■ SOLUTION

Let w represent the width of the garden. Then $w + 5$ represents the length.

$$2(w + 5) + 2w \le 68$$
$$2w + 10 + 2w \le 68$$
$$4w + 10 \le 68$$
$$4w \le 58$$
$$w \le 14.5$$

The greatest possible width for the garden is 14.5 feet.

Practice

Choose the letter preceding the word or expression that best completes the statement or answers the question.

1 Which could not be modeled by $n \le 2$?

A. A number n is not more than two.

B. A number n is not less than two.

C. A number n is less than or equal to two.

D. A number n is not greater than two.

2 Which describes all numbers r that are at most 5 units from zero on a number line?

A. $|r| < 5$

B. $|r| \le 5$

C. $|r| > 5$

D. $|r| \ge 5$

3 Today's high temperature of 54°F was more than 20°F above T, the normal high temperature. Which inequality can be used to represent this situation?

 A. $20 < T < 54$ **C.** $54 > 20 - T$

 B. $54 > 20 + T$ **D.** $T - 20 > 54$

4 The perimeter P of an equilateral triangle is given by the formula $P = 3s$, where s is the length of one side. In a certain equilateral triangle, the length of each side is a whole number of inches, and the perimeter is less than 15 inches. Which describes all possible values of s?

 A. $s < 5$

 B. $s \leq 4$

 C. $s = 1, s = 2, s = 3,$ or $s = 4$

 D. $s = 1, s = 2, s = 3,\ s = 4,$ or $s = 5$

5 A bag contains some red marbles and some blue marbles. There are fewer than 63 marbles in all. The ratio of red marbles to blue marbles is 5 to 3. If b represents the number of blue marbles, which inequality represents this situation?

 A. $b + \frac{3}{5}b < 63$ **C.** $b + \frac{5}{3}b \leq 63$

 B. $b + \frac{3}{5}b \leq 63$ **D.** $b + \frac{5}{3}b < 63$

In Exercises 6–18, solve the problem. Clearly show all necessary work.

6 Ten more than 3 times a real number j is greater than negative 31. What are the possible values of j?

7 Twice the sum of a whole number w and 5 is at most 15. What are all possible values of w?

8 Find all sets of three consecutive odd whole numbers whose sum is less than 45.

9 The cost of a gallon container of orange juice is $3.50. What is the maximum number of containers you can buy for $15?

10 To rent a car for one day, you must pay a base fee of $19.50. There is an additional charge of $.25 for each mile that you drive. You want to spend no more than $50 for the one-day rental. What is the greatest number of miles you can drive?

11 Jane is a salesperson at an automobile dealership. Each week she earns a base pay of $200, plus an 8% commission on her sales during the week. What must be the amount of her sales in one week if she wants her total earnings for the week to be at least $400?

12 A restaurant waiter earns a weekly base pay of $100, plus an average tip of $5 for each table served. In a five-day work week, how many tables must be served on average per day for the waiter to earn at least $450?

13 Ernest's job is to load shipping crates with cartons of merchandise. The weight of an empty shipping crate is 150 pounds. How many 35-pound cartons can Ernest load into a crate if the total weight of the crate and cartons may not exceed 850 pounds?

14 The perimeter of any triangle is the sum of the lengths of its sides. The lengths of the three sides of a certain triangle, in inches, are consecutive integers. The perimeter does not exceed 48 inches. What are all the possible measures for the longest side of this triangle?

15 The length and width of a rectangle are consecutive integers. The perimeter of this rectangle is at most 60 meters. What are the possible measures for the shorter side of this rectangle?

16 The Art Club is sponsoring a four-day art show. Their goal is for the average daily attendance to be between 100 and 120, inclusive. The attendance for the first three days of the show is 100, 105, and 91. What must be the attendance on the fourth day in order for the club to achieve its goal?

17 Two partners in a business share all profits in the ratio 4 to 5. They expect their profits for next month to be at least $1800 but no more than $3600. What amount of money might each partner expect to receive next month?

18 The formula $C = \frac{5}{9}(F - 32)$ gives the temperature C in degrees Celsius in terms of F degrees Fahrenheit. The temperature of a certain substance ranges from 20°C to 25°C inclusive. Find the corresponding range of temperatures in degrees Fahrenheit.

DIRECTIONS FOR QUESTIONS 1–22: For each of the questions below, select the answer choice that is best for each case.

1 If $3(x + 2) = -12$, then $x =$

A. -6 B. -2 C. 2 D. 6

2 If $-2d + 5 = -31$, then $3d - 9 =$

A. -63 B. -54 C. 18 D. 45

3 If $-4t + 4 + 2a = 3a - 12 - 5t$, then $t =$

A. $a - 3$ C. $a - 16$

B. $-a + 3$ D. $a - 8$

4 Last week a company's income was $530. From this, $50 was withheld for expenses. The rest was shared by two partners in the ratio 3 to 5. How much did each receive?

A. $180 and $300

B. $198.75 and $331.25

C. $72.50 and $457.50

D. $217.50 and $362.50

5 Each situation below gives an original amount followed by a new amount. Which illustrates the greatest percent of increase?

A. 230 pencils; 253 pencils

B. 12 gallons; 15 gallons

C. 18 miles; 21 miles

D. $12; $3

6 The total value of a collection of 34 nickels and quarters is at least $3.60. Let n represent the number of nickels. Which inequality models this situation?

A. $5n + 25(n - 34) \geq 360$

B. $5n + 25(34 - n) \geq 360$

C. $5n + 25(n - 34) \geq 3.60$

D. $5n + 25(34 - n) < 3.60$

7 A 14-ounce solution is made of water, salt, and sugar in the ratio 12 to 1 to 1. Which statement is false?

A. If x represents the number of ounces of sugar, then $12x + x + x = 14$.

B. Water, salt, and sugar are equal in amount.

C. The solution contains 12 ounces of water and 1 ounce each of salt and sugar.

D. The amount of water is 12 times the amount of salt.

8 If $|d| - 9 = 45$, then $d =$

A. 54 or -54 C. 6 or -6

B. 54 or 36   D. 36 or -36

9 What number is 110% of 19?

A. 29   B. 2.09   C. 17.3   D. 20.9

10 Which of the following is the ratio of 2 pounds to 48 ounces expressed as a fraction in lowest terms?

A. $\frac{1}{24}$ B. $\frac{1}{2}$ C. $\frac{2}{3}$ D. $\frac{1}{3}$

11 Solve the proportion: $\frac{5.4}{8} = \frac{t}{6}$

A. $t = 4.05$ C. $t = 1.43$

B. $t = 3.4$ D. $t = 7.2$

12 Solve the inequality: $15c - 4 \leq 12c + 5$

A. $c \geq 3$ C. $c \leq 3$

B. $c \leq \frac{1}{3}$ D. $c > \frac{1}{3}$

13 Which of the following includes all possible solutions of the inequality $-2 \leq -2m < 10$?

A. $1 \leq m < 5$ C. $-5 > m$

B. $m \geq 1$ D. $-5 < m \leq 1$

14 Which is the graph of the solution set of the inequality $p \le -1.5$?

A.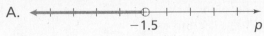
-1.5 p

B.
-1.5 p

C.
-1.5 p

D.
-1.5 p

15 The graph matches the solution set of which of the following inequalities?

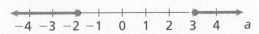
$-4\ -3\ -2\ -1\ \ 0\ \ 1\ \ 2\ \ 3\ \ 4$ a

A. $|4a - 2| \ge 10$

B. $|5a + 6| \le -4$

C. $|a| > 3$

D. $|3a + 4| > 13$

16 The graph matches the solution set of which of the following inequalities?

$-24\ -23\ -22\ -21\ -20\ -19\ -18\ -17$ k

A. $-23 \le k \le -18$

B. $-23 \ge k \ge -18$

C. $-19 < k + 4 < -14$

D. $-19 \ge k + 4 \ge -14$

17 Which of the following represents the set of all integers between -4 and 10 as a single inequality?

A. $-4 < x < 10$

B. $x < 10$

C. $x > -4$

D. $-4 > x > 10$

18 Which statement describes the set of all integers that satisfy $3(n - 5) \ge 20$ and $n \le 12$?

A. $\{11.6, 11.7, \ldots, 12\}$

B. all integers between 11.67 and 12

C. no solution

D. $\{12\}$

19 The ratio of right-handed students to left-handed students in a grade is $11:2$. There are 38 left-handed students in this grade. How many right-handed students are there?

A. 7   C. 47

B. 209   D. 437

20 Greg bought a television on sale for $336. The regular price was $420. What was the percent of decrease in the price?

A. 80%   C. 25%

B. 20%   D. 16%

21 The formula for calculating simple interest is $I = prt$, where I is the amount of interest, p is the amount invested, r is the annual rate of interest, and t is the time in years. Suppose that you invested $1200 for a period of six years and earned $396 simple interest. What was the annual rate of interest?

A. 0.055%   C. 0.55%

B. 18%   D. 5.5%

22 At Roosevelt High School, 12% of the students belong to the Drama Club. There are 66 students in the Drama Club. How many students are in the school altogether?

A. 550   C. 792

B. 616   D. 8

DIRECTIONS FOR QUESTIONS 23–25: Solve each problem and show your work.

23 A car left point X at noon, traveling along a straight road at exactly 60 miles per hour. It arrived at point Y at 1:00 P.M. on the same day. When this car was at point M, halfway between X and Y, a second car traveling at exactly 45 miles per hour left point X and traveled toward point Y along the same road.

X M Y

- What is the distance in miles from point X to point M.

- At what time did the second car reach point Y?

- How far had the second car traveled when the first car reached point Y?

- How long will it take the second car to travel from point X to point Y

24 The perimeter of any triangle is the sum of the lengths of its sides. The lengths of the sides of a certain triangle, in feet, are consecutive even numbers. The perimeter of this triangle is between 10 feet and 24 feet inclusive.

- Write 3 expressions that represent the lengths of the sides of the triangle.

- Write an inequality to describe the possible measures of the perimeter of the triangle.

- Solve the inequality.

- List all possible lengths for the longest side of the triangle.

25 A furniture store is having its annual spring sale. All furniture is on sale for 15% off. Janet purchases a sofa and receives an additional 10% off of the sale price. The original price of the sofa is $600.

- What is the price of the sofa before the additional 10% discount?

- How much more does Janet save with the additional 10% discount?

- Is the final sale price of the sofa the same as the price if the sale is 25% off the price of the sofa? Explain your reasoning.

3 Linear Equations and Inequalities in Two Variables

NEW JERSEY

Clara Barton

Clara Barton was born Clarissa Harlowe Barton on December 25, 1821 in Massachusetts. She became a teacher when she was 17.

During the Civil War, Clara worked to deliver medical aid to the wounded soldiers. She became known as the "Angel of the Battlefield." Later, Clara became involved in the women's suffragist movement, working with such individuals as Susan B. Anthony and Lucy Stone. Her greatest legacy, however, was establishing the American Red Cross in 1881. She also founded the National First Aid Society in 1904. Clara Barton received many honors for her accomplishments, including the Iron Cross, the Cross of Imperial Russia, and the International Red Cross Medal. She died in 1912 at the age of 90.

3.1 Lines in the Coordinate Plane

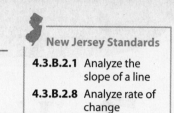

New Jersey Standards

4.3.B.2.1 Analyze the slope of a line

4.3.B.2.8 Analyze rate of change

The **coordinate axes system** is created by two intersecting number lines, one **horizontal axis** called the **x–axis** and one **vertical axis** called the **y–axis**. The intersection point is called the **origin**. The axes system divides the plane into points on the axes and into four regions called **quadrants**. Points in the plane are named by using a capital letter and an **ordered pair, P (a, b)**. Point P has **abscissa**, or **x–coordinate**, a, and **ordinate**, or **y–coordinate**, b. Point $F(2, -4)$ has abscissa 2 and ordinate -4. Point F is in the fourth quadrant.

Just as the graph of a real number is the point on the number line representing that number, the **graph of an ordered pair** (a, b) of real numbers a and b is the point P in the coordinate plane whose x-coordinate is a and whose y-coordinate is b. As shown at the right, the ordered pairs $(-5, 5)$ and $(0, 3)$ are represented by points $B(-5, 5)$ and $C(0, 3)$, respectively.

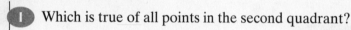

EXAMPLES 1 and 2 — Working with points in the coordinate plane

1 Which is true of all points in the second quadrant?

    A. positive x-coordinate; positive y-coordinate

    C. negative x-coordinate; positive y-coordinate

    B. negative x-coordinate; negative y-coordinate

    D. positive x-coordinate; negative y-coordinate

■ **SOLUTION**

To locate a point in the second quadrant, go left from the origin, and then go up.

go left: negative x-coordinate
go up: positive y-coordinate

The correct choice is C.

2 Which point lies in the third quadrant?

    A. $P(0, -5)$ **B.** $Q(-5, -11)$ **C.** $R(-5, 0)$ **D.** $T(-5, 11)$

■ **SOLUTION**

Points in the third quadrant have a negative x-coordinate $Q(-5, -11) \rightarrow$ Quadrant III and a negative y-coordinate. The correct choice is B.

Two points in the coordinate plane determine a line. The ratio of the vertical change to the horizontal change is the measure of the **slope of the line,** and the letter m is used to represent this measure. The horizontal change from point A to B is 5 units and the vertical change from A to B is 4 units.

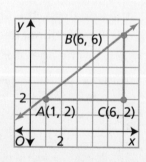

Slope of a Line

For any two points in the plane $P(x_1, y_1)$ and $Q(x_2, y_2)$ the slope can be represented in the following ways.

$$\text{slope} = m = \frac{\text{vertical change}}{\text{horizontal change}} = \frac{\text{rise}}{\text{run}} = \frac{\Delta y}{\Delta x} = \frac{y_1 - y_2}{x_1 - x_2} = \frac{y_2 - y_1}{x_2 - x_1}$$

Go Online
PHSchool.com
Visit: PHSchool.com
Web Code: ayp-0075

These diagrams illustrate a line with positive slope, line *m;* a line with negative slope, line *n;* and a line with 0 slope, line *z.*

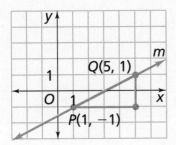
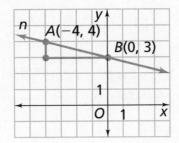
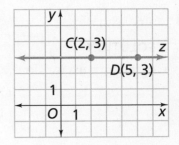

If the line is horizontal, then the vertical change $y_1 - y_2$, or rise, is equal to zero and the slope of the line is zero.

$$m = \frac{2 - 2}{1 - (-3)} = \frac{0}{4} = 0$$

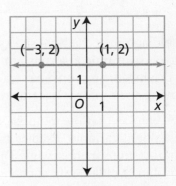

If the line is vertical, then the horizontal change, or run, is zero. A ratio is undefined when the denominator is zero and the numerator is nonzero. Therefore, **a vertical line has no slope.**

$$m = \frac{2 - 5}{1 - 1} = \frac{-3}{0} = \text{undefined}$$

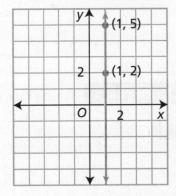

EXAMPLES 3 through 5 **Calculating the slope of a line**

Find the slope of the line containing the given points.

3 $P(1, -1)$ and $Q(5, 1)$

■ SOLUTION

$$m = \frac{1 - (-1)}{5 - 1} = \frac{2}{4} = \frac{1}{2}$$

4 $A(-4, 4)$ and $B(0, 3)$

■ SOLUTION

$$m = \frac{3 - 4}{0 - (-4)} = -\frac{1}{4}$$

5 $C(2, 3)$ and $D(5, 3)$

■ SOLUTION

$$m = \frac{3 - 3}{5 - 2} = 0$$

You can use what you know about slope to analyze and solve problems involving slopes of lines.

 EXAMPLES 6 and 7   **Solving problems that involve slope**

6 Which describes the slope of the line containing $W(-1, 5)$ and $Z(4, 5)$?

   A. positive   **B.** negative   **C.** 0   **D.** does not exist

   ■ **SOLUTION**

   The y-coordinates of W and Z are equal. So, the line is horizontal. The correct choice is C.

7 A line with slope $\frac{1}{3}$ contains $R(3, n)$ and $S(-2, 2)$. Find the value of n.

   ■ **SOLUTION**

   Use the formula for slope. $\frac{1}{3} = \frac{2-n}{-2-3}$ $\leftarrow$ $m = \frac{y_2 - y_1}{x_2 - x_1}$

                            $\frac{1}{3} = \frac{2-n}{-5}$

                            $n = \frac{11}{3}$

The diagram at the right shows the distance a certain motorist travels over time at a constant speed. Notice that after 2 hours of driving, the motorist has traveled 130 miles. After 4 hours of driving, the motorist has traveled 260 miles.

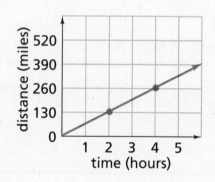

You can say that the motorist's speed is the ratio of the dependent variable, distance traveled, to the independent variable, time spent driving. This is an example of *rate of change*. You can calculate rate of change by finding the slope of the line.

$$\text{speed (rate of change)} = \frac{\text{change in distance}}{\text{change in time}} = \frac{260 - 130}{4 - 2} = 65$$

The motorist's speed is 65 miles per hour.

 EXAMPLE 8   **Using rate of change with data**

8 This table is a record of plant height over a period of time. Graph the data. Assuming that all data lie along a line, find the slope of the line. Interpret the slope.

day	1	2	3	4	5	6
height (inches)	1.0	1.5	2.0	2.5	3.0	3.5

   ■ **SOLUTION**

Record days on the horizontal axis and height on the vertical axis. Choose any two points from the data set. Use the formula for slope.

   day 2: height 1.5 inches   day 6: height 3.5 inches

$$\frac{\text{difference in height}}{\text{difference in days}} = \frac{3.5 - 1.5}{6 - 2} = \frac{1}{2}$$

Each day, plant height increased 0.5 inch.

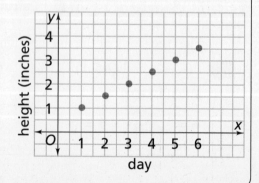

Practice

Choose the letter preceding the word or expression that best completes the statement or answers the question.

1 Which statement best describes a line with positive slope?

    A. From left to right, the line falls.

    B. From left to right, the line rises.

    C. The line is parallel to the x-axis.

    D. The line is parallel to the y-axis.

2 Which line has negative slope?

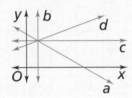

    A. a **B.** b **C.** c **D.** d

3 The slope of the line containing $G(-7, 4)$ and $H(6, -2)$ is

    A. $\frac{6}{13}$ **B.** $-\frac{13}{6}$ **C.** $-\frac{6}{13}$ **D.** $\frac{13}{6}$

4 Which ordered pairs represent X, Y, and Z?

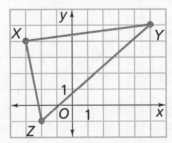

    A. $X(-3, 3)$, $Y(5, 4)$, and $Z(-2, -2)$

    B. $X(5, 5)$, $Y(-3, 4)$, and $Z(-2, -1)$

    C. $X(-3, 4)$, $Y(5, 5)$, and $Z(-2, 1)$

    D. $X(-3, 4)$, $Y(5, 5)$, and $Z(-2, -1)$

In Exercises 5–6, identify the figure determined by joining the points in the order given.

5 $A(-3, -5)$, $B(3, 5)$, and $C(10, -5)$

6 $C(0, 5)$, $D(-6, 0)$, $E(0, -5)$, and $F(6, 0)$

In Exercises 7–13, find the slope of the line containing each pair of points. If the line has no slope, so state.

7 $A(-3, -5)$, $B(3, 5)$ **8** $X(3, -7)$, $Y(-5, 11)$

9 $K(0, 5)$, $L(3, 0)$ **10** $P(4, 7)$, $Q(4, -7)$

11 $C(0, 5)$, $D(0, -6)$ **12** $R(-3, -3)$, $S(3, 3)$

13 $U(-0.5, 0.6)$, $V(-2.5, 1.4)$

In Exercises 14–19, point $P(x, y)$ has coordinates $x = -3$ and $y = 4$. Give the coordinates of each point.

14 $A(-x, -y)$ **15** $B(x, -y)$

16 $C(-x, y)$ **17** $P(-2x, 3y)$

18 $Q(x + 5, y - 3)$ **19** $F(-3x, y + 2.5)$

In Exercises 20–22, solve the problem. Clearly show all necessary work.

20 A line has slope -2 and contains $P(3, 4)$ and $Q(-4, a)$. Find the value of a.

21 Use this table to find the rate of change of distance (in miles) over time.

hour	1	2	3	4	5	6
distance	54	108	162	216	270	324

22 Which line is steeper, a line with slope 0.4 or a line with slope 0.6? Explain.

3.2 Relations and Functions

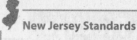

A student earns $4.50 per hour as a baby sitter. She is paid for a whole number of hours of work and works up to 6 hours at a time. The sitter can represent the relationship between time worked and money earned in a table, a list, an equation or rule, or a graph.

hours h	1	2	3	4	5	6
wage w	$4.50	$9.00	$13.50	$18.00	$22.50	$27.00

$$\{(1, 4.50), (2, 9.00), (3, 13.50), (4, 18.00), (5, 22.50), (6, 27.00)\}$$

$$w = 4.5h$$

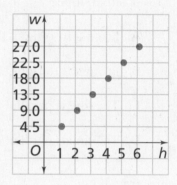

The relationship between hours worked and wages is an example of a *function*. A **function** is a relationship in which every member of one set, the **domain,** is assigned exactly one member of a second set, the **range.** Members of the range of a function are also called **values of a function.** If the function is defined by an equation, you *evaluate the function* to find its values.

EXAMPLES 1 and 2 Recognizing functions

1. Which list does not represent a function?

   A. $\{(1, 2), (3, 4), (5, 7), (7, 5)\}$ **C.** $\{(0, -3), (-2, 0), (7.5, 8.9), (-0.002, -0.002)\}$

   B. $\{(-2, 4), (0, 0), (1, 1), (2, 4)\}$ **D.** $\{(1, 1), (4, 2), (9, 3), (4, -2), (49, 7), (100, 10)\}$

   ■ **SOLUTION**

   In choice **D,** 4 is paired with 2 and with −2. So the list in choice D does not represent a function.

   domain 4 ⟨ 2 range
              −2

2. If domain members are represented by x and range members are represented by y, which does not represent a function?

   A. $y = 3x - 5$ **B.** $y^2 = x$ **C.** $y = x^2 - 5$ **D.** $y = |x|$

   ■ **SOLUTION**

   In choice **B,** $x = 9$ gives $y^2 = 9$. Both 3 and −3 satisfy $y^2 = 9$. The equation in choice B does not represent a function.

A **relation** is any correspondence between two sets, the **domain** and **range,** without requiring that each domain member be assigned only one range member. These *mapping diagrams* show the difference between a function and a relation.

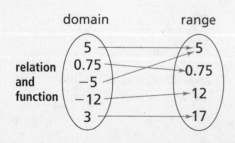

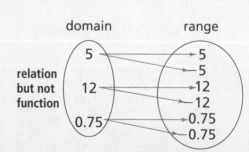

The domain and range of a function can be given using a list, interval notation, or a written description. You find the domain of a function by identifying all of the possible *x*-values of the function. You find the range of a function by identifying all of the possible *y*-values of the function.

Go Online
PHSchool.com
Visit:PHSchool.com
Web Code:ayp-0495

EXAMPLES 3 and 4   **Finding the domain and range of a function**

Find the domain and range of each function.

3 $\{(1, 5), (2, 10), (3, 15), (4, 20), (5, 25), (6, 30)\}$

■ **SOLUTION**

domain: first members in the ordered pairs
range: second members in the ordered pairs

domain: {1, 2, 3, 4, 5, 6}
range: {5, 10, 15, 20, 25, 30}

4 $y = x^2 + 2$

■ **SOLUTION**

For any real number $x, x^2 \geq 0$.
Thus, $x^2 + 2$ is always 2 or more.

domain: all real numbers
range: all real numbers 2 or more

The *vertical-line test* can help you determine whether a graph represents a function. If the graph does represent a function, you can use the graph to find the domain and range. The graph at the right does not represent a function because it does not pass the vertical-line test.

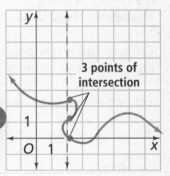

3 points of intersection

Vertical-Line Test

If every vertical line that intersects a graph does so in exactly one point, then the graph represents a function.

EXAMPLES 5 and 6   **Using graphs and the vertical-line test**

Does the graph represent a function? If it does, what are the domain and range?

5

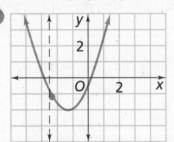

■ **SOLUTION**

Every vertical line intersects the graph in exactly one point. **The graph represents a function.**

domain: all real numbers
range: all real numbers −2 or more

6

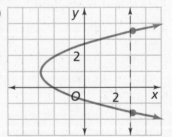

■ **SOLUTION**

Every vertical line with *x*-coordinate more than −3 intersects the graph in two points. For example, the line $x = 3$ intersects the graph in two points.

The graph does not represent a function.

You can use what you know to recognize relations and functions given in different representations, such as a list, table, graph, or equation.

EXAMPLE 7 **Recognizing a relation from different representations**

7 Which represents a relation that is not a function?

A. $\{(0,0), (0,7), (6,6), (6,-6)\}$ **C.** $y = -3.5x + 7$

B.

domain	range
-3	0
5	10
7	-5.4

D.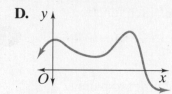

■ **SOLUTION**

In choice **A,** the domain values 0 and 6 are each assigned two range values. The list in choice **A** is a relation but not a function. The correct choice is A.

Practice

Choose the letter preceding the word or expression that best completes the statement or answers the question.

1 Which is a relation but not a function?

A. $\{(-2,3), (-1,1), (0,7), (2,3), (3,2)\}$

B. $\{(2,3), (3,4), (5,7), (1,2), (9,9)\}$

C. $\{(-2,4), (2,3), (5,6), (-2,6)\}$

D. $\{(-1,-1), (-2,-2), (-3,-3), (4,4)\}$

2 Given $y = 3x + 1$ and $x = 3$, find y.

A. 1   **B.** 3   **C.** 9   **D.** 10

3 If $\{-3, -1, 1, 2, 3\}$ is the domain, what is the range of $y = x^2 - x$?

A. $\{-3, -1, 1, 2\}$

B. $\{0, 2, 6, 12\}$

C. $\{1, 4, 9\}$

D. $\{-3, -2, -1, 1\}$

4 A graph passes the vertical-line test if

A. a vertical line intersects it at exactly one point.

B. a vertical line intersects it at two points.

C. a vertical line intersects it at more than one point.

D. a vertical line intersects at two or more points.

5 Which graph does not represent a function?

A. 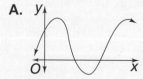   **C.**

B. 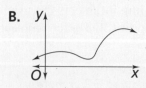   **D.**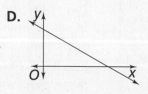

6 Which equation represents the verbal description of this function?

To change length f in feet to length I in inches, multiply f by 12.

A. $f = 12I$ C. $I = 12f$

B. $I = \frac{12}{f}$ D. $f = \frac{12}{I}$

7 The values of the independent variable for a function are also known as the

A. values.

B. domain.

C. range.

D. coordinates.

8 Given the function rule $g(x) = 2x - 1$, what is the value of $g(3)$?

A. 3   C. 5

B. 9   D. 10

9 $A = \{(1, 4), (4, 7), (3, 7), (5, 9), (9, 2)\}$. Which of the following statements is **not** true?

A. The domain of A is $\{1, 4, 3, 5, 7, 9\}$.

B. A is a function.

C. The range of A is $\{4, 7, 9, 2\}$.

D. A is a relation.

10 Which of the following lines has an undefined slope?

A. a line containing the points $(3, -4)$ and $(-4, 3)$

B. a line containing the points $(2, 1)$ and $(-2, -3)$

C. a horizontal line through the point $(3, 4)$

D. a vertical line through the point $(-1, 5)$

11 Determine whether the following graph represents a function.

In Exercises 12–16, write a formula for the relation described and give its domain and range.

12 To convert a length in inches i to centimeters c, multiply by 2.54.

13 The Coach USA Center seats 3200 fans. Tickets sell for $9. The number of seats sold determines the gross take G.

14 Your grade G on a test worth 80 points is the number of points you earned e divided by 0.8.

15 The points you earn p in basketball is 2 times the number of field goals f you make.

16 The area A of a square is the length of its side s multiplied by itself.

In Exercises 17–25, graph the function by using a table of values and state its domain and range.

17 $y = 2x - 1$

18 $f(x) = |x| - 1$

19 y is the quotient of some number and 3.

20 $y = -5x + 7$

21 $4x + 3y = 12$

22 $y = x$

23 $f(x) = |x + 1|$

24 y is the sum of 3 times x and 4.

25 $y = |x| - 5$

3.3 Linear Equations in Two Variables

A **linear equation in two variables** is any equation that can be written in the form $ax + by = c$, where a, b, and c are real numbers and a, $b \neq 0$. The equation $ax + by = c$ is called the **standard form** of a linear equation in two variables.

Examples:
$$y = 2x + 1$$
$$-3x + 2y = 6$$

A **solution to an equation in two variables** is any ordered pair (x, y) that makes the equation true.

The **graph of an equation in two variables** is the set of all points in the coordinate plane that correspond to solutions to the equation.

Graph of a Linear Equation in Two Variables

The graph of an equation of the form $ax + by = c$, where a, b, and c are real numbers and a, $b \neq 0$, is a line.

- A **y-intercept** of a graph is the y-coordinate of any point where the graph crosses the y-axis.

- An **x-intercept** of a graph is the x-coordinate of any point where the graph crosses the x-axis.

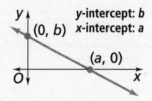

A linear equation in two variables can be written in **slope-intercept form**, $y = mx + b$, for real numbers m and b. The slope is m and the y-intercept is b.

EXAMPLE 1   Writing a linear equation in two variables in slope-intercept form

 Write $5x - 3y = 15$ in slope-intercept form. What are the slope and y-intercept?

■ SOLUTION
$$5x - 3y = 15$$
$$y = \tfrac{5}{3}x + (-5), \text{ or } y = \tfrac{5}{3}x - 5 \leftarrow \textbf{slope-intercept form}$$

The slope is $\tfrac{5}{3}$ and the y-intercept is -5.

You can use a table of solutions to graph an equation in two variables.
You can also graph a line by plotting the *y*-intercept and using the definition
of slope $= \frac{\text{rise}}{\text{run}}$ to plot additional points of the line.

    Graphing linear equations in two variables

2 Graph $y = 2x + 1$.

■ SOLUTION

Use a table of values.
Graph the points.

x	y
−1	2(−1) + 1 = −1
0	2(0) + 1 = 1
1	2(1) + 1 = 3

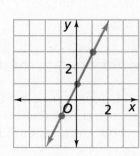

3 Graph $y = -\frac{2}{3}x + 3$.

■ SOLUTION

Use slope $-\frac{2}{3}$ and *y*-intercept 3.

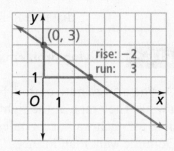

If *a* or *b* is zero in the equation $ax + b = c$, the resulting line is horizontal or
vertical respectively. Recall that line AB is horizontal; therefore, its slope is
zero. $y = (0)x + 2$ or $y = 2$ is the equation of the line.

Line BC is vertical and has no slope; therefore, the slope-intercept form
is of no help in writing the equation. Every point on this line has an
x-value of 4; therefore, the equation of the line is $x = 4$.

Equations of **vertical lines** are of the form $x = k$ and **horizontal lines** are
$y = k$.

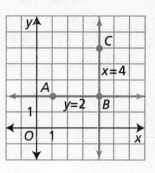

EXAMPLE 4   **Graphing a linear equation in two variables from standard form**

4 Graph $-3x + 2y = 6$, using any method.

■ SOLUTION 1

using the intercepts of the graph

If $x = 0$, then $2y = 6$. So, $(0, 3)$ is a
solution.

If $y = 0$, then $-3x = 6$.
So, $(-2, 0)$ is a solution.

Graph $(0, 3)$ and $(-2, 0)$. Draw the line.

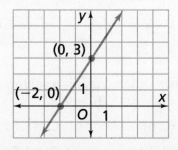

■ SOLUTION 2

solving for y in terms of x

If $-3x + 2y = 6$, then $y = \frac{3}{2}x + 3$.

Plot the *y*-intercept $(0, 3)$.

Use the slope $= \frac{3}{2} = \frac{\text{rise}}{\text{run}}$ to plot
additional points of the line. Draw the line.

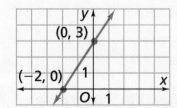

The amount of sales tax paid on a purchase depends on the value of the purchase. You can say that one variable, amount of purchase, is the **independent variable,** and a second variable, amount of tax, is the **dependent variable.** The amount of tax *varies directly* with amount of purchase.

In general, if the value of one variable y is found by multiplying the value of a second variable x by a constant nonzero real number k, the **constant of variation,** then the relationship is called a **direct variation.**

Go Online
PHSchool.com
Visit: PHSchool.com
Web Code: ayp-0169

If $y = kx$, where $k \neq 0$, then y varies directly with x.

An important direct-variation relationship involves distance, rate, and time.

$$\text{distance } d = \text{rate } r \times \text{time } t$$

EXAMPLE 5   **Solving problems involving distance, rate, and time**

 During a 50-minute period, Frances and Dominic went out for a walk. The graph at the right shows distance traveled over time for each walker. In miles per hour, how much faster did Dominic walk than Frances?

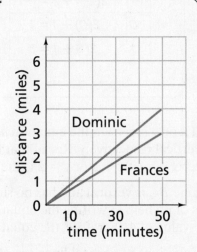

■ **SOLUTION**

In 50 minutes, $\frac{5}{6}$ of an hour, Dominic walked 4 miles and Frances walked 3 miles.

If $d = rt$, then $r = \frac{d}{t}$.

Dominic: $r = \dfrac{4}{\frac{5}{6}} = 4.8$ Frances: $r = \dfrac{3}{\frac{5}{6}} = 3.6$

Dominic walked 1.2 miles per hour faster than Frances.

Practice

Choose the letter preceding the word or expression that best completes the statement or answers the question.

1 Which of the following is not the equation of a line?

A. $y = 4$

B. $3x + 2y = 7$

C. $y = x^2 - 6$

D. $x = -5$

2 The equation of a line is $y = 3x - 7$. What is the y-intercept of the line?

A. 3   **C.** 7

B. 4   **D.** −7

3 Which equation represents variables that are directly related?

A. $y = 2x + 3$

B. $F = 1.8C + 32$

C. $zw = 6$

D. $y = 3f$

4 Which ordered pair is a solution to the equation $5x - 3y = 9$?

A. $(0,0)$ **C.** $(5,5)$

B. $(3,2)$ **D.** $(2,3)$

In Exercises 5–8, the equation $F = \frac{9}{5}C + 32$ relates temperature in degrees Fahrenheit (*F*) to degrees Celsius (*C*). Rewrite this equation as a function *C* in terms of *F*. Use the appropriate equation to calculate, to the nearest tenth, the corresponding temperature for each of the following.

5 $9°C$

6 $-20°C$

7 $0°F$

8 $95°F$

In Exercises 9–11, evaluate each function for the given member of the domain.

9 $y = \frac{2}{3}x + 9; x = -6$

10 $y = 1 - x^2; x = -3$

11 $y = \frac{2}{3}x - \frac{1}{2}; x = -6$

In Exercises 12–15, find the domain and range.

12 $y = 0.6x + 9$

13 $y = -0.25x$

14 $y = 1 - x^2$

15 $y = x^2 - 1$

In Exercises 16–27, graph each equation.

16 $y = -2x + 3$ **17** $y = 3x - 5$

18 $y = 2x - 1$ **19** $y = -3x$

20 $y = -\frac{1}{3}x - 2$ **21** $y = \frac{1}{2}x$

22 $-2x + y = 1$ **23** $x - y = 4$

24 $x + 3y = 3$ **25** $x + 2y = 2$

26 $-x + 2y = 3$ **27** $2x - 3y = 2$

28 During a 40-minute period, Dana and Li went out for a walk. The graph below shows distance traveled over time for each walker. In miles per hour, how much faster did Dana walk than Li?

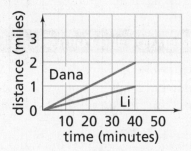

29 Marissa has $1.20 in nickels and dimes. Write an equation that represents this situation using *n* for the number of nickels and *d* for the number of dimes.

30 The sales tax in a certain area is 5%, or 5 cents on the dollar. Write an equation to represent the amount *a* of tax in terms of the cost *c* of a purchase.

31 Hank has $2.45 in nickels and dimes. Write an equation that represents this situation where *n* is the number of nickels and *d* is the number of dimes.

32 At a certain theater, an adult's ticket costs $9 and a child's ticket costs $5. The manager counted the receipts one night and determined that $2,250 was taken in. Write an equation to represent this situation, using *a* to represent the number of adults and *c* to represent the number of children.

33 A collection of 185 marbles consists of only red marbles, blue marbles, and 35 yellow marbles. Write an equation in *r* and *b* to represent the situation. List three possible solutions to the equation.

34 A choir sold fruit as represented below. Write an equation to represent this situation.

5-pound box	10-pound box	Total
f boxes	*t* boxes	200 pounds

Determine two possible numbers of cartons of 5-pound boxes and 10-pound boxes that satisfy the given conditions.

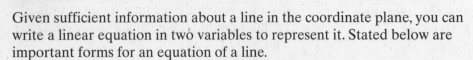

3.4 Writing Equations for Lines

Given sufficient information about a line in the coordinate plane, you can write a linear equation in two variables to represent it. Stated below are important forms for an equation of a line.

New Jersey Standards

4.3.B.1 Understand relations and functions

4.3.B.2.3 Analyze intercepts

4.3.B.2.1 Analyze the slope of a line

Slope-Intercept and Point-Slope Forms

A line with slope m and y-intercept b has **slope-intercept form:**

$$y = mx + b$$

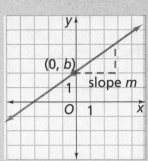

A line with slope m and containing $P(x_1, y_1)$ has **point-slope form:**

$$y - y_1 = m(x - x_1)$$

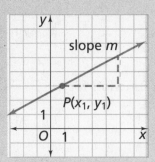

Any vertical line containing $P(x_1, y_1)$ has equation $x = x_1$. For example, if a vertical line contains the point $(5, 2)$, an equation for that line is $x = 5$.

Any horizontal line containing $P(x_1, y_1)$ has equation $y = y_1$. For example, if a horizontal line contains the point $(4, -8)$, an equation for that line is $y = -8$.

Go Online
PHSchool.com
Visit: PHSchool.com
Web Codes: ayp-0208
ayp-0215

EXAMPLES 1 and 2   Using slope and y-intercept to identify an equation for a line

1 Write an equation that represents the line with a slope of $-\frac{4}{5}$ and a y-intercept of 3.

■ **SOLUTION**
Use the slope-intercept form.

$$y = mx + b.$$

$$y = -\frac{4}{5}x + 3 \quad \leftarrow \text{ Replace } m \text{ with } -\frac{4}{5} \text{ and } b \text{ with 3.}$$

2 Which equation represents the line at the right?

A. $y = \frac{1}{4}x + 3$ **C.** $y = \frac{1}{4}x - 3$

B. $y = -\frac{1}{4}x + 3$ **D.** $y = -2x + 3$

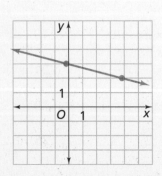

■ **SOLUTION**
The y-intercept is 3. The slope of the line is $-\frac{1}{4}$. Using the slope-intercept form, the correct choice is B.

When you are given the slope and a point on a line, you can use the point-slope form to write an equation for that line.

Go Online
PHSchool.com
Visit: PHSchool.com
Web Code: ayp-0214

EXAMPLES 3 through 5   **Writing an equation for a line by using slope and a point on the line**

Write an equation in slope-intercept form for each line, if possible.

3 the line with slope $\frac{3}{4}$ and containing $P(2, -3)$

■ **SOLUTION**

$$y - (-3) = \frac{3}{4}(x - 2)$$

$$y = \frac{3}{4}x - 4.5$$

4 the line with slope 0 and containing $P(2, -3)$

■ **SOLUTION**

Because the slope is 0, the line is horizontal.

$$y = -3$$

5 the line with no slope and containing $P(2, -3)$

■ **SOLUTION**

Because there is no slope, the line is vertical.

$$x = 2$$

You can also use the point-slope form to find an equation of a line through two specific points. The point-slope form requires that you first find the slope. Recall that slope $= m = \frac{y_2 - y_1}{x_2 - x_1}$. You can write an equation of a line in slope-intercept or standard form.

EXAMPLES 6 through 9   **Writing an equation for a line given two points**

Write an equation for

6 the line containing $L(-5, -6)$ and $M(3, -6)$.

■ **SOLUTION**

The y-coordinates of L and M are equal. The line is horizontal.

$$y = -6$$

7 the line containing $R(4.2, -6)$ and $S(4.2, 9)$.

■ **SOLUTION**

The x-coordinates of R and S are equal. The line is vertical.

$$x = 4.2$$

8 the line containing $A(-5, -6)$ and $B(3, 8)$.

■ **SOLUTION**

First determine the slope.

$$m = \frac{y_2 - y_1}{x_2 - x_1} = \frac{-6 - 8}{-5 - 3}$$

$$= \frac{-14}{-8} = \frac{7}{4}$$

Using the point $B(3, 8)$ and the point-slope form results in:

$$y - 8 = \frac{7}{4}(x - 3)$$

$$y - \frac{32}{4} = \frac{7}{4}x - \frac{21}{4}$$

$$y = \frac{7}{4}x + 2.75$$

9 $\overleftrightarrow{DG}$ containing $D(2, 3)$ and $G(8, 11)$ in standard form.

■ **SOLUTION**

First determine the slope.

$$m = \frac{y_2 - y_1}{x_2 - x_1} = \frac{11 - 3}{8 - 2} = \frac{8}{6}$$

Using the point $D(2, 3)$ and the point-slope form results in:

$$y - 3 = \frac{4}{3}(x - 2)$$

$$3y - 9 = 4x - 8$$

$$-4x + 3y = 1$$

The standard form for the equation is $-4x + 3y = 1$.

Use what you know to solve problems involving points on a line.

Solving problems about points on a line

10 The point $Z(3, w)$ is on the graph of $y = 2x + 5$. The value of w is

   A. -1 **B.** $w - 5$ **C.** 11   **D.** $2w + 5$

   ▪ **SOLUTION**

   If $x = 3$ and $y = w$, then $w = 2(3) + 5$; that is, $w = 11$.
   The correct choice is C.

11 Which point lies on the line containing $P(-3, -1)$ and $Q(5, 6)$?

   A. $A(-3, 0)$ **B.** $B(21, 19)$ **C.** $C(21, 20)$ **D.** $D(-3, -2)$

   ▪ **SOLUTION**

   $$m = \frac{6 - (-1)}{5 - (-3)} = \frac{7}{8} \quad \leftarrow \textbf{Determine the slope.}$$

   $$y = \frac{7}{8}(x - 5) + 6 \quad \leftarrow \textbf{Write an equation for the line containing } P \textbf{ and } Q.$$

   Because $\frac{7}{8}(21 - 5) + 6 = 20$, the correct choice is C.

Two lines in a plane either intersect or do not intersect. If the lines never intersect, they are **parallel.** If the lines intersect at a right angle, the lines are **perpendicular.**

$m: \ y = \frac{1}{2}x + 3$ $n: \ y = \frac{1}{2}x - 1$

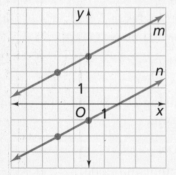

slope of m: $\frac{1}{2}$ slope of n: $\frac{1}{2}$

The lines are **parallel lines.**
The **slopes** of these lines are **equal.**

$p: \ y = -2x - 6$ $q: \ y = \frac{1}{2}x - 1$

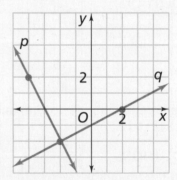

slope of p: -2 slope of q: $\frac{1}{2}$ Note:$-2 \cdot \frac{1}{2} = -1$

The lines are **perpendicular lines.**
The slopes are **negative reciprocals** of each other.

Parallel and Perpendicular Lines

- ▪ Two lines with slopes m_1 and m_2 are parallel if and only if $m_1 = m_2$.
  (Any two vertical or horizontal lines are parallel.)

- ▪ Two lines with slopes m_1 and m_2 are perpendicular if and only if
  $m_1 m_2 = -1$.
  (Every vertical line is perpendicular to every horizontal line.)

12   Which line is parallel to the graph of $5x - 6y = 2$?

   A. the line with slope $-\frac{5}{6}$ and y-intercept $-\frac{1}{3}$ **C.** the line with slope $-\frac{6}{5}$ and y-intercept $-\frac{1}{3}$

   B. the line with slope $\frac{5}{6}$ and y-intercept 3 **D.** the line with slope $\frac{6}{5}$ and y-intercept 3

■ **SOLUTION**

Write $5x - 6y = 2$ in slope-intercept form.

$$5x - 6y = 2$$
$$-6y = -5x + 2$$
$$y = \tfrac{5}{6}x - \tfrac{1}{3}$$

A line parallel to the graph of $5x - 6y = 2$ must have slope $\frac{5}{6}$.
Therefore, eliminate choices **A, C,** and **D.**
The correct choice is **B.**

> **Note**
>
> To see whether two distinct nonvertical lines are parallel, check to see whether:
> ■ slopes are equal;
> ■ y-intercepts are unequal.

13   Which line is parallel to $3x + 4y = 12$?

A. 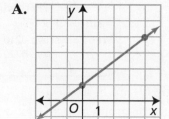   **C.**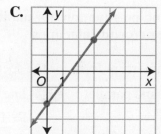

B. 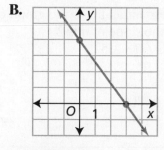   **D.**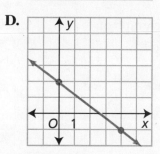

■ **SOLUTION**

Write $3x + 4y = 12$ in slope-intercept form.

$$y = -\tfrac{3}{4}x + 3$$

A line parallel to $3x + 4y = 12$ must have slope $-\frac{3}{4}$.

Therefore, eliminate choices **A** and **C.**

Find the slope of the line in choice **B.**

$$m = \frac{0 - 4}{3 - 0} = -\frac{4}{3}$$

The slope is not equal to $-\frac{3}{4}$; eliminate choice B.

Verify the slope of the line in choice D.

$$m = \frac{2 - (-1)}{0 - 4} = -\frac{3}{4}$$

The slope is equal to $-\frac{3}{4}$; the correct choice is D.

You can also use slope to identify perpendicular lines.

EXAMPLE 14   **Identifying a line perpendicular to a given line**

14 Which equation represents line q perpendicular to line p?

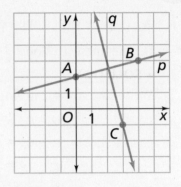

   A. $-x + 4y = -2$ **C.** $-x + 4y = -7$

   B. $4x + y = 11$ **D.** $4x + y = 2$

■ **SOLUTION**

Write each equation in slope-intercept form.

   A. $y = \frac{1}{4}x - \frac{1}{2}$ **C.** $y = \frac{1}{4}x - \frac{7}{4}$

   B. $y = -4x + 11$ **D.** $y = -4x + 2$

Because the slope of p is $\frac{1}{4}$, the slope of q is -4. Eliminate choices **A** and **C**. $C(3, -1)$ does not satisfy the equation in choice **D**. The correct choice is **B**.

You can find an equation of a line parallel or perpendicular to a given line.

Go Online
PHSchool.com
Visit: PHSchool.com
Web Codes: ayp-0218
           ayp-0220

EXAMPLES 15 and 16   **Finding equations for parallel or perpendicular lines**

Find an equation in slope-intercept form for the specified line.

15 line z containing $P(4, -3)$ and parallel to the graph of $y = \frac{1}{2}x + 3$

■ **SOLUTION**

Because z is parallel to the graph of $y = \frac{1}{2}x + 3$, the slope of z is $\frac{1}{2}$. Also, z contains $P(4, -3)$.

$$y - (-3) = \frac{1}{2}(x - 4)$$
$$y = \frac{1}{2}x - 5$$

16 line n containing $Q(-2, 5)$ and perpendicular to the graph of $y = -\frac{1}{2}x + 5$

■ **SOLUTION**

Because n is perpendicular to the graph of $y = -\frac{1}{2}x + 5$, the slope of n is 2. Also, n contains $Q(-2, 5)$.

$$y - 5 = 2(x - (-2))$$
$$y - 5 = 2(x + 2)$$
$$y = 2x + 9$$

Practice

Choose the letter preceding the word or expression that best completes the statement or answers the question.

1 What is the slope of a line parallel to a line with slope -2?

   A. 2   **B.** -2 **C.** $\frac{1}{2}$ **D.** $-\frac{1}{2}$

2 What is the slope of a line perpendicular to a line with slope -2?

   A. 2   **C.** $\frac{1}{2}$

   B. -2 **D.** $-\frac{1}{2}$

3 Which describes the relationship between two distinct nonvertical parallel lines?

   A. equal slopes; unequal y-intercepts

   B. unequal slopes; unequal y-intercepts

   C. equal slopes; equal y-intercepts

   D. unequal slopes; equal y-intercepts

4 Find the slope of a line perpendicular to line p.

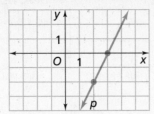

  A. 2   **B.** 0.5   **C.** -2 **D.** -0.5

5 Which equation represents the line with slope -3 and y-intercept -7?

  A. $y = -3x + 7$ **C.** $y = -3x - 7$

  B. $y = -7x + 3$ **D.** $y = 7x - 3$

6 What is the slope of a line parallel to m?

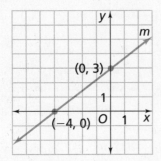

  A. $-\frac{4}{3}$ **B.** $\frac{4}{3}$ **C.** $-\frac{3}{4}$ **D.** 0.75

7 Which equation could not represent a line parallel to the graph of $y = -2.5x + 1$?

  A. $y = -2.5x + 3$ **C.** $y = -2.5x - 1$

  B. $y = 2.5x + 1$ **D.** $y = -2.5x$

In Exercises 8–16, write an equation in slope-intercept form for the specified line, where possible.

8 the line containing $A(0, 7)$ and $B(7, 0)$

9 the line containing $C(3, -7)$ and $D(-3, 5)$

10 slope: 2;
containing $P(4, 5)$

11 slope: -0.6;
containing $Z(-1, 1)$

12 slope: 0;
y-intercept -7

13 no slope;
x-intercept -11

14 containing $H(2, 2)$ and parallel to the graph of $y = x - 3$

15 containing $A(-2, -2)$ and parallel to the graph of $y = 2x - 1$

16 containing $M(1, 4)$ and perpendicular to the graph of $y = -\frac{2}{3}x + 5$

In Exercises 17–22, solve the problem. Clearly show all necessary work.

17 What are the coordinates of the point where the line containing $K(-3, 5)$ and $L(5, -4)$ crosses the y-axis?

18 Is the relationship between y and x linear? Explain your answer.

x	0	4	8	12
y	2	5	8	11

19 Write an equation in standard form for this graph.

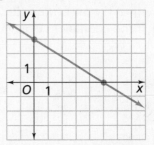

20 A student can work at a job that pays $4 an hour for 25 hours to earn $100 or can work at a second job that pays $5 per hour for 20 hours to earn $100. If the student spends time at each job, find two other amounts of time at each job needed to earn $100. Show your work.

21 Is $S(93, 83)$ on the line containing $P(-3, -1)$ and $Q(5, 6)$? Justify your response.

22 Is $K(-90, -232)$ on the line shown below?

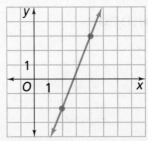

3.5 Graphs of Absolute Value Functions

New Jersey Standards

4.3.C.1.3 Use functions to solve absolute value problems

You have learned that the **absolute value** of a number is its distance from zero on a number line. The definition of the absolute value is

$$abs(x) = |x| = \begin{cases} x \ if \ x \geq 0 \\ -x \ if \ x < 0 \end{cases} \quad or \quad abs(x) = |x| = \begin{cases} x \ if \ x \ is \ positive \ or \ zero \\ the \ opposite \ of \ x \ if \ x \ is \ negative \end{cases}$$

You can use a graphing calculator to graph the $y = abs(x)$ function by entering it into the function list, selecting an appropriate window, and pressing the GRAPH key.

Note

The absolute value function is entered $y = abs(x)$ into the graphing calculator. It is commonly written $y = |x|$.

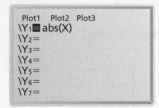
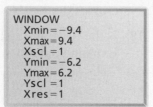
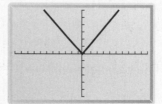

If you look at the table of values for this function, you will see that if x is negative, y is the opposite of x and if x is positive, y is equal to x.

If the cofficient of the absolute value term of the function is positive, the **V** points down; if the coefficient is negative, the **V** points up.

X	Y₁
−3	3
−2	2
−1	1
0	0
2	2
3	3

X=3

Note

The vertex of the absolute value function is the point where the function changes direction.

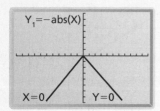
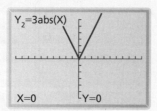
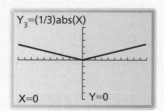

As you can see from the graphs above, if $y = a|x|$, the graph is narrower.

If $y = (1/a)|x|$, the graph is wider.

EXAMPLES 1 through 3   Graphing absolute value functions

Graph the following functions on a calculator.

1 $y = |x + 3|$

■ SOLUTION

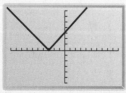

2 $y = |x - 3|$

■ SOLUTION

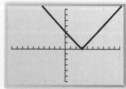

3 $y = |x| + 3$

■ SOLUTION

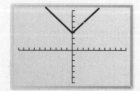

A **translation** is a shift of a graph vertically, horizontally, or both. The resulting graph is the same size and shape as the original but is in a different position in the plane.

Visit: PHSchool.com
Web Codes: ayp-0225
ayp-0226

Graphs of Absolute Value Functions

- If $y = |x + a|$, the graph translates a units to the left.
- If $y = |x - a|$, the graph translates a units to the right.
- If $y = |x| + a$, the graph translates a units up.
- If $y = |x| - a$, the graph translates a units down.

You can also write an equation of an absolute value function from its graph.

EXAMPLES 4 through 6   **Writing an equation of an absolute value function from its graph**

Write an equation for each translation of $y = |x|$ shown below.

4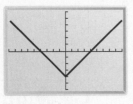

5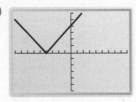

6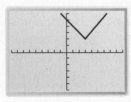

■ SOLUTION
$y = |x| - 4$

■ SOLUTION
$y = |x + 4|$

■ SOLUTION
$y = |x - 3| + 2$

Practice

In Exercises 1–2, use the graph below.

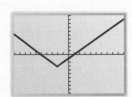

1 Which statement best describes the translation of $y = |x|$ shown in the graph above?

   A. 2 units up, 3 units left

   C. 2 units down, 3 units left

   B. 2 units left, 3 units down

   D. 2 units right, 3 units right

2 Which equation represents the graph?

   A. $y = |x + 2| - 3$ **C.** $y = |x - 2| + 3$

   B. $y = |x + 3| - 2$ **D.** $y = |x - 3| + 2$

In Exercises 3–6, graph each function and state its vertex.

3 $y = |x| + 2$ **4** $y = |x - 2|$

5 $y = |x| - 5$ **6** $y = |x - 1| + 3$

In Exercises 7–12, write an equation for each translation of $y = |x|$.

7 9 units up   **8** 6 units down

9 right 9 units   **10** left 0.5 units

11 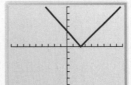   **12**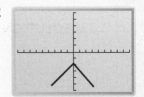

3.6 Special Functions

New Jersey Standards

4.3.C.1 Solve problems that involve varying quantities

When two quantities are related such that a change in one produces the opposite type of change in the other, the relationship is called **inverse variation.** For example, if the area of a rectangle is fixed at 72 square units, an increase in the length of the rectangle will cause a decrease in the width. The length varies inversely as the width.

Constant of Variation

When one quantity varies inversely as another, their product is a constant. If the variables are x and y, this can be written $xy = k$ or $y = \frac{k}{x}$, where $k \neq 0$. The number k is the **constant of variation.**

The graphs of the equations for inverse variation have the same general shape. The graph shows inverse variation functions with different values of k. When you know one pair of values of the variables that vary inversely, you can find the equation that relates them to each other.

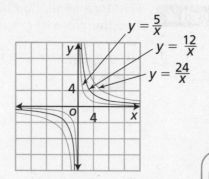

EXAMPLE 1   **Writing an equation for inverse variation**

Go Online
PHSchool.com

Visit: PHSchool.com
Web Code: ayp-0197

 Suppose that a varies inversely with b, and $a = 4$ when $b = 12$. Write an equation for the inverse variation.

■ **SOLUTION**

$ab = (4)(12) = 48$. The constant of variation is 48; therefore, the equation for the inverse variation is $a = \frac{48}{b}$.

You can determine whether variables vary inversely if the product of the corresponding values is constant.

EXAMPLE 2   **Writing an inverse variation equation**

2   Do the data in the table below vary inversely? If so, write an equation.

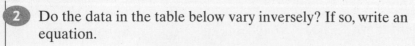

x	3	8	6	4
y	24	9	12	18

■ **SOLUTION**

The value of y varies inversely with the value of x because each product pair of values is 72. Therefore, the equation is $y = \frac{72}{x}$.

Most of the functions you will be considering will result in graphs that show a smooth, continuous line curve. Some functions, however, result in graphs that are not continuous. A function that results in a discontinuous line is referred to as a **step function**.

EXAMPLE 3   **Graphing a step function**

 During a recent cab ride, a passenger noticed that the taximeter remained at a certain dollar amount for a period of time and then advanced to the next dollar amount. It remained there for a period of time before advancing again. The taxi fare rate posted on the seat in front of the passenger read $2.50 + $0.25 per $\frac{1}{4}$ mile. The table at the right shows the cab fare for distances less than one mile. Graph the data.

TAXI FARE	
Distance (mi)	Fare ($)
$0 \leq m \leq 0.25$	2.50
$0.25 \leq m < 0.5$	2.75
$0.5 \leq m < 0.75$	3.00
$0.15 \leq m < 1$	3.25

■ SOLUTION

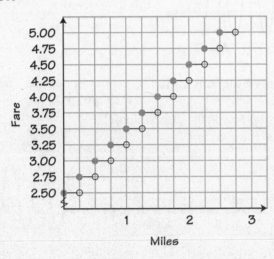

A special type of step function is the **greatest integer function**. The greatest integer function assigns to each real number the greatest integer that is less than or equal to that number. This function is written in symbols as $[x]$. Most calculators and computers denote the greatest integer function as INT(x).

EXAMPLES 4 through 7   **Finding the greatest integer function**

 $[6]$

■ SOLUTION

The greatest integer less than or equal to 6 is 6, so $[6] = 6$.

5 $[2.7]$

■ SOLUTION

The greatest integer less than or equal to 2.7 is 2, so $[2.7] = 2$.

6 $[-1.5]$

■ SOLUTION

The greatest integer less than or equal to -1.5 is -2, so $[-1.5] = -2$.

7 $[8.9]$

■ SOLUTION

The greatest integer less than or equal to 8.9 is 8, so $[8.9] = 8$.

85

The graph at the right shows the function $f(x) = [x]$. The domain of the greatest integer function is the set of real numbers and the range is the set of integers. Notice that the left endpoint of each segment is closed and therefore included. The right endpoint is open and therefore excluded. In a step function, there is a break in the y-values of the graph. Accordingly, the graph shows that point $(2, 2)$ is a member of the data set and point $(2, 1)$ is not.

A **periodic function** repeats at a set interval. An interval is the distance between cycles of an event. The interval is called the **period** of the function. The graph of a periodic function is shown below.

Period

EXAMPLES 8 and 9   Analyzing periodic functions

8 Use the graph of a periodic function to construct a table of values. Then identify the length of the interval.

■ **SOLUTION**

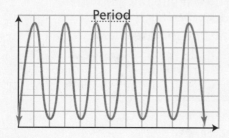

x	−3	−2.5	−2	−1.5	−1	−0.5	0	0.5	1	1.5	2	2.5	3
f(x)	0	−2	0	2	0	−2	0	2	0	−2	0	2	0

The values of f(x) repeat after every interval of 2.

9 A Ferris wheel with a radius of 30 feet completes one revolution every 20 seconds. The seats are 5 feet off the ground at the lowest position. One ride is six cycles. Construct a graph that models one complete ride on the Ferris wheel. Let $y = 0$ represent the ground. Let $x = 0$ represent the beginning of the ride.

radius = 30 ft

5 ft

■ **SOLUTION**

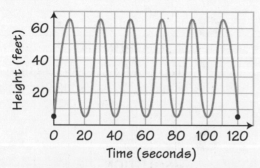

Height (feet) vs. Time (seconds)

Notice that the graph never goes below 5 feet because the seat is 5 feet off the ground at the lowest point. The height of the graph ($2r + 5$) is 65 feet. There are six periods because the ride is six cycles long.

Choose the letter preceding the word or expression that best completes the statement or answers the question.

1 The variables x and y vary inversely with a constant of variation of 32. What is the value of y when $x = 4$?

A. 128   **B.** 28   **C.** 8   **D.** 2

2 The variable x varies inversely with the variable y, and $x = 3$ when $y = 8$. What is the value of x when $y = 6$?

A. $\frac{5}{4}$ **B.** 2   **C.** 4   **D.** 6

3 Which equation is an example of inverse variation?

A. $y = 2x$ **C.** $x = \frac{7}{y}$

B. $y = \frac{-x}{3}$ **D.** $x = y - 2$

4 What is the value of $\lfloor 3.7 \rfloor$?

A. 3   **B.** 3.7   **C.** 4   **D.** -3

5 If $f(x) = 5 + \lfloor x \rfloor$, what is $f(-3.2)$?

A. 6.1   **B.** 1   **C.** 5   **D.** 8.2

6 The function $g(x)$ is periodic with a period of 3. If the point $(2, 7)$ is on the graph of $g(x)$, what is $g(5)$?

A. 2   **B.** 3   **C.** 5   **D.** 7

In Exercises 7–10, solve each problem and show your work.

7 Determine whether the data in the accompanying table represent inverse variation. Explain how you arrived at your answer and write the equation to model the data in the table.

r	s
3	12
6	6
9	4

8 The weight needed to balance a lever varies inversely with the distance from the fulcrum to the weight. Where should Sam, who weighs 150 lbs, sit to balance a lever if Betty, who weighs 120 lbs is 6 ft from the fulcrum?

9 The table shows the 2006 United States rates for mailing a first class letter weighing up to 8 ounces. Graph the cost of mailing a letter as a function of the weight of the letter.

First-Class Mail Rates	
Weight at most (ounces)	Rate
1	$0.39
2	$0.63
3	$0.87
4	$1.11
5	$1.35
6	$1.59
7	$1.83
8	$2.07

10 What is the period of the function shown in the graph?

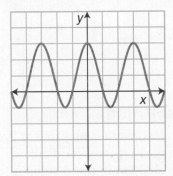

3.7 Matrix Algebra

4.1.B.3.1 Add and subtract
matrices

4.1.B.3.2 Multiply matrices
by scalars

A **matrix** is a rectangular array of numbers. Each number is called an
element of the matrix. An array with m rows and n columns is called an $m \times n$
(read "m by n") **matrix**. This matrix has dimensions m and n. If $m = n$, the
matrix is referred to as a square matrix.

A matrix is named by a capital letter. The rows of a matrix are numbered
from top to bottom and the columns are numbered from left to right. The
elements of a matrix are generally denoted by a lowercase letter, and
subscripts are used to denote the location of an element. Therefore, the entry
in row i, column j is denoted by a_{ij}. The element a_{23} is the element in the
second row, third column. The general form of a matrix is shown below.

$$A = \begin{bmatrix} a_{11} & a_{12} & a_{13} & \cdots & a_{1n} \\ a_{21} & a_{22} & a_{23} & \cdots & a_{2n} \\ a_{31} & a_{32} & a_{33} & \cdots & a_{3n} \\ \vdots & \vdots & \vdots & & \vdots \\ a_{m1} & a_{m2} & a_{m3} & \cdots & a_{mn} \end{bmatrix}$$

Go Online
PHSchool.com
Visit: PHSchool.com
Web Codes: ayp-0521

EXAMPLES 1 and 2   **Finding the dimension and entries of a matrix**

1   Determine the dimension of the following matrices.

$$A = \begin{bmatrix} 1 & -4 & 3 \\ -5 & 2 & 3 \end{bmatrix} \quad B = \begin{bmatrix} 7 \\ 2 \end{bmatrix} \quad C = \begin{bmatrix} -2 & 3 \\ 4 & -7 \end{bmatrix}$$

■ SOLUTION

Because matrix A has 2 rows and 3 columns, it is a **2 × 3 matrix**. Matrix
B has 2 rows and 1 column. Therefore, B is a **2 × 1 matrix**. Matrix C is a
square matrix with 2 rows and 2 columns, so C is a **2 × 2 matrix**.

2   Identify the entries in matrix T denoted by t_{24}, t_{12}, t_{31}.

$$T = \begin{bmatrix} -8 & 4 & 0 & 1 \\ 2 & -5 & 3 & -3 \\ 6 & 7 & -9 & 0 \end{bmatrix}$$

■ SOLUTION

t_{24} denotes the entry in row 2, column 4. This element is **−3**.
Similarly, t_{12} represents the entry in row 1, column 2; **4** and t_{31} denotes
the element in row 3 column 1; **6**.

Two matrices are equal if and only if they have the same dimension and
corresponding elements are equal. Consider the matrices

$$A = \begin{bmatrix} 2 & 7 \\ 3 & 5 \end{bmatrix}, B = \begin{bmatrix} 2 & 7 \\ 3 & -5 \end{bmatrix}, \text{ and } C = \begin{bmatrix} 2 & 7 \\ 3 & 5 \end{bmatrix}.$$

$A = C$ because the dimension of both matrices are the same and all
corresponding elements are equal. $A \neq B$ because $a_{22} \neq b_{22}$. Likewise,
$B \neq C$ because $b_{22} \neq c_{22}$.

EXAMPLE 3   **Finding elements of equal matrices**

Determine the values or w, x, y, z that make the following matrices equal.

$$\begin{bmatrix} w & -12 \\ 2x & 3z \end{bmatrix} = \begin{bmatrix} 3 & 3y \\ 10 & 9 \end{bmatrix}$$

■ SOLUTION

Corresponding elements of equal matrices must be equal; therefore, you can write the following equations.

$$w = 3 \qquad -12 = 3y \qquad 2x = 10 \qquad 3z = 9$$

Solving these equations, you find that $w = 3$, $y = -4$, $x = 5$, and $z = 3$.

You can perform the basic operations of addition and multiplication with matrices. The sum of two matrices is found by adding the corresponding elements. Therefore, only matrices of the same dimension can be added. When two matrices have different dimensions, their sum is undefined.

A matrix can be multiplied by a real number called a **scalar** by multiplying each element of the matrix by the scalar.

Go Online
PHSchool.com
Visit: PHSchool.com
Web Code: ayp-0152

EXAMPLE 4   **Finding sums and scalar products of matrices**

 Given the matrices $A = \begin{bmatrix} 3 & -2 \\ 5 & 1 \end{bmatrix}$ and $B = \begin{bmatrix} 1 & 2 \\ 6 & 8 \end{bmatrix}$, find $A + B$, $5A$, and $-B$.

■ SOLUTION

$$A + B = \begin{bmatrix} 3 & -2 \\ 5 & 1 \end{bmatrix} + \begin{bmatrix} 1 & 2 \\ 6 & 8 \end{bmatrix} = \begin{bmatrix} 3+1 & -2+2 \\ 5+6 & 1+8 \end{bmatrix} = \begin{bmatrix} 4 & 0 \\ 11 & 9 \end{bmatrix}$$

$$5A = 5\begin{bmatrix} 3 & -2 \\ 5 & 1 \end{bmatrix} = \begin{bmatrix} 5(3) & 5(-2) \\ 5(5) & 5(1) \end{bmatrix} = \begin{bmatrix} 15 & -10 \\ 25 & 5 \end{bmatrix}$$

$$-B = -\begin{bmatrix} 1 & 2 \\ 6 & 8 \end{bmatrix} = \begin{bmatrix} -1 & -2 \\ -6 & -8 \end{bmatrix}$$

Matrices are helpful in organizing data and can be used to manipulate several pieces of information at one time.

For example, the following monthly costs of phone, high speed internet, and digital cable are gathered from three different providers. Cablenet offers phone service for $39.99, internet for $24.99, and digital cable for $45.99. TRCable offers phone service for $29.99, internet for $29.99, and digital cable for $44.95. ALL4ONE offers phone service for $36.49, internet for $29.99, and digital cable for $35.00. You can use a matrix like the one at the right to organize and compare the costs.

$$C = \begin{bmatrix} \$39.99 & \$29.99 & \$36.49 \\ \$24.99 & \$29.99 & \$29.99 \\ \$45.99 & \$44.95 & \$35.00 \end{bmatrix}$$

EXAMPLE 5   Using matrices to solve problems

5   The maker of the music/video player MeVid has sales territories in four regions. The projected demand for the new 8-gig player in the first quarter of the year is 30,000 in the East; 25,000 in the Midwest; 40,000 in the West; and 20,000 in the South. The projected demand for the 40-gig player for the same period is 40,000 in the East; 30,000 in the Midwest, 50,000 in the West, and 24,000 in the South. Express the first-quarter demand for the two products as a 2 × 4 matrix. If the demand for the second quarter is projected to be 20 percent higher in each region, calculate the second-quarter demand matrix and the combined total two-quarter demand matrix.

■ **SOLUTION**

Step 1

Organize the data into a matrix.

$$D_{1quarter} = \begin{array}{c} \\ \text{8-gig} \\ \text{40-gig} \end{array} \begin{array}{cccc} \text{E} & \text{M} & \text{W} & \text{S} \\ \left[\begin{array}{cccc} 30{,}000 & 25{,}000 & 40{,}000 & 20{,}000 \\ 40{,}000 & 30{,}000 & 50{,}000 & 24{,}000 \end{array}\right] \end{array}$$

Step 2

Calculate the second-quarter demand matrix by multiplying by a scalar of 1.20.

$$D_{2quarter} = 1.2D_{1quarter} = \begin{bmatrix} 36{,}000 & 30{,}000 & 48{,}000 & 24{,}000 \\ 48{,}000 & 36{,}000 & 60{,}000 & 28{,}800 \end{bmatrix}$$

Step 3

Calculate the combined total two-quarter matrix by adding $D_{1quarter}$ and $D_{2quarter}$.

$$D = D_{1quarter} + D_{2quarter} = \begin{bmatrix} 66{,}000 & 55{,}000 & 88{,}000 & 44{,}000 \\ 88{,}000 & 66{,}000 & 110{,}000 & 52{,}800 \end{bmatrix}$$

To define the product of two matrices, the case where A is a $1 \times n$ matrix, called a **row matrix** and B is an $n \times 1$ matrix, called a **column matrix,** must be considered.

If $A = [a_1\ a_2\ a_3 \cdots a_n]$ and $B = \begin{bmatrix} b_1 \\ b_2 \\ b_3 \\ \vdots \\ b_n \end{bmatrix}$, the product of these two matrices

Note

The dot product of a row and column matrix can be described as either a numeral or a 1×1 matrix.

$A \cdot B$ is called the **dot product** and is the sum of the products of their corresponding elements. That is, $A \cdot B = [a_1b_1 + a_2b_2 + a_3b_3 + \cdots + a_nb_n]$.

The product of two matrices $A \cdot B$ will exist if the matrices are *compatible.* Two matrices are **compatible** if the number of columns in matrix A is the same as the number of rows in matrix B. If A is an $m \times n$ matrix and B is an $n \times p$ matrix they are compatible and the product will be an $m \times p$ matrix.

$$\begin{array}{ccccc} A & \times & B & = & AB \\ m \times n & & n \times p & & m \times p \end{array}$$

$$\underbrace{}_{Compatible}$$

You can determine the elements of the product matrix by finding all of the possible dot products for each corresponding placement in the product matrix. For example, the element in row i, column j of the product matrix is the dot product of the ith row of A and the jth column of B.

 EXAMPLES 6 and 7   **Finding the product of two matrices**

6 Given $A = \begin{bmatrix} 2 & 3 \\ 4 & 5 \end{bmatrix}$ and $B = \begin{bmatrix} 6 & 7 \\ 8 & 9 \end{bmatrix}$, find AB.

■ SOLUTION 1

$$\begin{bmatrix} 2 & 3 \\ 4 & 5 \end{bmatrix} \cdot \begin{bmatrix} 6 & 7 \\ 8 & 9 \end{bmatrix} = \begin{bmatrix} 2(6) + 3(8) & 2(7) + 3(9) \\ 4(6) + 5(8) & 4(7) + 5(9) \end{bmatrix}$$

$$= \begin{bmatrix} 12 + 24 & 14 + 27 \\ 24 + 40 & 28 + 45 \end{bmatrix} = \begin{bmatrix} 36 & 41 \\ 64 & 73 \end{bmatrix}$$

■ SOLUTION 2

You can use a calculator to verify this product.

```
[A]
            [ [2   3]
              [4   5] ]
[B]
            [ [6   7]
              [8   9] ]
■
```

```
[A] [B]
                [ [36   41]
                  [64   73] ]
```

7 Find $\begin{bmatrix} 2 & -3 & 5 \\ 1 & 4 & 7 \end{bmatrix} \cdot \begin{bmatrix} 1 & 8 & -4 & 3 \\ 5 & 2 & -2 & 7 \\ -11 & 9 & 6 & 0 \end{bmatrix}$.

■ SOLUTION 1

Multiply each row of the first matrix by each column of the second matrix.

$$\begin{bmatrix} 2 & -3 & 5 \\ 1 & 4 & 7 \end{bmatrix} \cdot \begin{bmatrix} 1 & 8 & -4 & 3 \\ 5 & 2 & -2 & 7 \\ -11 & 9 & 6 & 0 \end{bmatrix}$$

$$= \begin{bmatrix} 2(1) + -3(5) + 5(-11) & 2(8) + -3(2) + 5(9) & 2(-4) + -3(-2) + 5(6) & 2(3) + -3(7) + 5(0) \\ 1(1) + 4(5) + 7(-11) & 1(8) + 4(2) + 7(9) & 1(-4) + 4(-2) + 7(6) & 1(3) + 4(7) + 7(0) \end{bmatrix}$$

$$= \begin{bmatrix} -68 & 55 & 28 & -15 \\ -56 & 79 & 30 & 31 \end{bmatrix}$$

■ SOLUTION 2

You can use a calculator to verify this product.

```
[A]
            [ [2   -3   5]
              [1    4   7] ]
[B]
        [ [   1   8   -4   3]
          [   5   2   -2   7]
          [ -11   9    6   0] ]
■
```

```
[A] * [B]
[ [-68   55   28   -15...
  [-56   79   30    31...
```

Recall that you can only find the product of two matrices if they are compatible; otherwise the product is undefined.

EXAMPLE 8 **Finding the product of noncompatible matrices**

8 Given $A = \begin{bmatrix} 2 & 3 \\ -7 & 5 \end{bmatrix}$ and $B = \begin{bmatrix} 2 & 0 & -3 \\ 8 & 1 & 5 \\ -1 & 4 & 9 \end{bmatrix}$, find AB.

■ **SOLUTION 1**

Matrix A has 2 columns and Matrix B has 3 rows. Therefore, the matrices are not compatible and AB is undefined.

■ **SOLUTION 2**

You can use a calculator to verify that the product is undefined. As shown, the calculator indicates the error that the matrices have a "dimension mismatch."

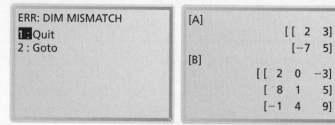

```
ERR: DIM MISMATCH
1:Quit
2 : Goto
```

```
[A]
                  [[ 2  3]
                   [-7  5]]
[B]
          [[ 2  0  -3]
           [ 8  1   5]
           [-1  4   9]]
```

An **identity matrix** is a square matrix with elements along the main diagonal (upper left to lower right) equal to 1 and all other elements equal to zero. For each dimension $n \times n$, there is a different identity matrix.

$$I_{2\times2} = \begin{bmatrix} 1 & 0 \\ 0 & 1 \end{bmatrix} \quad I_{3\times3} = \begin{bmatrix} 1 & 0 & 0 \\ 0 & 1 & 0 \\ 0 & 0 & 1 \end{bmatrix} \quad I_{4\times4} = \begin{bmatrix} 1 & 0 & 0 & 0 \\ 0 & 1 & 0 & 0 \\ 0 & 0 & 1 & 0 \\ 0 & 0 & 0 & 1 \end{bmatrix}$$

Note

If a matrix is multiplied on either side by its compatible identity matrix the matrix remains unchanged.

If A is a square matrix, its **inverse matrix** is a matrix that when multiplied by A results in the identity matrix. We denote the inverse of A as A^{-1}. This result written symbolically is $AA^{-1} = I$ and $A^{-1}A = I$. You can use a calculator to determine the inverse of a matrix.

EXAMPLE 9 **Finding the inverse of a matrix**

9 Given $A = \begin{bmatrix} 3 & 5 \\ 4 & 7 \end{bmatrix}$, use a calculator to find A^{-1}.

■ **SOLUTION**

Enter the matrix into the calculator. Next, list the matrix and use the x^{-1} key to communicate the inverse of the matrix, and then press ENTER.

You can also use a calculator to verify that the product of a matrix and its inverse is the identity matrix.

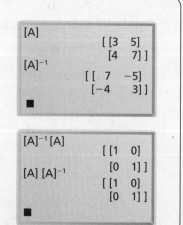

```
[A]
                  [[3  5]
                   [4  7]]
[A]⁻¹
              [[ 7  -5]
               [-4   3]]
■
```

```
[A]⁻¹[A]
                  [[1  0]
                   [0  1]]
[A][A]⁻¹
                  [[1  0]
                   [0  1]]
■
```

Choose the letter preceding the word or expression that best completes the statement or answers the question.

1 A matrix is

   A. a number.

   B. a variable.

   C. a rectangular array of numbers.

   D. a circular array of numbers.

2 The sum of two matrices can be found

   A. if they have the same number of rows as columns.

   B. only if they are square.

   C. only if they are equal.

   D. only if they have the same dimension.

3 If the dimension of a matrix is 3×4, then it is compatible with a matrix whose dimension is

   A. 4×5.   **C.** 3×4.

   B. 3×3.   **D.** 1×4.

4 The product of a 2×2 matrix and a 2×3 matrix is

   A. 2×2 matrix.   **C.** 3×3 matrix.

   B. 2×3 matrix.   **D.** undefined.

5 Which of the following is an identity matrix?

   A. $\begin{bmatrix} 1 & 1 \\ 1 & 1 \end{bmatrix}$ **C.** $\begin{bmatrix} 1 & 0 \\ 0 & 0 \end{bmatrix}$

   B. $\begin{bmatrix} 0 & 1 \\ 1 & 0 \end{bmatrix}$ **D.** $\begin{bmatrix} 1 & 0 \\ 0 & 1 \end{bmatrix}$

6 The product of a scalar and a 4×4 matrix will be

   A. a 4×4 matrix.   **C.** a 2×2 matrix.

   B. a scalar.   **D.** an identity matrix.

In Exercises 7–14, use the following matrices.

$$A = \begin{bmatrix} 1 & -2 \\ 3 & 5 \end{bmatrix}, B = \begin{bmatrix} 3 & 2 \\ -1 & 5 \end{bmatrix}$$

$$C = \begin{bmatrix} 2 & 1 & 4 \\ 4 & 3 & 1 \end{bmatrix}, \text{ and } D = \begin{bmatrix} 2 & 3 & 4 \\ 1 & 3 & 5 \\ 2 & 1 & 3 \end{bmatrix}$$

7 $A + B$ **8** $2C$

9 $A + C$ **10** AB

11 $3A + B$ **12** AC

13 $\frac{3}{4}D$ **14** CD

In Exercises 15–19, use the following information.

An electronics company has factories in two countries (C_1 and C_2) that manufacture DVD players, CD players, and cell phones for export to the United States. The costs of labor, materials, and transportation for each device vary. The figures in dollars per device are shown in the table.

Device	Labor C_1	Labor C_2	Materials C_1	Materials C_2	Transportation C_1	Transportation C_2
DVD	72	80	20	12	7	10
CD	40	52	20	12	10	12
Cell	80	84	35	25	5	9

15 Represent the costs of labor, material, and transportation in C_1 and C_2 as three 3×2 matrices.

16 Use matrix arithmetic to find the total cost per unit.

17 If DVD players sell for $160, CD players for $120, and cell phones for $200, represent the company's revenue per device as a matrix.

18 Represent the company's profit as the difference of two matrices and find the profit.

19 If there is a 25 percent increase in transportation costs, what is the effect on the transportation matrix?

3.8 Systems of Linear Equations

A **system of equations in two variables** is a set of equations in the same two variables as illustrated at the right. You can use a single brace { to indicate that a collection of equations is a system.

$$\begin{cases} x + y = 30 \\ x - y = 8 \end{cases}$$

New Jersey Standards

4.2.C.1.3 Finding the intersection of two lines

4.3.B.2.7 Intersecting points as solutions of systems of equations

EXAMPLES 1 and 2   Recognizing and representing a situation as a system of equations

1 The sum of two numbers x and y is 26. Twice x minus y equals 16. Which system could not represent this situation?

A. $\begin{cases} x + y = 26 \\ 2x - y = 16 \end{cases}$ **B.** $\begin{cases} 2x - y = 16 \\ x + y = 26 \end{cases}$ **C.** $\begin{cases} 26 = x + y \\ 16 = 2x - y \end{cases}$ **D.** $\begin{cases} x + y = 16 \\ 2x - y = 26 \end{cases}$

■ **SOLUTION**

The sum of two numbers is 26. $x + y = 26$
Twice x minus y equals 16. $2x - y = 16$

Only choice **D** does not contain these equations. The correct choice is D.

2 Club members at the Queen Video Store pay $24 to be members and pay $4 for each video rental. Those who are not members rent videos for $5.50 each. Represent total expense in terms of videos rented as a system of equations.

■ **SOLUTION**

Let n represent the number of videos rented. Let c represent total cost.

Member expense c: $4n + 24$ $c = 4n + 24$ $\begin{cases} c = 4n + 24 \\ c = 5.5n \end{cases}$

Nonmember expense c: $5.5n$ $c = 5.5n$

A **solution to a system of equations** in two variables x and y is any ordered pair (x, y) that makes each equation in the system true.

EXAMPLE 3   Verifying a solution to a system of equations

3 Which ordered pair (a, b) is a solution to $\begin{cases} a + 2b = 12 \\ 2a - 3b = -25 \end{cases}$?

A. $(7, -2)$ **B.** $(-2, 7)$ **C.** $(4, 4)$ **D.** $(-8, 3)$

■ **SOLUTION**

Test each ordered pair in each equation.

A. $(7, -2)$ $\begin{cases} 7 + 2(-2) \neq 12 \\ 2(7) - 3(-2) \neq -25 \end{cases}$ ✗   **C.** $(4, 4)$ $\begin{cases} 4 + 2(4) = 12 \\ 2(4) - 3(4) \neq -25 \end{cases}$ ✗

B. $(-2, 7)$ $\begin{cases} -2 + 2(7) = 12 \\ 2(-2) - 3(7) = -25 \end{cases}$ ✓   **D.** $(-8, 3)$ $\begin{cases} -8 + 2(3) \neq 12 \\ 2(-8) - 3(3) = -25 \end{cases}$ ✗

The correct choice is B.

By graphing each equation in a system of equations, you can approximate the coordinates of any solution.

 EXAMPLE 4 **Recognizing estimates of solutions to a system of equations**

4 Which best represents the coordinates of the point of intersection of these lines?

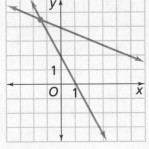

A. x is between -2 and -1.
y is between 3 and 4.

C. x is between -3 and -2.
y is between 4 and 5.

B. $x = -1.25$
$y = 4.\overline{3}$

D. x is between -2 and -1.
y is between 4 and 5.

■ **SOLUTION**

The x-coordinate is more than 1 unit but less than 2 units left of the origin.
The y-coordinate is more than 4 units but less than 5 units above the origin.
No further claim can be made of the solution. The correct choice is D.

You can use a graphing calculator to find more accurate solutions to systems of equations.

 EXAMPLE 5 **Finding a solution to a system of equations by graphing**

5 Solve the system $\begin{cases} y = 2x + 3 \\ y = -3x - 1 \end{cases}$.

■ **SOLUTION**

- Enter $y = 2x + 3$ and $y = -3x - 1$ into the function list.
- Set an appropriate window.
- Press **2nd** **CALC** #5Intersect.
- Choose the functions in response to the prompts.
- Enter a guess.
- The solution is displayed.

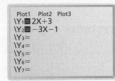 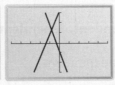 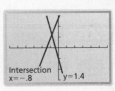

The solution is $(-0.8, 1.4)$.

You may have a system of equations in which y is not written in terms of x.
To solve by graphing, first solve each equation for y.

$$\begin{cases} x + y = 8 \\ x - 2y = 2 \end{cases}$$

$x + y = 8$ 　　　　 $x - 2y = 2$
$\quad y = -x + 8$ 　　　　 $\quad y = 0.5x - 1$

EXAMPLE 6   Solving systems by solving for the same variable

 Solve $\begin{cases} x + y = 8 \\ x - 2y = 2 \end{cases}$ graphically.

■ SOLUTION

Solve each equation for y in terms of x.

$$\begin{cases} x + y = 8 \\ x - 2y = 2 \end{cases} \rightarrow \begin{cases} y = -x + 8 \\ y = \frac{1}{2}x - 1 \end{cases}$$

Graph each equation on the same coordinate plane. Read the coordinates of the point of intersection. The solution is (6, 2), or $x = 6$ and $y = 2$.

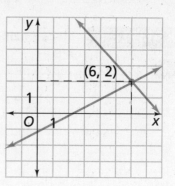

Not every pair of equations in the same two variables has a solution.

- If the system has exactly one solution, it is called **independent**.

$$\begin{cases} y = x - 2 \\ y = -2x + 10 \end{cases}$$

- If the graphs of the equations are **distinct** and **intersect**, then the system is independent.

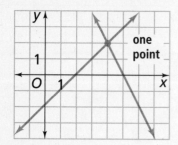

- If the system has infinitely many solutions, it is called **dependent**.

$$\begin{cases} y = x - 2 \\ x - y = 2 \end{cases}$$

- If the graphs of the equations **coincide**, then the system is dependent.

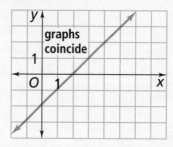

- If the system has no solution, it is called **inconsistent**.

$$\begin{cases} y = -x + 2 \\ y = -x \end{cases}$$

- If the graphs of the equations are parallel lines, then the system is inconsistent.

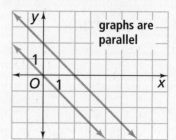

EXAMPLE 7   Identifying independent, dependent, and inconsistent systems

7 Which system of equations is independent?

A. $\begin{cases} x + y = 4 \\ 2x + y = 6 \end{cases}$ **B.** $\begin{cases} 2x + y = 4 \\ 2x + y = 9 \end{cases}$ **C.** $\begin{cases} x - y = 2 \\ 3x - 3y = 6 \end{cases}$ **D.** $\begin{cases} x - y = 0 \\ 3x - 3y = 0 \end{cases}$

■ SOLUTION

In each system, solve for y. Read slope and y-intercept.

A. $\begin{cases} y = -1x + 4 \\ y = -2x + 6 \end{cases}$ **B.** $\begin{cases} y = -2x + 4 \\ y = -2x + 9 \end{cases}$ **C.** $\begin{cases} y = 1x - 2 \\ y = 1x - 2 \end{cases}$ **D.** $\begin{cases} y = 1x \\ y = 1x \end{cases}$

The graphs in choice **A** have unequal slopes and unequal y-intercepts. The graphs intersect in exactly one point. The correct choice is A.

Visit: PHSchool.com
Web Code: ayp-0510

96

Practice

Choose the letter preceding the word or expression that best completes the statement or answers the question.

1 Which ordered pair is the solution to $\begin{cases} 2x - 5y = -11 \\ 2x - y = 1 \end{cases}$?

  A. $(-8, -1)$ **C.** $(3, 2)$

  B. $(3, 5)$ **D.** $(2, 3)$

2 Which best describes the solution to the system whose graphs are shown here?

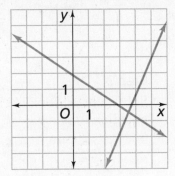

  A. x is between 3 and 4; y is between 0 and 1.

  B. x is between 3 and 4; y is between 0 and -1.

  C. x is between -4 and -3; y is between 0 and 1.

  D. x is between -4 and -3; y is between 0 and -1.

3 Which best describes $\begin{cases} y = 2x - 5 \\ y = 2x - 13 \end{cases}$?

  A. No solution; the slopes are equal and the y-intercepts are unequal.

  B. One solution; the slopes are equal and the y-intercepts are unequal.

  C. Two solutions; the slopes are equal and the y-intercepts are unequal.

  D. Infinite solutions; the slopes are equal and the y-intercepts are equal.

In Exercises 4–7, use graphs of the equations in each system to find the coordinates of any point of intersection.

4 $\begin{cases} x + y = 4 \\ -2x + y = 1 \end{cases}$ **5** $\begin{cases} y = 2x + 5 \\ y = 1 \end{cases}$

6 $\begin{cases} y = 3x + 1 \\ y = 4x + 2 \end{cases}$ **7** $\begin{cases} -7x + 5y = 10 \\ -2x + 5y = -15 \end{cases}$

In Exercises 8–11, represent each situation as a system of two equations in two variables. Identify the variables.

8 The larger of two numbers decreased by the smaller is 5. Twice the smaller number increased by the larger number is 41.

9 The Health Gym charges $50 plus $20 per month for membership. Chyna's Health Club charges $80 plus $15 per month for membership.

10 Kisha has $1.75 in nickels and dimes. She has 23 coins in all.

11 One number is twice another number. Their sum is 21.

In Exercises 12–16, solve the problem. Clearly show all necessary work.

12 Graph the equations in the system $\begin{cases} x + y = 7 \\ 3x - y = 7 \end{cases}$. Find consecutive integers between which the x- and y-coordinates of the solution lie.

13 What are the coordinates of the solution to the system whose graph is shown here?

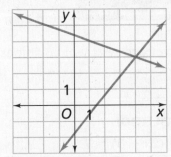

14 Is the system $\begin{cases} y = -2.5x - 3 \\ y = 2.2x - 10 \end{cases}$ independent, dependent, or inconsistent? Explain.

15 Is the system $\begin{cases} y = 3x + 5 \\ 4y = 12x + 20 \end{cases}$ independent, dependent, or inconsistent? Explain.

16 Graph $y = 1.5x - 1$, $x = 4$, and $y = -2$ on the same coordinate plane. Find the area of the triangle enclosed by the graphs.

3.9 Solving Systems of Equations

In the system of equations at the right, y is given in terms of x in each equation. Although you can solve this system graphically, there is an algebraic method you can use. It is called the **substitution method**.

$$\begin{cases} y = -x + 4 \\ y = 2x + 7 \end{cases}$$

When you use the substitution method, you transform a pair of equations in two variables into one equation in one variable.

If $y = -x + 4$ and $y = 2x + 7$, then $-x + 4 = 2x + 7$.

The solution to $-x + 4 = 2x + 7$ gives the value of x. The following example shows how to continue to get the complete solution.

Note

The *Transitive Property of Equality* states the following: If $a = b$ and $b = c$, then $a = c$.

EXAMPLE 1 Solving by simple substitution

1 Solve $\begin{cases} y = -x + 4 \\ y = 2x + 7 \end{cases}$ by substitution.

■ **SOLUTION**

Step 1

Equate the expressions for y.

$$-x + 4 = 2x + 7$$

The solution to the system is $(-1, 5)$.

Step 2

Solve $-x + 4 = 2x + 7$.

$$-x + 4 = 2x + 7$$
$$x = -1$$

Step 3

Substitute -1 for x in either equation to find y.

$$y = -(-1) + 4$$
$$= 5$$

Check: $\begin{cases} -(-1) + 4 = 5 \checkmark \\ 2(-1) + 7 = 5 \checkmark \end{cases}$

Sometimes you must first solve one of the equations for a specific value before you can use the substitution method.

Go Online
PHSchool.com

Visit: PHSchool.com
Web Code: ayp-0231

EXAMPLES 2 and 3 Solving by isolating one variable and then using substitution

Solve each system of equations by substitution.

2 $\begin{cases} x + y = 7 \\ y = 2x - 3 \end{cases}$

■ **SOLUTION**

$$x + (2x - 3) = 7$$
$$3x - 3 = 7$$
$$x = \frac{10}{3}$$

If $\frac{10}{3} + y = 7$, $y = \frac{11}{3}$. Solution: $\left(\frac{10}{3}, \frac{11}{3}\right)$

Check: $\begin{cases} \frac{10}{3} + \frac{11}{3} = \frac{21}{3} = 7 \qquad \checkmark \\ 2\left(\frac{10}{3}\right) - 3 = \frac{20}{3} - \frac{9}{3} = \frac{11}{3} \checkmark \end{cases}$

3 $\begin{cases} x + y = -2 \\ 3x + y = 5 \end{cases}$

■ **SOLUTION**

Solve $3x + y = 5$ for y. $y = -3x + 5$.

$$x + (-3x + 5) = -2$$
$$-2x + 5 = -2$$
$$x = \frac{7}{2}$$

If $\frac{7}{2} + y = -2$, $y = -\frac{11}{2}$. Solution: $\left(\frac{7}{2}, -\frac{11}{2}\right)$

Check: $\begin{cases} \frac{7}{2} + \left(-\frac{11}{2}\right) = -\frac{4}{2} = -2 \qquad \checkmark \\ 3\left(\frac{7}{2}\right) + \left(-\frac{11}{2}\right) = \frac{21}{2} - \frac{11}{2} = \frac{10}{2} = 5 \checkmark \end{cases}$

You can use the substitution method to solve problems involving systems of equations.

 Which system of equations has no solution?

A. $\begin{cases} y = x - 3 \\ 2x - 3y = 5 \end{cases}$ **B.** $\begin{cases} y = -5x - 3 \\ 2x - 2y = 5 \end{cases}$ **C.** $\begin{cases} y = x - 2.5 \\ 2x - 2y = -5 \end{cases}$ **D.** $\begin{cases} y = x - 3 \\ 2x - 2y = 5 \end{cases}$

■ SOLUTION

In choice **D**, $2x - 2(x - 3) = 5$. So, $6 = 5$. Choice D has no solution.

 Angela has 30 nickels and dimes totaling $2.40. How many of each has she?

■ SOLUTION

Let n and d represent the number of nickels and dimes, respectively.
In all, she has 30 coins.   → $n + d = 30$
In pennies, total worth is 240 cents.   → $5n + 10d = 240$

Use substitution to eliminate d from $5n + 10d = 240$.

$$5n + 10(30 - n) = 240 \quad \rightarrow \quad \text{because } d = 30 - n$$
$$-5n = -60$$
$$n = 12$$

Therefore, $d = 30 - 12 = 18$. So, Angela has 12 nickels and 18 dimes.

The **addition-multiplication method,** or **elimination method,** is a useful solution method if the variables in a system have coefficients other than 1. Use the properties of equality to make an **equivalent system,** a system that has the same solution set.

To make an equivalent system you multiply each term of an equation by a value that results in coefficients of matching terms that are opposites of each other.

$$\begin{cases} 4x + 2y = 7 \\ 2x + 5y = 4 \end{cases}$$

$$\begin{array}{c} -2(2x + 5y) = (4)(-2) \\ -4y - 10y = -8 \end{array} \quad \longrightarrow \quad \begin{cases} 4x + 2y = 7 \\ -4x - 10y = -8 \end{cases}$$

EXAMPLE 6   **Identifying equivalent systems of equations**

 Which system of equations is equivalent to $\begin{cases} -3x - 5y = -3 \\ 5x - 15y = 7 \end{cases}$?

A. $\begin{cases} -6x - 10y = -3 \\ 5x - 15y = 7 \end{cases}$ **B.** $\begin{cases} -3x - 5y = -2 \\ 5x - 15y = 7 \end{cases}$ **C.** $\begin{cases} -9x - 15y = -9 \\ 5x - 15y = 7 \end{cases}$ **D.** $\begin{cases} 6x - 10y = -6 \\ 5x - 15y = 7 \end{cases}$

■ SOLUTION

The system in choice C is equivalent to the given system.
$3(-3x - 5y) = -9x - 15y$ and $3(-3) = -9$ ✓

In the following example, the coefficients of each of the x-terms are opposites. When you add the terms of an equation, the x-term will be eliminated. Then you solve a simple one-variable equation.

Visit: PHSchool.com
Web Code: ayp-0233

EXAMPLE 7   **Solving a system with coefficients of one variable being opposites**

 Solve $\begin{cases} -2x + 7y = 11 \\ 2x - 5y = -1 \end{cases}$ using the addition-multiplication method.

■ **SOLUTION**

Step 1 Use the Addition Property of Equality.

$$
\begin{array}{rcr}
-2x + 7y & = & 11 \\
+\;\; 2x - 5y & = & +\; -1 \\
\hline
2y & = & 10
\end{array}
$$

$$y = 5.$$

Step 2 If $y = 5$, then $-2x + 7(5) = 11$. So, $x = 12$.
The solution is $(12, 5)$.

You can carefully consider the equations of a system to determine which equation to rewrite.

Visit: PHSchool.com
Web Code: ayp-0234

EXAMPLE 8   **Using addition and one multiplier to solve a system**

 Solve $\begin{cases} 4a + 2b = 7 \\ 2a + 5b = 4 \end{cases}$ by using addition and multiplication.

■ **SOLUTION**

Step 1 Multiply each side of $2a + 5b = 4$ by -2.
$$-4a - 10b = -8$$

Step 2 Add.

$$
\begin{array}{rcr}
4a + \;\; 2b & = & 7 \\
+\;-4a - 10b & = & +\; -8 \\
\hline
-8b & = & -1
\end{array}
$$

$$b = \frac{1}{8}$$

Step 3 If $b = \frac{1}{8}$, then

$$2a + 5\left(\frac{1}{8}\right) = 4.$$

$$a = \frac{27}{16}$$

The solution to the system is $\left(\frac{27}{16}, \frac{1}{8}\right)$.

Sometimes you need to use the Multiplication Property of Equality twice to solve a system of equations.

9 Solve $\begin{cases} 2x + 3y = 15 \\ 5x - 2y = -29 \end{cases}$ by using the addition-multiplication method.

■ **SOLUTION**

$$\begin{cases} 2x + 3y = 15 \\ 5x - 2y = -29 \end{cases} \rightarrow \begin{cases} 2(2x + 3y) = 2(15) \\ 3(5x - 2y) = 3(-29) \end{cases} \rightarrow$$

$$\begin{array}{r} 4x + 6y = \quad 30 \\ + \ 15x - 6y = + \ -87 \\ \hline 19x \qquad\qquad -57 \end{array}$$

Therefore, $x = -3$. Substitute -3 for x in one of the given equations.

$$2(-3) + 3y = 15$$
$$y = 7$$

So, the solution is $(-3, 7)$.

Check: $\begin{cases} 2(-3) + 3(7) = -6 + 21 = 15 \quad \checkmark \\ 5(-3) - 2(7) = -15 - 14 = -29 \ \checkmark \end{cases}$

Another solution method that can be implemented by using a calculator is a matrix solution. From the system below we can form a **coefficient matrix,** a **variable matrix,** and a **solution matrix.**

$$\begin{cases} 2x + 3y = 15 \\ 5x - 2y = -29 \end{cases}$$

$$A = \begin{bmatrix} 2 & 3 \\ 5 & -2 \end{bmatrix} \qquad \begin{bmatrix} x \\ y \end{bmatrix} \qquad B = \begin{bmatrix} 15 \\ -29 \end{bmatrix}$$

coefficient   variable   solution
matrix   matrix   matrix

```
[A]
              [[ 2  3 ]
               [ 5 -2]]
[B]
              [[ 1 5 ]
               [ -29 ]]
■
```

You can enter these matrices into the calculator and multiply both sides of the equation by the inverse of $[A]$, $[A]^{-1}$, to solve the following matrix equation:

$$[A] \cdot \begin{bmatrix} x \\ y \end{bmatrix} = [B]$$

```
                 [ 5  -2]]
[B]
                [ [ 15 ]
                  [ -29 ]]
[A]⁻¹[B]
                 [[ -3 ]
                  [ 7 ]]
```

The solution is shown in the final matrix, $x = -3$ and $y = 7$.

A second matrix solution is to enter the augmented matrix C and execute a rref calculation. The solution is shown in the last column of the result $x = -3$ and $y = 7$.

```
[C]
     [[ 2   3    15 ]
      [ 5  -2  -29 ]]
```

```
NAMES MHTH EDIT
7↟augment (
8:Matr▶list (
9:List▶matr (
0:cumSum (
A:ref (
B:rref (
C:↓rowSwap (
```

```
rref ([C])
            [[ 1 0 -3]
  ■         [ 0 1  7 ]]
```

You can use a system of equations to solve problems that describe two equations.

EXAMPLE 10 **Using the addition-multiplication method to solve real-world problems**

10 Twice one integer plus 3 times a second integer equals 9. Five times the first integer plus 4 times the second integer equals 5. What are the numbers?

■ **SOLUTION**

Step 1 Write a system of equations.

Twice one integer m plus 3 times a second integer n equals 9. → $2m + 3n = 9$

Five times the first integer m plus 4 times the second integer n equals 5. → $5m + 4n = 5$

Step 2 Solve the system of equations.

Multiply by 5. $\begin{cases} 2m + 3n = 9 \\ 5m + 4n = 5 \end{cases}$ → $\begin{cases} 10m + 15n = 45 \\ -10m - 8n = -10 \end{cases}$ →

$$\begin{array}{rr} 10m + 15n = & 45 \\ + \;\; -10m - 8n = & + \;\; -10 \\ \hline 7n = & 35 \end{array}$$

Multiply by -2.

Therefore, $n = 5$. Substitute 5 for n in $2m + 3n = 9$ to find m.
$$2m + 3(5) = 9$$
$$m = -3$$

Step 3 Answer the question. The first number is -3. The second number is 5.

Check: $\begin{cases} 2(-3) + 3(5) = -6 + 15 = 9 \;\checkmark \\ 5(-3) + 4(5) = -15 + 20 = 5 \;\checkmark \end{cases}$

Practice

Choose the letter preceding the word or expression that best completes the statement or answers the question.

1 Which ordered pair (a, b) is the solution to $\begin{cases} b = 3.5a \\ b = 2a - 3 \end{cases}$?

A. $(0, 0)$ **C.** $(2, -3.5)$

B. $(2, -8)$ **D.** $(-2, -7)$

2 A line segment 15 inches long is separated into two smaller segments. The length y of the longer segment is 3 inches more than twice the length x of the shorter segment. Which system cannot represent this situation?

A. $\begin{cases} x + y = 15 \\ y = 2x + 3 \end{cases}$ **C.** $\begin{cases} x + y = 15 \\ x = 2y + 3 \end{cases}$

B. $\begin{cases} y = 2x + 3 \\ x + y = 15 \end{cases}$ **D.** $\begin{cases} y = 15 - x \\ y = 2x + 3 \end{cases}$

3 Which system of equations represents this situation?

Nikki has 20 dimes and quarters in all. Their total value is $3.80.

Let d represent the number of dimes and q represent the number of quarters.

A. $\begin{cases} d + q = 20 \\ 25q + 10d = 3.80 \end{cases}$

B. $\begin{cases} d + q = 20 \\ d + q = 3.80 \end{cases}$

C. $\begin{cases} d + q = 20 \\ 10d + 25q = 3.80 \end{cases}$

D. $\begin{cases} d + q = 20 \\ 0.1d + 0.25q = 3.80 \end{cases}$

4 Which system of equations has the same solution as $\begin{cases} 5x - 3y = 24 \\ 2x - 7y = 11 \end{cases}$?

A. $\begin{cases} 10x - 6y = 48 \\ 2x - 7y = 11 \end{cases}$

B. $\begin{cases} 5x - 3y = 48 \\ 2x - 7y = 11 \end{cases}$

C. $\begin{cases} 10x - 6y = 24 \\ 2x - 7y = 11 \end{cases}$

D. $\begin{cases} 5x - 3y = 24 \\ 10x - 35y = 11 \end{cases}$

In Exercises 5–12, solve each system of equations.

5 $\begin{cases} x = 2y - 3 \\ 2x - 3y = -5 \end{cases}$

6 $\begin{cases} y = 4 - 4x \\ 3x + y = 5 \end{cases}$

7 $\begin{cases} x = 3y + 5 \\ y = 2x + 1 \end{cases}$

8 $\begin{cases} 2x + 3y = 0 \\ -2x + 5y = 8 \end{cases}$

9 $\begin{cases} 3x - 7y = 13 \\ 6x + 5y = 7 \end{cases}$

10 $\begin{cases} 2x + 3y = 21 \\ 5x - 2y = -14 \end{cases}$

11 $\begin{cases} 2x = y + 12 \\ 3x + 2y = -3 \end{cases}$

12 $\begin{cases} 5x = 4y + 15 \\ 6y = 3x - 9 \end{cases}$

In Exercises 13–20, use a system of equations to solve each problem.

13 The larger of two supplementary angles is 15° more than twice the measure of the smaller angle. Find each angle measure.

14 Top Tunes sells CDs for a single price and sells tapes for a single price. Bianna bought 3 CDs and 2 tapes for $58. Ramon bought 1 CD and 4 tapes for $46. Determine the selling price for 1 CD and for 1 tape.

15 The sum of two numbers is 70. The difference of the these numbers is 24. What are the numbers?

16 Tickets for the school play sell for $3 for a student and $5 for an adult. One night, 595 people bought tickets. The school took in $1951. How many adult tickets and how many student tickets were sold?

17 There are 250 students in the freshman class. The number of girls is 20 fewer than twice the number of boys. How many boys and how many girls are in the class?

18 The length of a rectangular flower garden is 6 feet more than three times the width. The perimeter of the garden is 32 feet. What is the area of the garden?

19 Stefan has a collection of nickels, dimes, and quarters. In all, he has 24 coins. Seven of the coins are quarters. The total value of the collection is $2.90. How many nickels and how many dimes does he have?

20 Delila has $1200 in a savings account and in a checking account. The ratio of money in savings to money in checking is 3 to 2. Use a system of equations to find how much money is in each account.

In Exercises 21–25, solve the problem. Clearly show all necessary work.

21 For what value of k will the system of equations below have no solution? Explain.

$$\begin{cases} 2x - 4y = 6 \\ kx - 4y = 9 \end{cases}$$

22 The graphs of $kx + 2y = 2$ and $2x + hy = 10$ intersect at $(2, -2)$. Find h and k.

23 What are the coordinates of the point where the graphs of the equations below intersect?

$$3x - 5y = 4 \text{ and } 4x + 7y = 19$$

24 Find the measures in degrees of the angles indicated by x and y. The measure of angle y is 15 degrees more than 3 times the measure of angle x.

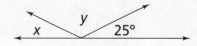

25 Find k such that the graphs of $y = 3x + 4$ and $y = kx - 5$ do not intersect.

3.10 Linear Inequalities in Two Variables

New Jersey Standards

4.3.C.1.4 Use functions to solve problems involving inequalities

On a number line, the graph of $x \geq 3$ is a closed ray. In the coordinate plane, the graph of $x \geq 3$ is a **closed half-plane.** The graph of $x > 3$ is an **open half-plane.**

The **boundary** of the graph is the line separating it from the rest of the plane.

- If the inequality contains $\leq$ or $\geq$, the boundary is part of the solution.

  $\leq$ or $\geq$ solid line

- If the inequality contains $>$ or $<$, the boundary is not part of the solution.

  $>$ or $<$ dashed line

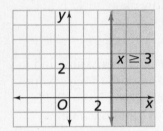 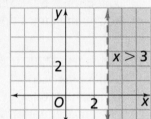 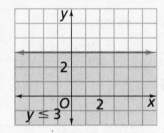 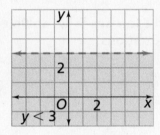

A **linear inequality in two variables** x and y is any inequality that can be written in one of these forms:

$$ax + by \geq c \quad ax + by > c \quad ax + by \leq c \quad ax + by < c,$$

where a, b, and c are real numbers and not both a and b equal 0. A **solution to an inequality in two variables** is any ordered pair that makes the inequality true. The **graph of an inequality in two variables** is the set of the graphs of all solutions.

EXAMPLES 1 and 2   **Graphing a linear inequality in two variables**

Graph each linear inequality in two variables.

1 $y > x - 2$

■ SOLUTION

Graph $y = x - 2$ with a dashed line because the given inequality involves $>$. The solution region is all points above the graph of $y = x - 2$.

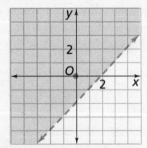

To check, test a point in the plane. For example, $(0, 0)$ satisfies $y > x - 2$. So, it is in the solution region.

2 $y \leq -2x - 2$

■ SOLUTION

Graph $y = -2x - 2$ with a solid line because the given inequality involves $\leq$. The solution region is all points on or below the graph of $y = -2x - 2$.

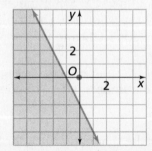

To check, test a point in the plane. For example, $(0, 0)$ does not satisfy $y \leq -2x - 2$. So, it is not in the solution region.

Sometimes it is easier to solve the inequality for *y* before graphing.

EXAMPLES 3 and 4   **Graphing a linear inequality in which *y* is not isolated**

Graph each linear inequality in two variables.

3 $2x + 3y < 9$

- **SOLUTION**
Solve for *y*. $y < -\frac{2}{3}x + 3$

Graph $y = -\frac{2}{3}x + 3$ with a dashed line.
Shade the region below the line.

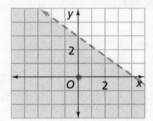

Because $(0, 0)$ satisfies $2x + 3y < 9$,
the solution contains the origin.

4 $2x - 3y \geq 9$

- **SOLUTION**
Solve for *y*. $y \leq \frac{2}{3}x - 3$

Graph $y = \frac{2}{3}x - 3$ with a solid line. Shade
the line and the region below the line.

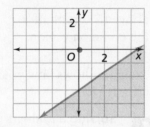

Because $(0, 0)$ does not satisfy $2x - 3y \geq 9$,
the solution does not contain the origin.

A **system of inequalities in two variables** is a set of inequalities in those
variables as illustrated below. A **solution to a system of inequalities** is
any ordered pair that makes all of the inequalities in the system true.

$$\begin{cases} y \geq -x + 2 \\ x \geq 0 \\ y \geq 0 \end{cases}$$

EXAMPLE 5   **Recognizing the correct solution region for a system**

5 Which system of inequalities represents the solution region
shown here?

A. $\begin{cases} y \geq -x \\ x > -2 \\ y > -2 \end{cases}$ **B.** $\begin{cases} y \geq -x \\ x > -2 \\ y < -2 \end{cases}$ **C.** $\begin{cases} y \geq -x \\ x < -2 \\ y < -2 \end{cases}$ **D.** $\begin{cases} y \geq -x \\ x < -2 \\ y > -2 \end{cases}$

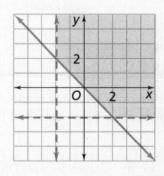

- **SOLUTION**
The shaded region lies entirely to the right of $x = -2$ and above
$y = -2$. Only choice **A** meets all these conditions. The correct
choice is A.

A system of linear inequalities can also consist of a pair of inequalities in
two variables.

EXAMPLE 6 — Graphing systems of linear inequalities

6 Graph this system of linear inequalities.

$$\begin{cases} 2x + 3y \le 6 \\ -5x + 2y > -4 \end{cases}$$

- **SOLUTION**

Solve for y. $\begin{cases} y \le -\frac{2}{3}x + 2 \\ y > \frac{5}{2}x - 2 \end{cases}$

Graph $y = -\frac{2}{3}x + 2$ with a solid line, and graph

$y = \frac{5}{2}x - 2$ with a dashed line.

Shade below the graph of $y = -\frac{2}{3}x + 2$.

Shade above the graph of $y = \frac{5}{2}x - 2$.
Shade the common region.

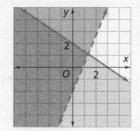

The following example shows how you can use a system of inequalities to solve a real-world problem.

EXAMPLE 7 — Solving a real-world problem by using a system of inequalities

7 A gardener wants to use at least 40 feet and no more than 120 feet of fencing to enclose a rectangular garden. The length is equal to or greater than its width. What possible dimensions may the garden have if dimensions are multiples of 10 feet?

- **SOLUTION**

Let L represent length in feet and W represent width in feet. Graph the solution to the system at the right. Mark points whose coordinates are multiples of 10. Keep in mind that length and width must be positive.

$$\begin{cases} L + W \ge 20 \\ L + W \le 60 \\ L \ge W \end{cases}$$

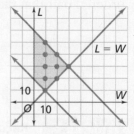

Make a table listing ordered pairs that satisfy all conditions.

Width	10	10	10	10	10	20	20	20	30
Length	10	20	30	40	50	20	30	40	30

Practice

Choose the letter preceding the word or expression that best completes the statement or answers the question.

1 A rectangular garden is to have a perimeter no more than 66 feet. The length of the garden is to be at least twice the width. Which dimensions satisfy these conditions?

- **A.** length 20 feet and width 20 feet
- **B.** length 40 feet and width 20 feet
- **C.** length 30 feet and width 10 feet
- **D.** length 20 feet and width 8 feet

2 Sheila has nickels and dimes but not more than 25 coins. The value of the coins is between $2.00 and $3.00. Which combination of coins is not possible?

- **A.** 6 nickels and 18 dimes
- **B.** 8 nickels and 10 dimes
- **C.** 7 nickels and 18 dimes
- **D.** 1 nickel and 21 dimes

3 Which is a solution to $\begin{cases} y \le 3x + 5 \\ y \ge -x - 5 \end{cases}$?

A. $x = 0, y = 5$ **C.** $x = 4, y = -10$

B. $x = -3, y = -7$ **D.** $x = 0, y = -6$

4 Which system has the shaded region as its solution?

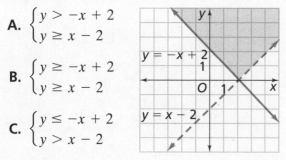

A. $\begin{cases} y > -x + 2 \\ y \ge x - 2 \end{cases}$

B. $\begin{cases} y \ge -x + 2 \\ y \ge x - 2 \end{cases}$

C. $\begin{cases} y \le -x + 2 \\ y > x - 2 \end{cases}$

D. $\begin{cases} y \ge -x + 2 \\ y > x - 2 \end{cases}$

5 Which accurately describes the solution region for $y \le -4x + 11$?

A. all points on or below the graph of $y = -4x + 11$

B. all points on or above the graph of $y = -4x + 11$

C. all points below but not on the graph of $y = -4x + 11$

D. all points above but not on the graph of $y = -4x + 11$

6 Which point is in the shaded region?

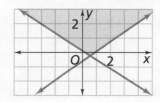

A. $(-99, 0)$ **C.** $(-99, -99)$

B. $(1, 99)$ **D.** $(99, -99)$

7 Which inequality symbol will make the solution region all points above but not on the graph of $y = 13x + 9$?

$$y \underline{\hspace{1cm}} 13x + 9$$

A. $\le$ **B.** $\ge$ **C.** $<$ **D.** $>$

8 The length of a board in feet is between 14 and 16. The board is cut into two unequal pieces. Which pair of lengths is possible?

A. 7 and 6   **C.** 7 and 8

B. 7.5 and 7.5   **D.** 9 and 8

In Exercises 9–16, graph each linear inequality in two variables.

9 $y > x$ **10** $y \le x$

11 $y \ge 2x - 3$ **12** $y \le -x + 4$

13 $2x + y < 3$ **14** $2x + 3y \ge 6$

15 $x - 2y > -1$ **16** $2x + 5y < 10$

In Exercises 17–20, graph each system of linear inequalities in two variables.

17 $\begin{cases} y \le x + 2 \\ y \ge x - 2 \end{cases}$ **18** $\begin{cases} y \ge 3 \\ y > x \end{cases}$

19 $\begin{cases} y \le 3x + 2 \\ y < -2x + 1 \end{cases}$ **20** $\begin{cases} y < \frac{3}{5}x + 4 \\ -3x + 5y \ge -5 \end{cases}$

In Exercises 21–24, solve the problem. Clearly show all necessary work.

21 Today Jessica and Melissa are having a birthday. Both girls are at least 9 years old but not older than 16. If Melissa is 2 years older than Jessica, how old can they be? Show your work.

22 The sum of two positive integers is at most 5. What could the integers be if they are unequal? Show your work and explain your reasoning.

23 Graph the solution to $y \ge x$, $y \le 3$, and $y \ge -2x + 1.5$. Describe the solution region.

24 Jeremy is thinking of two positive integers. He says that their sum is less than 6 and both numbers are at least 2. What could the numbers be? Show your work and explain your reasoning.

DIRECTIONS FOR QUESTIONS 1–20: For each of the questions below, select the answer choice that is best for each case.

1 Which is the slope of the line containing $P(-5, 6)$ and $Q(3, -1)$?

A. $-\frac{8}{7}$ C. $\frac{7}{2}$

B. $-\frac{7}{8}$ D. $\frac{5}{2}$

2 Which is true of all points in the third quadrant?

A. positive x-coordinate; positive y-coordinate

B. negative x-coordinate; negative y-coordinate

C. negative x-coordinate; positive y-coordinate

D. positive x-coordinate; negative y-coordinate

3 Which of the following is not a value in the range of the function $\{(-2, 4), (0, -4), (1, -2), (3, 14)\}$?

A. 1   C. 14

B. -2 D. -4

4 If $y = \frac{2}{3}x - 4$ and $x = 15$, find y.

A. 6   C. 14

B. 26   D. $\frac{37}{2}$

5 Which of the following is the equation in slope-intercept form for the line containing $P(4, 1)$ with slope $\frac{3}{4}$?

A. $y = \frac{3}{4}x + 1$ C. $y = \frac{3}{4}x - \frac{13}{4}$

B. $y = \frac{3}{4}x - 2$ D. $y = \frac{3}{4}x + 4$

6 Which point lies along the line containing $P(-1, 2)$ and $Q(2, -4)$?

A. $(-1, -2)$ C. $(6, 12)$

B. $(1, 2)$ D. $(2, -4)$

7 Which ordered pair (a, b) is a solution to $\begin{cases} 3a + b = 5 \\ a - 5b = -9 \end{cases}$?

A. $(4, -7)$ C. $(3, -4)$

B. $(1, 2)$ D. $(-4, 1)$

8 The sum of two numbers x and y is 49. Twice one number less 14 is the other number. Which system could not represent this situation?

A. $\begin{cases} x + y = 49 \\ 14 - 2x = 49 \end{cases}$

B. $\begin{cases} x + y = 49 \\ 2x - 14 = y \end{cases}$

C. $\begin{cases} 49 = x + y \\ y = 2x - 14 \end{cases}$

D. $\begin{cases} 2x - 14 = y \\ x + y = 49 \end{cases}$

9 Which system of equations is dependent?

A. $\begin{cases} y = 3x - 2 \\ y = x + 1 \end{cases}$ C. $\begin{cases} x + y = 5 \\ y = x + 5 \end{cases}$

B. $\begin{cases} y = x - 1 \\ y - 1 = x \end{cases}$ D. $\begin{cases} y = \frac{2}{5}x - 4 \\ 5y = 2x - 20 \end{cases}$

10 Which system of equations has no solution?

A. $\begin{cases} y = x + 4 \\ 3x - 2y = 10 \end{cases}$ C. $\begin{cases} y = x - 2 \\ 3x + 3y = 12 \end{cases}$

B. $\begin{cases} y = -3x - 5 \\ 2x - 2y = 50 \end{cases}$ D. $\begin{cases} y = x - 4 \\ 3x - 3y = 15 \end{cases}$

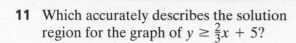
11 Which accurately describes the solution region for the graph of $y \geq \frac{2}{3}x + 5$?

   A. all points on or below the graph of $y \geq \frac{2}{3}x + 5$

   B. all points on or above the graph of $y \geq \frac{2}{3}x + 5$

   C. all points below but not on the graph of $y \geq \frac{2}{3}x + 5$

   D. all points above but not on the graph of $y \geq \frac{2}{3}x + 5$

12 Brian and Lauren are at least 20 years old but not older than 30. If Lauren is 8 years younger than Brian, what could their ages be?

   A. 23 and 27

   B. 18 and 26

   C. 20 and 27

   D. 21 and 29

13 The vertex of $y + 3 = |x + 2|$ is

   A. $(2, 3)$.

   B. $(-2, 3)$.

   C. $(-2, -3)$.

   D. $(2, -3)$.

14 Which is the slope of a line perpendicular to the graph of $y = \frac{5}{4}x + 8$?

   A. -0.8

   B. 0.8

   C. 1.25

   D. -1.25

15 A collection of dimes and quarters has a value of $4.60. The number of dimes is d and the number of quarters is q. Which equation represents this situation?

   A. $10d + 25q = 4.60$

   B. $25d + 10q = 460$

   C. $1.0d + 2.5q = 4.60$

   D. $0.1d + 0.25q = 4.60$

16 What is the value of $\lfloor -2.3 \rfloor$?

   A. -3 **B.** -2 **C.** 2 **D.** 3

17 The variable x varies inversely with y with a constant of variation of 24. What is the value of x when $y = 3$?

   A. 8 **B.** 21 **C.** 27 **D.** 72

18 The function $g(x)$ is periodic with a period of 4. If $g(2) = 5$ and $g(6) = -2$, what is $g(10)$?

   A. -10 **B.** -2 **C.** 3 **D.** 5

19 Which best describes the relationship between the matrices $\begin{bmatrix} 1 & 3 \\ 2 & -1 \end{bmatrix}$ and $\begin{bmatrix} 0 & 5 \\ -4 & 7 \end{bmatrix}$?

   A. They can be added and multiplied.

   B. They can be added but not multiplied.

   C. They can be multiplied but not added.

   D. They cannot be added or multiplied.

20 If $A = \begin{bmatrix} 1 & 0 \\ 0 & 1 \end{bmatrix}$, how can you describe BA?

   A. $BA = A$

   B. Add 1 to each element in B to find BA.

   C. BA is the inverse of B.

   D. $BA = B$.

DIRECTIONS FOR 21–23: Solve each problem and show your work.

21 A line passes through the point $(1, 3)$ and has a slope of 4.

- Write an equation for the line.
- Find the equation of the line that is perpendicular to the first line and passes through $(1, 3)$.
- Graph both lines on the same coordinate grid.

22 The following table shows distance of a car for given times.

Time (hr)	0	2	3	5	6	8
Distance (miles)	0	80	120	200	240	320

- Find the average rate of change of distance over time.
- Write an equation that gives the distance traveled of the car given time.
- Do distance and time vary directly, indirectly, or neither?

23 A box contains a combination of dimes and quarters.

- Write a system of inequalities to describe the possible combinations if there are at most 50 coins in the box and between $7.00 and $9.00.
- Graph the system of inequalities.
- If there are 25 quarters in the box, what is the least number of dimes that could be in the box? Describe how this is reflected in the graph.

4 More About Exponents and Exponential Functions

NEW JERSEY

Discovering New Jersey

Ellis Island

During the late 1800s and early 1900s, Ellis Island was the leading port for immigrants entering the United States. From 1892 to 1954, more than 12 million immigrants passed through Ellis Island in their quest to seek a new home and citizenship in the United States.

Ellis Island became part of the Statue of Liberty National Monument in 1965. The main building on the island, which houses the Ellis Island Immigration Museum, is open to the public, with nearly 2 million visitors each year.

Ellis Island is located at the mouth of the Hudson River and is within the boundaries of Jersey City, New Jersey. Landfill was used to enlarge the original three acre island to its present-day 31 acres.

4.1 Properties of Exponents

New Jersey Standards

4.1.B.2 Rational exponents
4.1.B.4 Laws of exponents

The exponential expression a^n is read as "a to the nth power." In this expression, a is the **base** and n is the **exponent**. The number represented by a^n is called *the nth power of a*.

When n is a positive integer, you can interpret a^n as follows.

$$a^n = \underbrace{a \cdot a \cdot a \cdot \ldots \cdot a}_{n \text{ factors}}$$

Now observe how this interpretation can help you simplify products such as the following.

$p^5 \cdot p^3 = (p \cdot p \cdot p \cdot p \cdot p) \cdot (p \cdot p \cdot p) = p^8$ ← Notice that $5 + 3 = 8$.

$(q^2)^3 = (q^2)(q^2)(q^2) = (q \cdot q) \cdot (q \cdot q) \cdot (q \cdot q) = q^6$ ← Notice that $2 \cdot 3 = 6$.

$(rs)^4 = (r \cdot s)(r \cdot s)(r \cdot s)(r \cdot s) = (r \cdot r \cdot r \cdot r)(s \cdot s \cdot s \cdot s) = r^4 s^4$

These examples are generalized in the following properties of exponents.

Note

Notice that you can add exponents only when the bases are the same.

Multiplication Properties of Exponents

Let m and n represent integers and a and b represent nonzero real numbers.

Product of Powers Property
$$a^m \cdot a^n = a^{m+n}$$

Power of a Power Property
$$(a^m)^n = a^{mn}$$

Power of a Product Property
$$(ab)^m = a^m b^m$$

You can use the multiplication properties of exponents to simplify the following exponential expressions.

Go Online
PHSchool.com
Visit: PHSchool.com
Web Code: ayp-0250

EXAMPLES 1 through 7   **Using the multiplication properties of exponents**

Simplify each expression. Write answers using positive exponents.

1 $2^3 \cdot 2^4$ ■ SOLUTION $2^3 \cdot 2^4 = 2^{3+4} = 2^7 = 128$

2 $(n^3)^3$ ■ SOLUTION $(n^3)^3 = n^{3 \cdot 3} = n^9$

3 $(-2x)^3$ ■ SOLUTION $(-2x)^3 = (-2)^3 x^3 = -8x^3$

4 $(yz^4)^2$ ■ SOLUTION $(yz^4)^2 = (y^1 z^4)^2 = (y^1)^2 (z^4)^2 = y^{1 \cdot 2} z^{4 \cdot 2} = y^2 z^8$

5 $(pq)^3 \cdot (pq)^5$ ■ SOLUTION $(pq)^3 \cdot (pq)^5 = (pq)^{3+5} = (pq)^8 = p^8 q^8$

6 $(-3s^3 t^2)^4$ ■ SOLUTION $(-3s^3 t^2)^4 = (-3)^4 (s^3)^4 (t^2)^4 = 81 s^{3 \cdot 4} t^{2 \cdot 4} = 81 s^{12} t^8$

7 $(df)^2 (gh)^5$ ■ SOLUTION $(df)^2 (gh)^5 = d^2 f^2 g^5 h^5$

Notice that in order to apply the product property of exponents, you add exponents when you are multiplying powers of like bases. In some numerical expressions, however, you can apply this property if the given bases are not alike but can be changed to like bases.

EXAMPLE 8   **Applying the product property of exponents to a numerical expression**

 Which is equivalent to $3^5 \cdot 9^4$?

A. 3^{11} **B.** 3^{13} **C.** 27^9 **D.** 27^{20}

■ SOLUTION

The bases of the factors are not alike; however, 9 can be written as an exponent with a base of 3. $9 = 3^2$

Rewrite the expression, substituting 3^2 for 9. $3^5 \cdot 9^4 = 3^5 \cdot (3^2)^4 = 3^5 \cdot 3^8 = 3^{13}$

The correct choice is B.

When you understand the multiplication properties of exponents, you can multiply terms by using the following procedure.

Multiplying Terms

Step 1 Multiply the coefficients, using the rules for multiplying signed numbers.

Step 2 Multiply the variable factors, using the multiplication properties of exponents.

Step 3 Write the product of the results from Steps 1 and 2.

EXAMPLES 9 and 10   **Multiplying terms**

Go Online
PHSchool.com
Visit: PHSchool.com
Web Code: ayp-0248

Simplify each expression. Write answers using positive exponents.

 $(3a^2)(5a^4)$

■ SOLUTION

$(3a^2)(5a^4)$
$= 3 \cdot 5 \cdot a^2 \cdot a^4$
$= 15 \cdot a^2 \cdot a^4$
$= 15 \cdot a^{2+4}$
$= 15a^6$

10 $(2rs^3)(5r^3s)^2$

■ SOLUTION

$(2rs^3)(5r^3s)^2$
$= (2r^1s^3)(5^1r^3s^1)^2$
$= (2r^1s^3)(5^2r^6s^2)$
$= 2 \cdot 5^2 \cdot r^1 \cdot r^6 \cdot s^3 \cdot s^2$
$= 50 \cdot r^{1+6} \cdot s^{3+2}$
$= 50r^7s^5$

Now examine these quotients involving exponents.

$$\frac{x^9}{x^2} = \frac{\overset{1}{\cancel{x}} \cdot \overset{1}{\cancel{x}} \cdot x \cdot x \cdot x \cdot x \cdot x \cdot x \cdot x}{\underset{1}{\cancel{x}} \cdot \underset{1}{\cancel{x}}} = \frac{x^7}{1} = x^7 \leftarrow \text{Notice that } 9 - 2 = 7.$$

$$\left(\frac{v}{w}\right)^5 = \frac{v}{w} \cdot \frac{v}{w} \cdot \frac{v}{w} \cdot \frac{v}{w} \cdot \frac{v}{w} = \frac{v \cdot v \cdot v \cdot v \cdot v}{w \cdot w \cdot w \cdot w \cdot w} = \frac{v^5}{w^5}$$

Note

A quotient involving exponents is also called **a ratio of powers.**

113

The results of the divisions on the preceding page are generalized in the following properties of exponents.

Division Properties of Exponents

Let m and n represent integers and a and b represent nonzero real numbers.

Quotient of Powers Property

$$\frac{a^m}{a^n} = a^{m-n}$$

Power of a Quotient Property

$$\left(\frac{a}{b}\right)^m = \frac{a^m}{b^m}$$

You can now divide terms by using the following procedure.

Dividing Terms

Step 1 Divide the coefficients, using the rules for dividing signed numbers.

Step 2 Divide the variable factors, using the division properties of exponents.

Step 3 Write the product of the results from Steps 1 and 2.

EXAMPLES 11 through 14   Dividing terms

Simplify each expression. Write each answer using positive exponents.

11 $\dfrac{5^6}{5^3}$ ▪ SOLUTION $\dfrac{5^6}{5^3} = 5^{6-3} = 5^3$

12 $\left(\dfrac{2}{z^3}\right)^2$ ▪ SOLUTION $\left(\dfrac{2}{z^3}\right)^2 = \dfrac{2^2}{(z^3)^2} = \dfrac{4}{z^6}$

13 $\dfrac{6r^8}{3r^2}$ ▪ SOLUTION $\dfrac{6r^8}{3r^2} = 2r^{8-2} = 2r^6$

14 $\dfrac{32m^5n^3}{2^3m^4n^2}$ ▪ SOLUTION $\dfrac{32m^5n^3}{2^3m^4n^2} = \dfrac{2^5m^5n^3}{2^3m^4n^2} = 2^{5-3}m^{5-4}n^{3-2} = 2^2m^1n^1 = 4mn$

Practice

Choose the letter preceding the word or expression that best completes the statement or answers the question.

1 Which is equivalent to r^4s^8?

   A. $(rs)^{12}$ **C.** $(rs^2)^4$

   B. $(r^4s^4)^2$ **D.** $r^4 + s^4 + s^4$

2 Which expression is equivalent to $\dfrac{4^{12}}{2^6}$?

   A. 2^6 **C.** 4^8

   B. 2^4 **D.** 2^{18}

3 Which is not equivalent to $(-w)^2$?

   A. $-w^2$ **C.** w^2

   B. $w \cdot w$ **D.** $(-w)(-w)$

4 Which is the product of pr^3 and p^2q^2r?

   A. $p^3q^2r^4$ **C.** $p^3q^2r^3$

   B. $p^5q^2r^4$ **D.** $\dfrac{r^2}{pq^2}$

5 Which is not equivalent to n^4?

    A. $n^2 \cdot n^2$ **C.** $\frac{n^4}{n}$

    B. $(n^2)^2$ **D.** $\frac{1}{n^{-4}}$

6 If $a = -2$ and $b = 3$, find the value of $\frac{a^2 b^3}{a^3 b^2}$.

    A. $-\frac{3}{2}$ **C.** $-\frac{2}{3}$

    B. $\frac{3}{2}$ **D.** $\frac{2}{3}$

7 The expression $[(2a)(2b)]^2$ is equivalent to

    A. $4a^2 b^2$.   **C.** $8a^2 b^2$.

    B. $16ab^2$.   **D.** $16a^2 b^2$.

8 Which is the quotient of $18gh^3 k^5$ and $20g^6 hk^3$?

    A. $\frac{10g^5}{9h^2 k^2}$ **C.** $\frac{9h^2 k^2}{10g^5}$

    B. $\frac{9g^5 h^2}{10k^2}$ **D.** $\frac{10h^2 k^2}{9g^5}$

9 Evaluate $(6^4)(3^5)$.

    A. 39   **C.** 1,539

    B. 314,928   **D.** 360

10 Which is the product of $(4a^3 b^2)^3$ and $(2ab)^3$?

    A. $512a^{12} b^9$ **C.** $512a^{10} b^9$

    B. $72a^9 b^8$ **D.** $18a^9 b^9$

11 If $g^x \cdot g^3 = g^{12}$, find x.

    A. $x = 4$ **C.** $x = 36$

    B. $x = 15$ **D.** $x = 9$

12 If $\left(\frac{r^8}{r^x}\right)^2 = r^{16}$, find x.

    A. $x = 4$ **C.** $x = 0$

    B. $x = 1$ **D.** $x = 12$

In Exercises 13–15, simplify each expression.

13 $3^3 \cdot 3^2$ **14** $\frac{5^4}{5^7}$ **15** $\left(-\frac{1}{2}\right)^3$

In Exercises 16–30, simplify each expression. Write answers using positive exponents.

16 $(-5r^2 s^2)(-3r^2 s)$ **17** $(12x^2 y)(4x^5)(-2z)$

18 $(-3a^3 b^2 c)^3$ **19** $(x^3 y^2)^2 (xy^3)^4$

20 $\frac{p^6 q^{10}}{p^3 q^8}$ **21** $\frac{3v^2 w^4}{9vw^3}$

22 $\left(\frac{3a}{7b}\right)^2$ **23** $\left(\frac{x^3}{y^7}\right)^2$

24 $\left(\frac{-2ab}{c}\right)^2$ **25** $\left(\frac{-2y^5}{3x^3}\right)^3$

26 $\left(\frac{c^3 d^3}{c^2}\right)^3$ **27** $\frac{(5ab^4)^2}{5ab^4}$

28 $\frac{(3y^2)(2y^3)}{3y^4}$ **29** $\frac{(-4n^5)(2n^3)}{2n^4}$

30 $\frac{(9x^2 y)(3x^3 y^2)}{-27x^5 y}$

In Exercises 31–36, find the value of x that makes each statement true. Assume that no base is equal to zero.

31 $r^x \cdot r^2 = r^6$ **32** $(r^x)^2 = r^6$

33 $r^x \cdot r^2 = 1$ **34** $(r^x)^2 = 1$

35 $\frac{r^2}{r^x} = r^6$ **36** $\left(\frac{r}{r^x}\right)^2 = r^6$

In Exercises 37–38, solve the problem. Clearly show all necessary work.

37 Are -5^2 and $(-5)^2$ equivalent expressions? Explain your answer.

38 Given that m and n are integers and x is a nonzero real number, is it true that $(x^m)^n = (x^n)^m$? Justify your answer.

4.2 Zero and Negative Exponents

You can use the division property of exponents to develop a rule for negative exponents. Recall that $\frac{b^m}{b^n} = b^{m-n}$. If n is greater than m, then $m - n$ is negative. The problem below shows how you can simplify a ratio of powers when the degree of the numerator is less than the degree of the denominator.

$$\frac{s^3}{s^5} = \frac{s \cdot s \cdot s}{s \cdot s \cdot s \cdot s \cdot s} = \frac{\cancel{s} \cdot \cancel{s} \cdot \cancel{s}}{\cancel{s} \cdot \cancel{s} \cdot \cancel{s} \cdot s \cdot s} = \frac{1}{s \cdot s} = \frac{1}{s^2}; \text{ therefore, } \frac{1}{s^2} = s^{-2}$$

Likewise, $\frac{s^3}{s^5} = s^{3-5} = s^{-2}$.

Visit: PHSchool.com
Web Code: ayp-0039

EXAMPLES 1 through 3 — **Using the division property of exponents**

Simplify the following expressions using the division property of exponents.

1 $\frac{5^2}{5^6}$ ■ **SOLUTION** $\frac{5^2}{5^6} = 5^{2-6} = 5^{-4} = \frac{1}{5^4} = \frac{1}{625}$

2 $\frac{12m^3n^5}{4m^7n^3}$ ■ **SOLUTION** $\frac{12m^3n^5}{4m^7n^3} = 3m^{3-7}n^{5-3} = 3m^{-4}n^2 = \frac{3n^2}{m^4}$

3 $\frac{15rs^5}{-3r^3s^{-2}}$ ■ **SOLUTION** $\frac{15rs^5}{-3r^3s^{-2}} = -5r^{1-3}s^{5-(-2)} = -5r^{-2}s^{5+2} = -5r^{-2}s^7 = \frac{-5s^7}{r^2}$

If the degree of the numerator is equal to the degree of the denominator, the division property will result in an exponent of zero.

$$\frac{5^3}{5^3} = 5^{3-3} = 5^0. \text{ Similarly, } \frac{5^3}{5^3} = \frac{125}{125} = 1. \text{ Therefore, } \frac{5^3}{5^3} = 5^0 = 1.$$

EXAMPLES 4 through 7 — **Simplifying expressions with exponents equal to zero**

> **Note**
> For any real number x, $x^1 = x$. For any non zero real number x, $x^0 = 1$. For any non zero real number x and any integer n, $x^{-n} = \frac{1}{x^n}$.

Simplify each of the following exponential expressions.

4 $(fg^3)^0$

■ **SOLUTION**
$(fg^3)^0 = f^0g^{(3)(0)} = (1)(1) = 1$

5 $x^0y^3z^2$

■ **SOLUTION**
$x^0y^3z^2 = (1)(y^3)(z^2)$
$= y^3z^2$

6 $\left(\frac{2x^2y^0}{3x^0y^2}\right)^2$

■ **SOLUTION**
$\left(\frac{2x^2y^0}{3x^0y^2}\right)^2 = \frac{2^2x^{(2)(2)}y^{(0)(2)}}{3^2x^{(0)(2)}y^{(2)(2)}}$

$= \frac{4x^4y^0}{9x^0y^4}$

$= \frac{4x^4}{9y^4}$

7 $\frac{16a^0b^3}{2a^4}$

■ **SOLUTION**
$\frac{16a^0b^3}{2a^4} = 8a^{0-4}b^3$

$= 8a^{-4}b^3$

$= \frac{8b^3}{a^4}$

You can use all of the rules of exponents to simplify exponential expressions.

EXAMPLES 8 through 10 — Simplifying exponential expressions

Simplify each expression. Write each answer using positive exponents.

8 $(v^{-2}w^3)^{-2}$ ■ **SOLUTION** $(v^{-2}w^3)^{-2} = (v^{-2})^{-2}(w^3)^{-2}$

$$= v^{(-2)(-2)}w^{(3)(-2)} = v^4 w^{-6} = \frac{v^4}{w^6}$$

9 $\left(\dfrac{2z^3r^{-2}}{3zr^4}\right)^3$ ■ **SOLUTION** $\left(\dfrac{2z^3r^{-2}}{3zr^4}\right)^3 = \dfrac{2^3z^{(3)(3)}r^{(-2)(3)}}{3^3z^{(1)(3)}r^{(4)(3)}} = \dfrac{8z^9r^{-6}}{27z^3r^{12}} = \dfrac{8z^6}{27r^{18}}$

10 $\dfrac{-36a^0b^3}{9a^5b}$ ■ **SOLUTION** $\dfrac{-36a^0b^3}{9a^5b} = -4a^{0-5}b^{3-1} = -4a^{-5}b^2 = \dfrac{-4b^2}{a^5}$

Recall that a number written in scientific notation has the following form.

The first factor is a number that is at least 1, but is less than 10. $\rightarrow a \times 10^n \leftarrow$ **The second factor is an integer power of 10, expressed in exponential form.**

The properties of exponents can be used when performing operations on numbers written in scientific notation.

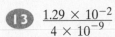
Go Online
PHSchool.com
Visit: PHSchool.com
Web Code: ayp-0940

EXAMPLES 11 through 13 — Multiplying and dividing with numbers in scientific notation

Simplify each expression. Write answers in scientific notation.

11 $5000 \times (1.39 \times 10^{-8})$ **12** $(6 \times 10^4)^2$ **13** $\dfrac{1.29 \times 10^{-2}}{4 \times 10^{-9}}$

■ **SOLUTION**

$5000 \times (1.39 \times 10^{-8})$
$= (5 \times 10^3) \times (1.39 \times 10^{-8})$
$= (5 \times 1.39) \times (10^3 \times 10^{-8})$
$= 6.95 \times (10^3 \times 10^{-8})$
$= 6.95 \times 10^{3+(-8)}$
$= 6.95 \times 10^{-5}$

■ **SOLUTION**

$(6 \times 10^4)^2$
$= (6)^2 \times (10^4)^2$
$= 36 \times (10^4)^2$
$= 36 \times 10^{4 \cdot 2}$
$= 36 \times 10^8$
$= 3.6 \times 10^1 \times 10^8$
$= 3.6 \times 10^9$

■ **SOLUTION**

$\dfrac{1.29 \times 10^{-2}}{4 \times 10^{-9}}$

$= \dfrac{1.29}{4} \times \dfrac{10^{-2}}{10^{-9}}$

$= 0.3225 \times \dfrac{10^{-2}}{10^{-9}}$

$= 0.3225 \times 10^{-2-(-9)}$

$= 0.3225 \times 10^7$

$= 3.225 \times 10^{-1} \times 10^7$

$= 3.225 \times 10^6$

Most calculators display numbers written in scientific notation without the base *10* showing. The symbol *E* represents multiplying by 10, and the number following is the exponent. For example, if the calculator displays 5.68 E −8, that represents the number 5.68×10^{-8} or 0.0000000568.

The solutions to the example problems above performed on a calculator are displayed in the accompanying figure.

5000∗(1.39ᴇ⁻8)
                6.95ᴇ⁻5
(6ᴇ4)²
                3.6ᴇ9
(1.29ᴇ⁻2)/(4ᴇ⁻9)
                3.225ᴇ6
■

Choose the letter preceding the word or expression that best completes
the statement or answers the question.

1 Which is a true statement?

A. $\dfrac{z^6}{z^2} = z^3$

B. $\dfrac{z^3}{z^5} = \dfrac{1}{z^{-2}}$

C. $\dfrac{z^0}{z^{-3}} = z^3$

D. $\dfrac{z^{-4}}{z^2} = z^{-2}$

2 Simplify the expression $\dfrac{k^4 l^2}{k^{-3} l^6}$.

A. kl^4

B. $k^7 l^4$

C. $\dfrac{k^7}{l^4}$

D. $\dfrac{k}{l^4}$

3 Which is equivalent to $\dfrac{8.125 \times 10^{-8}}{3.25 \times 10^3}$?

A. 2.5×10^{-11}

B. 4.875×10^{-11}

C. 2.5×10^{-5}

D. 4.875×10^{-5}

4 Which is the proper way to write
$(3.62 \times 10^{-3})^2$ in standard form?

A. 0.0000131044   C. 0.000000362

B. 13,104,400,000   D. 36,200,000

5 What value of x will make the equation
$\dfrac{6^6}{6^x} = 1$ true?

A. 0   B. -6 C. 1   D. 6

6 What value of x will make the equation
$\dfrac{r^3 s^7}{r^x s^2} = r^7 s^5$ true?

A. 4   B. 2   C. -4 D. -2

7 If the length of one side of a cube is denoted
by x, the volume of the cube would be
denoted as which of the following?

A. $3x$ B. 3^x C. x^3 D. $(3x)^3$

8 If the length of one side of a rectangular
garden is denoted by l and the width is
4 units shorter than the length, the area of
the garden would be denoted as which of
the following?

A. $l - 4$ C. $l(l + 4)$

B. $(l - 4)^2$ D. $l^2 - 4l$

9 If $k = 3.2 \times 10^{-4}$, what is the value of $3k^2$?

A. 3.072×10^{-7}

B. 9.216×10^{-7}

C. 30,720,000

D. 0.00000003072

10 If $b = 1.8 \times 10^5$, what is the value of $2b^2$?

A. 3.6×10^7 C. 12.96×10^{10}

B. 6.48×10^{10} D. 3.6×10^{10}

Solve the following problems. Clearly show all necessary work.

11 The planet Earth is approximated by a sphere with a radius of 6.4×10^6 meters. Use the formula $S = 4\pi r^2$ to approximate the surface area of the Earth.

12 If the area of a rectangle is represented by $60a^2b^5$ and its width is represented by $12ab$, express the length of the rectangle in terms of a and b.

13 The national debt was approximately 8.5 trillion dollars in August of 2006. At that time, the population of the United States was 300 million. If the debt were divided equally among all of the people in the United States, how much would each person owe?

In Exercises 14–30, simplify each expression. Write each answer using positive exponents.

14 $b^{-4} \cdot b^{-3} \cdot b^5$

15 $k^{-7} \cdot (k^2)^5$

16 $(m^{-3}n^4)^{-4}$

17 $(2^3 a^5)^2 (16a^{-5})$

18 $2^3 \cdot 7^4 \cdot 2^{-3} \cdot 7^{-4}$

19 $\dfrac{a^2 b^2}{a^3 b^2}$

20 $\dfrac{15c^8 d^3}{-3c^{10} d^{-2}}$

21 $\left(\dfrac{c^3 d^3}{c^2}\right)^4$

22 $\left(\dfrac{-2x^3 y^{-3}}{x^2 y^5}\right)^3$

23 $\dfrac{(-3n^{-5})(4n^3)}{(2n^{-2})}$

24 $\left(\dfrac{s^3 t^{-5}}{s^{-1} t^{-4}}\right)^2$

25 $\dfrac{(2a^3)^{-2}(3a^4 b^0)}{6a^{-2}}$

26 $(4g^3 h^3)^{-4}(-2gh)^3$

27 $(m^2)^{-4}(m^2 n^3)^2$

28 $\dfrac{r^3 s^{-1}}{r^2 s^6}$

29 $\dfrac{3j^{-3} k^{-5}}{2j^{-5} k^{-3}}$

30 $\left(\dfrac{a^{-2} b^{-1}}{a^{-5} b^3}\right)^{-3}$

In Exercises 31–36, simplify each expression. Write each answer in scientific notation.

31 $(2.6 \times 10^{-9})(3 \times 10^2)$

32 $12{,}000 \times (6.5 \times 10^{-11})$

33 $(3 \times 10^{-4})^2$

34 $(1.6 \times 10^4)^3$

35 $\dfrac{4.8 \times 10^8}{7.5 \times 10^2}$

36 $\dfrac{2.43 \times 10^{-9}}{7.5 \times 10^{-10}}$

In Exercises 37–39, solve the problem. Clearly show all necessary work.

37 There are approximately 6.02×10^{23} molecules in one mole of a substance. How many molecules are in 5,000 moles?

38 When the planet Mars is closest to Earth, the distance between Earth and Mars is about 3.38×10^7 miles. Suppose that you were to travel this distance at an average speed of 60 miles per hour. How many years would it take to travel to Mars?

39 In 1998, municipalities in the United States recovered about 7×10^{10} pounds of waste paper. The population of the United States in 1998 was about 2.7×10^8. How many pounds of waste paper were recovered per person? Round your answer to the nearest pound.

4.3 Recursive and Explicit Formulas

New Jersey Standards

4.3.C.3 Convert recursive formulas to linear formulas

In a **recursive sequence,** subsequent terms of a given sequence are defined in relation to the preceding term or terms in the sequence. Because any given term is dependent on the preceding term(s), the seed or starting number(s) must be identified. The Fibonacci sequence is a simple example of a recursive sequence. The first ten terms of the Fibonacci sequence are 0, 1, 1, 2, 3, 5, 8, 13, 21, and 34. The seed numbers are 0 and 1.

A **recursive formula** can be derived by identifying the recurring pattern in the number sequence. The recursive formula for the Fibonacci sequence is based on adding the two previous terms in the sequence to get the next term. This can be expressed mathematically as $a_n = a_{n-1} + a_{n-2}$, where (n) is the number of the term, and (a) is the value of (n). The value (a) of the 11th term (n) can be determined by using the formula.

$$a_{11} = a_{11-1} + a_{11-2}$$
$$a_{11} = a_{10} + a_9$$
$$a_{11} = 34 + 21$$
$$a_{11} = 55$$

Therefore, the 11th term of the Fibonacci sequence is 55.

EXAMPLE 1 — Finding terms in a recursive sequence

 Determine the recursive formula and the next four values of the sequence to complete the table below. The seed number is $a_1 = 1$.

Term (n)	1	2	3	4	5	6	7	8	9	10
Value (a)	1	3	7	15	31	63				

■ **SOLUTION**

Notice that the value of any given term is 2 times the value of the preceding term plus 1. In other words, the value of the third term is twice the value of the second term plus 1, or 2(3) + 1. The value of the third term is 7. This can be written as the formula $a_n = 2(a_{n-1}) + 1$.

Completing the table, the four missing terms can be found using the formula.

$a_7 = 2(a_{7-1}) + 1$ $a_8 = 2(a_{8-1}) + 1$ $a_9 = 2(a_{9-1}) + 1$ $a_{10} = 2(a_{10-1}) + 1$

$a_7 = 2(a_6) + 1$ $a_8 = 2(a_7) + 1$ $a_9 = 2(a_8) + 1$ $a_{10} = 2(a_9) + 1$

$a_7 = 2(63) + 1$ $a_8 = 2(127) + 1$ $a_9 = 2(255) + 1$ $a_{10} = 2(511) + 1$

$a_7 = 127$ $a_8 = 255$ $a_9 = 511$ $a_{10} = 1023$

Term (n)	1	2	3	4	5	6	7	8	9	10
Value (a)	1	3	7	15	31	63	127	255	511	1023

Unlike a recursive sequence, an **explicit** sequence does not depend on previous terms in order to find the nth term. The value of a_n is dependent only on term n. Assume that 4, 7, 12, 19, and 28 are the first five terms of a sequence. The recursive formula for this sequence can be written as $a_n = a_{n-1} + 2n - 1$; however, the value of the preceding term must be known in order to solve for a given term n.

In order to determine an explicit function for this sequence, it is helpful to assign a term number for each value, as shown in the chart below.

Term (n)	1	2	3	4	5	6	7	8
Value (a)	4	7	12	19	28			

Rather than considering the sequential change in values, consider the value in relation to the term. In this case, the explicit formula is $f(n) = (n)^2 + 3$. To complete the chart, simply apply the formula as shown at the right.

$$f(6) = (6)^2 + 3; f(6) = 39$$
$$f(7) = (7)^2 + 3; f(7) = 52$$
$$f(8) = (8)^2 + 3; f(8) = 67$$

Furthermore, the value (a) for any term (n) can be found using the same method.

Go Online
PHSchool.com
Visit: PHSchool.com
Web Code: ayp-0664

EXAMPLE 2   Finding terms of an explicit sequence

2 Find an explicit formula for the sequence, then find the 15th term.

Term (n)	1	2	3	4	5
Value (a)	9	16	25	36	49

▪ **SOLUTION**

Notice that each value (a) is a perfect square. The square root of each value (a) results in the values 3, 4, 5, 6, and 7. Compare these values with the term (n): 1:3, 2:4, 3:5, 4:6, 5:7. Notice that the value (a) is 2 more than the term (t). The explicit formula to the sequence is $f(n) = (n + 2)^2$.

Use the formula to find the 15th term as follows:

$$f(n) = (n + 2)^2$$
$$f(15) = (15 + 2)^2 = (17)^2$$
$$f(15) = 289$$

Note

Notice that the value of the terms between 5 and 15 are not needed in order to find the 15th term because this is an explicit sequence.

Practice

Choose the letter preceding the word or expression that best completes the statement or answers the question.

1 What is the recursive formula for the sequence 5, 10, 30, 120, 600?

A. $a_n = (a_{n-1})$ **C.** $a_n = n(a_{n-1})$

B. $a_n = n(a_{n+1})$ **D.** $a_n = (a_{n+1})$

2 What are the first four terms of the explicit sequence $f(n) = 3^{n-1}$?

A. 0, 3, 6, 9   **C.** 1, 3, 9, 27

B. 0, 3, 9, 27   **D.** 3, 9, 27, 81

3 A sequence is defined recursively as $a_1 = 3$ and $a_n = 3a_{n-1}$. Determine the first five values in the sequence. Write the explicit formula for this sequence.

4 Consider the sequence $\frac{1}{2}, \frac{1}{4}, \frac{1}{8}, \frac{1}{16}, \frac{1}{32}$. Write a recursive formula for this sequence. Write an explicit formula for this sequence.

4.4 Exponential Functions

New Jersey Standards

4.3.B.1 Convert functions among equations, tables, and graphs

4.3.B.4.1 Understand exponential functions

Many teenagers would like to persuade their parents to pay them an allowance in the following way. One cent (1¢) is paid on the first day of the month and doubled each successive day. The table shows the amount to be paid each day for the month of February.

Day	x	Amount	Day	x	Amount
1	0	$.01	15	14	$163.84
2	1	$.02	16	15	$327.68
3	2	$.04	17	16	$655.36
4	3	$.08	18	17	$1,310.72
5	4	$.16	19	18	$2,621.44
6	5	$.32	20	19	$5,242.88
7	6	$.64	21	20	$10,485.76
8	7	$1.28	22	21	$20,971.52
9	8	$2.56	23	22	$41,943.04
10	9	$5.12	24	23	$83,886.08
11	10	$10.24	25	24	$167,772.16
12	11	$20.48	26	25	$335,544.32
13	12	$40.96	27	26	$671,088.64
14	13	$81.92	28	27	$1,342,177.28

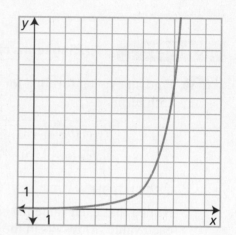

The amount due on the last day is over one million dollars, and it all started with just one penny!

The equation that determines the amount paid each day is $y = 0.01(2^x)$. The graph of this function is shown in the diagram above. This type of function is known as an **exponential function**.

Exponential Functions

An exponential function is of the form $y = a \cdot b^x$ where a is nonzero, $b > 0$, $b \neq 1$, and x is a real number.

Go Online
PHSchool.com
Visit: PHSchool.com
Web Code: ayp-0131

EXAMPLE 1   **Graphing exponential functions from a table**

1   Use the table to graph the exponential function

■ SOLUTION

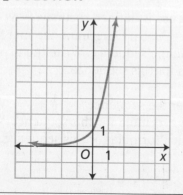

x	y
−2	0.04
−1	0.2
0	1
1	5
2	25

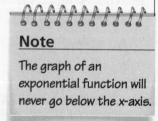

Note

The graph of an exponential function will never go below the x-axis.

122

Examples of the exponential functions $y = 2^x$, $y = 3^x$, and $y = 5^x$ and their graphs are shown below.

x	2^x	3^x	5^x
−1	$2^{-1} = \frac{1}{2}$	$3^{-1} = \frac{1}{3}$	$5^{-1} = \frac{1}{5}$
0	$2^0 = 1$	$3^0 = 1$	$5^0 = 1$
1	$2^1 = 2$	$3^1 = 3$	$5^1 = 5$
2	$2^2 = 4$	$3^2 = 9$	$5^2 = 25$
3	$2^3 = 8$	$3^3 = 27$	$5^3 = 125$

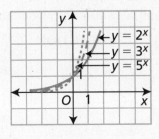

Notice that the point $(0, 1)$ is the y-intercept for each of these graphs. Also notice that none of these graphs crosses the x-axis. There is no value of x for which y will be negative.

Go Online
PHSchool.com
Visit: PHSchool.com
Web Code: ayp-0257

EXAMPLES 2 and 3   **Evaluating exponential functions**

Evaluate the following functions for $x = \{-2, -1, 0, 1, 2\}$. As the values of x increase, determine whether the values of the function increase or decrease.

2 $y = 4^x$ ▪ **SOLUTION**

x	4^x
−2	$4^{-2} = \frac{1}{4^2} = \frac{1}{16}$
−1	$4^{-1} = \frac{1}{4}$
0	$4^0 = 1$
1	$4^1 = 4$
2	$4^2 = 16$

Increase

3 $y = \left(\frac{1}{3}\right)^x$ ▪ **SOLUTION**

x	$\left(\frac{1}{3}\right)^x$
−2	$\left(\frac{1}{3}\right)^{-2} = \frac{1^{-2}}{3^{-2}} = \frac{\frac{1}{1^2}}{\frac{1}{3^2}} = \frac{1}{1^2} \cdot \frac{3^2}{1} = \frac{9}{1} = 9$
−1	$\left(\frac{1}{3}\right)^{-1} = \frac{1^{-1}}{3^{-1}} = \frac{\frac{1}{1}}{\frac{1}{3}} = \frac{1}{1} \cdot \frac{3}{1} = \frac{3}{1} = 3$
0	$\left(\frac{1}{3}\right)^0 = 1$
1	$\left(\frac{1}{3}\right)^1 = \frac{1^1}{3^1} = \frac{1}{3}$
2	$\left(\frac{1}{3}\right)^2 = \frac{1^2}{3^2} = \frac{1}{9}$

Decrease

You can use a chart of values to graph exponential functions.

Go Online
PHSchool.com
Visit: PHSchool.com
Web Code: ayp-0258

EXAMPLES 4 and 5   **Graphing exponential functions**

Graph the following exponential functions.

4 $y = 4^x$ ■ **SOLUTION**

x	4^x
−2	$4^{-2} = \frac{1}{16}$
−1	$4^{-1} = \frac{1}{4}$
0	$4^0 = 1$
1	$4^1 = 4$
2	$4^2 = 16$
3	$4^3 = 64$

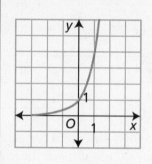

Notice that the curve of the function $y = 4^x$ rises from left to right.

5 $y = 3(4^x)$ ■ **SOLUTION**

x	$3(4^x)$
−2	$3(4^{-2}) = \frac{3}{16}$
−1	$3(4^{-1}) = \frac{3}{4}$
0	$3(4^0) = 3$
1	$3(4^1) = 12$
2	$3(4^2) = 48$
3	$3(4^3) = 192$

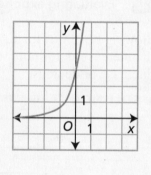

Notice that changing the function $y = 4^x$ to $y = 3(4^x)$ changes the y-intercept from 1 to 3. The steepness of the function's curve also decreases.

Observe what happens when you graph an exponential function with a base that is less than 1.

EXAMPLE 6   **Graphing exponential functions with a base that is less than 1**

 6   Graph $y = 0.25^x$

■ **SOLUTION**

x	0.25^x
−2	$0.25^{-2} = 16$
−1	$0.25^{-1} = 4$
0	$0.25^0 = 1$
1	$0.25^1 = 0.25$
2	$0.25^2 = \frac{1}{16}$
3	$0.25^3 = \frac{1}{64}$

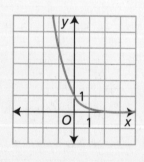

Notice that when the base is less than 1, the function's curve decreases from left to right.

Choose the letter preceding the word or expression that best completes the statement or answers the question.

1 Which function is shown in the graph?

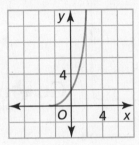

A. $y = -0.5^x$ **C.** $y = \left(\frac{1}{4}\right)^x$

B. $y = 2(4^x)$ **D.** $y = -(3)^x$

2 Which of the following is not an exponential function?

A. $y = 0.2(8^x)$ **C.** $y = 4x^2$

B. $y = \left(\frac{1}{4}\right)^x + 2$ **D.** $y = 2^x$

3 The graph of which function is shown below?

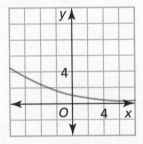

A. $y = \left(\frac{3}{4}\right)^x$ **C.** $y = 0.5^x$

B. $y = 2\left(\frac{3}{4}\right)^x$ **D.** $y = 2(0.5)^x$

In Exercises 4–6, solve the problem. Clearly show all necessary work.

4 When an exponential function has a base that is ≥ 1, does its graph rise or fall from left to right? Explain.

5 When an exponential function has a base that is ≤ 1, does its graph rise or fall from left to right? Explain.

6 Does the graph of an exponential function have an x-intercept? Explain.

In Exercises 7–9, evaluate each function for $x = \{-2, -1, 0, 1, 2, 3\}$. As the values for x increase, determine whether the values of the function increase or decrease.

7 $y = 2.5^x$ **8** $f(x) = 5(4^x)$ **9** $y = \left(\frac{2}{3}\right)^x$

In Exercises 10–13, match each of the following functions to its graph.

10 $y = 2^x$ **11** $y = \left(\frac{1}{2}\right)^x$

12 $y = -(2^x)$ **13** $y = 5(2^x)$

A.   C.

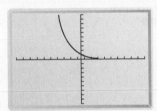 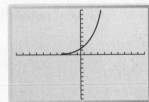

B.   D.

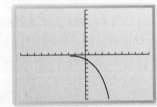 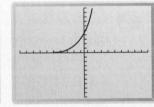

In Exercises 14–20, evaluate each function for $x = \{-2, -1, 0, 1, 2\}$ and graph the function.

14 $y = 2^x$ **15** $y = 0.5^x$

16 $y = 2(3^x)$ **17** $y = \left(\frac{1}{3}\right)^x$

18 $f(x) = 0.4^x$ **19** $f(x) = -\left(\frac{3}{4}\right)^x$

20 $f(x) = -5^x$

4.5 Exponential Growth and Decay

New Jersey Standards

4.3.B.1 Convert functions among equations, tables, and graphs

4.3.C.1.1 Exponential growth and decay

Recall that an exponential function is of the form $y = a \cdot b^x$ where a is nonzero, $b > 0$, $b \neq 1$, and x is a real number. If the value of a is positive and the value of b is greater than 1, this function models growth.

Exponential Growth

Exponential growth can be modeled by the function

$$y = a \cdot b^x \text{ with } a > 0 \text{ and } b > 1.$$

a = the starting amount when $x = 0$.
b = is the growth factor and is greater than one.
x is the exponent.

Go Online
PHSchool.com

Visit: PHSchool.com
Web Code: ayp-0260

EXAMPLES 1 and 2 **Solving problems involving exponential growth**

1 If the population of Ontario County, New York, was 102,500 in 2003 and has been increasing at an average rate of 2.2% per year, find the projected population of the county in 2010.

■ **SOLUTION**

To determine the population of Ontario County, we can use the following formula.

Current population
↓
$P = 102{,}500(1.022)^x$ ⟶ **Number of years since 2003**
↑
Growth rate

$P = 102{,}500(1.022)^7 = 1.193658612 \cdot 10^5 \approx 119{,}366 \text{ people}$

2 Suppose that you deposit $1,000 in a savings account that pays 5.6% interest compounded annually. Write an equation to model the account balance, and determine what the balance will be after 4 years.

■ **SOLUTION**

$A = 1{,}000(1.056)^t$
$A = 1{,}000(1.056)^t = 1{,}000(1.056)^4 = 1{,}243.528298 \approx \$1{,}243.53$

A function in the form $y = a \cdot b^x$ where a is greater than zero and b is between zero and one models exponential decay.

Exponential Decay

Exponential decay can be modeled by the function

$$y = a \cdot b^x \text{ with } a > 0 \text{ and } 0 < b < 1.$$

a = the starting amount when $x = 0$.
b = is the decay factor and is between zero and one.
x is the exponent.

The radioactive half-life of a substance is the length of time it takes for one half of the substance to decay.

Go Online
PHSchool.com
Visit: PHSchool.com
Web Code: ayp-0262

EXAMPLE 3   **Solving problems involving half-life with exponential decay**

 Radioactive iodine is used to treat some medical conditions. The half-life of iodine-131 is 8 days. A doctor administers a 12-unit treatment to a patient. How much iodine-131 is left in the patient after 24 days?

■ **SOLUTION**

In 24 days, there are three 8-day half-lives.
After one half-life, there are **6 units.**
After the second half-life, there are **3 units.**
Finally, after the third half-life, there are **1.5 units.**

This result can also be obtained in the following way:
$y = 12(0.5)^3 = 1.5$

Note

When a quantity is decreased by 10%, the result is 90% of the original quantity. When thinking of the decay factor, think of 100% minus the percent by which the quantity is decreasing.

You can also use exponential decay to model a decrease in population.

EXAMPLES 4 and 5   **Solving problems involving population decrease with exponential decay**

 An antidote is introduced into a colony of bacteria that contains 1 million bacteria. If the antidote reduces the population by 25% every hour, what is the population after 24 hours?

■ **SOLUTION**

1,000,000	← **This is the initial bacteria population.**
$1 - 0.25 = 0.75$	← **This is the decay factor.**
$1,000,000(0.75)^x$	← **This equation models the declining population.**
$1,000,000(0.75)^{24}$	← **This equation models the population after 24 hours.**
$1,000,000(0.75)^{24} = 1,003.3912$	← **This is the population after 24 hours.**
$\approx 1,003$	

5 In 2000, the population of Someplace was 702,000 people. The population decreases about 1.7% per year. Predict the population of Someplace in 2010.

■ **SOLUTION**

702,000	← **This is the initial number of people.**
$1 - 0.017 = 0.983$	← **This is the decay factor.**
$y = 702,000(0.983)^x$	← **This equation models the population since 2000.**
$y = 702,000(0.983)^x$	
$= 702,000(0.983)^{10}$	
$= 591,387.70$	
$\approx 591,388$	← **This is the projected population in 2010.**

You can determine the equation of a function given a set of data.

EXAMPLE 6   Determining a function that models given data

6 The data from the table are shown in the accompanying scatter plot. Write an equation to model the data.

x	y
−1	12
0	6
1	3
2	1.5
3	0.75
4	0.375
5	0.1875

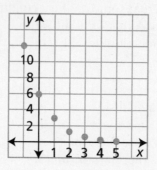

■ SOLUTION

The graph of the data suggests an exponential model. Test for a common ratio.

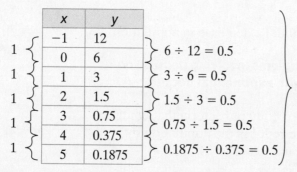

x	y
−1	12
0	6
1	3
2	1.5
3	0.75
4	0.375
5	0.1875

$6 \div 12 = 0.5$

$3 \div 6 = 0.5$

$1.5 \div 3 = 0.5$

$0.75 \div 1.5 = 0.5$

$0.1875 \div 0.375 = 0.5$

The common ratio is 0.5.

The initial value $y = 6$ when $x = 0$ determines the value of a.
The common ratio determines the decay factor. Therefore, the equation that models this data is $y = 6\left(\frac{1}{2}\right)^x = 6(0.5)^x$.

Practice

Choose the letter preceding the word or expression that best completes the statement or answers the question.

1 Which of the following is an exponential decay function with an initial amount of 2?

A. $y = 5 \cdot 4^x$

C. $y = 2(0.75)^x$

B. $g(x) = \frac{1}{2}(3)^x$

D. $f(t) = \frac{3}{4}\left(\frac{2}{3}\right)^t$

In Exercises 2–6, use the following information.

Suppose that the population of a city is 75,000 and is growing 2.5% per year.

2 What is the initial amount a?

3 What is the growth factor b?

4 What do you multiply 75,000 by to find the population after one year?

5 Write an equation to find the population after x years.

6 Use the equation to predict the population after 25 years.

In Exercises 7–11, use the following information.

Suppose that the population of a large city was 8,000,000 six years ago, but since then it has been declining at an average rate of 1.75% per year.

7 What is the initial amount *a*?

8 What is the decay factor *b*?

9 Write an equation to find the population after *x* years.

10 Use the equation to predict the population after 6 years.

11 The value of a new car decreases exponentially at a rate of 15% per year. A new car has an initial value of $24,000. What is the value of the car after 5 years?

In Exercises 12–17, identify the functions as *linear*, *exponential*, or *neither*.

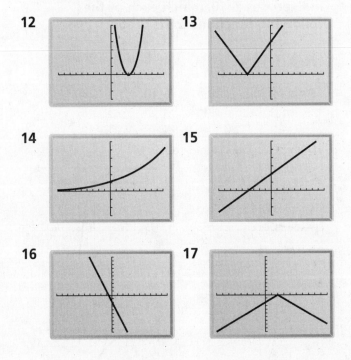

In Exercises 18–25, solve the problem. Clearly show all necessary work.

18 Write an exponential equation to represent the growth of an account with a $4,000 principal that earns a rate of 4.5% compounded annually.

19 Determine whether the data in the accompanying table represent a linear, absolute value, or exponential function. Explain your reasoning.

x	y
1	3
2	9
3	27
4	81

20 If the half-life of a certain compound is eight hours, how many half-lives occur in a two-day period?

21 The half-life of a certain substance is four days. If you have 100 grams of the substance, how much of it will remain after twelve days?

22 Suppose that a town had a population of 1,250 people in 2001. Over the next five years, however, the population decreased at an average rate of 1.3% per year. At this rate, what will be the town's population in the year 2010?

23 A common bacteria grows at a rate described by the function $B(t) = (3)^t$ where *t* is number of hours. How many bacteria are expected to have grown after 7 hours?

24 The amount in grams of a radioactive substance is given by the function $y = 50(1.7)^{-0.3t}$ where *t* is time in years. Find the number of grams of the substance after 20 years.

25 New vehicles lose value at a rate of 18.5% per year. Write an equation to calculate the value of a vehicle with an original value of $21,000 after *t* years.

DIRECTIONS FOR QUESTIONS 1–18: For each of the questions below, select the answer choice that is best for each case.

1 Which of the following statements is true?

   A. Any number raised to the zero power is zero.

   B. Any number raised to a negative power is a negative number.

   C. The product of two powers with the same base equals the base raised to the sum of the powers.

   D. The quotient of two powers with the same base equals the base raised to the quotient of the powers.

2 Determine the value of $\dfrac{-5x^3y^5}{15x^{-7}y^5z^{-2}}$ when $x = -1, y = 5,$ and $z = 3$.

   A. -9 C. -1

   B. -3 D. 0

3 Determine the value of $\dfrac{-6a^{-2}bc^6}{24a^3c^{-4}}$ when $a = 2, b = 4,$ and $c = -1$.

   A. -32 C. -2

   B. $\frac{1}{2}$ D. $-\frac{1}{32}$

4 Which of the following best describes the graph below?

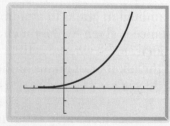

   A. Linear growth

   B. Exponential growth

   C. Exponential decay

   D. Quadratic growth

5 What are the first four terms of the recursive sequence $a_n = a_{n-1} + 3$ when $a_1 = 1$?

   A. $1, 3, 5, 6$ C. $3, 4, 5, 6$

   B. $1, 4, 7, 10$ D. $4, 7, 10, 13$

6 What is the explicit formula for the sequence $3, 6, 9, 12, 15$?

   A. $a_n = a_{n-1} + 3$

   B. $a_n = 3a_{n-1}$

   C. $f(n) = n + 3$

   D. $f(n) = 3n$

In Exercises 7–10, match each of the following functions to its graph.

7 $y = \left(\dfrac{1}{4}\right)^x$ **8** $y = -2(4^x)$

9 $y = 3^x$ **10** $y = -(6^x)$

A.

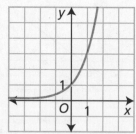

C.

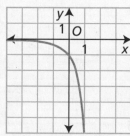

B.

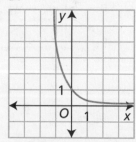

D.

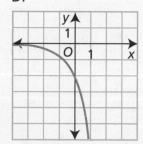

In Exercises 11–16, simplify each expression.

11 $(-3)^{-3}$

    A. 27

    B. $-\frac{1}{27}$

    C. $-\frac{1}{9}$

    D. $\frac{1}{27}$

12 $\dfrac{9a^2b^{-3}}{18a^5b^{-5}}$

    A. $2a^3b^8$

    B. $\dfrac{a^7}{2b^8}$

    C. $\dfrac{-9}{a^3b^2}$

    D. $\dfrac{b^2}{2a^3}$

13 $(z^3s^{-5}q^2)^0$

    A. 1

    B. zsq

    C. $\dfrac{z^3q^2}{s^5}$

    D. 0

14 $(2wz^2)(3wz^3)^2$

    A. $18w^2z^{12}$

    B. $18w^3z^8$

    C. $36w^4z^{10}$

    D. $12w^3z^7$

15 Which is equivalent to $\dfrac{1.92 \times 10^5}{2 \times 10^{-4}}$?

    A. -0.08×10^1

    B. 0.096×10^0

    C. 0.96×10^9

    D. 9.6×10^{-9}

16 Which is equivalent to $2000(1.27 \times 10^0)$?

    A. 2540×10^1

    B. 0.00254×10^0

    C. 2.54×10^3

    D. 2.54×10^{-3}

In Exercises 17–18, use the following information.

20% of a particular medicine is absorbed by the bloodstream every hour. A patient takes a 40 milligram dose of this medicine at 9 A.M.

17 Which function describes the amount of medicine absorbed in the bloodstream after x hours?

    A. $y = 20(40)^x$

    B. $\dfrac{1}{32}$

    C. $y = 40(0.8)^x$

    D. $y = 40(0.20)^x$

18 How many milligrams of medicine is absorbed in the bloodstream at 2 P.M.?

    A. 13.11 mg

    B. 160 mg

    C. 0.0128 mg

    D. 4,000 mg

19 Which of the following is not an exponential function?

    A. $5^x - 3$

    B. $3\left(\dfrac{5}{2}\right)^x$

    C. $5x^3$

    D. $(0.25)^x$

20 Which exponential equation represents exponential decay?

    A. $y = 0.5(1.5)^x$

    B. $y = 1.5(3)^x$

    C. $y = \dfrac{7}{2}(2)^x$

    D. $y = 3\left(\dfrac{2}{7}\right)^x$

DIRECTIONS FOR 21–23: Solve each problem and show your work.

21 In the 2004 presidential election, George W. Bush received 62,040,610 votes, John Kerry received 59,028,111 votes, and other candidates received 1,224,611 votes.

- Express the number of votes received by Bush in scientific notation.

- Express the number of votes received by Kerry in scientific notation.

- Express the number of votes received by Bush as a percentage of total votes in scientific notation.

- Express the number of votes received by Kerry as a percentage of total votes in scientific notation.

22 Suppose that you deposit $750 in a savings account that pays 4.8% interest compounded annually.

- Identify the initial amount.

- Identify the growth factor.

- Write an exponential growth equation that models the interest earned on the savings account.

- Assuming no withdrawals or additional deposits, what is the balance after six years?

23 A sequence is defined explicitly by the formula $f(n) = 4(n + 1)$.

- Determine the first five values in the sequence.

- Write a recursive formula for this sequence.

5 Polynomials and Factoring

Discovering New Jersey

The First Drive-In Theater

Richard Hollingshead, an inventor from Riverton, opened the first drive-in theater in the world, on June 6, 1933 in Camden New Jersey.

Approximately 600 people came to opening night. The cost for the movie was 25 cents per car and 25 cents per person, with a maximum of one dollar per carload. People remained in their cars as they watched a movie shown on a large outdoor screen. Speakers mounted next to the movie screen provided adequate sound for the movie.

Drive-ins became very popular around the country, and the number of theaters rose very quickly. The popularity of drive-ins waned over the years, and the majority of theaters closed, but the nostalgia of drive-in theaters remains and their popularity is growing again.

5.1 Addition and Subtraction of Polynomials

New Jersey Standards

4.3.D.1.1 Add and subtract polynomials

A single-term algebraic expression is called a **monomial.** A monomial is the product of real numbers and variables with nonnegative exponents.

EXAMPLE 1   Recognizing monomials

 Which of the following are monomials?

   A. $-3abc$ **B.** $\frac{4}{x}$ **C.** $-2r^2s$ **D.** $\frac{2}{3x}$ **E.** xy^{-2}

■ **SOLUTION**

$-3abc$ and $-2r^2s$ are monomials. $\frac{4}{x}, \frac{2}{3x}$, and xy^{-2} are not because each has an unknown value in the denominator.

> **Note**
>
> No monomial may have a variable in the denominator because it may result in values for which the expression is undefined.

Recall that the number in front of the variable, or numerical factor, is called the **numerical coefficient** of the term, or **coefficient.**

Expression	Coefficient
$3x^2$	3
$-4y$	-4
$\frac{5c}{6}$	$\frac{5}{6}$

If no coefficient is indicated, then it is understood to be 1. For example, abc^2 has a numerical coefficient of 1.

Terms that have the same variable factors are **like terms.** Monomials with the same like terms can be combined.

EXAMPLES 2 and 3   Combining monomials

 Can the terms $7x^3y^2$ and $-3x^3y^2$ be combined? Explain why or why not and describe the resulting expression.

■ **SOLUTION**

$7x^3y^2$ and $-3x^3y^2$ can be combined because x^3 and y^2 are the same in both monomials. We apply the rule for addition of signed numbers on the coefficients and attach the variable expressions. So $7x^3y^2$ and $-3x^3y^2$ become $(7-3)x^3y^2$, or the monomial $4x^3y^2$.

3 Can the terms $2xy$ and y be combined?

■ **SOLUTION**

The monomials $2xy$ and y cannot be combined because one monomial has x and y as its variables and the second monomial has only y. Therefore, the monomials are not like terms. The resulting expression will remain $2xy + y$.

A **polynomial** is a monomial or a sum of monomials. Each of the monomials is a term of the polynomial. To write a polynomial in its simplest form, you must combine any like terms.

EXAMPLES 4 and 5   **Simplifying a polynomial**

4 Simplify $3a - 2ab + 4a$.

- **SOLUTION**

$$3a - 2ab + 4a$$
$$[3a + 4a] - 2ab \quad \leftarrow \text{Group like terms.}$$
$$7a - 2ab \quad \leftarrow \text{Add the coefficients of } a.$$

5 Simplify $5r^2s + 10rs^2 - 8r^2s$.

- **SOLUTION**

$$5r^2s + 10rs^2 - 8r^2s$$
$$[5r^2s - 8r^2s] + 10rs^2 \quad \leftarrow \text{Group like terms.}$$
$$-3r^2s + 10rs^2 \quad \leftarrow \text{Subtract the coefficients of } r^2s.$$

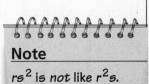

Note

rs^2 is *not* like r^2s.

A polynomial in one variable is written in *descending order* when the powers of the variable decrease from left to right. It is written in *ascending order* when the powers of the variable increase from left to right. When a polynomial in one variable has no like terms, and the terms are written in descending order, the polynomial is said to be in **standard form**.

EXAMPLE 6   **Writing a polynomial in standard form**

6 Write $-8 + 4x^2 + 5 - 3x^2 + 2x$ in standard form.

- **SOLUTION**

$$-8 + 4x^2 + 5 - 3x^2 + 2x$$
$$(-8 + 5) + (4x^2 - 3x^2) + 2x \quad \leftarrow \text{Group like terms.}$$
$$-3 \quad + \quad 1x^2 \quad + 2x \quad \leftarrow \text{Simplify.}$$
$$x^2 + 2x - 3 \quad \leftarrow \text{Use descending order: } x^2 + 2x^1 - 3x^0$$

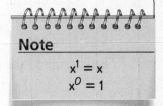

Note

$x^1 = x$
$x^0 = 1$

You can classify some polynomials by their number of terms. Polynomials with one, two, or three terms have special names.

Classifying Polynomials by Number of Terms		
Number of Terms	**Classification**	**Examples**
one	monomial	m, n^5, xy, $-5ab^2$, r^2st^3, 9
two	binomial	$3x + 4y$, $jk - 3$, $a^2 + 7a$, $p^3qr - 5p^2q^4$
three	trinomial	$r + s - t$, $-4x^2 + 8xy - 5y^2$, $a^2 + 2a - 6$

Go Online
PHSchool.com
Visit: PHSchool.com
Web Code: ayp-0133

EXAMPLE 7   **Classifying polynomials by number of terms**

7 Classify $4x + 7$ as a monomial, binomial, or trinomial.

- **SOLUTION**

$4x + 7$ has 2 terms; therefore, it is a **binomial**.

If a term of a polynomial has just one variable, the **degree of the term** is the exponent of the variable. A term that has no variable part is called a **constant term,** or simply a **constant.** The degree of a constant term is 0.

$$10k^4 \rightarrow \text{The degree is } 4.$$
$$-2t = -2t^1 \rightarrow \text{The degree is } 1.$$
$$6 = 6x^0 \rightarrow \text{The degree is } 0.$$

The **degree of a polynomial** is the greatest degree of any of its terms after it has been simplified. The term with the greatest degree is called the **leading term** of the polynomial. The coefficient of the leading term is called the **leading coefficient.**

Identifying the degree provides another means for classifying polynomials.

Note

When the term of a polynomial has more than one variable, the degree of the term is the sum of the exponents of the variables of the leading term.

$5x^4y^2 \rightarrow$ The degree is 6.

Classifying Polynomials by Degree		
Degree of Polynomial	Classification	Examples
one	linear	$x,\ -6d,\ 5s - 3,\ 7 + 8y$
two	quadratic	$x^2,\ 3m^2,\ 9z^2 + 3z,\ k - k^2,\ 4 - 2g + 6g^2$
three	cubic	$x^3,\ -8b^3 + 5b,\ 4b^3 - b^2 + 7b + 6$

EXAMPLES 8 and 9 Classifying polynomials by number of term and degree

Go Online
PHSchool.com
Visit: PHSchool.com
Web Code: ayp-0263

8 Which phrase best describes $-z^3 + 3z^2 - 2z - 3z^2$?

    A. cubic trinomial   **C.** cubic monomial
    B. quadratic trinomial   **D.** cubic binomial

▪ SOLUTION

First simplify the polynomial.
$$-z^3 + 3z^2 - 2z - 3z^2$$
$$-z^3 + (3z^2 - 3z^2) - 2z$$
$$-z^3 + 0 - 2z$$
$$-z^3 - 2z$$

The simplified polynomial has two terms, so it is a *binomial*.
The greatest degree of any of its terms is 3, so it is *cubic*.
The correct choice is D.

9 Which phrase best describes $9x^2y + 3x^2 - 2x^2y - 5xy^2 - 4x^2$?

    A. quadratic binomial   **C.** cubic binomial
    B. quadratic trinomial   **D.** cubic trinomial

▪ SOLUTION

First simplify the polynomial.
$$9x^2y + 3x^2 - 2x^2y - 5xy^2 - 4x^2$$
$$-5xy^2 + (9x^2y - 2x^2y) + (3x^2 - 4x^2)$$
$$-5xy^2 + 7x^2y - x^2$$

The simplified polynomial has 3 terms, so it is a *trinomial*.
The greatest degree of any of its terms is 3, so it is *cubic*.
The correct choice is D.

To find a sum of polynomials, you add the like terms from all the polynomials. You can do this using either a horizontal or vertical format.

Go Online
PHSchool.com
Visit: PHSchool.com
Web Code: ayp-0135

EXAMPLES 10 and 11 **Adding polynomials**

Simplify each expression.

10 $(3x + x^2 - x^3) + (4x^3 + 2x^2 + 5x)$

■ SOLUTION 1
Group like terms.
Then add their coefficients.

$(3x + x^2 - x^3) + (4x^3 + 2x^2 + 5x)$
$= (-x^3 + 4x^3) + (x^2 + 2x^2) + (3x + 5x)$
$= 3x^3 + 3x^2 + 8x$

■ SOLUTION 2
Line up like terms in columns.
Then add their coefficients.

$$\begin{array}{r} -x^3 + x^2 + 3x \\ + 4x^3 + 2x^2 + 5x \\ \hline 3x^3 + 3x^2 + 8x \end{array}$$

11 $(3n^2 - 2n) + (-5n^3 + n^2) + (2n - 5)$

■ SOLUTION 1
$(3n^2 - 2n) + (-5n^3 + n^2) + (2n - 5)$
$= -5n^3 + (3n^2 + n^2) + (-2n + 2n) - 5$
$= -5n^3 + 4n^2 - 5$

■ SOLUTION 2
$$\begin{array}{r} 3n^2 - 2n \\ -5n^3 + n^2 \\ + 2n - 5 \\ \hline -5n^3 + 4n^2 - 5 \end{array}$$

To subtract one polynomial from another, you add the opposite, or additive inverse. In order to do this, it will be helpful to first review the procedure for finding the additive inverse of a polynomial.

EXAMPLE 12 **Finding the additive inverse of a polynomial**

12 Find the additive inverse of $-6a^3 - 5a^2 + 3a + 1$.

■ SOLUTION
The sum of a number and its additive inverse is 0.
Find the polynomial that gives a sum of 0 when added to $-6a^3 - 5a^2 + 3a + 1$.

$$\begin{array}{r} -6a^3 - 5a^2 + 3a + 1 \\ + ? \\ \hline 0 \end{array} \quad \rightarrow \quad \begin{array}{r} -6a^3 - 5a^2 + 3a + 1 \\ + 6a^3 + 5a^2 - 3a - 1 \\ \hline 0 \end{array} \quad \begin{array}{l} \text{Write the opposite} \\ \leftarrow \text{of each term.} \end{array}$$

So the additive inverse of $-6a^3 - 5a^2 + 3a + 1$ is $6a^3 + 5a^2 - 3a - 1$.

You can find the additive inverse of a polynomial by finding the additive inverse of each term.

Opposites of Sums and Differences

For all real numbers a and b: $-(a + b) = -a + (-b) = -a - b$

$-(a - b) = -a + b$

Just as with addition, you can find a difference of polynomials using either a horizontal or vertical format.

 **Go Online**
PHSchool.com
Visit: PHSchool.com
Web Code: ayp-0136

EXAMPLES 13 and 14   **Subtracting polynomials**

13 Simplify $(3c^2 - 8c + 4) - (7 + c^2 - 8c)$.

■ **SOLUTION 1**

Change the subtraction to addition. Then write the opposite of each term of the polynomial being subtracted. Finally, combine like terms.

$(3c^2 - 8c + 4) - (7 + c^2 - 8c)$
$= (3c^2 - 8c + 4) + (-7 - c^2 + 8c)$
$= (3c^2 - c^2) + (-8c + 8c) + (4 - 7)$
$= 2c^2 - 3$

■ **SOLUTION 2**

Line up like terms in columns. Write the opposite of each term of the polynomial being subtracted. Finally, combine like terms.

$$\begin{array}{r} 3c^2 - 8c + 4 \\ + \underline{-c^2 + 8c - 7} \\ 2c^2 - 3 \end{array}$$

14 Simplify the result when $(5d^2 - 2d^3 + 3)$ is subtracted from $(d^2 + 8 - 5d)$.

■ **SOLUTION 1**

Subtract horizontally.

$(d^2 + 8 - 5d) - (5d^2 - 2d^3 + 3)$
$= (d^2 + 8 - 5d) + (-5d^2 + 2d^3 - 3)$
$= 2d^3 + (d^2 - 5d^2) - 5d + (8 - 3)$
$= 2d^3 - 4d^2 - 5d + 5$

■ **SOLUTION 2**

Subtract vertically.

$$\begin{array}{r} d^2 - 5d + 8 \\ + \underline{2d^3 - 5d^2 - 3} \\ 2d^3 - 4d^2 - 5d + 5 \end{array}$$

Practice

Choose the letter preceding the word or expression that best completes the statement or answers the question.

1 Which best describes $-3x^2 + 3 - x + 3x^2$?

   A. quadratic expression with four terms

   B. linear binomial

   C. polynomial with degree 2

   D. not a polynomial

2 Which is a quadratic binomial when written in simplest form?

   A. $(-z^2 + 3z) + (-z^2 - 3z)$

   B. $(-z^2 + 3z) + (z^2 - 3z)$

   C. $(-z^2 - 3z) + (-z^2 - 3z)$

   D. $(-z^2 + 3z) + (z^2 + 3z)$

3 Which polynomial added to $3d^2 - 3d + 1$ will result in a sum of 0?

   A. $-3d^2 - 3d + 1$

   B. $-3d^2 + 3d + 1$

   C. $-3d^2 + 3d - 1$

   D. $3d^2 - 3d + 1$

4 What is the result when $2c^2 - 3c + 6$ is subtracted from $c^2 + c - 2$?

   A. $c^2 - 4c + 8$

   B. $-c^2 - 2c + 4$

   C. $c^2 + 4c + 8$

   D. $-c^2 + 4c - 8$

5 The perimeter of a polygon is the sum of the lengths of its sides. Which does not represent the perimeter of the polygon below?

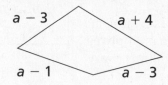

A. $(a - 3) + (a - 3) + (a - 1) + (a + 4)$

B. $2(a - 3) + (a - 1) + (a + 4)$

C. $4a + 3$

D. $4a - 3$

In Exercises 6–9, simplify each expression.

6 $yz^3 + 2y^3z - 4yz^3 - y^3z$

7 $5m^2n^2 - 4mn^2 - 9m^2n + 7mn^2$

8 $-4a^2b^2 + 3ab - a^3b - 8ba$

9 $2c^2d - 6d - 7d + 3cd^2 + c^4$

In Exercises 10–15, write each polynomial in standard form.

10 $y^2 - 7y - 3y^3$

11 $4b^3 + 1 - b + 9b^2$

12 $3x^2 - 2x + 5x - 6x^3$

13 $v^2 + v - 3v^3 - v^2$

14 $-7q^2 + 2q + 3q^2 - 2q + 5q^2$

15 $4w - 3w^2 + 7w^3 - w^3 - 7$

In Exercises 16–21, classify each polynomial by its degree and by its number of terms.

16 $3d^2$

17 $y^2 - 3y - 7$

18 $-g - 4g^3 + 5g$

19 $5d + 9$

20 $2m^2 + 3m^3 - 2m - 5m^2$

21 $b^3 - 2b - b^3 - 2b$

In Exercises 22–37, simplify each expression. Write answers in standard form.

22 $(n^3 + 8n^2 + 6n) + (8n^3 + 2n^2 - 6n)$

23 $(5s^2 + 7s - 11) + (4 + s - 5s^2)$

24 $(x^4 + x - 2) + (2x^4 + x^3 - 5)$

25 $(3a + 4a^3 - 8) + (a^2 + 2a - 7)$

26 $(3y^3 + 8y - 3) + (2y - 5y^2)$

27 $(-4r^3 + 2r - 3r^2 + 1) + (2r^3 - 5r + 1)$

28 $(5h^2 + 4h + 8) - (3h^2 + h + 3)$

29 $(-7z^3 + 2z - 7) - (2z^3 - z - 3)$

30 $(3c^2 + 4c - 6) - (3c - 8 + 5c^2)$

31 $(-a^2 - 3 + 7a) - (2a^3 - 7a)$

32 $(n^3 + n^2) - (2n^3 + 3n^2 - 2n)$

33 $(-2w^3 - 9 + 8w) - (2w^4 + 6w^3 - 11w^2)$

34 $(x^2 + 5) + (3x + 8) + (5x^2 + 3x)$

35 $(5j^2 + 3j) + (j^2 + 4j + 4) - (2j - 3)$

36 $(-5p^3 + 6p) - (2p^3 + 8p^2) + (6p + 2p^3)$

37 $(2z^2 - 4) - (z^2 - 4) - (-3z^2 - 2)$

In Exercises 38–42, solve the problem. Clearly show all necessary work.

38 Find the difference when $x^2 + 8 - 2x$ is subtracted from $2x - 10x^2 + 7$.

39 Is $2x^{-3} + x^2 + x - 4$ a polynomial? Explain your answer.

40 The perimeter of a polygon is the sum of the lengths of its sides. Write a simplified expression for the perimeter of this polygon.

$m + n$

$2m + 3$ $4m - 2$

$3m + 15$

41 The perimeter of the polygon below can be represented by the expression $12t - 5$. Write a simplified expression for the length of the side that is not labeled.

$4t + 10$

$2t + 5$ $3t - 4$

42 Is the sum of two binomials always a binomial? Explain your answer.

5.2 Multiplication and Division with Polynomials

New Jersey Standards

4.3.D.1.2 Multiply polynomials

4.3.D.1.3 Divide polynomials

Recall that a polynomial is simply the sum of monomials; therefore, the same rules that apply for multiplication of monomials also apply when multiplying a polynomial by a monomial. Use the distributive property to multiply every term of the polynomial by the monomial.

EXAMPLES 1 through 3   **Multiplying a polynomial by a monomial: one variable**

Simplify each expression.

1 $3(5z - 6)$

■ **SOLUTION**

$3(5z - 6)$	**Use the distributive**
$3(5z) - 3(6)$	← **property.**
$15z - 3(6)$	← Simplify $3(5z)$.
$15z - 18$	← Simplify $3(6)$.

2 $-7a(-2a + 9)$

■ **SOLUTION**

$-7a(-2a + 9)$
$(-7a)(-2a) + (-7a)(9)$
$14a^2 + (-63a)$
$14a^2 - 63a$

3 $2xy(-3x + 2y - 4)$

■ **SOLUTION**

$2xy(-3x + 2y - 4)$
$2xy(-3x) + 2xy(2y) - 2xy(4)$
$-6x^2y + 4xy^2 - 8xy$

Sometimes you must multiply polynomials before solving an equation.

EXAMPLES 4 and 5   **Multiplying polynomials in equation solving**

Go Online

PHSchool.com

Visit: PHSchool.com

Web Code: ayp-0269

4   Solve $(3b^2 + 2b - 1) - 3b(b + 5) = 12$.

■ **SOLUTION**

$$(3b^2 + 2b - 1) - 3b(b + 5) = 12$$
$$(3b^2 + 2b - 1) + (-3b)(b + 5) = 12 \quad \leftarrow \textbf{Rewrite the subtraction as addition.}$$
$$(3b^2 + 2b - 1) + (-3b)(b) + (-3b)(5) = 12 \quad \leftarrow \textbf{Apply the distributive property.}$$
$$(3b^2 + 2b - 1) + (-3b^2) + (-15b) = 12 \quad \leftarrow \textbf{Simplify } (-3b)(b) \text{ and } (-3b)(5).$$
$$[3b^2 + (-3b^2)] + [2b + (-15b)] - 1 = 12 \quad \leftarrow \textbf{Combine like terms.}$$
$$-13b - 1 = 12 \quad \leftarrow \textbf{Solve.}$$
$$-13b = 13$$
$$b = -1$$

5   Solve $3(2m^2 + 5) = 3m(2m + 7) - 3m - 3$.

■ **SOLUTION**

$$3(2m^2 + 5) = 3m(2m + 7) - 3m - 3$$
$$3(2m^2) + 3(5) = 3m(2m) + 3m(7) - 3m - 3 \quad \leftarrow \textbf{Apply the distributive property.}$$
$$6m^2 + 15 = 6m^2 + 21m - 3m - 3 \quad \leftarrow \textbf{Simplify.}$$
$$6m^2 + 15 = 6m^2 + 18m - 3 \quad \leftarrow \textbf{Combine like terms.}$$
$$6m^2 - 6m^2 + 15 = 6m^2 - 6m^2 + 18m - 3 \quad \leftarrow \textbf{Solve.}$$
$$15 + 3 = 18m - 3 + 3$$
$$18 = 18m$$
$$1 = m$$

To multiply a polynomial by a binomial, you must apply the distributive property more than once. You begin by distributing the first term in the binomial factor to each term in the polynomial, and then you distribute the second term in the binomial factor to each term in the polynomial.

Go Online
PHSchool.com
Visit: PHSchool.com
Web Code: ayp-0270

EXAMPLES 6 and 7   **Multiplying by a binomial**

Simplify each expression.

6 $(2y - 3)(y + 2)$

■ **SOLUTION 1**

Multiply horizontally.

$$(2y - 3)(y + 2)$$
$(2y - 3)y + (2y - 3)2$ ← **Distribute** $(2y - 3)$.
$2y^2 - 3y + (2y - 3)2$ ← **Simplify** $(2y - 3)y$.
$2y^2 - 3y + 4y - 6$ ← **Simplify** $(2y - 3)2$.
$2y^2 + y - 6$ ← **Combine like terms.**

■ **SOLUTION 2**

Multiply vertically.

$$
\begin{array}{r}
2y - 3 \\
\times \quad y + 2 \\
\hline
4y - 6 \\
2y^2 - 3y \quad\quad \\
\hline
2y^2 + y - 6
\end{array}
$$
← **Multiply** $2(2y - 3)$.
← **Multiply** $y(2y - 3)$.
← **Combine like terms.**

7 $(n + 4)(2n^2 - 3n + 3)$

■ **SOLUTION 1**

Multiply horizontally.

$$(n + 4)(2n^2 - 3n + 3)$$
$n(2n^2 - 3n + 3) + 4(2n^2 - 3n + 3)$
$2n^3 - 3n^2 + 3n + 4(2n^2 - 3n + 3)$
$2n^3 - 3n^2 + 3n + 8n^2 - 12n + 12$
$2n^3 + 5n^2 - 9n + 12$

■ **SOLUTION 2**

Multiply vertically.

$$
\begin{array}{r}
2n^2 - 3n + 3 \\
\times \quad\quad\quad n + 4 \\
\hline
8n^2 - 12n + 12 \\
2n^3 - 3n^2 + 3n \quad\quad\quad \\
\hline
2n^2 + 5n^2 - 9n + 12
\end{array}
$$

You may also need to multiply polynomials before you can simplify an algebraic expression.

Go Online
PHSchool.com
Visit: PHSchool.com
Web Code: ayp-0939

EXAMPLE 8   **Using multiplication to simplify a polynomial**

8 Simplify the expression $(b^2 + 2b - 1) - (b - 5)(b + 6)$.

■ **SOLUTION**

$(b^2 + 2b - 1) - (b - 5)(b + 6)$
$(b^2 + 2b - 1) - [(b - 5)b + (b - 5)6]$ ← **Distribute** $(b - 5)$.
$(b^2 + 2b - 1) - [b^2 - 5b + (b - 5)6]$ ← **Simplify** $(b - 5)b$.
$(b^2 + 2b - 1) - [b^2 - 5b + 6b - 30]$ ← **Simplify** $(b - 5)6$.
$(b^2 + 2b - 1) - [b^2 + b - 30]$ ← **Combine like terms** $-5b$ and $6b$.
$(b^2 + 2b - 1) - b^2 - b + 30$ ← **Distribute** -1.
$b + 29$ ← **Combine like terms.**

When you use the Distributive Property to multiply binomials. You can use the letters in the word FOIL to help you remember which terms of two binomials are multiplied.

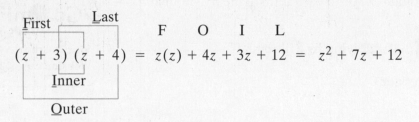

$$\begin{array}{cccccc} & \text{F} & \text{O} & \text{I} & \text{L} \\ (z + 3)(z + 4) = & z(z) & + 4z & + 3z & + 12 & = z^2 + 7z + 12 \end{array}$$

A special product, called a **perfect square trinomial**, results when a binomial is squared. Another pattern emerges, called the **difference of two squares,** when you multiply the sum of two terms by the difference of the same two terms. Look for the patterns in the following examples.

Go Online
PHSchool.com

Visit: PHSchool.com
Web Code: ayp-0271

EXAMPLES 9 and 10   **Squaring a binomial**

Simplify each expression.

 9 $(c + 4)^2 = (c + 4)(c + 4)$

■ **SOLUTION**

$$c^2 + 4c + 4c + 4^2$$
$$c^2 + 2(4c) + 4^2$$
$$c^2 + 8c + 16$$

10 $(m + 5)(m - 5)$

■ **SOLUTION**

$$m^2 + (-5m) + 5m + 5(-5)$$
$$m^2 + 0m + (-25)$$
$$m^2 - 25$$

These patterns are often generalized as follows.

Squaring Patterns of Binomials

For all real numbers a and b: $(a + b)^2 = a^2 + 2ab + b^2$
$$(a - b)^2 = a^2 - 2ab + b^2$$
$$(a + b)(a - b) = a^2 - b^2$$

The same rules that apply for division of monomials will apply for division of a polynomial by a monomial. Every term of the polynomial in the numerator will be divided by the monomial in the denominator.

For all real numbers a and b and all nonzero real numbers c,

$$\frac{a + b}{c} = \frac{a}{c} + \frac{b}{c} \quad \text{and} \quad \frac{a - b}{c} = \frac{a}{c} - \frac{b}{c}.$$

$$\frac{2 + 5}{9} = \frac{2}{9} + \frac{5}{9} = \frac{7}{9} \quad \text{and} \quad \frac{8 - 3}{7} = \frac{8}{7} - \frac{3}{7} = \frac{5}{7}$$

EXAMPLES 11 and 12   **Dividing a polynomial by a monomial**

Simplify each expression.

11 $\dfrac{8a^2 - 12a}{4a}$

   ■ **SOLUTION**

   $\dfrac{8a^2 - 12a}{4a}$

   $\dfrac{8a^2}{4a} - \dfrac{12a}{4a}$ ← **Divide each term by $4a$.**

     $2a - 3$

12 $\dfrac{16yz^2 - 8y^2z + 10yz}{-2yz}$

   ■ **SOLUTION**

   $\dfrac{16yz^2 - 8y^2z + 10yz}{-2yz}$

   $\dfrac{16yz^2}{-2yz} - \dfrac{8y^2z}{-2yz} + \dfrac{10yz}{-2yz}$ ← **Divide each term by $-2yz$.**

     $-8z - (-4y) + (-5)$

     $-8z + 4y - 5$

Practice

Choose the letter preceding the word or expression that best completes the statement or answers the question.

1   The expression $(s - 3)^2$ is equivalent to

   A. $s^2 + 9$ **C.** $s^2 + 6s + 9$

   B. $s^2 - 9$ **D.** $s^2 - 6s + 9$

2   The product of $4g^3 + 4g^2 + 2g$ and $2g$ is

   A. $2g^2 + 2g$ **C.** $8g^2 + 8g + 4$

   B. $2g^2 + 2g + 1$ **D.** $8g^4 + 8g^3 + 4g^2$

3   Which is equivalent to $23^2 - 13^2$?

   A. 10^2 **C.** 36^2

   B. 10×36 **D.** $2(23 - 13)$

4   Which is the value of $\dfrac{6a^4 - 2a^3 - 2a^2}{2a^2}$ when $a = -2$?

   A. 13   **B.** 9   **C.** 0   **D.** -11

5   Simplify $(5z - 9) - 4(-2z - 3)$.

   A. $13z - 3$ **C.** $13z + 3$

   B. $-3z + 21$ **D.** $3z - 8$

6 $4y^2 - 12y + 9$ is the perfect square of which binomial?

   A. $(-2y + 3)$ **C.** $(y - 3)$

   B. $(-2y - 3)$ **D.** $(2y + 3)$

In Exercises 7–21, simplify each expression.

7 $6(4a - 2)$ **8** $(8v - 3)(-5v)$

9 $(2y + 3)(y - 2)$ **10** $(2t - 5)(5t - 2)$

11 $(3w + 7)(2w - 5)$ **12** $(2d + 4)^2$

13 $(-3q - 4)^2$ **14** $(v + 9)(v - 9)$

15 $\dfrac{6k^2 + 15k}{3k}$

16 $(a^2b^2 + ab - 4)(-2a)$

17 $-5p^2(p^2 + 2p + 1)$

18 $(x^2 + 3x - 2)(x + 3)$

19 $(2n - 7)(n^2 - n + 3)$

20 $\dfrac{2w^3 + 6w^2 - 5w}{-2w}$

21 $\dfrac{15z^4 - 25z^3 - 20z^2}{5z^2}$

In Exercises 22–24, solve each equation.

22 $2(3n + 2) = 5n - 4$

23 $8w - 5(2w + 7) = 2w - 9$

24   Mark says that $(m + n)^2$ and $m^2 + n^2$ are equivalent expressions. Do you agree or disagree? Explain.

5.3 Factoring Polynomials

New Jersey Standards

4.3.D.2.2 Factor quadratics

When multiplying monomials, you write a simplified expression for their product. The reverse of this process is called *factoring the monomial*.

To **factor** a monomial, you start with the simplified expression and find a multiplication equivalent of it. For instance, using whole number coefficients, there are five ways to factor $9x^2$. These are shown at the right. From these factorizations, you arrive at the following list of factors.

factors of $9x^2$: $1, 3, 9, x, 3x, 9x, x^2, 3x^2, 9x^2$

$$9x^2 = 1 \cdot 9x^2$$
$$9x^2 = 3 \cdot 3x^2$$
$$9x^2 = 9 \cdot x^2$$
$$9x^2 = x \cdot 9x$$
$$9x^2 = 3x \cdot 3x$$

The **greatest common factor (GCF)** of two or more monomials is the product of the greatest common factor of their numerical coefficients and the greatest common factor of their variable parts.

EXAMPLE 1   **Finding the GCF of monomials**

 Find the GCF of $12x^3$, $30x^2$, and $42x$.

- **SOLUTION**

Step 1

Write the factored form of each monomial. Circle the factors common to all the monomials.

$12x^3 = ②\cdot 2 \cdot ③ \cdot ⓧ \cdot x \cdot x$
$30x^2 = ② \cdot ③ \cdot 5 \cdot ⓧ \cdot x$
$42x = ② \cdot ③ \cdot 7 \cdot ⓧ$

Step 2

Multiply the circled factors.
$2 \cdot 3 \cdot x = 6x$

The GCF of $12x^3$, $30x^2$, and $42x$ is $6x$.

When the terms of a polynomial have a GCF other than 1, you can factor the polynomial by using the distributive property.

EXAMPLES 2 and 3   **Common monomial factoring with a numerical GCF**

Factor each expression using the GCF of the terms.

2 $3a + 6$ ■ SOLUTION
  $3a + 6$ ← The GCF of $3a$ and 6 is 3.
  $3a + 3(2)$ ← Rewrite each term as a product.
  $3(a + 2)$ ← Apply the distributive property.

3 $8x^2 - 12y + 20$ ■ SOLUTION
  $8x^2 - 12y + 20$ ← The GCF of $8x^2$, $12y$, and 20 is 4.
  $4(2x^2) - 4(3y) + 4(5)$ ← Rewrite each term as a product.
  $4(2x^2 - 3y + 5)$ ← Apply the distributive property.

In Example 3, notice that it is also possible to factor $8x^2 - 12y + 20$ as $2(4x^2 - 6y + 10)$. However, the GCF was not used in this factoring. As a result, $4x^2 - 6y + 10$ can be factored further as $2(2x^2 - 3y + 5)$. This means that $2(4x^2 - 6y + 10)$ is considered only a *partial* factorization.

In general, your goal is to factor polynomials *completely*. A polynomial is factored completely when it is expressed as a product of one or more polynomials that cannot be factored further.

Common monomial factoring with a variable expression as the GCF

Factor each expression completely.

4 $6r^4 + 9r^2 + 4r$

■ SOLUTION

$6r^4 + 9r^2 + 4r$
$r(6r^3) + r(9r) + r(4)$
$r(6r^3 + 9r + 4)$

← The GCF of $6r^4$, $9r^2$, and $4r$ is r.

5 $4mn - 10m$

■ SOLUTION

$4mn - 10m$
$2m(2n) - 2m(5)$
$2m(2n - 5)$

← The GCF of $4mn$ and $10m$ is $2m$.

6 $8a^3b^2 + 16\,a^2b^2 - 4ab$

■ SOLUTION

$8a^3b^2 + 16\,a^2b^2 - 4ab$
$4ab(2a^2b) + 4ab(4ab) - 4ab(1)$
$4ab(2a^2b + 4ab - 1)$

← The GCF of $8a^3b^2$, $16a^2b^2$, and $4ab$ is $4ab$.

Many trinomials are the product of two binomial factors. The general formula for these trinomials is $ax^2 + bx + c$, where c is a constant term. Study the products in the following table.

Factors		Quadratic Term		Linear Term		Constant Term
$(x + 2)(x + 5) = x^2 + 5x + 2x + 10 =$		x^2	$+$	$7x$	$+$	10
$(x - 3)(x - 1) = x^2 - 1x - 3x + 3 =$		x^2	$-$	$4x$	$+$	3
$(x + 6)(x - 4) = x^2 - 4x + 6x - 24 =$		x^2	$+$	$2x$	$-$	24
$(x - 8)(x + 7) = x^2 + 7x - 8x - 56 =$		x^2	$-$	x	$-$	56

Notice that the terms of the trinomials are related to the terms of their binomial factors. The constant term is the product of the last terms of the factors. The coefficient of the linear term is the sum of the last terms of the factors. You can use these relationships to factor many quadratic trinomials.

Factoring trinomials of the form $ax^2 + bx + c$ **where** $a = 1$ **and** $c > 0$

Factor each expression completely.

7 $h^2 + 8h + 15$

■ SOLUTION

Look for factors of 15 whose sum is 8.

Factors of 15	Sum of Factors
1, 15	16
3, 5	8

← Both factors must be positive.

The numbers 3 and 5 have a product of 15 and a sum of 8.
So $h^2 + 8h + 15 = (h + 3)(h + 5)$.

8  $y^2 - 10y + 16$

■ SOLUTION

Look for factors of 16 whose sum is −10.

Factors of 16	Sum of Factors
−1, −16	−17
−2, −8	−10
−4, −4	−8

← Both factors must be negative.

The numbers −2 and −8 have a product of 16 and a sum of −10.
So $y^2 - 10y + 16 = (y - 2)(y - 8)$.

ADP standard

If every term of a quadratic trinomial is positive, then the second term of each binomial will be positive. If the second term of the trinomial is negative and the last term is positive, then the second term of each binomial will be negative.

If the second term of a trinomial is positive and the third term is negative, then each binomial will be opposite in sign and the sign of the number with the largest absolute value will be positive. If the second and third terms of a trinomial are negative, then each binomial will be opposite in sign and the sign of the number with the largest absolute value will be negative.

Go Online
PHSchool.com
Visit: PHSchool.com
Web Code: ayp-0276

EXAMPLES 9 and 10 | **Factoring trinomials of the form $ax^2 + bx + c$ where $c < 0$**

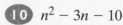

Factor each expression completely.

9 $n^2 + 3n - 10$

■ SOLUTION

Look for factors of -10 with sum 3.

Factors	Sum
$-1, 10$	9
$1, -10$	-9
$-2, 5$	3
$2, -5$	-3

← The factors must have opposite signs.

The numbers -2 and 5 have a product of -10 and a sum of 3. So $n^2 + 3n - 10 = (n - 2)(n + 5)$.

10 $n^2 - 3n - 10$

■ SOLUTION

Look for factors of -10 with sum -3.

Factors	Sum
$-1, 10$	9
$1, -10$	-9
$-2, 5$	3
$2, -5$	-3

← The factors must have opposite signs.

The numbers 2 and -5 have a product of -10 and a sum of -3. So $n^2 - 3n - 10 = (n + 2)(n - 5)$.

Sometimes you must factor a trinomial of the form $ax^2 + bx + c$ when a is a whole number greater than 1. In these cases you must consider not only the factors of the constant c, but also the factors of the leading coefficient a.

Go Online
PHSchool.com
Visit: PHSchool.com
Web Code: ayp-0278

EXAMPLE 11 | **Factoring trinomials of the form $ax^2 + bx + c$ where $a > 1$**

11 Factor the expression $2w^2 - w - 6$.

■ SOLUTION

Step 1

List the factors of the leading coefficient, which is 2:

1 and 2

List the factors of the constant, which is -6:

1 and -6
-1 and 6
2 and -3
-2 and 3

Step 2

Use the factors from Step 1 to write pairs of binomial factors. Look for $-1w$ as the middle term.

$(1w + 1)(2w - 6) \rightarrow -6w + 2w = -4w$
$(1w - 6)(2w + 1) \rightarrow 1w + (-12w) = -11w$
$(1w - 1)(2w + 6) \rightarrow 6w + (-2w) = 4w$
$(1w + 6)(2w - 1) \rightarrow -1w + 12w = 11w$
$(1w + 2)(2w - 3) \rightarrow -3w + 4w = 1w$
$(1w - 3)(2w + 2) \rightarrow 2w + (-6w) = -4w$
$(1w + 3)(2w - 2) \rightarrow -2w + 6w = 4w$
$(1w - 2)(2w + 3) \rightarrow 3w + (-4w) = -1w$ ✔

So $2w^2 - w - 6 = (w - 2)(2w + 3)$.

Recall that squares of sums and differences result in perfect square trinomials.

For all real numbers a and b: $(a + b)^2 = a^2 + 2ab + b^2$
$(a - b)^2 = a^2 - 2ab + b^2$

You can use what you know about the squares of sums and differences to factor perfect square trinomials. The steps are described below.

To Factor a Perfect Square Trinomial

- Find the square root of the first and last terms.
- If the sign of the middle term is positive then the second term of the factor is positive.
- If the sign of the middle term is negative then the second term of the factor is negative.
- Check to make sure that twice the product of the first and last terms equals the middle term.

EXAMPLES 12 and 13 **Factoring perfect square trinomials**

 $x^2 + 6x + 9$

■ SOLUTION

$x^2 + 2(3)x + 3^2 = (x + 3)^2$

13 $a^2 - 8ab + 16b^2$

■ SOLUTION

$a^2 - 4(2)b + (4b)^2 = (a - 4b)^2$

Recall the rule for the product of the **difference of two squares.**

For all real numbers a and b: $(a - b)(a + b) = a^2 - b^2$

You can use what you know about the product of $(a - b)(a + b)$ to factor the difference of two squares. The steps are described below.

To Factor the Difference of 2 Squares

- Find the square root of each term.
- Write two binomials that are the sum and difference of those square roots.

Visit: PHSchool.com
Web Code: ayp-0282

EXAMPLES 14 and 15 **Factoring the difference of 2 squares**

 $4x^4 - 9y^6$

■ SOLUTION

$(2x^2)^2 - (3y^3)^2 = (2x^2 - 3y^3)(2x^2 + 3y^3)$

15 $25a^2 - 49b^2$

■ SOLUTION

$(5a)^2 - (7b)^2 = (5a - 7b)(5a + 7b)$

147

You may be asked to determine the correctly factored form of a polynomial.

EXAMPLE 16   **Recognizing the correct factored form**

16 Which product is equivalent to $m^2 - 5m + 6$?

A. $(m + 3)(m - 2)$ **C.** $(m + 3)(m + 2)$
B. $(m - 3)(m - 2)$ **D.** $(m - 3)(m + 2)$

■ **SOLUTION**

Examine the choices.

A and **D**   These products will each have a negative constant term.

C   This product will have a positive constant term, but the coefficient of the linear term will also be positive.

B   By a process of elimination, choice B must be the correct factorization. You can check any factorization by multiplying:

$$(m - 3)(m - 2) = m^2 - 2m - 3m + (-3)(-2) = m^2 - 5m + 6 \quad ✔$$

The correct choice is B.

In some cases, factoring completely will involve two types of factorization. In general, you should always begin by looking for a common monomial factor.

EXAMPLES 17 and 18   **Factoring in two steps**

Factor each expression completely.

17 $5v^2 - 5$ ■ **SOLUTION** $5v^2 - 5$ ← The GCF of $5v^2$ and 5 is 5.
                                     $5(v^2 - 1)$ ← $v^2 - 1$ is a difference of two squares.
                                       $5(v + 1)(v - 1)$

18 $6h^3 + 9h^2 - 6h$ ■ **SOLUTION** $6h^3 + 9h^2 - 6h$ ← The GCF of $6h^3$, $9h^2$, and $6h$ is $3h$.
                                          $3h(2h^2 + 3h - 2)$ ← $2h^2 + 3h - 2$ has two binomial factors.
                                          $3h(2h - 1)(h + 2)$

Practice

Choose the letter preceding the word or expression that best completes the statement or answers the question.

1 What is the greatest common factor of $24c^2d$, $18c^2d^2$, and $12cd^2$?

A. $72c^2d^2$ **C.** $6cd$

B. $6c^2d$ **D.** $2c^2d$

2 Which is a perfect square trinomial?

A. $x^2 - 8x + 16x^2$ **C.** $x^2 - 8x + 16$

B. $x^2 + 8x - 16$ **D.** $x^2 - 8x - 16$

3 Which is not a true statement?

A. $a^2 + 2ab + b^2 = (a + b)^2$

B. $a^2 - 2ab + b^2 = (a - b)^2$

C. $a^2 + 2ab - b^2 = (b - a)^2$

D. $a^2 - b^2 = (a + b)(a - b)$

4 Which expression is a factor of $9m^2 - 9m - 10$?

   A. $3m - 5$ **C.** $9m + 1$

   B. $3m - 2$ **D.** $9m - 1$

5 Which is equivalent to $9r^2 - 16s^2$?

   A. $(3r + 4s)(3r - 4s)$

   B. $(3r - 4s)^2$

   C. $(9r + 16s)(9r - 16s)$

   D. $(9r - 16s)^2$

6 Which expression cannot be factored over the integers?

   A. $z^2 + 7z + 6$ **C.** $z^2 + 5z - 6$

   B. $z^2 + 7z - 6$ **D.** $z^2 + 5z + 6$

In Exercises 7–10, find the GCF.

7 $9t^2, 15t, 12$ **8** $2y^3, 10y^2, 20y$

9 $4r^2s^2, 12rs^2, 9r^2s$ **10** a^3b^3, a^2b^3, a^2b

In Exercises 11–54, factor each expression completely. If it is not possible to factor over the integers, write *cannot be factored*.

11 $8n - 72$ **12** $9b^2 + 17b$

13 $12r^2 + 18r$ **14** $8v^3 - 36v$

15 $v^6 + v^3 + v$ **16** $3x^5 - 15x^3 + 9x^2$

17 $16j^2k^2 - 40jk$ **18** $4cd^2 + 2c^2d - 6cd$

19 $c^2 + 14c + 45$ **20** $a^2 - 16a + 28$

21 $x^2 - x - 30$ **22** $q^2 + 2q - 63$

23 $y^2 - 16y + 48$ **24** $b^2 - 14b - 72$

25 $h^2 + h - 42$ **26** $s^2 - 10s + 9$

27 $3d^2 + 8d + 5$ **28** $5m^2 - 11m + 2$

29 $3t^2 - 7t - 6$ **30** $3j^2 + 7j - 10$

31 $6x^2 - 19x + 15$ **32** $4y^2 - 4y - 15$

33 $b^2 + 4b + 4$ **34** $n^2 - 24n + 144$

35 $w^2 - 10w + 25$ **36** $r^2 + 8r + 16$

37 $9z^2 + 30z + 25$ **38** $4c^2 - 60c + 225$

39 $4p^2 + 44p + 121$ **40** $16g^2 - 72g + 81$

41 $u^2 - 100$ **42** $9k^2 - 49$

43 $36a^2 - 1$ **44** $144c^2 - 25$

45 $4n^2 - 16$ **46** $12w^2 - 27$

47 $5z^2 + 25z + 30$ **48** $40d^2 - 10d - 15$

49 $50t^3 - 32t$ **50** $16y^3 + 48y^2 + 36y$

51 $k^6 - 9k^4$ **52** $b^4 - 1$

53 $9c^2 - 100d^2$ **54** $4r^2 + 2rs - 6s^2$

In Exercises 55–59, solve the problem. Clearly show all necessary work.

55 What are all the possible values of n that make $x^2 + nx - 10$ a factorable expression over the integers?

56 For what value(s) of m is $x^2 + 2x + m$ a perfect square trinomial?

57 For what value(s) of p is $x^2 + px + 81$ a perfect square trinomial?

58 Explain why there is no integer value of q for which $x^2 + 7x + q$ is a perfect square.

59 Selena says that $(a - b)^2$ and $(b - a)^2$ are equivalent expressions. Do you agree or disagree? Explain.

Preparing for the New Jersey HSPA

DIRECTIONS FOR QUESTIONS 1–26: For each of the questions below, select the answer choice that is best for each case.

1 What is the difference when $3r^2 + 5$ is subtracted from $3r^3 + 3r^2 + 2r$?

  A. $-3r^2 - 2r + 5$ C. $3r^3 + 2r - 5$

  B. $3r^2 + 2r$ D. $3r^3 + 6r^2 + 2r + 5$

2 Which is not equal to $5^2 \cdot 5^{-3}$?

  A. 5^{2-3} C. $\dfrac{5^2}{5^3}$

  B. 5^{-1} D. $(5^2)^{-3}$

3 Which is equivalent to the expression $(4w - 2)(3w - 5)$?

  A. $7w - 7$ C. $7w^2 - 14w - 7$

  B. $-2w - 5$ D. $12w^2 - 26w + 10$

4 Which of the following is a cubic binomial?

  A. $-6x^3$ C. $5x^3 - 2x$

  B. $3x^2 + 3x$ D. $-7x^3 + 4x + x^2$

5 What is the result when $2c^2 - 3c + 6$ is subtracted from $c^2 + c - 2$?

  A. $c^2 - 4c + 8$

  B. $-c^2 - 2c + 4$

  C. $c^2 - 4c + 8$

  D. $-c^2 + 4c - 8$

6 Which of the following is the product of $(4x - 2)(5 - 3x)$?

  A. $-12x^2 + 14x - 10$

  B. $20x^2 + 12x - 10$

  C. $-12x^2 + 26x - 10$

  D. $-12x^2 + 20x$

7 Compare the degrees of the expressions $4x(x^2 + 5x)$ and $2x^2(4x + 10)$. Which has the greater degree?

  A. The degree of $4x(x^2 + 5x)$ is greater.

  B. The degree of $2x^2(4x + 10)$ is greater.

  C. The two degrees are equal.

  D. Cannot be determined

8 Which of the following are factors of $2x^2 - 5x - 12$?

  A. $(2x + 3)(x - 4)$ C. $(2x - 5)(x - 7)$

  B. $(2x - 3)(x + 4)$ D. $(2x - 2)(x - 6)$

9 Which is *not* equivalent to $-\dfrac{x + 5}{x - 1}$?

  A. $\dfrac{-x + 5}{x - 1}$ C. $\dfrac{x + 5}{1 - x}$

  B. $\dfrac{-x - 5}{x - 1}$ D. $\dfrac{x + 5}{-x + 1}$

10 What is equivalent to the expression $(6c^2 + 5c - 3) - (3c^2 + 8c - 1)$?

  A. $3c^2 + 13c - 4$ C. $3c^2 - 3c - 2$

  B. $3c^2 - 3c - 4$ D. $3c^2 + 13c - 2$

11 What is the product of $(-3x^3y^2)(5xy^5)$?

  A. $-15x^4y^7$ C. $-15x^3y^{10}$

  B. $2x^4y^7$ D. $2x^3y^{10}$

12 Which is equivalent to the expression $(3xy)(2x^2y)^3$?

  A. $18x^6y^5$ C. $216x^9y^6$

  B. $24x^7y^4$ D. $18x^6y^3$

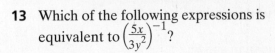

13 Which of the following expressions is equivalent to $\left(\frac{5x}{3y^2}\right)^{-1}$?

A. $\frac{3y^2}{5x}$ B. $\frac{3x}{5y^2}$ C. $-\frac{5x}{3y^2}$ D. $-\frac{3y^2}{5x}$

14 Simplify the expression $(w - 8) + 2(4w - 1)$.

A. $9w - 10$ C. $9w - 9$

B. $-23w + 6$ D. $10w - 18$

15 What is the product of $(2a - 5)(3a + 1)$?

A. $6a^2 - 5$ C. $6a^2 - 13a - 5$

B. $5a - 4$ D. $6a^2 - 17a - 5$

16 Which trinomial is equivalent to $(2r - 1)^2$?

A. $4r^2 + 1$ C. $4r^2 + 4r + 1$

B. $4r^2 - 4r + 1$ D. $4r - 2$

17 Solve the equation $-4n + 7 = (n - 1)(-3)$.

A. $n = 10$ C. $n = 4$

B. $n = -\frac{10}{7}$ D. $n = -4$

18 Which of the following is the solution for $5j - 3(2j - 1) = 3j + 8$?

A. 10 B. -3 C. $-\frac{5}{4}$ D. $-\frac{9}{4}$

19 Simplify the expression $(5j^2 + 3j) + (j^2 + 4j + 4) - (2j - 3)$.

A. $11j^2 - 1$ C. $6j^2 + 5j - 1$

B. $6j^2 + 5j + 7$ D. $11j^2 - 7$

20 Which of the following is equivalent to the expression $(2z^2 - 4) - (z^2 - 4) - (3z^2 - 2)$?

A. $4z^2 + 2$ C. $-2z^2 + 2$

B. $-2z^2 - 10$ D. $4z^2 - 10$

21 What is the GCF of the terms of the trinomial $3x^5 - 15x^3 + 9x^2$?

A. 3 B. x C. $3x$ D. $3x^2$

22 Which is the completely factored form of $5z^2 + 5z - 30$?

A. $(5z + 15)(z - 2)$ C. $(5z - 10)(z + 3)$

B. $5(z + 3)(z - 2)$ D. $5(z - 3)(z - 2)$

23 The length of a triangular-shaped sail is represented by $2x + 5$, and the height is represented by $2x - 4$. Which expression represents the area of the sail?

A. $4x + 1$ C. $2x^2 + x - 10$

B. $4x^2 - 20$ D. $x^2 + x - 20$

24 The length of a rug is represented by $x + 6$, and the width is represented by $x - 2$. Which expression represents the area of the rug?

A. $2x + 4$ C. $x^2 - 12$

B. $x^2 + 4x - 12$ D. $x^2 - 8x - 12$

25 Two cars leave the same location at the same time. One car drives due east and the other travels south. The southbound car travels 12 mi less than the other. Which expression describes the distance between the two cars at that point?

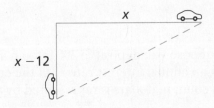

A. $\sqrt{2x - 12}$ C. $\sqrt{2x^2 + 144}$

B. $\sqrt{x^2 - 12x}$ D. $\sqrt{2x^2 - 24x + 144}$

26 Factor $2a^2 + 7a - 4$ completely.

A. $(2a + 1)(a - 4)$

B. $2(a + 4)(a - 1)$

C. $(a + 4)(2a - 1)$

D. $(2a + 4)(a - 1)$

DIRECTIONS FOR 27–29: Solve each problem and show your work.

27 A rectangular pool is being constructed according to the plan shown below. The formula for the area A of a rectangle is $A = lw$, where l is the length of the rectangle and w is the width.

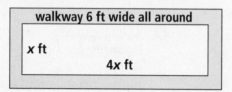

walkway 6 ft wide all around

x ft

$4x$ ft

- Write a simplified expression for the area in square feet of the pool, not including the walkway. Explain your work.

- Write a simplified expression for the area in square feet of the pool and the walkway combined. Explain your work.

- What is the area in square feet of the pool and walkway, given that $x = 12$? Explain the steps you took to find the answer.

28 The volume V of a rectangular prism is given by the formula $V = lwh$, where l is the length of the prism, w is its width, and h is its height. The length of a certain rectangular prism is three times its width, and its height is 2 ft less than its width.

- Write a simplified expression for the length of the prism.

- Write a simplified expression that represents the volume of the prism in cubic feet.

- Calculate the volume of the prism if the width w equals 6 ft.

29 Suppose you deposit $1200 into an account that pays simple interest at an annual interest rate r. At the end of two years, the amount in the account in dollars is represented by the expression $1200(1 + r)^2$.

- Simplify this expression and write the result in standard form.

- Assuming no additional deposits or withdrawals, what is the total amount in the account after two years if r is 3%?

- Assuming no additional deposits or withdrawals, what is the total amount in the account after two years if r is 3.5%?

- Assuming no additional deposits or withdrawals, how much money is in the account after two years if r is 3.5% with an initial deposit of $2000?

6 Quadratic Equations and Functions

Discovering New Jersey

Grover Cleveland

Stephen Grover Cleveland was born on March 18, 1837 in Caldwell, New Jersey. He grew up in New York and became involved in politics while helping with the presidential campaign of James Buchanan. He became the mayor of Buffalo, New York in 1881. The following year he became the governor of New York.

Grover Cleveland was elected as the 22nd President of the United States in 1884. In 1892 he was elected as the 24th President, becoming the first and only president to serve two nonconsecutive terms.

In 1908 Cleveland died in Princeton, New Jersey.

6.1 Solving Quadratic Equations Using Square Roots

New Jersey Standards

4.3.D.2.1 Solving quadratic equations

A **quadratic equation** is any equation that can be written in the form

$$ax^2 + bx + c = 0,\text{ where } a, b, \text{ and } c \text{ are real numbers and } a \neq 0.$$

This is the **standard form of a quadratic equation** in x.

The following examples describe both quadratic and nonquadratic equations.

Equation	Description	Classification
$3x + 2 = 7x - 5$	Both $3x + 2$ and $7x - 5$ are linear polynomials in x.	not quadratic
$n^2 = 25$	The greatest power of n is 2.	quadratic not in standard form
$6x^2 + 5x - 7 = 0$	The greatest power of x is 2.	quadratic in standard form
$27a^3 = 9$	The equation contains a power of a greater than 2.	not quadratic

EXAMPLES 1 and 2   **Writing quadratic equations in standard form**

Write each quadratic equation in standard form.

 1 $6 - n^2 = 5n$

2 $5x^2 = 3x - 2$

■ SOLUTION

$$6 - n^2 = 5n$$
$$6 - n^2 - 5n = 5n - 5n$$
$$6 - n^2 - 5n = 0$$
$$-n^2 - 5n + 6 = 0$$

■ SOLUTION

$$5x^2 = 3x - 2$$
$$5x^2 + 2 = 3x - 2 + 2$$
$$5x^2 + 2 = 3x$$
$$5x^2 + 2 - 3x = 0$$
$$5x^2 - 3x + 2 = 0$$

A **solution to a quadratic equation** in one variable is any number that makes the equation true. For example, if $b^2 + b = 6$, you can conclude that $b = 2$ and $b = -3$ are solutions since $(2)^2 + 2 = 4 + 2 = 6$ and $(-3)^2 + (-3) = 9 - 3 = 6$. Solutions are also called **roots.**

If the value of b (the coefficient of the x term in a quadratic equation) is zero, the equation can be written as $x^2 = k$. If $k \geq 0$, this equation can be solved by using square roots. There are no real solutions for the quadratic equation if k is negative ($k < 0$).

For example, you can solve the equation $x^2 = 64$ by finding the square root of each side of the equation. Therefore, $x = \pm\sqrt{64}$; $x = \pm 8$.

EXAMPLES 3 through 8 | Solving quadratic equations in one variable

Solve each of the following quadratic equations.

3 $x^2 = 9$

■ SOLUTION
$x^2 = 9$
$x = \pm\sqrt{9}$
$x = \pm 3$

4 $5s^2 = 125$

■ SOLUTION
$5s^2 = 125$
$\dfrac{5s^2}{5} = \dfrac{125}{5}$
$s^2 = 25$
$s = \pm\sqrt{25} = \pm 5$

5 $x^2 - 61 = 20$

■ SOLUTION
$x^2 - 61 = 20$
$x^2 = 81$
$x = \pm\sqrt{81} = \pm 9$

6 $3m^2 - 24 = 2m^2 + 40$

■ SOLUTION
$3m^2 - 24 = 2m^2 + 40$
$3m^2 = 2m^2 + 64$
$m^2 = 64$
$m = \pm\sqrt{64} = \pm 8$

7 $x^2 + 40 = 15$

■ SOLUTION
$x^2 + 40 = 15$
$x^2 = -25$
$x = \pm\sqrt{-25}$
no real solution

8 $3(h + 5)^2 = 48$

■ SOLUTION
$3(h + 5)^2 = 48$
$(h + 5)^2 = 16$
$\sqrt{(h + 5)^2} = \pm\sqrt{16}$
$h + 5 = \pm 4$
$h + 5 = 4 \quad or \quad h + 5 = -4$
$h = -1 \quad or \quad h = -9$

If the value of k in the equation $x^2 = k$ is not a perfect square, then the roots are irrational. You can use a calculator to approximate the root to the desired degree of accuracy.

EXAMPLES 9 through 11 | Solving quadratic equations with irrational roots

Solve each of the following equations and round your answers to the nearest hundredth.

9 $12n^2 = 60$

■ SOLUTION
$12n^2 = 60$
$n^2 = 5$
$n = \pm\sqrt{5}$
$n = \pm 2.24$

10 $3y^2 - 144 = 30$

■ SOLUTION
$3y^2 - 144 = 30$
$3y^2 = 174$
$y^2 = 58$
$y = \pm\sqrt{58}$
$y = \pm 7.62$

11 $2(x - 5)^2 - 10 = 24$

■ SOLUTION
$2(x - 5)^2 - 10 = 24$
$2(x - 5)^2 = 34$
$(x - 5)^2 = 17$
$x - 5 = \pm\sqrt{17}$
$x - 5 = \pm 4.12$
$x = 4.12 + 5 \ or \ x = -4.12 + 5$
$x = 9.12 \quad or \quad x = 0.88$

Certain verbal problems translate to a quadratic equation. You can use what you know about quadratic equations to solve these types of equations.

EXAMPLES 12 and 13   **Using quadratic equations to solve verbal problems**

Solve the following problems using a quadratic equation.

12 The sum of a number and 5 is squared. The result is 81. What are the numbers that make this statement true?

■ **SOLUTION**

Let n represent the number.

$(n + 5)^2 = 81$

$n + 5 = \pm\sqrt{81}$

$n + 5 = \pm 9$

$n + 5 = 9 \text{ or } n + 5 = -9$

$n = 4 \text{ or } n = -14$

13 Five times the square of the sum of two and a number is equal to 45. What are the numbers that make this statement true?

■ **SOLUTION**

Let n represent the number.

$5(n + 2)^2 = 45$

$n + 2 = \pm\sqrt{9}$

$n + 2 = \pm 3$

$n + 2 = 3 \text{ or } n + 2 = -3$

$n = 1 \text{ or } n = -5$

Quadratic equations can be used to describe the area of some shapes algebraically. You can use these equations to find side lengths and areas.

It is important to check the solutions of a quadratic equation with the information in the problem. Often a solution will be rejected because it does not make sense in the context of the problem. For example, if you are asked to find a side length, a negative solution does not make sense.

EXAMPLE 14   **Using a quadratic equation to solve an area problem**

14 Write an expression in x for the area of the shaded region. Find x such that the area of the shaded region equals 75% of the full square.

■ **SOLUTION**

area of full square − area of small square

$16^2 - x^2$

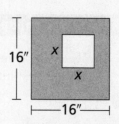

Since 75% = 0.75, solve $16^2 - x^2 = 0.75 \times 16^2$.

$16^2 - x^2 = 0.75 \times 256$

$256 - x^2 = 192$

$-x^2 = -64$ ← **Use the Addition Property of Equality.**

$x = \pm 8$

$x = 8$ ← **Reject the negative solution.**

The desired value of x is 8 inches.

Note

Because the length of a square must be a positive number, keep 8 as a solution and reject −8 as a possible solution.

156

Practice

Choose the letter preceding the word or expression that best completes the statement or answers the question.

1 Which is not a quadratic equation?

    A. $x^2 = 81$

    B. $3x^2 = 5x - 7$

    C. $4x + 5 = 9 - 2x$

    D. $5x - 7x^2 = 21$

2 Which equation has the same solutions as $2(b^2 - 5) = 18$?

    A. $b^2 = 14$ **C.** $2b^2 = 23$

    B. $b^2 = 8$ **D.** $b^2 = \frac{18}{2} - 5$

3 Which numbers are the solutions to $n^2 = 2.25$?

    A. $0.15; -0.15$ **C.** $1.5; -1.5$

    B. $0.05; -0.05$ **D.** $1.125; -1.125$

4 Suppose x represents a real number. Which statement is true?

    A. $\sqrt{x^2} = x$ for all x

    B. $\sqrt{x^2} = -x$ for all x

    C. $\sqrt{x^2} = \frac{1}{2}x$ for all x

    D. $\sqrt{x^2} = x$ for all x zero or more

In Exercises 5–14, solve each quadratic equation. Give exact solutions. If the equation has no solutions, so state.

5 $x^2 = 49$ **6** $-x^2 = -9$

7 $3a^2 = 48$ **8** $12x^2 = 3$

9 $3a^2 - 5 = 43$ **10** $12m^2 + 3 = 3$

11 $12m^2 - 23 = -11$

12 $5x^2 + 6x - 7 = 3x^2 + 6x - 5$

13 $5n^2 + n + 4 = 6n^2 + n - 5$

14 $5k^2 - 2k + 18 = 9k^2 - 2k - 82$

In Exercises 15–20, solve each quadratic equation. Give solutions rounded to the nearest hundredth. If the equation has no solutions, so state.

15 $-x^2 = -10$ **16** $-4t^2 = -48$

17 $3a^2 = 2a^2 + 2$ **18** $-3c^2 = 2c^2 - 10$

19 $3(x - 5)^2 = 120$

20 $5x^2 + x + 8 = 3x^2 + x + 30$

In Exercises 21–26, solve the problem. Clearly show all necessary work.

21 The ratio of 90 to some number is equal to the ratio of that number to 40. What is the number?

22 Suppose that you want to build a square garden whose area is to be 729 square feet. What should the length of one side be?

23 The area A of a circle with radius r is given by $A = \pi r^2$. If the area of a circular pond is 1156 square feet, what is the radius to the nearest tenth of a foot?

24 The length of a rectangular sign is three times its width. What are the dimensions of the sign if its area is 192 square feet?

25 Write an expression in m for the shaded region. For what m will the area of the shaded region be 175 square units?

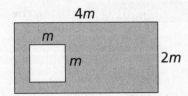

26 What are the lengths of the height and the base of this right triangle?

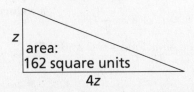

6.2 Solving Quadratic Equations by Various Methods

New Jersey Standards

4.3.D.2.1 Solving quadratic equations

4.3.D.2.2 Using different methods to solve quadratic equations

Suppose that each card below has a number written on the reverse side. If you are told $ab = 0$, you must conclude that at least one of the cards has 0 written on it. For example, if card a has 2 written on it, then $2b = 0$. Therefore, b must equal 0.

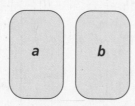

The *Zero-Product Property* is a generalization of this discussion.

Zero-Product Property

If a and b are real numbers and $ab = 0$, then either $a = 0$ or $b = 0$.

If $2x = 0$, then $x = 0$.   If $-3(x - 5) = 0$, then $x - 5 = 0$.   If $x(x - 2) = 0$, then $x = 0$ or $x - 2 = 0$.

EXAMPLE 1   Reading solutions from a product equal to 0

 Which is true given that $(n - 5)(n + 4) = 0$?

A. $n - 5 = 0$ and $n + 4 = 0$ **C.** $n - 5 = 0$ or $n + 4 = 0$
B. $n - 5 = 0$ and $n + 4 \neq 0$ **D.** $n - 5 \neq 0$ and $n + 4 = 0$

■ SOLUTION

By the Zero-Product Property, one or the other factor in $(n - 5)(n + 4)$ equals 0. Therefore, $n - 5 = 0$ or $n + 4 = 0$. The correct choice is C.

You can use the Zero-Product Property to solve a quadratic equation written in factored form.

EXAMPLES 2 and 3   Using the Zero-Product Property with factored form

Solve each equation.

 $3h(h + 7) = 0$

■ SOLUTION

$3h(h + 7) = 0$

$3h = 0$ or $h + 7 = 0$ ← Apply the Zero-Product Property.

$h = 0$ or $h = -7$

The solutions are 0 and −7.

3 $(x + 5)(x + 6) = 0$

■ SOLUTION

$(x + 5)(x + 6) = 0$

$x + 5 = 0$ or $x + 6 = 0$ ← Apply the Zero-Product Property.

$x = -5$ or $x = -6$

The solutions are −5 and −6.

You can use the Zero-Product Property to solve quadratic equations not written in factored form like those shown below.

$$b^2 + 3b = 0 \qquad m^2 + m - 6 = 0 \qquad z^2 + 4z + 4 = 0$$

You can use these steps to solve quadratic equations by factoring.

Solving a Quadratic Equation by Factoring

Step 1 Write the given quadratic equation in standard form, if it is not already.

Step 2 Factor the quadratic expression into a pair of linear expressions.

Step 3 Use the Zero-Product Property to write a pair of linear equations.

Step 4 Solve the linear equations.

Step 5 The solutions to the linear equations are the solutions to the given equation.

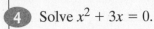 **EXAMPLES 4 through 6**

Solving a quadratic equation by factoring

 Go Online
PHSchool.com
Visit: PHSchool.com
Web Code: ayp-0295

4 Solve $x^2 + 3x = 0$.

■ **SOLUTION**

$$x^2 + 3x = 0$$

$$x(x + 3) = 0 \qquad \leftarrow \textbf{Factor the quadratic expression.}$$

$$x = 0 \text{ or } x = -3 \qquad \leftarrow \textbf{Apply the Zero-Product Property.}$$

5 Solve $\frac{z}{2} = \frac{z - 2}{z + 6}$.

■ **SOLUTION**

$$z(z + 6) = 2(z - 2) \qquad \leftarrow \textbf{Cross multiply.}$$

$$z^2 + 6z = 2z - 4$$

$$z^2 + 4z + 4 = 0$$

$$(z + 2)(z + 2) = 0 \qquad \leftarrow z^2 + 4z + 4 \textbf{ is a perfect square trinomial.}$$

$$z + 2 = 0 \text{ or } z + 2 = 0 \qquad \leftarrow \textbf{Apply the Zero-Product Property.}$$

$$z = -2 \text{ or } z = -2 \qquad \leftarrow -2 \textbf{ is called a double root.}$$

6 Solve $6w^2 - 28 = 13w$.

■ **SOLUTION**

$$6w^2 - 28 = 13w$$

$$6w^2 - 13w - 28 = 0 \qquad \leftarrow \textbf{Write in standard form.}$$

$$(2w - 7)(3w + 4) = 0 \qquad \leftarrow \textbf{Apply the Zero-Product Property.}$$

$$2w - 7 = 0 \text{ or } 3w + 4 = 0$$

$$w = \frac{7}{2} \text{ or } w = -\frac{4}{3}$$

Note

The quadratic must be equal to zero to use the Zero-Product Property.

Recall that quadratic equations can be used to solve area problems.

EXAMPLE 7   **Using factoring to solve an area problem**

7 The area of a rectangle is 220 square inches. The length of the rectangle is
12 inches more than its width. What are the dimensions of the rectangle?

■ **SOLUTION**

Step 1 Represent the given information in an equation.
Let w represent the width of the rectangle. Then $w + 12$ represents
the length.
$$(w + 12)w = 220 \qquad \leftarrow \text{length} \times \text{width} = \text{area}$$

Step 2 Solve the equation.
$$w^2 + 12w - 220 = 0 \qquad \leftarrow \text{Write in standard form.}$$
$$(w + 22)(w - 10) = 0 \qquad \leftarrow \text{Factor } w^2 + 12w - 220.$$
$$w = -22 \text{ or } w = 10 \qquad \leftarrow \text{Use the Zero-Product Property.}$$

Step 3 Interpret the solution.
Because length must be positive, length cannot be -22 inches.
The rectangle has a width of 10 inches. So the length is 22 inches.

Another way to solve a quadratic equation is to use the **quadratic formula**.
You can use it to find the roots of the quadratic equation.

Solving a Quadratic Equation by Using the Quadratic Formula

If $ax^2 + bx + c = 0$, a, b, and c are real numbers, and $a \neq 0$,

$$x = \frac{-b \pm \sqrt{b^2 - 4ac}}{2a}.$$

- If $b^2 - 4ac > 0$, there are
  two distinct real solutions.
- If $b^2 - 4ac = 0$, there is
  one real solution.
- If $b^2 - 4ac < 0$, there are
  no real solutions.

EXAMPLE 8   **Using the quadratic formula to solve an equation**

Go Online
PHSchool.com
Visit: PHSchool.com
Web Code: ayp-0602

8 Solve $n^2 + 5n - 7 = 0$. Approximate irrational solutions to the
nearest hundredth.

■ **SOLUTION**

$$n^2 + 5n - 7 = 0$$
$$n = \frac{-5 \pm \sqrt{5^2 - 4(1)(-7)}}{2(1)} \qquad \leftarrow a = 1, b = 5, c = -7$$
$$n = \frac{-5 + \sqrt{53}}{2} \approx 1.14 \text{ or } n = \frac{-5 - \sqrt{53}}{2} \approx -6.14$$

You can use the quadratic formula to solve quadratic equations that can also
be solved by factoring. Consider $6x^2 + x = 12$.

$$6x^2 + x = 12$$
$$6x^2 + x - 12 = 0$$
$$(2x + 3)(3x - 4) = 0$$
$$x = -\frac{3}{2} \text{ or } x = \frac{4}{3}$$

$$6x^2 + x = 12$$
$$6x^2 + x - 12 = 0$$
$$x = \frac{-1 \pm \sqrt{1^2 - 4(6)(-12)}}{2(6)}$$
$$x = \frac{-1 \pm 17}{12} = -\frac{3}{2} \text{ or } x = \frac{4}{3}$$

160

Practice

Choose the letter preceding the word or expression that best completes the statement or answers the question.

1 The solutions to $(z + 1)(z + 2) = 0$ are

   A. 1 and 2.   **C.** -1 and -2.

   B. 0 and -2.   **D.** 0 and -1.

2 The solutions to $a^2 - 10a = 0$ are

   A. 0 and -10.   **C.** 1 and 10.

   B. 0 and 10.   **D.** 1 and -10.

3 The solutions to $n(n + 1)(n - 2) = 0$ are

   A. 0, 1, and 2.   **C.** -1 and -2.

   B. 0 and -2.   **D.** 0, -1, and 2.

In Exercises 4–12, solve each equation.

4 $x^2 + 5x + 6 = 0$ **5** $x^2 + 7x = 8$

6 $a^2 - 5a = 0$ **7** $x^2 - 64 = 0$

8 $x^2 = 20 - 8x$ **9** $2b^2 - b - 21 = 0$

10 $18d - 81 = d^2$ **11** $r^3 - 7r^2 - 18r = 0$

12 $4x^3 - 100x = 0$

In Exercises 13–20, solve the problem. Clearly show all necessary work.

13 The altitude of a model rocket is given by $h = -16t^2 + 160t$ where h is the altitude in feet and t is elapsed time in seconds. After how many seconds of flight will the rocket hit the ground?

14 The length and width of a rectangle are represented by consecutive even integers. The area of the rectangle is 224 square inches. What are the length and the width?

15 A positive number is 5 more than another. Their product is 36. What are the numbers?

16 A rectangle is 8 feet long and 6 feet wide. If each side is increased by the same amount, the area of the new rectangle is 72 square feet more than the area of the original rectangle. Find the length and width of the new rectangle in feet.

17 The volume of a rectangular solid is the product of its length, width, and height. The volume of this solid is 440 cubic feet. What are the dimensions of the base?

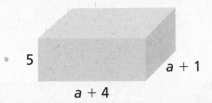

18 One number is 3 more than another. The sum of their squares is 89. What are the numbers?

19 The figure below shows a square inside a rectangle. If the area of the shaded region is 55 square units, determine the value of x.

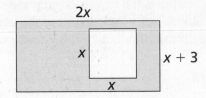

20 The product of two consecutive integers is 132. What is the sum of the numbers?

In Exercises 21–26, solve by using the quadratic formula. Give solutions to the nearest tenth. If the equation has no solutions, so state.

21 $n^2 + n - 1 = 0$

22 $p^2 + p - 3 = 0$

23 $-2h^2 + h + 1 = 0$

24 $3d^2 - 8d + 3 = 0$

25 $3z^2 - 3z - 1 = 2z^2 - z + 3$

26 $-m^2 - m + 10 = 10m - 1$

6.3 Quadratic Functions and Parabolas

New Jersey Standards

4.3.B.2.3 Analyze the intercepts of a function

4.3.B.2.5 Analyze the maximum/minimum of a quadratic

4.3.B.2.6 Estimate the roots of a quadratic

Recall that the graph of a linear equation in two variables is a line. The equation $y = ax^2 + bx + c$, where a, b, and c are real numbers and $a \neq 0$ represents a **quadratic function.** Its graph is a **parabola,** a smooth and symmetric U-shape.

For example, a table of values for $y = x^2 - 2x - 4$ and its graph are shown here.

x	−1	0	1	2	3
y	−1	−4	−5	−4	−1

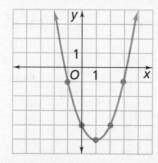

Characteristics of a Parabola

- The **axis of symmetry** is the line that divides the parabola into two matching parts. Its equation is $x = -\frac{b}{2a}$.

- The highest or lowest point on a parabola is called the **vertex** (also called a *turning point*). Its x-coordinate is the value of $-\frac{b}{2a}$.

If $a > 0$, the parabola opens upward. The vertex is the lowest point on the parabola. The y-coordinate of the vertex is the **minimum** value of the function.

If $a < 0$, the parabola opens downward. The vertex is the highest point on the parabola. The y-coordinate of the vertex is the **maximum** value of the function.

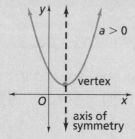

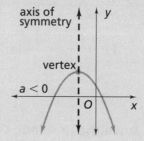

EXAMPLE 1   **Identifying the axis of symmetry of a parabola**

1   Which is true of the graph of $y = 2x^2 - 4x + 5$?

A. axis of symmetry: $x = 1$; graph opens down   **C.** axis of symmetry: $x = 1$; graph opens up

B. axis of symmetry: $x = -4$; graph opens up   **D.** axis of symmetry: $x = 5$; graph opens down

- **SOLUTION**

Identify the values of a and b in $y = 2x^2 - 4x + 5$. $a = 2$ and $b = -4$
Because $a > 0$, the graph *opens up*. Eliminate choices **A** and **D**.

Calculate the value of $-\frac{b}{2a}$. $\rightarrow$ $-\frac{-4}{2(2)} = 1$

An equation for the axis of symmetry is $x = 1$. The correct choice is *C*.

You can also identify the vertex and the axis of symmetry from the graph of a parabola.

EXAMPLE 2   **Identifying the vertex and axis of symmetry of a parabola**

 Find the vertex and the equation for the axis of symmetry of the parabola shown.

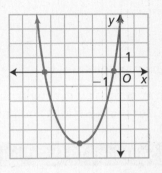

- **SOLUTION**

Because the vertex is either the lowest or highest point of a parabola, the vertex of this parabola is $(-3, -5)$. The equation of the axis of symmetry is $x = $ 'the x-coordinate of the vertex'; therefore, the equation is $x = -3$.

You can use the characteristics of a parabola to match an equation to its graph.

EXAMPLE 3   **Recognizing an equation for a parabola**

 Which equation represents the graph shown here?

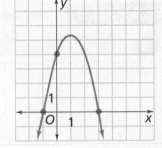

A. $y = -\frac{4}{3}x^2 + \frac{8}{3}x + 4$ **C.** $y = \frac{4}{3}x^2 - \frac{8}{3}x + 4$

B. $y = -\frac{4}{3}x^2 - \frac{8}{3}x - 4$ **D.** $y = \frac{4}{3}x^2 - \frac{8}{3}x - 4$

- **SOLUTION**

Eliminate choices **C** and **D** because the graphs of these equations open upward. Because $y = 4$ when $x = 0$, the graph crosses the y-axis at $(0, 4)$. Eliminate choice **B**. The correct choice is A.

You can graph a quadratic function by making a table of values. Finding the coordinates of the vertex first can reduce the work involved.

EXAMPLE 4   **Using the vertex to help sketch a parabola**

 Graph $y = -x^2 - 2x + 4$ using the vertex and a table of values. Label the axis of symmetry.

- **SOLUTION**

Identify the values of a and b in $y = -x^2 - 2x + 4$. $a = -1$ and $b = -2$

Calculate the value of $-\frac{b}{2a}$. $-\frac{-2}{2(-1)} = -1$

An equation for the axis of symmetry is $x = -1$. Make a table containing five x-values with -1 being the third x-value.

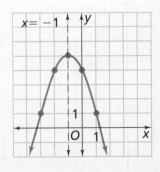

x	-3	-2	-1	0	1
y	1	4	5	4	1

Graph the ordered pairs in the table as shown here. Draw a smooth curve through them. Notice that the parabola opens downward because $a < 0$.

Let's look at how the real-number solutions of $x^2 - 4 = 0$ are related to the x-intercepts of the graph of $y = x^2 - 4$.

$$x^2 - 4 = 0$$
$$(x + 2)(x - 2) = 0$$
$$x + 2 = 0 \text{ or } x - 2 = 0$$
$$x = -2 \text{ or } x = 2$$

The real solutions to $x^2 - 4 = 0$ are **−2** and **2**.

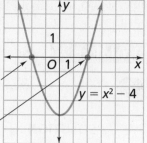

x-intercept: −2

$y = x^2 - 4$

x-intercept: 2

In general, you can make the following statements relating solutions to quadratic equations and graphs of quadratic functions.

> ## Solutions to Quadratic Equations and Graphs of Quadratic Functions
>
> - The real numbers that are solutions to $ax^2 + bx + c = 0$ are the x-intercepts of the graph of $y = ax^2 + bx + c$.
>
> - The x-intercepts of the graph of $y = ax^2 + bx + c$ are the real solutions to $ax^2 + bx + c = 0$.

EXAMPLE 5   **Finding real solutions from the *x*-intercepts of a graph**

5 The diagram represents the graph of a quadratic function. Which are the solutions of the corresponding quadratic equation?

   A. −2 and −4   **B.** −2 and 4   **C.** 2 and −4   **D.** 2 and 4

   ■ **SOLUTION**

   The graph crosses the x-axis at $(-2, 0)$ and $(4, 0)$. Therefore, the x-intercepts are −2 and 4. The correct choice is **B**.

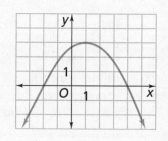

You can also use the functions of a graphing calculator to find the solutions of a quadratic equation.

Go Online
PHSchool.com

Visit: PHSchool.com
Web Code: ayp-0293

EXAMPLE 6   **Finding real solutions of a quadratic equation in *x* from a graph**

6 Solve $x^2 + 5x - 7 = 0$ graphically. Approximate the roots to the nearest tenth.

   ■ **SOLUTION**

   Graph $y = x^2 + 5x - 7$.

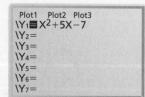

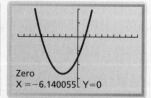

Plot1 Plot2 Plot3	WINDOW
\Y₁ = X²+5X−7	Xmin = −9.4
\Y₂ =	Xmax = 9.4
\Y₃ =	Xscl = 1
\Y₄ =	Ymin = −18
\Y₅ =	Ymax = 10
\Y₆ =	Yscl = 5
\Y₇ =	Xres = 1

Zero
X = −6.140055   Y = 0

Zero
X = 1.1400549   Y = 0

To the nearest tenth, the *roots are $x = -6.1$ and $x = 1.1$.*

The nature of the roots of a quadratic equation can be determined by looking at its graph. One diagram below shows the graphs of three different quadratic equations. Equation A has one real root because it has one x-intercept. Equation B has two real roots because it has two x-intercepts. Finally, equation C has no real roots because it never crosses the x-axis. The other diagram shows the graph of a polynomial equation that has three real roots because it has three x-intercepts.

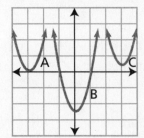
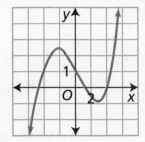

You can use the graph of a polynomial to determine the roots of a polynomial equation. You can solve the equation $x^3 - x^2 - 4x + 4 = 0$ by graphing $y = x^3 - x^2 - 4x + 4$ and determining the x-intercepts. The roots are $x = 1$, $x = 2$, and $x = -2$.

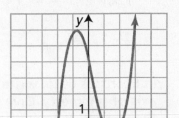

Note

The x-intercept is the point where the graph crosses the x-axis. A graph can have more than one x-intercept.

These roots can be used further to determine that the factors of $x^3 - x^2 - 4x + 4 = (x - 1)(x - 2)(x + 2)$.

EXAMPLE 7   **Finding the number and type of roots of a quadratic equation**

7 Identify the number and type of solutions of the polynomial graphed at the right.

■ **SOLUTION**

Because the graph has three x-intercepts, the polynomial has **three real solutions.**

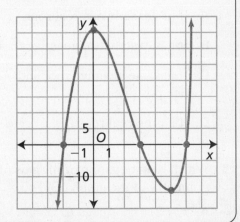

Practice

Choose the letter preceding the word or expression that best completes the statement or answers the question.

1 The graph of an equation of the form $y = ax^2 + bx + c$ is shown. Which is true?

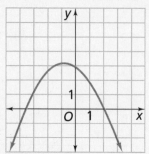

   A. $a > 0$ and $c > 0$

   B. $a > 0$ and $c < 0$

   C. $a < 0$ and $c < 0$

   D. $a < 0$ and $c > 0$

2 Which of the following statements is true of the equation graphed below?

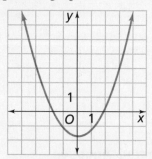

   A. It has exactly one real root.

   B. It has exactly two negative roots.

   C. It has one negative root and one positive root.

   D. It has no real roots.

3 Which is an equation of the axis of symmetry of the graph of $y = 3x^2 - 12x$?

   A. $x = 2$ **C.** $x = -5$

   B. $x = \frac{1}{5}$ **D.** $x = \frac{1}{2}$

4 Which represents the coordinates of the vertex of the graph of $y = x^2 - 6x - 10$?

   A. $(-6, 10)$

   B. $(3, -19)$

   C. $(3, -22)$

   D. $(6, 10)$

5 The graph of which equation has a maximum?

   A. $y = \frac{1}{3}x^2 - 3x + 2$

   B. $y = -5x + \frac{1}{2}x^2 - 5$

   C. $y - \frac{1}{2}x^2 = 4x + 6$

   D. $y = 6x - \frac{1}{3}x^2 + 2$

In Exercises 6–15, write an equation for the axis of symmetry. Give the coordinates of the ve rtex. Tell whether the graph opens up or down and whether the vertex is the minimum or maximum of the graph.

6 $y = 2x^2$

7 $y = -2x^2$

8 $y = -x^2 + 2$

9 $y = 5 - 3x^2$

10 $y = 1.5x^2 + 3x$

11 $y = 2.5x^2 - 3x$

12 $y = \frac{1}{2}x^2 + 4x$

13 $y = -\frac{1}{2}x^2 + \frac{1}{3}x$

14 $y = 2x^2 + 4x - 5$

15 $y = -x^2 + 6x - 1$

In Exercises 16–18, the graph of a quadratic function, $y = ax^2 + bx + c$, is given. Find the solutions to the related equation $ax^2 + bx + c = 0$.

16
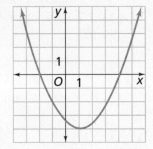

17
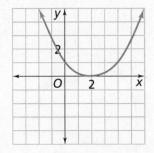

18
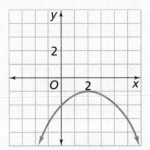

In Exercises 19–24, sketch each parabola.

19 $y = x^2 - 3x$

20 $y = (x + 2)^2$

21 $y = x^2 - 2x + 2$

22 $y = 0.5x^2 - 4x$

23 $y = \frac{1}{3}x^2 - 2$

24 $y = x^2 - 3x + 2$

In Exercises 25–31, solve the problem. Clearly show all necessary work.

25 Profit P in dollars made by a manufacturing company that makes w units of a product is given by $P = w^2 - 25w + 5000$. Determine the minimum profit for this company.

26 Write an equation of a parabola that has a y-intercept 6 and x-intercepts -3 and 4. Explain how you arrived at your answer.

27 The square shown below has sides 18 units in length. The shaded region has area 100π square units. Find the radius of the circle to the nearest tenth.

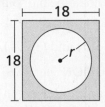

28 Write an equation for the set of all points in the coordinate plane whose y-coordinate is 2 less than half the square of the x-coordinate. Sketch that set of points.

29 Becky drops a coin into a well 64 feet deep. If the distance d in feet the coin falls is given by $d = 16t^2$, how many seconds t will it take the coin to hit the bottom?

30 Use a graph or an analysis of a graph to show that $x^2 + 5 = 4x$ has no real solutions.

31 Andre threw a ball into the air from the top of a building as shown. An equation for the altitude h of the ball in feet is given by $h = -16t^2 + 64t + 60$, where t is elapsed time in seconds. What is the maximum altitude of the ball?

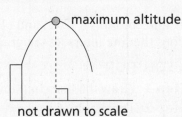

maximum altitude

not drawn to scale

6.4 Quadratic and Linear Equations in Two Variables

New Jersey Standards

4.3.B. 2.3 Analyze intercepts

4.3.B. 2.6 Estimate quadratic roots

4.3.D.2.3 Solve quadratics

You have already learned how to find solutions to a pair of linear equations in the same two variables. The solution to the pair of equations is the point of intersection of the graphs.

A system of equations may contain a linear and a quadratic equation.

The graph of this type of system includes a line and a parabola. The line may intersect the parabola at zero, one, or two points. You can use the graph of a linear-quadratic system to find its solutions.

EXAMPLE 1 Reading solutions from graphs

1 Which could be the solution(s) to equations whose graphs are shown?

A. only $(-2, 4)$ **C.** only $(3, 3)$
B. $(-3, 3)$ and $(-2, 4)$ **D.** $(3, 3)$ and $(-2, 4)$

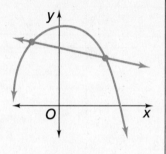

- **SOLUTION**

The graphs intersect in two poiznts, not a single point. Eliminate choices **A** and **C**. The points of intersection are in the first and second quadrants. The correct choice is D.

To find the number of solutions of a system of equations, you can count the intersection points of the graphs.

EXAMPLES 2 and 3 Counting points of intersection

2 In how many points does the graph of $y = x^2 - 4x - 1$ intersect the line $y = 3$?

- **SOLUTION**

The graph of $y = x^2 - 4x - 1$ is a parabola opening up with vertex $(2, -5)$.

$x = -\frac{b}{2a}$ → $x = -\frac{-4}{2(1)} = 2$ So $y = (2)^2 - 4(2) - 1 = -5$

Therefore, the vertex = $(2, -5)$.

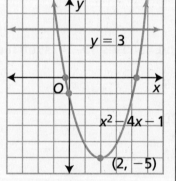

The horizontal line $y = 3$ is above the vertex. This parabola intersects the horizontal line $y = 3$ in **two points**.

3 A line contains $(-2, 3)$ and $(1, 1)$. In how many points does the line intersect the graph of $y = x^2 - 4x + 7$?

- **SOLUTION**

Step 1 Draw the line containing $(-2, 3)$ and $(1, 1)$.

Step 2 The graph of $y = x^2 - 4x + 7$ is a parabola with vertex $(2, 3)$. On the same sketch, draw the parabola.

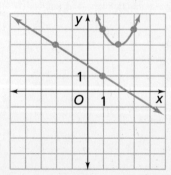

The graph shows that there are **zero points of intersection**.

The graphs of a linear equation and a quadratic equation in two variables may intersect in two points, intersect in one point, or not intersect at all.

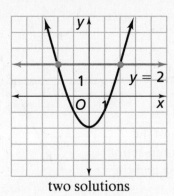
two solutions

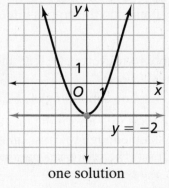
one solution

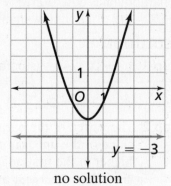
no solution

If $ax^2 + bx + c = 0$, then $b^2 - 4ac$ is called the **discriminant of the quadratic equation.** There is a connection between the sign of the discriminant and the number of real solutions of a quadratic equation.

Let $ax^2 + bx + c = 0$, where a, b, and c are real numbers and $a \neq 0$.

- If $b^2 - 4ac > 0$, the equation has two real solutions.
- If $b^2 - 4ac = 0$, the equation has one real solution.
- If $b^2 - 4ac < 0$, the equation has no real solutions.

You can use the discriminant to determine the number and type of solutions of a quadratic and linear system of equations.

Go Online
PHSchool.com
Visit: PHSchool.com
Web Code: ayp-0301

EXAMPLE 4 **Using the discriminant to count solutions**

4 In how many points do the graphs of $y = -x$ and $y = x^2 + x + 1$ intersect?

■ **SOLUTION**

Step 1 Set the expressions for y equal. Write the resulting equation in standard form.
$$x^2 + x + 1 = -x$$
$$x^2 + 2x + 1 = 0 \quad \leftarrow \text{ standard form}$$

Step 2 Determine whether the value of $b^2 - 4ac$ is positive, 0, or negative.
$$2^2 - 4(1)(1) = 0 \quad \leftarrow a = 1, b = 2, \text{ and } c = 1$$

Step 3 Interpret Step 2.
Because $2^2 - 4(1)(1) = 0$, $x^2 + x + 1 = -x$ has 1 real solution.
The graphs have 1 *point of intersection.*

In some problems, you can use reasoning to find the number of solutions of a system containing one linear equation in two variables and one quadratic equation in two variables.

EXAMPLE 5 | **Using reasoning to count solutions to a linear-quadratic system**

5 A parabola has equation $x^2 + 2x + 4$. A line has equation $y + 2 = 2(x - 1)$. In how many points do the graphs intersect?

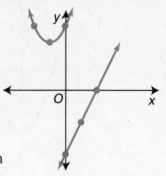

■ **SOLUTION**

Step 1 $x^2 + 2x + 4 \rightarrow$ a parabola with vertex $(-1, 3)$ and
y-intercept $(0, 4)$
$y - (-2) = 2(x - 1) \rightarrow$ a line containing $(1, -2)$

Step 2 The vertex of the parabola is well above the line and the slope of the line is not steep enough to cause an intersection higher in the first quadrant. Therefore, *the parabola and the line do not intersect at any point.*

You may be asked to find how many points of intersection a pair of equations has. You may also be asked for the coordinates of the points of intersection.

EXAMPLES 6 and 7 | **Solving a simple linear-quadratic system**

Solve each system of equations.

6 $y = x^2$ and $y = 2x$

■ **SOLUTION**

$$x^2 = 2x$$
$$x^2 - 2x = 0$$
$$x(x - 2) = 0$$
$$x = 0 \text{ or } x = 2$$

If $x = 0$, then $y = 0$.
If $x = 2$, then $y = 4$.
The solutions are $(0, 0)$ and $(2, 4)$.

7 $y = x$ and $y = x^2 - 2$

■ **SOLUTION**

$$x = x^2 - 2 \qquad \leftarrow \text{since } y = x$$
$$0 = x^2 - x - 2$$
$$0 = (x - 2)(x + 1)$$
$$x = 2 \text{ or } x = -1$$

If $x = 2$, then $y = 2$.
If $x = -1$, then $y = -1$.
The solutions are $(2, 2)$ and $(-1, -1)$.

There are pairs of equations whose graphs never intersect. These systems have no solution.

EXAMPLE 8 | **Solving a linear-quadratic system of equations that has no solution**

8 Find all solutions to $y = x - 3$ and $y = x^2 + 1$.

■ **SOLUTION** **Step 1** Write a single quadratic equation in x.
$$x^2 + 1 = x - 3$$
$$x^2 - x + 4 = 0$$

Step 2 Calculate the discriminant.
$$x^2 + (-1)x + 4 = 0 \qquad a = 1, b = -1, \text{ and } c = 4.$$
$$(-1)^2 - 4(1)(4) = -15$$

Step 3 Because the discriminant is negative, $x^2 + 1 = x - 3$ has no solution. Therefore, the system has *no solution.*

170

Sometimes an equation is written in standard form. You can solve the equation for y and then use substitution to solve the system.

EXAMPLES 9 and 10   **Using substitution to find the points of intersection**

9 What are the coordinates of any points of intersection of the graphs of $y + 3x = 4$ and $y = x^2 - 2x - 8$?

■ **SOLUTION**

Step 1 Solve $y + 3x = 4$ for y.

$$y = -3x + 4$$

Step 2 Set the expressions for y equal.

$$x^2 - 2x - 8 = -3x + 4$$

Step 3 Solve $x^2 - 2x - 8 = -3x + 4$.

$$x^2 - 2x - 8 = -3x + 4$$
$$x^2 + x - 12 = 0 \qquad \leftarrow \text{Write in standard form.}$$
$$(x - 3)(x + 4) = 0 \qquad \leftarrow \text{Factor } x^2 + x - 12.$$
$$x = 3 \text{ or } x = -4 \qquad \leftarrow \text{Use the Zero-Product Property.}$$

Step 4 Evaluate $-3x + 4$ for $x = 3$ and $x = -4$.

$$-3(3) + 4 = -5 \qquad -3(-4) + 4 = 16$$

The graphs intersect at $(3, -5)$ and $(-4, 16)$.

10 Find the coordinates of any points of intersection of the graphs of $y - 4 = x - 3$ and $y = x^2 + x$.

■ **SOLUTION**

Step 1 Solve $y - 4 = x - 3$ for y.

$$y = x + 1$$

Step 2 Set the expressions for y equal.

$$x + 1 = x^2 + x$$

Step 3 Solve $x + 1 = x^2 + x$.

$$x = x^2 + x - 1$$
$$0 = x^2 - 1$$
$$0 = (x - 1)(x + 1) \qquad \leftarrow \text{Factor } x^2 - 1.$$
$$x = 1 \text{ or } x = -1 \qquad \leftarrow \text{Apply the Zero-Factor Property.}$$

Step 4 Evaluate $x + 1$ for $x = -1$ and for $x = 1$.

$$(-1) + 1 = 0 \qquad (1) + 1 = 2$$

The solutions are $(-1, 0)$ and $(1, 2)$.

You can also solve a system of equations graphically. You can use a graphing calculator to quickly find the intersection points of two or more equations.

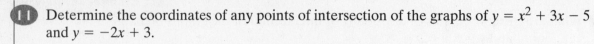

EXAMPLES 11 and 12   Using a graphing calculator to solve a linear-quadratic system

11 Determine the coordinates of any points of intersection of the graphs of $y = x^2 + 3x - 5$ and $y = -2x + 3$.

■ **SOLUTION**

Step 1 Graph the functions $y = x^2 + 3x - 5$ and $y = -2x + 3$.

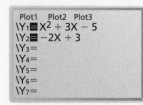 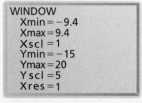 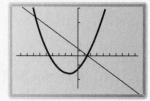

Step 2 After graphing the two functions, use the calculation feature to determine the points of intersection.

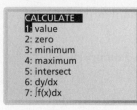 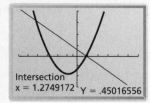 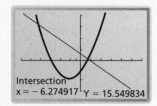

12 Determine the coordinates of any points of intersection of the graphs of $y = x^2 - 3x - 2$ and $y = -5x - 3$.

■ **SOLUTION**

Step 1 Graph the functions $y = x^2 - 3x - 2$ and $y = -5x - 3$.

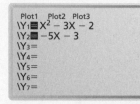 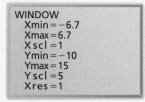 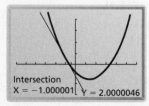

Step 2 After graphing the two functions, use the calculation feature to determine the points of intersection. There is only one answer in this situation where the line appears to be tangent to the parabola. What is the point of tangency? The answer is very close to $x = -1$ and $y = 2$.

Step 3 This answer can be verified on the calculator and algebraically as shown below.

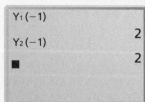

$x^2 - 3x - 2 = (-1)^2 - 3(-1) - 2 = 1 + 3 - 2 = 2$

$-5x - 3 = -5(-1) - 3 = 5 - 3 = 2$

Practice

Choose the letter preceding the word or expression that best completes the statement or answers the question.

1 In how many points does the graph of $y = (x - 3)(x + 5)$ intersect the x-axis?

    A. none   **C.** two

    B. one   **D.** three

2 A linear and a quadratic function are graphed on the same coordinate plane. Which are solution(s) to both equations?

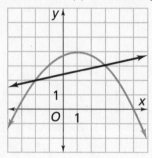

    A. $(-2, 2)$

    B. $(3, 3)$

    C. $(3, 3)$ and $(-2, 2)$

    D. $(-3, 3)$ and $(2, 2)$

3 A parabola and a line lie in the same coordinate plane. Which situation is not possible?

    A. The graphs do not intersect.

    B. The graphs can intersect in one point.

    C. The graphs can intersect in two points.

    D. The graphs can intersect in three points.

4 A parabola opens up with its vertex at the origin. For which equation will the parabola and the line not intersect?

    A. $x = 2$ **C.** $y = 4$

    B. $y = 2$ **D.** $y = -5$

5 For which equation will the graph of $y = x^2 + 1$ and the line intersect in two points?

    A. $y = -2x$ **C.** $y = 2$

    B. $x = 1$ **D.** $y = 2x$

6 For which equations will the graphs intersect in two points?

    A. $x = 0; y = x^2$ **C.** $y = -1; y = x^2$

    B. $y = 2; y = x^2$ **D.** $y = 0; y = x^2$

In Exercises 7–14, solve each pair of equations. If there is no solution, so state.

7 $y = 2x + 3$ and $y = x^2$

8 $y = x$ and $2y = x^2$

9 $y = x^2 - 4x + 8$ and $y + x = 1$

10 $x^2 + y = 25$ and $x = y + 7$

11 $y = x^2 - 3x - 10$ and $y = 2x - 4$

12 $y = 5 - 4x - x^2$ and $y = 4x + 21$

13 $y = \frac{x^2}{2} + 2x + 3$ and $y + 3 = \frac{x}{2}$

14 $x^2 + y = 5$ and $y - 3 = -(x + 4)$

In Exercises 15–16, use graphs to show that the pair of equations has no solution.

15 $y = x - 10$ **16** $y = x^2 + 1$
    $y = x^2 + 2x - 5$ $y = -x^2 - 2$

In Exercises 17–19, determine the number of points of intersection of the specified graphs. Justify your response.

17 A parabola opens up and has vertex $P(-2, 3)$. A line has equation $y = 3$.

18 A parabola opens down and has vertex $P(-2, 3)$. A line has equation $y = 3$.

19 A parabola opens up and has vertex $P(0, 0)$. A line has equation $y = 2x$.

6.5 Transforming Functions

New Jersey Standards

4.3.B.3.1 Transformations on functions

4.3.B.3.2 Transformations on linear and quadratic functions

The graphs of all quadratic functions of the form $y = ax^2 + bx + c$ are parabolas. You know that the graph of the most basic quadratic function $y = x^2$ is a parabola that opens up with its vertex at the origin $(0, 0)$. $y = x^2$ is called the **parent function** of the family of quadratic functions because all graphs of quadratic functions have the same parabolic shape but may open down, or be shifted along one or both of the x-axis and y-axis.

EXAMPLES 1 and 2 — Comparing quadratic functions to $y = x^2$

Graph the following quadratic functions. Compare the graph with the graph of $y = x^2$.

1 $y = (x - 1)^2$

■ SOLUTION

x	y
-2	9
-1	4
0	1
1	0
2	1

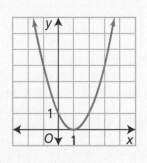

The graph of $y = (x - 1)^2$ is shifted 1 unit to the right on the x-axis.

2 $y = -\frac{1}{3}(x + 2)^2 - 1$

■ SOLUTION

x	y
-2	9
-1	4
0	1
1	0
2	1

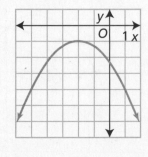

The graph of $y = -\frac{1}{3}(x + 2)^2 - 1$ opens down, is wider, and is shifted 2 units left on the y-axis and 1 unit down on the x-axis.

You can also apply a basic geometric transformation, called a reflection, to a quadratic function. If the graph of the function $y = x^2$ is reflected over the line $y = x$, the result will be the graph of $x = y^2$.

You can use function notation to show how a transformation changes the graph of the function. The table below shows how the graph of $f(x)$ is transformed to the graph of the new function. The constants h and k are positive real numbers.

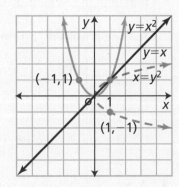

Function	Transformation
$f(x + h)$	Shift h units to the left
$f(x - h)$	Shift h units to the right
$f(x) + k$	Shift k units up
$f(x) - k$	Shift k units down
$-f(x)$	Reflect over x-axis
$f(-x)$	Reflect over y-axis

You can use this notation to graph a function quickly and accurately.

EXAMPLE 3   **Transforming the graph of $f(x) = x^2$**

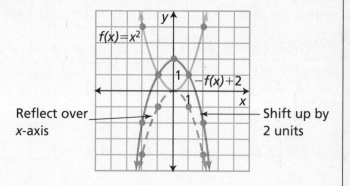

3 Graph the function $-f(x) + 2$ where of $f(x) = x^2$.

■ **SOLUTION**

The graph of $-f(x) + 2$ is the graph of $f(x) = x^2$ reflected over the x-axis and shifted 2 units up on the y-axis.

Reflect over x-axis

Shift up by 2 units

Practice

Choose the letter preceding the word or expression that best completes the statement or answers the question.

1 The graph of $f(-x)$ relates to the graph of $f(x)$ because it is reflected over

   A. the x-axis.   **C.** the line $y = x$.

   B. the y-axis.   **D.** the line $x = -1$.

2 Which function when graphed is the graph of $g(x)$ shifted down by 3 units and to the right by 1 unit?

   A. $g(x + 3) - 1$

   B. $g(x - 3) + 1$

   C. $g(x - 1) - 3$

   D. $g(x + 1) + 3$

3 If you know that the point $(-3, 10)$ is on the graph of $f(x)$, what point do you know is on the graph of $f(-x) + 5$?

   A. $(-8, 10)$ **C.** $(2, 10)$

   B. $(-3, 15)$ **D.** $(3, 15)$

In Exercises 4–7, use the graph of $f(x)$ shown, drawn with a unit scale, to sketch each transformation.

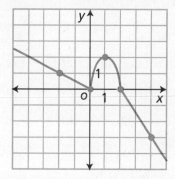

4 $f(x - 4)$ **5** $f(x) + 3$

6 $f(x + 2) - 3$ **7** $-f(x)$

In Exercises 8–13, describe the transformation of $f(x)$ for each function.

8 $f(x - 5) + 3$ **9** $-f(x + 2)$

10 $f(-x) - 6$ **11** $-f(x + 1) - 4$

12 $f\left(-\frac{1}{2}x\right) + 5$ **13** $-f(x - 3) - 7$

175

DIRECTIONS FOR QUESTIONS 1–23: For each of the questions below, select the answer choice that is best for each case.

1 Which is an equation of a parabola whose vertex is the origin and opens down?

A. $y = 3x^2$ C. $y - x^2 = 1$

B. $y = -3x^2$ D. $y + 1 = x^2$

2 Which graph crosses $y = 0$ in two points?

A. $y = x^2 - 6x + 8$

B. $y = x^2 + 6x + 9$

C. $y = x^2 - 6x + 10$

D. $y = x^2 + 6x + 11$

3 In how many points does the parabola with vertex $(3, -4)$ that opens up intersect the line with equation $x = 3$?

A. 1   B. 3   C. 2   D. 0

4 Which is equivalent to $6x^2 + 19x + 10 = 0$?

A. $(3x + 2)(2x + 5) = 0$

B. $(3x - 2)(2x - 5) = 0$

C. $(x + 2)(6x + 5) = 0$

D. $(6x - 5)(x - 2) = 0$

5 Which are the solutions to $19n = 4n^2 + 19n - 9$?

A. $\frac{3}{2}$ and $-\frac{3}{2}$ C. $\frac{2}{3}$ and $-\frac{2}{3}$

B. only $\frac{3}{2}$ D. no solution

6 Which is true of the graph of $y = -x^2 + 12x$?

A. The graph opens down and the axis of symmetry is $x = -12$.

B. The graph opens down and the axis of symmetry is $x = 12$.

C. The graph opens up and the axis of symmetry is $x = 6$.

D. The graph opens down and the axis of symmetry is $x = 6$.

7 Which equation does not have the same solutions as $3x^2 = 6x - 9$?

A. $3x^2 - 6x + 9 = 0$

B. $3x^2 - 6x = -9$

C. $3x^2 - 6x - 9 = 0$

D. $x^2 - 2x + 3 = 0$

8 Which equation has exactly one solution?

A. $(c - 3)^2 = 0$

B. $(c - 3)^2 = 5$

C. $(c - 3)^2 = -5$

D. $c - (2c^2 + 1) = -5$

9 Which is equivalent to $n^2 + n = 30$?

A. $(n + 6)(n - 5) = 0$

B. $(n - 6)(n + 5) = 0$

C. $(n - 6)(n - 5) = 0$

D. $(n + 6)(n + 5) = 0$

10 How many solutions does $q^2 - 2q + 1 = 0$ have?

A. one   C. two

B. none   D. infinitely many

11 Which does not represent a rectangle with length $m + 2$, width $m + 4$, and area 63?

A. $(m + 2)(m + 4) = 63$

B. $(m + 2)(m + 4) - 63 = 0$

C. $m^2 + 6m + 8 = 63$

D. $m^2 + 6m + 71 = 0$

12 The solutions to $s(s - 3)(s + 8) = 0$ are

A. $0, 3,$ and $8.$ C. $0, 3,$ and $-8.$

B. -3 and $8.$ D. $0, -3,$ and $8.$

13 If the value of the discriminant is 0, how many solutions will the quadratic have?

A. zero   C. two

B. one   D. four

14 The roots of a quadratic are $x = -5$ and $x = 3$. Which of the following are possible factors of the quadratic?

A. $(x - 5)$ and $(x + 3)$

B. $(x + 5)$ and $(x - 3)$

C. $x = -5$ and $x = 3$

D. $(x - 5)$ and $(x - 3)$

In Exercises 15–17, solve the quadratic equation.

15 $4h^2 = 2h^2 + 32$

A. 8 and -8 C. -4 and 4

B. 16   D. 8

16 $4p^2 = -16$

A. 4 and -4 C. -2

B. 2 and -2 D. no solution

17 $2a^2 = 13a + 7$

A. -7 and $\frac{1}{2}$ C. $-\frac{1}{2}$ and 7

B. 1 and $\frac{7}{2}$ D. -1 and $\frac{7}{2}$

18 In how many points does the parabola with equation $x^2 - 6x + 9 = y$ intersect the line with equation $y = 3x$?

A. 0   B. 1   C. 2   D. 3

19 Which points are the zeros of the equation $x^2 - 2x - 15 = 0$?

A. $(-3, 0)$ and $(5, 0)$

B. $(0, -3)$ and $(0, 5)$

C. $(3, 0)$ and $(-5, 0)$

D. $(0, -2)$ and $(0, -15)$

20 Which is not true of the parabola with equation $y = -3x^2 + 2x - 4$?

A. The parabola opens down.

B. The parabola has a minimum.

C. The parabola has vertex $\left(\frac{1}{3}, -\frac{11}{3}\right)$.

D. The axis of symmetry is $x = \frac{1}{3}$.

21 The graph of which equation has a maximum?

A. $y = \frac{1}{2}x^2 - 6x + 5$

B. $y = -2x + \frac{3}{4}x^2 - 1$

C. $y = 3x - \frac{7}{8}x^2 + 2$

D. $y - \frac{2}{3}x^2 = 7x + 5$

22 What is the value of the discriminant of $2x^2 - 3x + 5 = 0$?

A. $x = -49$

B. $y = -7$

C. $y = -31$

D. $x = -46$

23 A line given by $f(x)$ passes through the origin. Which could be the function shown in the graph?

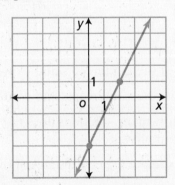

A. $f(x - 3)$ C. $f(x) - 3$

B. $f(x + 3)$ D. $f(x) + 3$

DIRECTIONS FOR 24–26: Solve each problem and show your work.

24 The altitude of an object in feet is given by
$h = -16t^2 + 8t + 48$.

- What is its maximum altitude?

- After how many seconds t will it strike the ground?

25 The shaded area is 324 square feet.

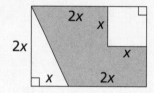

- Write an expression for the area of the square shown.

- Write an expression for the area of the right triangle shown.

- Find x.

26 The diagram below shows the graph of $y = x^3 + x^2 - 5x - 7$ and
$y = x - 4$.

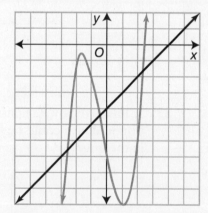

- List the x-intercepts and y-intercepts of the line.

- List the x-intercepts and y-intercepts of the curve.

- How many solutions does this system of equations have? Explain your answer.

- Estimate the coordinates of the solutions of the system.

7 Rational and Radical Expressions and Equations

NEW JERSEY

7.1 Rational Expressions

New Jersey Standards

4.1.B.1 Understand real numbers

4.3.D.1.4 Use rational expressions

4.3.D.1.5 Evaluate rational expressions

Recall that a rational number is any number that can be written in the form $\frac{a}{b}$, where a and b are integers and $b \neq 0$. It is necessary to exclude 0 because the fraction $\frac{a}{b}$ represents $a \div b$, and division by zero is undefined.

A **rational expression** is an expression that can be written in the form $\frac{P}{Q}$, where P and Q are polynomials and the value of Q is not zero. The following are some examples of rational expressions.

$$\frac{-3}{2} \qquad \frac{y^2 - 1}{4} \qquad \frac{5}{x + 2} \qquad \frac{t^2 + 5t + 6}{t + 3} \qquad \frac{ab^2}{c} \qquad \frac{m^2 - 3m}{m - n}$$

Like a rational number, a rational expression represents a division, and so the denominator cannot be 0. A rational expression is said to be *undefined* for any value of a variable that results in a denominator of zero.

Recall that the **domain** or **replacement set** is the set of all possible numbers that can be used to substitute for the variable in an algebraic expression. The domain for a rational expression will be **restricted** to all real numbers except those that make the denominator equal to zero.

EXAMPLES 1 through 4 **Recognizing when a rational expression is undefined**

Describe the circumstances, if any, in which the given expression is undefined.

1 $\frac{n}{6}$

▪ **SOLUTION** The denominator is 6, which is a constant. So the expression is defined for all real-number values of n.

2 $\frac{6}{n}$

▪ **SOLUTION** The denominator is n, which is a variable. So the expression is undefined when $n = 0$.

3 $\frac{6}{n + 1}$

▪ **SOLUTION** The denominator is $n + 1$. When $n = -1, n + 1 = 0$. So the expression is undefined when $n = -1$.

4 $\frac{6}{n^2 + 1}$

▪ **SOLUTION** The denominator is $n^2 + 1$, which is a variable expression. However, there is no real number n for which $n^2 + 1 = 0$. So the expression is defined for all real-number values of n.

Any value of a variable for which a rational expression is undefined is called an **excluded value** of the variable. It is said that the excluded values are *restricted from the domain* of that variable.

To find the excluded values of a variable, you can use what you learned about solving equations.

Finding values for which a rational expression is undefined

Note

Recall the Zero-Product Property: If a and b are real numbers and $ab = 0$, then either $a = 0$ or $b = 0$.

State any restrictions on the domain of the variable in each expression.

5 $\dfrac{w}{3w + 2}$

6 $\dfrac{2b}{b^2 + 4b + 3}$

■ **SOLUTION**

Solve $3w + 2 = 0$.

$$3w + 2 = 0 \qquad \leftarrow 3w + 2 = 0 \text{ is}$$
$$3w = -2 \qquad \text{a linear equation.}$$
$$w = -\tfrac{2}{3}$$

The only excluded value is $-\tfrac{2}{3}$.

You write: $w \neq -\tfrac{2}{3}$

■ **SOLUTION**

Solve $b^2 + 4b + 3 = 0$.

$$b^2 + 4b + 3 = 0 \qquad \leftarrow b^2 + 4b + 3 = 0 \text{ is}$$
$$(b + 1)(b + 3) = 0 \qquad \text{a quadratic equation.}$$
$$b = -1 \text{ or } b = -3$$

The excluded values are -1 and -3.

You write: $b \neq -1, b \neq -3$

Recall that an arithmetic fraction is in *lowest terms* if the GCF of its numerator and denominator is 1. You can rewrite a fraction in lowest terms by dividing both its numerator and denominator by their GCF.

$$\frac{16}{24} = \frac{16 \div 8}{24 \div 8} = \frac{2}{3} \qquad \leftarrow \text{The GCF of 16 and 24 is 8.}$$

Similarly, a rational expression is in *simplest form* if the GCF of its numerator and denominator is 1. You can use the following procedure to simplify a rational expression.

Simplifying a Rational Expression

Step 1 Factor both the numerator and the denominator, if necessary.

Step 2 Divide both the numerator and the denominator by their GCF.

EXAMPLE 7 **Simplifying a rational expression: monomial GCF**

Simplify the expression. State any restrictions on the domain of the variable.

7 $\dfrac{a^2 b - ab}{a^2 b}$

■ **SOLUTION**

$$\frac{a^2 b - ab}{a^2 b} = \frac{ab(a - 1)}{a^2 b} \qquad \leftarrow \text{Factor.}$$

$$= \frac{\overset{1}{ab}(a - 1)}{a \cdot \underset{1}{ab}} \qquad \leftarrow \text{The GCF is } ab.$$

$$= \frac{1 \cdot (a - 1)}{a \cdot 1}$$

$$= \frac{a - 1}{a}$$

To find the restrictions on the domains of a and b, solve $a^2 b = 0$.

$$a^2 b = 0$$
$$a^2 = 0 \text{ or } b = 0$$
$$a = 0 \text{ or } b = 0$$

The simplest form is $\frac{a - 1}{a}$, with the restrictions $a \neq 0, b \neq 0$.

181

Notice that $\frac{a-1}{a}$ cannot be simplified further, even though the variable a appears in both the numerator and denominator. When simplifying, you must look for *factors* that are common to the numerator and denominator. In $\frac{a-1}{a}$, the a in the numerator is a term, not a factor.

Also notice that, although the variable b does not appear in the simplified expression in Example 7, there is a restriction on b. When determining restrictions on the variables, you must examine the original expression.

Go Online
PHSchool.com

Visit: PHSchool.com
Web Code: ayp-0324

EXAMPLE 8   **Simplifying a rational expression: binomial GCF**

8 Simplify $\frac{d^2 - 9d + 18}{d^2 - 6d + 9}$. State any restrictions on the domain of the variable.

■ SOLUTION

$\frac{d^2 - 9d + 18}{d^2 - 6d + 9} = \frac{(d-3)(d-6)}{(d-3)(d-3)}$ ← **Factor.**

$= \frac{\overset{1}{(d-3)}(d-6)}{\underset{1}{(d-3)}(d-3)}$ ← **The GCF is $(d-3)$.**

$= \frac{1 \cdot (d-6)}{1 \cdot (d-3)}$

$= \frac{d-6}{d-3}$

To find the restrictions on the domain of d, solve $d^2 - 6d + 9 = 0$.

$d^2 - 6d + 9 = 0$
$(d-3)^2 = 0$
$d = 3$

So the simplest form is $\frac{d-6}{d-3}$, with the restriction $d \neq 3$.

Recall that we can reverse the signs of a polynomial by factoring -1 from every term. Therefore,

$$b - a = (-1)(-b + a) \text{ or } (-1)(a - b).$$

EXAMPLE 9   **Simplifying a rational expression: binomial factors that are opposites**

9 Simplify $\frac{w-4}{16-w^2}$. State any restrictions on the domain of the variable.

■ SOLUTION

$\frac{w-4}{16-w^2} = \frac{w-4}{(4-w)(4+w)}$ ← **Factor.**

$= \frac{w-4}{(-1)(w-4)(4+w)}$ ← $4 - w = (-1)(w-4)$

$= \frac{\overset{1}{w-4}}{(-1)(\underset{1}{w-4})(4+w)}$ ← **The GCF is $(w-4)$.**

$= \frac{1}{(-1)(1)(4+w)}$

$= \frac{1}{-(4+w)}$

$= \frac{1}{-4-w} \text{ or } \frac{-1}{4+w}$

To find the restrictions on the domain of w, solve $16 - w^2 = 0$.

$16 - w^2 = 0$
$(4+w)(4-w) = 0$
$w = -4 \text{ or } w = 4$

So the simplest form is $\frac{1}{-4-w}$, with the restrictions $w \neq -4$, $w \neq 4$.

Practice

Choose the letter preceding the word or expression that best completes the statement or answers the question.

1 Given the expression $\dfrac{3}{x^3 - 4x}$, what are the excluded values of x?

 A. 2 and -2 **C.** $-2, 0,$ and 2

 B. 0 and 2 **D.** 0 and 4

2 If $a \neq b$, which is equivalent to $\dfrac{a^2 - b^2}{a - b}$?

 A. $a - b$ **C.** 1

 B. $a + b$ **D.** 0

3 Which expression is equivalent to -1 for all values of n for which it is defined?

 A. $\dfrac{n - 2}{n^2 - 2}$ **C.** $\dfrac{(n - 2)^2}{n^2 - 4}$

 B. $\dfrac{n^2 - 4}{4 - n^2}$ **D.** $\dfrac{n + 1}{n - 1}$

4 Which is $\dfrac{4a^2 - 20ab}{4a^2 - 100b^2}$ in simplest form?

 A. $\dfrac{1 - 2ab}{1 - 10b^2}$

 B. $\dfrac{a(a - 5b)}{(a - 5b)(a - 5b)}$

 C. $\dfrac{4a(a - 5b)}{(2a - 10b)(2a + 10b)}$

 D. $\dfrac{a}{a + 5b}$

5 Which best describes the restrictions on the variables in $\dfrac{a^2 - 10ab + 25b^2}{a^2 - 25b^2}$?

 A. $a \neq 5b, a \neq -5b$

 B. $a \neq 5b, b \neq 5a$

 C. $a \neq 5, a \neq -5$

 D. $a \neq 5, a \neq -5, b \neq 5, b \neq -5$

In Exercises 6–11, state any restrictions on the domains of the variables in each expression.

6 $\dfrac{5}{2x - 8}$ **7** $\dfrac{h^2 - 36}{h^2}$

8 $\dfrac{p^2 - 2p - 3}{p^2 - 9}$ **9** $\dfrac{m^2 - 4m + 4}{m^2 + 4}$

10 $\dfrac{s^2 + t^2}{s^2 - t^2}$ **11** $\dfrac{a^2 - ab + b^2}{a^2 - ab}$

In Exercises 12–31, simplify each expression. State any restrictions on the domains of the variables.

12 $\dfrac{3j - 9}{3j}$ **13** $\dfrac{5u}{5u + 10}$

14 $\dfrac{x^2 - 2x}{x}$ **15** $\dfrac{2t}{4t^2 - 2t}$

16 $\dfrac{6z - 9}{4z - 6}$ **17** $\dfrac{c + 3}{c^2 + 3c}$

18 $\dfrac{s^3 - 2s^2}{2s^2 - 4s}$ **19** $\dfrac{3w - 6w^2}{2w^3}$

20 $\dfrac{p^2 - p}{pq - p}$ **21** $\dfrac{x^2 - xy}{x^2 + xy}$

22 $\dfrac{n^2 - 5n + 6}{n - 3}$ **23** $\dfrac{v + 7}{v^2 - 49}$

24 $\dfrac{b^2 - 36}{b^2 + 4b - 12}$ **25** $\dfrac{r^2 - r - 6}{r^2 + r - 12}$

26 $\dfrac{6k - 15}{2k^2 - 3k - 5}$ **27** $\dfrac{4z^2 + 3z - 1}{8z - 2}$

28 $\dfrac{5d + 20}{16 - d^2}$ **29** $\dfrac{2g^2 + 3g - 9}{3 - 2g}$

30 $\dfrac{b^2 + 2b + 1}{1 - b^2}$ **31** $\dfrac{m^2 - mn}{n^2 - mn}$

In Exercises 32–33, use the expression given to solve the problem.

32 Given $\dfrac{c + 4}{c - 4}$, explain why 4 is excluded from the domain of c, but -4 is not.

33 Is the expression $\dfrac{3p^2 - 27q^2}{p^2 - 9q^2}$ defined when $p = 3$ and $q = -1$? Show your work.

7.2 Multiplication and Division with Rational Expressions

New Jersey Standards

4.3.D.1.4 Perform operations on rational expressions

4.3.D.1.5 Evaluate rational expressions

When you multiply arithmetic fractions, you multiply the numerators and multiply the denominators. Then, if necessary, you simplify the result.

$$\frac{4}{5} \cdot \frac{15}{16} = \frac{4 \cdot 15}{5 \cdot 16} = \frac{60}{80} = \frac{60 \div 20}{80 \div 20} = \frac{3}{4}$$

The procedure for multiplying rational expressions is similar to the procedure for multiplying arithmetic fractions.

Multiplying Rational Expressions

If $\frac{P}{Q}$ and $\frac{R}{S}$ are rational expressions, and the values of Q and S are not zero, then:

$$\frac{P}{Q} \cdot \frac{R}{S} = \frac{PR}{QS}$$

When you are performing operations with rational expressions in this book, you may assume that the domain of each variable is restricted so that no denominator has a value of zero.

- You can multiply rational expressions by first multiplying the numerators and denominators and then reducing the resulting rational expression by the common monomial factor (the GCF) of both the numerator and denominator.

- You can also divide the numerators and denominators by the common factors first and then multiply the remaining factors.

EXAMPLE 1 Multiplying $\frac{P}{Q} \cdot \frac{R}{S}$: monomial numerators and denominators

 Simplify $\frac{7x}{9} \cdot \frac{3}{4x^2}$.

■ SOLUTION 1
Multiply first.

$$\frac{7x}{9} \cdot \frac{3}{4x^2} = \frac{21x}{36x^2}$$

$$= \frac{21x \div 3x}{36x^2 \div 3x} \quad \leftarrow \text{Find the common factor.}$$

$$= \frac{7}{12x} \quad \leftarrow \text{Divide by the common factor.}$$

■ SOLUTION 2
Factor first.

$$\frac{7x}{9} \cdot \frac{3}{4x^2}$$

$$= \frac{7 \cdot x}{3 \cdot 3} \cdot \frac{3}{4 \cdot x \cdot x} \quad \leftarrow \text{Factor first.}$$

$$= \frac{7 \cdot 1 \cdot 1}{3 \cdot 4 \cdot x} = \frac{7}{12x}$$

You may use the second method if the rational expressions have polynomials in the numerator and denominator. Because both numerators and denominators are multiplied, the common factors can be removed from any numerator and denominator.

Go Online
PHSchool.com
Visit: PHSchool.com
Web Code: ayp-0638

Simplify each expression.

2 $\dfrac{3v-6}{5v+25} \cdot \dfrac{v+5}{9v-18}$

■ SOLUTION

$\dfrac{3v-6}{5v+25} \cdot \dfrac{v+5}{9v-18}$

$= \dfrac{3(v-2)}{5(v+5)} \cdot \dfrac{v+5}{9(v-2)}$

$= \dfrac{3(v-2)}{5(v+5)} \cdot \dfrac{(v+5)}{9(v-2)}$

$= \dfrac{1 \cdot 1 \cdot 1}{5 \cdot 1 \cdot 3 \cdot 1}$

$= \dfrac{1}{15}$

3 $\dfrac{c^2+4c-12}{4c-6} \cdot \dfrac{8c^2-18}{5c+30}$

■ SOLUTION

$\dfrac{c^2+4c-12}{4c-6} \cdot \dfrac{8c^2-18}{5c+30}$

$= \dfrac{(c+6)(c-2)}{2(2c-3)} \cdot \dfrac{2(2c+3)(2c-3)}{5(c+6)}$

$= \dfrac{(c+6)(c-2)}{2(2c-3)} \cdot \dfrac{2(2c+3)(2c-3)}{5(c+6)}$

$= \dfrac{1 \cdot (c-2) \cdot 1 \cdot (2c+3) \cdot 1}{1 \cdot 1 \cdot 5 \cdot 1}$

$= \dfrac{(c-2)(2c+3)}{5}$ or $\dfrac{2c^2-c-6}{5}$

Recall that any whole number is a rational number whose denominator is 1. Therefore, you can multiply a rational expression by a polynomial by writing the polynomial as a rational expression with a denominator of 1, for example,

$$2x^2 + 3 = \dfrac{2x^2+3}{1}.$$

EXAMPLE 4   **Multiplying a rational expression by a polynomial**

4 Simplify $\dfrac{5x+10}{x^2+7x+10} \cdot x^2 + 8x + 15$.

■ SOLUTION

$\dfrac{5x+10}{x^2+7x+10} \cdot x^2 + 8x + 15 = \dfrac{5(x+2)}{(x+5)(x+2)} \cdot \dfrac{(x+3)(x+5)}{1} = 5(x+3)$

When you divide two arithmetic fractions, you multiply the dividend by the reciprocal of the divisor and simplify the result.

$$\dfrac{3}{4} \div \dfrac{5}{6} = \dfrac{3}{4} \cdot \dfrac{6}{5} = \dfrac{3 \cdot 6}{4 \cdot 5} = \dfrac{18}{20} = \dfrac{18 \div 2}{20 \div 2} = \dfrac{9}{10}$$

The procedure for dividing rational expressions is similar.

Note

Recall that the reciprocal of any rational number $\frac{a}{b}$ is $\frac{b}{a}$, provided that $a \neq 0$ and $b \neq 0$.

Dividing Rational Expressions

If $\frac{P}{Q}$ and $\frac{R}{S}$ are rational expressions, and the values of Q, R, and S are not zero, then:

$$\dfrac{P}{Q} \div \dfrac{R}{S} = \dfrac{P}{Q} \cdot \dfrac{S}{R} = \dfrac{PS}{QR}$$

EXAMPLES 5 and 6 — Dividing $\frac{P}{Q} \div \frac{R}{S}$: monomial numerators and denominators

Simplify each expression. Write each answer using positive exponents.

5 $\frac{9h^2}{35} \div \frac{h^3}{7}$

■ **SOLUTION**

$$\frac{9h^2}{35} \div \frac{h^3}{7} = \frac{9h^2}{35} \cdot \frac{7}{h^3}$$

$$= \frac{9h^2}{\underset{5}{35}} \cdot \frac{\overset{1}{7}}{\underset{h}{h^3}}$$

$$= \frac{9}{5h}$$

6 $\frac{6a}{5b} \div \frac{3b}{5a}$

■ **SOLUTION**

$$\frac{6a}{5b} \div \frac{3b}{5a} = \frac{6a}{5b} \cdot \frac{5a}{3b}$$

$$= \frac{\overset{2}{6a}}{\underset{1}{5b}} \cdot \frac{\overset{1}{5a}}{\underset{1}{3b}}$$

$$= \frac{2a^2}{b^2}$$

To divide a rational expression by a polynomial, you must multiply by the reciprocal of the polynomial. For example, to divide a rational expression by $2x + 3$, you would multiply by $\frac{1}{2x+3}$.

Go Online
PHSchool.com
Visit: PHSchool.com
Web Code: ayp-0639

EXAMPLES 7 and 8 — Dividing polynomial expressions

Simplify each expression.

7 $\frac{3y + 12}{y - 4} \div \frac{y^2 + 4y}{2y - 8}$

■ **SOLUTION**

$$\frac{3y + 12}{y - 4} \div \frac{y^2 + 4y}{2y - 8}$$

$$= \frac{3y + 12}{y - 4} \cdot \frac{2y - 8}{y^2 + 4y}$$

$$= \frac{3(y + 4)}{y - 4} \cdot \frac{2(y - 4)}{y(y + 4)}$$

$$= \frac{3\,\overset{1}{\cancel{(y + 4)}}}{\underset{1}{\cancel{y - 4}}} \cdot \frac{2\,\cancel{(y - 4)}}{y\,\underset{1}{\cancel{(y + 4)}}}$$

$$= \frac{6}{y}$$

8 $\frac{m^2 - 4}{m^2 + 6m + 9} \div \frac{m^2 - 2m - 8}{m^2 - m - 12}$

■ **SOLUTION**

$$\frac{m^2 - 4}{m^2 + 6m + 9} \div \frac{m^2 - 2m - 8}{m^2 - m - 12}$$

$$= \frac{m^2 - 4}{m^2 + 6m + 9} \cdot \frac{m^2 - m - 12}{m^2 - 2m - 8}$$

$$= \frac{(m - 2)(m + 2)}{(m + 3)(m + 3)} \cdot \frac{(m - 4)(m + 3)}{(m - 4)(m + 2)}$$

$$= \frac{(m - 2)\,\cancel{(m + 2)}}{(m + 3)\,\underset{1}{\cancel{(m + 3)}}} \cdot \frac{\overset{1}{\cancel{(m - 4)}}\,\overset{1}{\cancel{(m + 3)}}}{\underset{1}{\cancel{(m - 4)}}\,\underset{1}{\cancel{(m + 2)}}}$$

$$= \frac{m - 2}{m + 3}$$

When performing multiplications and divisions with rational expressions, you may need to work with binomial factors that are opposites of each other.

EXAMPLE 9 — Dividing rational expressions when binomial factors are opposites

9 Simplify $\frac{z - 6}{5} \div \frac{6 - z}{2}$.

■ **SOLUTION**

$$\frac{z - 6}{5} \div \frac{6 - z}{2} = \frac{z - 6}{5} \cdot \frac{2}{6 - z} = \frac{z - 6}{5} \cdot \frac{2}{(-1)(z - 6)} = \frac{\overset{1}{\cancel{z - 6}}}{5} \cdot \frac{2}{(-1)\,\underset{1}{\cancel{(z - 6)}}} = \frac{2}{-5} = -\frac{2}{5}$$

Practice

Choose the letter preceding the word or expression that best completes the statement or answers the question.

1 Which is equivalent to $\dfrac{16r^2}{5s^2} \div \dfrac{4r^2}{5s}$?

A. $\dfrac{5s^2}{16r^2} \cdot \dfrac{4r^2}{5s}$

C. $\dfrac{5s^2}{16r^2} \cdot \dfrac{5s}{4r^2}$

B. $\dfrac{16r^2}{5s^2} \cdot \dfrac{5s}{4r^2}$

D. $\dfrac{4r^2}{5s} \div \dfrac{16r^2}{5s^2}$

2 Which is equivalent to $\dfrac{4}{n-6} \div \dfrac{n+6}{4}$?

A. $\dfrac{n+6}{n-6}$

C. $\dfrac{16}{n^2-36}$

B. $\dfrac{n-6}{n+6}$

D. $\dfrac{4n+24}{4n-24}$

3 Simplify $\dfrac{a+2}{a-2} \cdot \dfrac{2-a}{2+a}$.

A. -2

C. 0

B. -1

D. 1

4 Which is not equivalent to $\dfrac{b-1}{b} \cdot (1-b)$?

A. $\dfrac{b-1}{b} \cdot \dfrac{1-b}{1}$

B. $\dfrac{b-1}{b} \cdot \dfrac{-(b-1)}{1}$

C. $\dfrac{-(b-1)^2}{b}$

D. $-\dfrac{1}{b}$

In Exercises 5–30, simplify each expression. Write answers using positive exponents.

5 $\dfrac{9}{j} \cdot \dfrac{3}{j}$

6 $\dfrac{4}{t} \div \dfrac{16}{t}$

7 $\dfrac{2c^2}{7} \cdot \dfrac{21}{12c^3}$

8 $\dfrac{6}{5s} \cdot \dfrac{s^3}{8}$

9 $\dfrac{m^4}{9} \div \dfrac{3}{2m^2}$

10 $\dfrac{1}{10v^3} \div \dfrac{35}{v}$

11 $\dfrac{4y^2}{3} \cdot 12y$

12 $\dfrac{1}{d^3} \div 5d^2$

13 $\dfrac{3}{xy} \cdot \dfrac{5}{2xy}$

14 $\dfrac{7p}{2q^2} \cdot \dfrac{3p^2}{q}$

15 $\dfrac{2-t}{t} \cdot \dfrac{4}{4+t}$

16 $\dfrac{2x}{2x+8} \cdot \dfrac{x+4}{3x^2}$

17 $\dfrac{4}{2c-3} \div \dfrac{3}{4c-6}$

18 $\dfrac{6z+6}{z} \div \dfrac{z+1}{z^3}$

19 $\dfrac{3y+12}{y-4} \div \dfrac{3y}{2y-8}$

20 $\dfrac{4s}{s-5} \cdot \dfrac{4s-20}{s+4}$

21 $\dfrac{g}{g^2+6g-7} \cdot \dfrac{g^2+7g}{g^3}$

22 $\dfrac{6w^3}{w^2-3w} \div \dfrac{3w^2}{w^2-9}$

23 $\dfrac{b^2-b-6}{b^2-4b+4} \cdot \dfrac{b-2}{b-3}$

24 $\dfrac{q-9}{q+2} \div \dfrac{q^2-81}{q^2-2q-8}$

25 $\dfrac{n^2+6n+8}{n-1} \div \dfrac{n^2-4}{n-1}$

26 $\dfrac{u^2-3u-10}{u-2} \cdot \dfrac{u-5}{u^2-10u+25}$

27 $(6h-36) \cdot \dfrac{h^2+h-12}{h^2-2h-24}$

28 $\dfrac{t^2-6t-27}{t^2+2t-3} \cdot (t^2-1)$

29 $\dfrac{y^2+y-30}{y^2+3y-10} \div (y+6)$

30 $(m-4) \div \dfrac{m^2-16}{m^2+5m+4}$

7.3 Addition and Subtraction with Rational Expressions

New Jersey Standards

4.3.D.1.4 Perform operations on rational expressions

4.3.D.1.5 Evaluate rational expressions

When you add or subtract arithmetic fractions with like denominators, you add or subtract the numerators. Then you place the sum or difference over the common denominator and simplify the result.

$$\frac{3}{7} + \frac{2}{7} = \frac{3+2}{7} = \frac{5}{7} \qquad \frac{3}{7} - \frac{2}{7} = \frac{3-2}{7} = \frac{1}{7}$$

The procedure for adding and subtracting rational expressions is similar.

Adding and Subtracting Rational Expressions

If $\frac{P}{Q}$ and $\frac{R}{Q}$ are rational expressions, and the value of Q is not zero, then:

$$\frac{P}{Q} + \frac{R}{Q} = \frac{P+R}{Q} \qquad \text{and} \qquad \frac{P}{Q} - \frac{R}{Q} = \frac{P-R}{Q}$$

EXAMPLES 1 through 4 Simplifying $\frac{P}{Q} + \frac{R}{Q}$ and $\frac{P}{Q} - \frac{R}{Q}$: monomial numerators

Simplify each expression.

1 $\frac{9}{4s} - \frac{1}{4s}$

- SOLUTION $\quad \frac{9}{4s} - \frac{1}{4s} = \frac{9-1}{4s} = \frac{8}{4s} = \frac{\overset{2}{\cancel{8}}}{\underset{1}{\cancel{4s}}} = \frac{2}{s}$

2 $\frac{2}{p-1} - \frac{7}{p-1}$

- SOLUTION $\quad \frac{2}{p-1} - \frac{7}{p-1} = \frac{2-7}{p-1} = \frac{-5}{p-1}$

3 $\frac{2a}{a+b} + \frac{6a}{a+b}$

- SOLUTION $\quad \frac{2a}{a+b} + \frac{6a}{a+b} = \frac{2a+6a}{a+b} = \frac{8a}{a+b}$

4 $\frac{m}{n+3} - \frac{3}{n+3}$

- SOLUTION $\quad \frac{m}{n+3} - \frac{3}{n+3} = \frac{m-3}{n+3}$

Often you must perform additions or subtractions in which the numerators are polynomials with more than one term. In such cases, you will need to apply what you have learned about adding and subtracting polynomials. When subtracting, be especially careful to use the rules for opposites of sums and differences that are summarized at the right.

$$-(a+b) = -a - b$$
$$-(a-b) = -a + b$$

EXAMPLES 5 and 6 Simplifying $\frac{P}{Q} + \frac{R}{Q}$ and $\frac{P}{Q} - \frac{R}{Q}$: polynomial numerators

Simplify each expression.

5 $\frac{c+2}{c-6} + \frac{c-3}{c-6}$

- SOLUTION

$$\frac{c+2}{c-6} + \frac{c-3}{c-6} = \frac{(c+2)+(c-3)}{c-6}$$
$$= \frac{(c+c)+(2-3)}{c-6}$$
$$= \frac{2c-1}{c-6}$$

6 $\frac{5z}{2z+7} - \frac{z-1}{2z+7}$

- SOLUTION

$$\frac{5z}{2z+7} - \frac{z-1}{2z+7} = \frac{5z-(z-1)}{2z+7}$$
$$= \frac{5z-z+1}{2z+7}$$
$$= \frac{4z+1}{2z+7}$$

To simplify some sums or differences, you may need to factor expressions in the numerator or denominator.

Go Online
PHSchool.com

Visit: PHSchool.com
Web Codes: ayp-0334
ayp-0335

EXAMPLES 7 and 8   Further simplifying $\frac{P}{Q} + \frac{R}{Q}$ and $\frac{P}{Q} - \frac{R}{Q}$

Simplify each expression.

7 $\dfrac{w+1}{3w+2} + \dfrac{5w+3}{3w+2}$

■ **SOLUTION**

$$\frac{w+1}{3w+2} + \frac{5w+3}{3w+2} = \frac{(w+1)+(5w+3)}{3w+2}$$

$$= \frac{6w+4}{3w+2}$$

$$= \frac{2(3w+2)}{3w+2}$$

$$= \frac{2(3w+2)^{1}}{3w+2_{1}}$$

$$= 2$$

8 $\dfrac{k^2+k}{k-1} - \dfrac{k+1}{k-1}$

■ **SOLUTION**

$$\frac{k^2+k}{k-1} - \frac{k+1}{k-1} = \frac{(k^2+k)-(k+1)}{k-1}$$

$$= \frac{k^2+k-k-1}{k-1}$$

$$= \frac{k^2-1}{k-1}$$

$$= \frac{(k+1)(k-1)}{k-1}$$

$$= \frac{(k+1)(k-1)^{1}}{k-1_{1}}$$

$$= k+1$$

In some additions and subtractions, the denominators are opposite binomials. You can use the basic relationship shown at the right to rewrite one of the expressions so that the denominators are like.

$$\frac{a}{-b} = \frac{-a}{b}$$

EXAMPLE 9   **Working with binomial denominators that are opposites**

9   Simplify $\dfrac{g}{g-5} - \dfrac{5}{5-g}$.

■ **SOLUTION**

$$\frac{g}{g-5} - \frac{5}{5-g} = \frac{g}{g-5} - \frac{5}{-(g-5)} = \frac{g}{g-5} - \frac{-5}{g-5} = \frac{g-(-5)}{g-5} = \frac{g+5}{g-5}$$

When you add or subtract numeric fractions with unlike denominators, you first rewrite one or both fractions with their least common denominator (LCD).

$$\frac{1}{6} + \frac{4}{15} = \frac{1}{2 \cdot 3} + \frac{4}{3 \cdot 5} \qquad \leftarrow \text{ Find the prime factorization of 6 and of 15.}$$

$$= \frac{1 \cdot 5}{2 \cdot 3 \cdot 5} + \frac{2 \cdot 4}{2 \cdot 3 \cdot 5} \qquad \leftarrow \text{ The LCD is } 2 \cdot 3 \cdot 5 \text{, or 30.}$$

$$= \frac{5}{30} + \frac{8}{30}$$

$$= \frac{5+8}{30}$$

$$= \frac{13}{30}$$

The procedure for adding and subtracting rational expressions with unlike denominators is similar. Although you can use any common denominator, your work generally is easier if you use the following method to find the LCD.

Go Online
PHSchool.com

Visit: PHSchool.com
Web Codes: ayp-0036
   ayp-0037

Finding the LCD of Rational Expressions

Step 1 Factor each denominator completely, writing the prime factorization of any numerical factors.

Step 2 Write the product of the factors that appear in any of the denominators, using each factor the greatest number of times it appears.

EXAMPLES 10 through 15   Simplifying $\frac{P}{Q} + \frac{R}{S}$ and $\frac{P}{Q} - \frac{R}{S}$

Simplify each expression.

10 $\frac{3}{x} + \frac{4}{y}$

■ SOLUTION

$$\frac{3}{x} + \frac{4}{y} = \frac{3 \cdot y}{x \cdot y} + \frac{4 \cdot x}{x \cdot y} = \frac{3y + 4x}{xy}$$

11 $\frac{5}{8} + \frac{1}{6d}$

■ SOLUTION

$$\frac{5}{8} + \frac{1}{6d} = \frac{5 \cdot 3d}{8 \cdot 3d} + \frac{1 \cdot 4}{6d \cdot 4} = \frac{15d + 4}{24d}$$

12 $\frac{2}{a} - \frac{3}{a^2}$

■ SOLUTION

$$\frac{2}{a} - \frac{3}{a^2} = \frac{2}{a} - \frac{3}{a \cdot a}$$
$$= \frac{2 \cdot a}{a \cdot a} - \frac{3}{a \cdot a}$$
$$= \frac{2a - 3}{a^2}$$

13 $\frac{m}{5} - \frac{m + 1}{m}$

■ SOLUTION

$$\frac{m}{5} - \frac{m + 1}{m} = \frac{m \cdot m}{5 \cdot m} - \frac{5 \cdot (m + 1)}{5 \cdot m}$$
$$= \frac{m^2 - 5(m + 1)}{5m}$$
$$= \frac{m^2 - 5m - 5}{5m}$$

14 $\frac{4}{3h + 6} - \frac{3}{2h + 4}$

■ SOLUTION

$$\frac{4}{3h + 6} - \frac{3}{2h + 4}$$
$$= \frac{4}{3(h + 2)} - \frac{3}{2(h + 2)}$$
$$= \frac{2 \cdot 4}{2 \cdot 3 \cdot (h + 2)} - \frac{3 \cdot 3}{2 \cdot 3 \cdot (h + 2)}$$
$$= \frac{8}{6(h + 2)} - \frac{9}{6(h + 2)}$$
$$= \frac{8 - 9}{6(h + 2)}$$
$$= \frac{-1}{6(h + 2)} \text{ or } \frac{-1}{6h + 12}$$

15 $\frac{5}{r^2 - 4} - \frac{7}{r + 2}$

■ SOLUTION

$$\frac{5}{r^2 - 4} - \frac{7}{r + 2}$$
$$= \frac{5}{(r + 2)(r - 2)} - \frac{7}{(r + 2)}$$
$$= \frac{5}{(r + 2)(r - 2)} - \frac{7(r - 2)}{(r + 2)(r - 2)}$$
$$= \frac{5 - 7(r - 2)}{(r + 2)(r - 2)}$$
$$= \frac{5 - 7r + 14}{(r + 2)(r - 2)}$$
$$= \frac{-7r + 19}{(r + 2)(r - 2)} \text{ or } \frac{-7r + 19}{r^2 - 4}$$

Choose the letter preceding the word or expression that best completes the statement or answers the question.

1 In simplest form, $\frac{4x + 6}{3} + \frac{5x + 9}{3}$ is

A. $\frac{9x + 15}{3}$.

C. $3x + 5$.

B. $\frac{9x + 15}{6}$.

D. $\frac{x + 3}{3}$.

2 Simplify $\frac{1}{c - 1} - \frac{1}{1 - c}$.

A. 0

C. $\frac{2}{c - 1}$

B. 2

D. $\frac{2}{c^2 - 1}$

3 Which is equivalent to $\frac{1}{a + b} + \frac{1}{a}$?

A. $\frac{2}{a + b}$

C. $\frac{2}{a^2 + b}$

B. $\frac{2a + b}{a^2 + ab}$

D. $\frac{2}{a^2 + ab}$

4 Which is equivalent to $\frac{m}{n} - \frac{1}{3}$?

A. $\frac{m - 1}{n - 3}$

C. $\frac{3m - n}{n - 3}$

B. $\frac{m - 1}{3n}$

D. $\frac{3m - n}{3n}$

In Exercises 5–31, simplify each expression. Write answers using positive exponents.

5 $\frac{7}{8} + \frac{3}{8}$

6 $\frac{8}{j} + \frac{1}{k}$

7 $-\frac{4}{3r} - \frac{2}{3r}$

8 $\frac{1}{z^2} + \frac{1}{z}$

9 $\frac{6}{v} + \frac{3}{v}$

10 $\frac{3}{2x} + \frac{3}{4x^2}$

11 $\frac{2}{c} + \frac{1}{5}$

12 $\frac{2}{25b^3} - \frac{1}{5b^2}$

13 $\frac{2b}{2b + 6} - \frac{4b}{2b + 6}$

14 $\frac{x}{x - y} - \frac{2y}{x - y}$

15 $\frac{r}{5r + 5s} + \frac{s}{5r + 5s}$

16 $\frac{8m}{4m - n} - \frac{2n}{4m - n}$

17 $\frac{5a}{a - 4} - \frac{3a}{4 - a}$

18 $\frac{p}{3p - 3} + \frac{1}{3p - 3}$

19 $\frac{q}{q + 1} + \frac{q - 9}{q + 1}$

20 $\frac{3g - h}{2g - 3h} - \frac{h}{2g - 3h}$

21 $\frac{z - 1}{z - 3} + \frac{z - 7}{z - 3}$

22 $\frac{8m - 1}{2m + 5} - \frac{6m - 6}{2m + 5}$

23 $\frac{2}{k + 1} + \frac{1}{2k + 2}$

24 $\frac{d}{3d + 9} - \frac{5}{4d + 12}$

25 $\frac{1}{y - 4} + \frac{3}{4}$

26 $\frac{3}{3s - 6} - \frac{2}{s^2 - 2s}$

27 $\frac{2}{x + 2} + \frac{8}{x^2 - 4}$

28 $\frac{2v}{v^2 - 1} - \frac{3}{v + 1}$

29 $\frac{1}{a + b} + \frac{1}{a - b}$

30 $\frac{4}{2c + d} + \frac{3}{2c - d}$

31 $\frac{2a}{a - 4} - 7$

7.4 Solving Rational Equations

New Jersey Standards

4.3.D.1.4 Perform operations on rational expressions

4.3.D.1.5 Evaluate rational expressions

4.3.C.1.4 Use equation to model real-world phenomena

A **rational equation** is an equation that contains one or more rational expressions. Rational equations are generally easier to solve if you first eliminate all denominators other than 1. You can solve rational equations by using the following procedure.

Solving a Rational Equation

Step 1 Find the LCD of all the denominators.

Step 2 Multiply all terms on each side of the equation by the LCD.

Step 3 Simplify the terms and solve the resulting equation.

EXAMPLES 1 and 2   **Solving rational equations by using the LCD: monomial denominators**

① Solve $\frac{b}{3} + \frac{1}{2} = \frac{4}{5}$.

■ **SOLUTION**

$$\frac{b}{3} + \frac{1}{2} = \frac{4}{5}$$ ← The denominators are 3, 2, and 5. The LCD is 30.

$$30\left(\frac{b}{3} + \frac{1}{2}\right) = 30\left(\frac{4}{5}\right)$$ ← Multiply each side by 30.

$$30\left(\frac{b}{3}\right) + 30\left(\frac{1}{2}\right) = 30\left(\frac{4}{5}\right)$$ ← Apply the Distributive Property.

$$10b + 15 = 24$$ ← Simplify each term.

$$10b = 9$$ ← Solve.

$$b = 0.9$$

Check: $\frac{b}{3} + \frac{1}{2} = \frac{4}{5} \rightarrow \frac{0.9}{3} + \frac{1}{2} = \frac{4}{5}$

$$0.3 + 0.5 = 0.8 \checkmark$$

② Solve $\frac{5}{4} + \frac{1}{2y} = \frac{7}{6}$.

■ **SOLUTION**

$$\frac{5}{4} + \frac{1}{2y} = \frac{7}{6}$$ ← The denominators are 4, 2y, and 6. The LCD is 12y.

$$12y\left(\frac{5}{4} + \frac{1}{2y}\right) = 12y\left(\frac{7}{6}\right)$$ ← Multiply each side by 12y.

$$12y\left(\frac{5}{4}\right) + 12y\left(\frac{1}{2y}\right) = 12y\left(\frac{7}{6}\right)$$ ← Apply the Distributive Property.

$$15y + 6 = 14y$$ ← Simplify each term.

$$y + 6 = 0$$ ← Solve.

$$y = -6$$

Check: $\frac{5}{4} + \frac{1}{2y} = \frac{7}{6} \rightarrow \frac{5}{4} + \frac{1}{2(-6)} = \frac{7}{6}$

$$\frac{15}{12} + \frac{-1}{12} = \frac{14}{12} \checkmark$$

When checking a solution to any equation, you must check it in the *original equation*, not in any of the subsequent equations. This procedure is especially important with rational equations. You must make sure that no proposed solution results in a denominator of zero in the original equation.

EXAMPLE 3   **Solving rational equations by using the LCD: polynomial denominators**

3 Solve $\dfrac{1}{m-4} + \dfrac{1}{m+4} = \dfrac{8}{m^2-16}$.

■ **SOLUTION**

$$\frac{1}{m-4} + \frac{1}{m+4} = \frac{8}{m^2-16}$$

$$\frac{1}{m-4} + \frac{1}{m+4} = \frac{8}{(m+4)(m-4)}$$

$$(m+4)(m-4)\left[\frac{1}{m-4} + \frac{1}{m+4}\right] = (m+4)(m-4)\left[\frac{8}{(m+4)(m-4)}\right]$$

$$(m+4)(m-4)\left[\frac{1}{m-4}\right] + (m+4)(m-4)\left[\frac{1}{m+4}\right] = (m+4)(m-4)\left[\frac{8}{(m+4)(m-4)}\right]$$

$$(m+4) + (m-4) = 8$$

$$2m = 8$$

$$m = 4$$

Check 4:

$$\frac{1}{m-4} + \frac{1}{m+4} = \frac{8}{m^2-16} \rightarrow \frac{1}{4-4} + \frac{1}{4+4} = \frac{8}{4^2-16} \rightarrow \frac{8}{0}$$

Replacing m with 4 in the original equation results in denominators of zero. Therefore, the equation has *no solution*.

When each side of a rational equation is a single rational expression, you can solve the equation by using the cross products property of proportions.

EXAMPLES 4 and 5   **Solving rational equations by using cross products**

4 Solve $\dfrac{k}{9} = \dfrac{36}{k}$.

■ **SOLUTION**

$$\frac{k}{9} = \frac{36}{k}$$
$$k \cdot k = 9 \cdot 36 \quad \leftarrow \text{Write the cross}$$
$$k^2 = 324 \qquad \text{products.}$$
$$k = 18 \text{ or } k = -18$$

Check 18:

$$\frac{k}{9} = \frac{36}{k} \rightarrow \frac{18}{9} = \frac{36}{18} \checkmark$$

Check −18:

$$\frac{k}{9} = \frac{36}{k} \rightarrow \frac{-18}{9} = \frac{36}{-18} \checkmark$$

Therefore, the solutions are 18 and −18.

5 Solve $\dfrac{1}{x+3} = \dfrac{4}{x^2-9}$.

■ **SOLUTION**

$$\frac{1}{x+3} = \frac{4}{x^2-9}$$
$$1(x^2-9) = (x+3)(4) \quad \leftarrow \text{Write the cross}$$
$$x^2 - 9 = 4x + 12 \quad \leftarrow \text{Simplify each side.}$$
$$x^2 - 4x - 21 = 0 \quad \leftarrow \text{Solve.}$$
$$(x-7)(x+3) = 0$$
$$x = 7 \text{ or } x = -3$$

Check 7:

$$\frac{1}{x+3} = \frac{4}{x^2-9} \rightarrow \frac{1}{7+3} = \frac{4}{7^2-9}$$
$$\frac{1}{10} = \frac{4}{40} \checkmark$$

Check −3:

$$\frac{1}{x+3} = \frac{4}{x^2-9} \rightarrow \frac{1}{-3+3} = \frac{4}{(-3)^2-9}$$
$$\frac{1}{0} = \frac{4}{0}$$

Replacing x with −3 in the original equation results in denominators of zero. Therefore, the only solution is 7.

You can use rational equations to solve word problems.

EXAMPLES 6 and 7   **Using a rational equation to solve problems**

6 One copy machine can complete a job in 25 minutes. This machine and
a newer machine working together can complete the same job in
10 minutes. How long would it take the newer machine, working
by itself, to complete the job?

■ SOLUTION

Let m represent the time in minutes for the newer machine to do
the job. Then the following are the work rates.

The first machine does 1 job in 25 minutes, so it does $\frac{1}{25}$ of the job in 1 minute.

The newer machine does 1 job in m minutes, so it does $\frac{1}{m}$ of the job in 1 minute.

The two machines do 1 job in 10 minutes, so they do $\frac{1}{10}$ of the job in 1 minute.

Step 1

Translate the situation into an equation.

part of job done by first machine in one minute	plus	part of job done by newer machine in one minute	equals	part of job done by both machines in one minute
↓	↓	↓	↓	↓
$\frac{1}{25}$	$+$	$\frac{1}{m}$	$=$	$\frac{1}{10}$

Step 2

Solve the equation.

$$\frac{1}{25} + \frac{1}{m} = \frac{1}{10}$$
$$50m\left(\frac{1}{25} + \frac{1}{m}\right) = 50m\left(\frac{1}{10}\right)$$
$$50m\left(\frac{1}{25}\right) + 50m\left(\frac{1}{m}\right) = 50m\left(\frac{1}{10}\right)$$
$$2m + 50 = 5m$$
$$50 = 3m$$
$$\frac{50}{3} = m$$
$$m = \frac{50}{3}, \text{ or } 16\frac{2}{3}$$

Working by itself, the newer machine can do the job in $\frac{50}{3}$ minutes, or $16\frac{2}{3}$ minutes.

7 When $\frac{2}{3}$ is subtracted from the quotient of a number n divided by 3, the result
equals the ratio of 1 to n. What is n?

■ SOLUTION

Step 1

Translate the situation into an equation.

The quotient of n divided by three	minus	two thirds	equals	the ratio of one to n
↓	↓	↓	↓	↓
$\frac{n}{3}$	$-$	$\frac{2}{3}$	$=$	$\frac{1}{n}$

Step 2

Solve the equation.

$$\frac{n}{3} - \frac{2}{3} = \frac{1}{n}$$
$$\frac{n-2}{3} = \frac{1}{n}$$
$$(n-2)n = 3(1)$$
$$n^2 - 2n = 3$$
$$n^2 - 2n - 3 = 0$$
$$(n-3)(n+1) = 0$$
$$n = 3 \text{ or } n = -1$$

The number n is either 3 or −1.

194

Choose the letter preceding the word or expression that best completes the statement or answers the question.

1 The solution set of $\frac{1}{r+1} = \frac{3}{r^2-1}$ consists of

   A. 4 and -1 **C.** only -1

   B. only 4   **D.** -4 and 1

2 Which equation is equivalent to $\frac{3}{a} - \frac{1}{a^2} = 2$?

   A. $3 - a = 2a^2$

   B. $2a^2 - 3a + 1 = 0$

   C. $3a^2 - a = 2a^2$

   D. $\frac{48}{a^2} = 2a$

3 Which equation has at least one solution?

   A. $\frac{3}{m-1} = \frac{4}{m-1}$

   B. $\frac{p}{5} = \frac{-5}{p}$

   C. $\frac{7}{2x-5} = \frac{3}{2x-5}$

   D. $\frac{3}{d+1} = \frac{d+1}{3}$

4 For which equation is 6 the only solution?

   A. $\frac{s}{6} = \frac{6}{s}$ **C.** $\frac{s}{6} = \frac{36}{s}$

   B. $\frac{s}{6} = \frac{-6}{s}$ **D.** $\frac{s}{s+2} = \frac{3}{4}$

In Exercises 5–22, solve each equation. If there is no solution, so state.

5 $\frac{w}{6} - \frac{1}{3} = \frac{1}{2}$ **6** $\frac{1}{3} + \frac{d}{9} = \frac{5}{6}$

7 $\frac{3r}{8} + \frac{5}{2} = \frac{r}{3}$ **8** $2 = \frac{5z}{8} - \frac{1}{2}$

9 $\frac{2}{a} + \frac{1}{2} = 3$ **10** $\frac{3}{h} - \frac{3}{4} = 4$

11 $\frac{3}{5n} - \frac{3}{2} = \frac{2}{3}$ **12** $\frac{1}{5} = \frac{3}{2y} + \frac{3}{10}$

13 $\frac{6}{j+1} = 1 + \frac{2}{j}$ **14** $\frac{6}{t} - 1 = \frac{3}{t+2}$

15 $\frac{1}{n-1} + \frac{2}{n+1} = \frac{2n+1}{n^2-1}$

16 $\frac{4s}{s^2-25} = \frac{1}{s+5} - \frac{2}{s-5}$

17 $\frac{8}{q} = \frac{q}{8}$

18 $\frac{k}{4} = \frac{25}{k}$

19 $\frac{4}{m-1} = \frac{6}{m-5}$

20 $\frac{2}{z+2} = \frac{8}{z-1}$

21 $\frac{d-1}{d-4} = \frac{10}{d-2}$

22 $\frac{4}{b+5} = \frac{b-5}{4}$

In Exercises 23–26, solve the problem.

23 When a number is divided by 3 the quotient is the same as the quotient obtained when 27 is divided by the number. What is the number?

24 Paul can complete a plumbing job in 3 hours. If he and his friend Sam work together, they can complete the same job in 2 hours. How many hours would it take Sam, working alone, to complete this job?

25 Jessica can wash the family dog in 45 minutes. Her brother can wash the dog in just 30 minutes. How long would it take them, working together, to wash the dog?

26 Two pipes can fill a storage tank in 9 hours. The larger pipe fills the tank three times as fast as the smaller one. How long would it take the smaller pipe alone to fill the tank?

7.5 Radical Expressions and Equations

New Jersey Standards

4.1.B.1 Understand real numbers

4.3.D.2.1 Solve linear equations

Recall that when solving equations like $x^2 = 144$, $x = \pm12$. However, when asked to evaluate or simplify a radical, we will consider only the positive or **principal square root**.

The square root $\sqrt{}$ symbol is also called a **radical sign**. An expression that involves a radical sign is called a **radical expression**. The expression under the radical is called the **radicand**.

$$^{\text{radical}}\sqrt{16}_{\text{radicand}} = 4_{\text{root}}$$

You can simplify some radical expressions by using the definition of square root.

$$\sqrt{144} = 12 \text{ because } 12 \cdot 12 = 12^2 = 144.$$
$$\sqrt{\frac{1}{9}} = \frac{1}{3} \text{ because } \frac{1}{3} \cdot \frac{1}{3} = \left(\frac{1}{3}\right)^2 = \frac{1}{9}.$$

To simplify other radical expressions, you may need to apply one of the following properties of square roots.

Visit: PHSchool.com
Web Code: ayp-0171

Properties of Square Roots

Let a and b represent real numbers.

Product Property

If $a \geq 0$ and $b \geq 0$,

then $\sqrt{ab} = \sqrt{a} \cdot \sqrt{b}$.

Quotient Property

If $a \geq 0$ and $b > 0$,

then $\sqrt{\frac{a}{b}} = \frac{\sqrt{a}}{\sqrt{b}}$.

EXAMPLES 1 through 4

Using the properties of square roots to simplify rational square roots

Simplify each expression.

1 $\sqrt{1600}$

■ **SOLUTION**

$$\sqrt{1600} = \sqrt{16 \cdot 100}$$
$$= \sqrt{16} \cdot \sqrt{100}$$
$$= 4 \cdot 10$$
$$= 40$$

2 $\sqrt{\frac{81}{64}}$

■ **SOLUTION**

$$\sqrt{\frac{81}{64}} = \frac{\sqrt{81}}{\sqrt{64}}$$
$$= \frac{9}{8}$$

3 $\sqrt{2916}$

■ **SOLUTION**

$$\sqrt{2916} = \sqrt{36 \cdot 81}$$
$$= \sqrt{36} \cdot \sqrt{81}$$
$$= 6 \cdot 9$$
$$= 54$$

4 $\sqrt{\frac{16}{144}}$

■ **SOLUTION**

$$\sqrt{\frac{16}{144}} = \frac{\sqrt{16}}{\sqrt{144}}$$
$$= \frac{4}{12} \text{ or } \frac{1}{3}$$

When the square root of a number is rational, the number is a **perfect square.** In the set of whole numbers, the perfect squares less than or equal to 100 are 1, 4, 9, 16, 25, 36, 49, 64, 81, and 100. Most whole numbers are not perfect squares and do not have rational square roots. These non-perfect squares have *irrational* square roots.

Recall that an irrational number is a non-terminating, non-repeating decimal. Therefore, if you are trying to find the square root of a non-perfect square the closest decimal answer will be an approximation.

You can use a calculator to find an approximation by entering the number and then pressing the  or key. The $\sqrt{5} \approx 2.236067978$. You press the key and then the number on a graphing calculator to approximate a root.

Some radical expressions containing non-perfect squares can also be simplified.

A radical expression is in simplest form if:

- the radicand contains no perfect-square factors other than 1;
- the radicand contains no fractions; and
- no denominator contains a radical.

To find the simplest form of an irrational square root, you can use the product and quotient properties of square roots.

| EXAMPLES 5 through 8 | **Using the product and quotient properties of square roots to simplify irrational square roots** |

Simplify each expression.

5 $\sqrt{72}$

■ SOLUTION

$$\sqrt{72} = \sqrt{36 \cdot 2}$$
$$= \sqrt{36} \cdot \sqrt{2} \quad \leftarrow \sqrt{ab} = \sqrt{a} \cdot \sqrt{b}$$
$$= 6\sqrt{2}$$

6 $\sqrt{48}$

■ SOLUTION

$$\sqrt{48} = \sqrt{2 \cdot 2 \cdot 2 \cdot 2 \cdot 3} \quad \leftarrow \text{If at first you}$$
$$= \sqrt{2^2 \cdot 2^2 \cdot 3} \qquad \text{cannot identify}$$
$$= \sqrt{2^2} \cdot \sqrt{2^2} \cdot \sqrt{3} \qquad \text{a perfect-square factor,}$$
$$= 2 \cdot 2 \cdot \sqrt{3} \qquad \text{write the}$$
$$= 4\sqrt{3} \qquad \text{prime factors.}$$

7 $\sqrt{\dfrac{5}{49}}$

■ SOLUTION

$$\sqrt{\frac{5}{49}} = \frac{\sqrt{5}}{\sqrt{49}} \quad \leftarrow \sqrt{\frac{a}{b}} = \frac{\sqrt{a}}{\sqrt{b}}$$
$$= \frac{\sqrt{5}}{7}, \text{ or } \frac{1}{7}\sqrt{5}$$

8 $\sqrt{\dfrac{8}{25}}$

■ SOLUTION

$$\sqrt{\frac{8}{25}} = \frac{\sqrt{8}}{\sqrt{25}}$$
$$= \frac{\sqrt{8}}{5}$$
$$= \frac{\sqrt{4 \cdot 2}}{5}$$
$$= \frac{\sqrt{4} \cdot \sqrt{2}}{5}$$
$$= \frac{2\sqrt{2}}{5}, \text{ or } \frac{2}{5}\sqrt{2}$$

You can apply the product and quotient properties to simplify square roots that include variable expressions.

EXAMPLES 9 and 10   **Using properties of square roots to simplify variable expressions**

Simplify each expression.

9 $\sqrt{24y^3}$

■ SOLUTION

$$\sqrt{24y^3} = \sqrt{4 \cdot 6 \cdot y^2 \cdot y}$$
$$= \sqrt{4} \cdot \sqrt{6} \cdot \sqrt{y^2} \cdot \sqrt{y}$$
$$= 2 \cdot \sqrt{6} \cdot y \cdot \sqrt{y}$$
$$= 2y\sqrt{6y}$$

10 $\sqrt{\dfrac{a^7}{16}}$

■ SOLUTION

$$\sqrt{\frac{a^7}{16}} = \frac{\sqrt{a^7}}{\sqrt{16}}$$
$$= \frac{\sqrt{a^6 \cdot a}}{\sqrt{16}}$$
$$= \frac{\sqrt{a^6} \cdot \sqrt{a}}{\sqrt{16}}$$
$$= \frac{a^3\sqrt{a}}{4}$$

You also use the product and quotient properties of square roots when multiplying and dividing with radical expressions.

EXAMPLES 11 through 14   **Using properties of square roots to simplify products and quotients**

11 Simplify each expression.

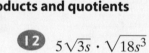

$\sqrt{15} \cdot \sqrt{6}$

■ SOLUTION

$$\sqrt{15} \cdot \sqrt{6} = \sqrt{15 \cdot 6}$$
$$= \sqrt{90}$$
$$= \sqrt{9 \cdot 10}$$
$$= \sqrt{9} \cdot \sqrt{10}$$
$$= 3\sqrt{10}$$

12 $5\sqrt{3s} \cdot \sqrt{18s^3}$

■ SOLUTION

$$5\sqrt{3s} \cdot \sqrt{18s^3} = 5\sqrt{3s \cdot 18s^3}$$
$$= 5\sqrt{54s^4}$$
$$= 5\sqrt{9 \cdot 6 \cdot s^4}$$
$$= 5 \cdot \sqrt{9} \cdot \sqrt{6} \cdot \sqrt{s^4}$$
$$= 5 \cdot 3 \cdot \sqrt{6} \cdot s^2$$
$$= 15s^2\sqrt{6}$$

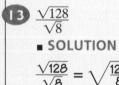

13 $\dfrac{\sqrt{128}}{\sqrt{8}}$

■ SOLUTION

$$\frac{\sqrt{128}}{\sqrt{8}} = \sqrt{\frac{128}{8}}$$
$$= \sqrt{16}$$
$$= 4$$

14 $\dfrac{\sqrt{48b^2}}{\sqrt{6b}}$

■ SOLUTION

$$\frac{\sqrt{48b^2}}{\sqrt{6b}} = \sqrt{\frac{48b^2}{6b}}$$
$$= \sqrt{8b}$$
$$= \sqrt{4 \cdot 2 \cdot b}$$
$$= \sqrt{4} \cdot \sqrt{2b}$$
$$= 2\sqrt{2b}$$

Go Online   PHSchool.com
Visit: PHSchool.com
Web Code: ayp-0304

Go Online   PHSchool.com
Visit: PHSchool.com
Web Code: ayp-0307

In a simplified radical expression, no denominator contains a radical. So if an expression has a radical in the denominator, and if that radical is not a perfect square, then you must *rationalize the denominator*. You do this by multiplying both numerator and denominator by the radical in the denominator.

Go Online
PHSchool.com
Visit: PHSchool.com
Webcode: ayp-0307

 EXAMPLES 15 and 16 **Rationalizing the denominator**

Simplify each expression.

15 $\sqrt{\dfrac{4}{3}}$

■ SOLUTION

$\sqrt{\dfrac{4}{3}} = \dfrac{\sqrt{4}}{\sqrt{3}}$

$= \dfrac{2}{\sqrt{3}}$

$= \dfrac{2}{\sqrt{3}} \cdot \dfrac{\sqrt{3}}{\sqrt{3}}$ ← Multiply by $\dfrac{\sqrt{3}}{\sqrt{3}} = 1$.

$= \dfrac{2 \cdot \sqrt{3}}{\sqrt{3} \cdot \sqrt{3}}$

$= \dfrac{2\sqrt{3}}{3}$, or $\dfrac{2}{3}\sqrt{3}$

16 $\sqrt{\dfrac{5}{2n^3}}$

■ SOLUTION

$\sqrt{\dfrac{5}{2n^3}} = \dfrac{\sqrt{5}}{\sqrt{2n^3}}$

$= \dfrac{\sqrt{5}}{n\sqrt{2n}}$

$= \dfrac{\sqrt{5}}{n\sqrt{2n}} \cdot \dfrac{\sqrt{2n}}{\sqrt{2n}}$

$= \dfrac{\sqrt{5 \cdot 2n}}{n\sqrt{2n \cdot 2n}}$

$= \dfrac{\sqrt{10n}}{n \cdot 2n} = \dfrac{\sqrt{10n}}{2n^2}$

Radical expressions with exactly the same radicand are called **like radicals**.

Examples of like radicals	Examples of unlike radicals
$\sqrt{2}$ and $5\sqrt{2}$	$2\sqrt{3}$ and $2\sqrt{5}$
$4\sqrt{a}$ and $7\sqrt{a}$	$3\sqrt{m}$ and $3\sqrt{m^2}$

You add and subtract radical expressions in much the same way that you add and subtract variable expressions. That is, you can use the Distributive Property to combine like radicals.

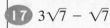 **EXAMPLES 17 and 18** **Adding and subtracting radical expressions**

Simplify each expression.

17 $3\sqrt{7} - \sqrt{7}$

■ SOLUTION

$3\sqrt{7} - \sqrt{7}$

$= 3\sqrt{7} - 1\sqrt{7}$

$= (3 - 1)\sqrt{7}$

$= 2\sqrt{7}$

18 $\sqrt{8} + \sqrt{50}$

■ SOLUTION

$\sqrt{8} + \sqrt{50}$

$= \sqrt{4 \cdot 2} + \sqrt{25 \cdot 2}$ ← Rewrite unlike radicals.

$= 2\sqrt{2} + 5\sqrt{2}$ ← Simplify.

$= (2 + 5)\sqrt{2}$ ← Apply the Distributive Property.

$= 7\sqrt{2}$ ← Add.

To simplify certain radical expressions, you must use the Distributive Property.

Go Online
PHSchool.com
Visit: PHSchool.com
Web Code: ayp-0309

EXAMPLES 19 and 20

Using the Distributive Property to simplify a product involving radical expressions

Simplify each expression.

19 $\sqrt{2}(10 + 4\sqrt{7})$

■ SOLUTION

$$\sqrt{2}(10 + 4\sqrt{7}) = \sqrt{2} \cdot 10 + \sqrt{2} \cdot 4\sqrt{7}$$
$$= 10\sqrt{2} + 4\sqrt{2 \cdot 7}$$
$$= 10\sqrt{2} + 4\sqrt{14}$$

20 $\sqrt{3}(\sqrt{12} + 2\sqrt{15})$

■ SOLUTION

$$\sqrt{3}(\sqrt{12} + 2\sqrt{15}) = \sqrt{3} \cdot \sqrt{12} + \sqrt{3} \cdot 2\sqrt{15}$$
$$= \sqrt{3 \cdot 12} + 2\sqrt{3 \cdot 15}$$
$$= \sqrt{36} + 2\sqrt{45}$$
$$= 6 + 2\sqrt{5 \cdot 9}$$
$$= 6 + 6\sqrt{5}$$

A **radical equation** contains one or more radicals with variables in the radicand. To solve a radical equation, you can use the following procedure.

Solving a Radical Equation

Step 1 Isolate the radical on one side of the equation and simplify.

Step 2 Square each side of the equation to eliminate the radical.

Step 3 Solve the resulting equation.

EXAMPLES 21 and 22

Solving radical equations

Solve each equation.

21 $\sqrt{r} + 5 = 9$

■ SOLUTION

$$\sqrt{r} + 5 = 9$$
$$\sqrt{r} + 5 - 5 = 9 - 5 \qquad \leftarrow \text{Subtract 5 from each side.}$$
$$\sqrt{r} = 4 \qquad \leftarrow \text{Simplify.}$$
$$(\sqrt{r})^2 = (4)^2 \qquad \leftarrow \text{Square each side.}$$
$$r = 16$$

Check 16:
$$\sqrt{r} + 5 = 9 \quad \rightarrow \quad \sqrt{16} + 5 = 9$$
$$4 + 5 = 9 \quad \checkmark$$

Therefore, the solution is 16.

22 $\sqrt{a - 5} = 3$

■ SOLUTION

$$\sqrt{a - 5} = 3 \qquad \leftarrow \text{The radical is already isolated.}$$
$$(\sqrt{a - 5})^2 = (3)^2 \qquad \leftarrow \text{Square each side.}$$
$$a - 5 = 9 \qquad \leftarrow \text{Simplify.}$$
$$a = 14 \qquad \leftarrow \text{Solve.}$$

Check 14:
$$\sqrt{a - 5} = 3 \quad \rightarrow \quad \sqrt{14 - 5} = 3$$
$$\sqrt{9} = 3 \quad \checkmark$$

Therefore, the solution is 14.

Practice

Choose the letter preceding the word or expression that best completes the statement or answers the question.

1 Which statement is false?

   A. $\sqrt{5} \cdot \sqrt{6} = \sqrt{30}$

   B. $\sqrt{5} + \sqrt{6} = \sqrt{11}$

   C. $(\sqrt{5})^2 = 5$

   D. $\sqrt{5^2} = 5$

2 Which expression is in simplest form?

   A. $\sqrt{12}$ **C.** $\sqrt{19}$

   B. $\sqrt{\frac{1}{3}}$ **D.** $\frac{2}{\sqrt{5}}$

3 Which shows the expression $\sqrt{250}$ in simplest form?

   A. $125\sqrt{2}$ **C.** $5\sqrt{10}$

   B. $25\sqrt{10}$ **D.** $5\sqrt{5}$

4 Which expression is equivalent to $2\sqrt{72} - \sqrt{2}$?

   A. $2\sqrt{70}$ **C.** $11\sqrt{2}$

   B. $71\sqrt{2}$ **D.** 12

In Exercises 5–47, simplify each expression.

5 $\sqrt{324}$ **6** $\sqrt{1089}$ **7** $\sqrt{40{,}000}$

8 $\sqrt{\frac{1}{36}}$ **9** $\sqrt{\frac{169}{25}}$ **10** $\sqrt{\frac{441}{10{,}000}}$

11 $\sqrt{\frac{10}{9}}$ **12** $\sqrt{\frac{12}{49}}$ **13** $\sqrt{\frac{50}{81}}$

14 $\sqrt{64h^2}$ **15** $\sqrt{49w^6}$ **16** $\sqrt{100q^3}$

17 $\sqrt{x^2 y^6}$ **18** $\sqrt{m^3 n^5}$ **19** $\sqrt{abc^2}$

20 $\sqrt{\frac{y^6}{4}}$ **21** $\sqrt{\frac{16v^3}{25}}$ **22** $\sqrt{\frac{28v^5}{9}}$

23 $\sqrt{8} \cdot \sqrt{32}$ **24** $\sqrt{5} \cdot \sqrt{30}$

25 $\frac{\sqrt{120}}{\sqrt{15}}$ **26** $\frac{\sqrt{8}}{\sqrt{50}}$

27 $\sqrt{35t} \cdot \sqrt{5t}$ **28** $\sqrt{8a} \cdot \sqrt{22a^5}$

29 $\frac{\sqrt{32d^5}}{\sqrt{8d^2}}$ **30** $\frac{\sqrt{3z}}{\sqrt{75z^3}}$

31 $6\sqrt{11} - 2\sqrt{11}$ **32** $-8\sqrt{15} + 9\sqrt{15}$

33 $3\sqrt{2} + \sqrt{8}$ **34** $4\sqrt{3} - \sqrt{12}$

35 $\sqrt{75} - \sqrt{48}$ **36** $2\sqrt{20} + \sqrt{45}$

37 $\sqrt{2}(\sqrt{2} + \sqrt{3})$

38 $\sqrt{3}(\sqrt{6} - \sqrt{5})$

39 $\sqrt{5}(3\sqrt{5} - 2\sqrt{2})$

40 $2\sqrt{3}(7\sqrt{2} - \sqrt{6})$

41 $(\sqrt{2} + 1)(\sqrt{2} - 3)$

42 $(\sqrt{5} + 2)(2\sqrt{5} - 2)$

43 $(2\sqrt{3} + 3)(2\sqrt{3} - 3)$

44 $(2\sqrt{5} + 3)^2$

45 $\sqrt{27} - \sqrt{24} - \sqrt{54} + \sqrt{48}$

46 $2\sqrt{75} + 4\sqrt{12} - 2\sqrt{18}$

47 $\sqrt{16n + 32} + \sqrt{4n + 8}$

In Exercises 48–53, solve each equation.

48 $\sqrt{j} - 6 = 3$ **49** $4 + \sqrt{2x} = 10$

50 $\sqrt{s + 1} = 7$ **51** $2 = \sqrt{v - 8}$

52 $g = \sqrt{g + 12}$ **53** $\sqrt{2 - y} = y$

DIRECTIONS FOR QUESTIONS 1–21: For each of the questions below, select the answer choice that is best for each case.

1 In $\frac{1}{v^2 - 9}$, all excluded values of v are

    A. 0 and 3.

    B. $-3, 0$, and 3.

    C. -3 and 3.

    D. -9 and 9.

2 What is $\frac{1}{c} + \frac{c + 4}{c^2}$ as a single fraction?

    A. $\frac{2c + 4}{c^2}$

    B. $\frac{c + 5}{c^2}$

    C. $\frac{c + 4}{c^3}$

    D. $\frac{c + 5}{c^2 + c}$

3 If a, b, and z are positive numbers, simplify the expression $\sqrt{az} \cdot \sqrt{bz}$.

    A. $\sqrt{abz}$

    B. $z\sqrt{ab}$

    C. $z\sqrt{a + b}$

    D. $z^2\sqrt{ab}$

4 For which value of x is $\sqrt{3x - 5}$ a real number?

    A. 1   B. 0   C. 2   D. -1

5 Simplify $\sqrt{\frac{49}{84}}$.

    A. $\frac{7}{\sqrt{84}}$ C. $\frac{7\sqrt{21}}{2}$

    B. $\frac{7}{2\sqrt{21}}$ D. $\frac{\sqrt{21}}{6}$

6 Approximate $\sqrt{93}$ to the nearest thousandth.

    A. 9.644   C. 0.964

    B. 9.643   D. 0.963

7 Find the value $-\sqrt{225}$.

    A. 15   C. $15(-15)$

    B. ± 15 D. -15

8 Which of the following is irrational?

    A. $\sqrt{\frac{9}{25}}$

    B. $-\sqrt{625}$

    C. $\sqrt{\frac{200}{50}}$

    D. $\sqrt{0.90}$

9 Which expression is equivalent to $\sqrt{27} + \sqrt{48}$?

    A. $7\sqrt{3}$ C. $5\sqrt{3}$

    B. $\sqrt{75}$ D. $7\sqrt{6}$

10 Compare the values $16\sqrt{2}$ and $\frac{16\sqrt{8}}{2}$. Which statement is true?

    A. The value of $16\sqrt{2}$ is greater than $\frac{16\sqrt{8}}{2}$.

    B. The value of $\frac{16\sqrt{8}}{2}$ is greater than $16\sqrt{2}$.

    C. The two values are equal.

    D. Nothing can be determined.

11 What is $\sqrt{2} \cdot \sqrt{128}$ simplified?

    A. $\sqrt{256}$ C. 16

    B. $8\sqrt{2}$ D. $6\sqrt{2}$

12 Simplify $\frac{10x}{5x + 20}$.

A. $\frac{1}{10}$

B. $\frac{2}{x + 4}$

C. $\frac{x}{5x + 2}$

D. $\frac{2x}{x + 4}$

13 Divide. Express the answer in simplest form.

$$\frac{4x + 12}{x^2 + x - 30} \div \frac{3x^2 + 5x - 12}{3x^2 - 15x}$$

A. $\frac{3x^2 + 14x - 24}{12x}$

B. $\frac{12x}{3x^2 + 14x - 24}$

C. $\frac{4x^2 - 20x}{(x^2 + x - 30)(3x + 4)}$

D. $\frac{4}{3x^2 - 15x}$

14 Simplify $\frac{2m + 6}{3m^2 + 11m + 6}$.

A. $\frac{4m}{3m^2 + 11m}$

B. $\frac{4}{3m^2 + 11}$

C. $\frac{2}{3m + 2}$

D. $\frac{1}{3m}$

15 Which is the product of $\frac{3x^2}{8y} \cdot \frac{20}{9x}$ expressed in simplest form?

A. $\frac{5x}{6y}$

C. $\frac{23x^2}{17xy}$

B. $\frac{20x}{24y}$

D. $\frac{60x}{72y}$

16 Solve for m.

$$\frac{3}{m + 4} + 2 = \frac{5}{m}$$

A. -5 and 2

B. -2 and 5

C. 9

D. -9

17 Simplify $\sqrt{72x^5}$.

A. $3x\sqrt{8x^3}$ C. $6\sqrt{2x^5}$

B. $3x^2\sqrt{8x}$ D. $6x^2\sqrt{2x}$

18 Find the difference.

$$\frac{8x}{x - 9} - \frac{5x + 2}{x - 9}$$

A. $\frac{3x - 2}{-18}$ C. $\frac{3x - 2}{x - 9}$

B. $\frac{3x + 2}{x - 9}$ D. $\frac{x}{x - 9}$

19 Find the sum.

$$\frac{2n}{n + 3} + \frac{5}{n + 8}$$

A. $\frac{2n + 5}{n^2 + 11}$

B. $\frac{23n + 3}{n^2 + 11n + 24}$

C. $\frac{2n^2 + 5n + 11}{n^2 + 11n + 24}$

D. $\frac{2n^2 + 21n + 15}{n^2 + 11n + 24}$

20 The quotient of a number divided by 6 is subtracted from $\frac{3}{4}$. The result is $\frac{5}{12}$. What is the number?

A. 1   B. 2   C. 4   D. 5

21 Solve $\sqrt{r - 9} = 7$.

A. 10   B. 58   C. 100   D. 256

DIRECTIONS FOR 22–24: Solve each problem and show your work.

22 The motion of a pendulum is approximated by the equation
$T = 2\pi\sqrt{\frac{L}{9.8}}$, where T is the time of one swing, and L is the length of
the pendulum.

- Find the time, approximated to the nearest tenth, of one swing of the
  pendulum if the length is 10 units.

- Find the length of the pendulum, rounded to the nearest tenth, if it
  takes 2 seconds for each swing of the pendulum.

- Does the time of one pendulum swing T increase or decrease as the
  length L increases? Explain your reasoning and justify your solution
  mathematically.

23 Jake can unload a delivery truck in 40 minutes, and Jennie can unload the
same truck in 60 minutes.

- Write an equation of rational expressions to find how long it would
  take Jake and Jennie to unload the truck together.

- How long would it take Jake and Jennie to unload the truck together?

24 Ed rode his bike for 2 more hours than Ann rode hers. Ed rode
24 miles, and Ann rode 6 miles.

- Write an equation that can be used to find how many hours Ed rode
  his bike if he rode at the same speed as Ann.

- If they both rode at the same speed, how long did Ed ride his bike?

8 Probability

NEW JERSEY

Princeton University

Princeton University is the fourth oldest college in the United States. The College of New Jersey, as it was originally named, was chartered in 1746 in Elizabeth, New Jersey. In 1756, after a brief move to Newark, the college moved to its current location in Princeton, New Jersey. In 1896, the college gained university status and officially became Princeton University.

In January 1758, Jonathan Edwards, commonly recognized as the most eminent American philosopher and theologian, became Princeton's third president. Although he died only two months later, Edwards is probably the most famous of Princeton's presidents.

Princeton University is one of eight private colleges that comprise the Ivy League.

8.1 Experimental and Theoretical Probability

New Jersey Standards

4.4.B.3 Solve probability problems

4.4.B.5 Use experimental and theoretical probabilities

Probability is a measure of the likelihood that an event will occur. You can represent a probability using a ratio or a percent. Some events will never occur, others will always occur, and the likelihood of many events is uncertain.

There are two types of probability: a priori, or theoretical probability, and experimental probability.

In general, you can define the probability of flipping heads as the ratio 1 out of 2, or $\frac{1}{2}$. This is called the **a priori,** or **theoretical probability,** of flipping heads.

Theoretical probability is a calculation of the ratio of the number of favorable outcomes to the total number of outcomes. You can express probability as a fraction, percent, or decimal.

Experimental probability is determined by collecting data from an *experiment*. The sum of the probabilities of all of the events of an experiment is always equal to 1. Suppose you flip a coin and record the occurrence of heads.

Number of flips	10	10	10	10	10
Number of heads	4	5	5	6	5
ratio	4 of 10	5 of 10	5 of 10	6 of 10	5 of 10

In each experiment, heads occur about 5 times in every 10 flips. You can say that the experimental or **empirical probability** of heads' occurring is about 1 out of 2 for this coin.

Theoretical Probability of an Event

If an event E contains m favorable outcomes in a sample space containing n outcomes, the **theoretical probability** of E, denoted $P(E)$, is found as follows.

$$P(E) = \frac{\text{number } m \text{ of favorable outcomes}}{\text{total number } n \text{ of outcomes}} = \frac{m}{n}$$

Note

"At random" means that the selection is made without any preference or bias for one outcome over another.

EXAMPLE 1   **Calculating theoretical probabilities**

 In a local district, there are 1300 Democratic, 1100 Republican, and 400 Independent registered voters. If a voter is selected at random, what is the probability to the nearest whole percent, that the voter selected is Republican?

■ **SOLUTION**

Calculate the total number of voters in the district. $1300 + 1100 + 400 = 2800$

$$P(\text{Republican}) = \frac{\text{number of Republicans}}{\text{total number of registered voters}} = \frac{1100}{2800} \approx 0.39$$

The probability of selecting a Republican is about 39%.

Go Online
PHSchool.com

Visit: PHSchool.com
Web Code: ayp-0871

Sample space is the set of all possible outcomes in a given situation. An **event** is any set of outcomes in the sample space. You can use a table or a tree diagram to identify a sample space.

 EXAMPLE 2   Using a table or tree diagram to identify a sample space

Note

There are four outcomes. H and T is different from T and H.

2 What is the sample space when two coins are flipped consecutively?

■ **SOLUTION**

Determine all of the possible outcomes of flipping two coins consecutively.

coin 1 \ coin 2	H	T
H	H H	H T
T	T H	T T

coin 1   coin 2   outcome

H < H → H and H
    T → H and T

T < H → T and H
    T → T and T

The sample space is HH, HT, TH, TT.

The table below shows all possible ordered pairs (cube X, cube Y) in the sample space for rolling two number cubes. Notice that there are 36 outcomes in all.

cube X/cube Y	1	2	3	4	5	6
1	(1, 1)	(1, 2)	(1, 3)	(1, 4)	(1, 5)	(1, 6)
2	(2, 1)	(2, 2)	(2, 3)	(2, 4)	(2, 5)	(2, 6)
3	(3, 1)	(3, 2)	(3, 3)	(3, 4)	(3, 5)	(3, 6)
4	(4, 1)	(4, 2)	(4, 3)	(4, 4)	(4, 5)	(4, 6)
5	(5, 1)	(5, 2)	(5, 3)	(5, 4)	(5, 5)	(5, 6)
6	(6, 1)	(6, 2)	(6, 3)	(6, 4)	(6, 5)	(6, 6)

If one cube shows 1, there are 6 possibilities for the second cube.

EXAMPLES 3 through 5   Using probability facts with ordered pairs

Find each of the following probabilities using the sample space for rolling a pair of number cubes. Write the probabilities as fractions in lowest terms.

 P(sum equals 3) P(same number on each) P(sum not equal to 12)

■ **SOLUTION**

The only ordered pairs whose numbers total 3 are $(1, 2)$ and $(2, 1)$. There are two favorable outcomes.

P(sum equals 3)

$= \frac{2}{36}$, or $\frac{1}{18}$

■ **SOLUTION**

The six ordered pairs $(1, 1)$, $(2, 2), (3, 3), (4, 4), (5, 5)$, and $(6, 6)$ are the only outcomes with identical numbers.

P(same number on each)

$= \frac{6}{36}$, or $\frac{1}{6}$

■ **SOLUTION**

There is exactly one ordered pair whose numbers total 12. It is $(6, 6)$.

P(sum not equal to 12)

$= 1 - P$(sum equal to 12)

$= 1 - \frac{1}{36} = \frac{35}{36}$

You can say the outcomes from rolling a single number cube are **equally likely.**

$$P(1) = \tfrac{1}{6} \quad P(2) = \tfrac{1}{6} \quad P(3) = \tfrac{1}{6} \quad P(4) = \tfrac{1}{6} \quad P(5) = \tfrac{1}{6} \quad P(6) = \tfrac{1}{6}$$

If you roll a pair of number cubes, the probability of rolling one sum is not necessarily equal to the probability of rolling another sum. You can say that the outcomes from rolling a pair of number cubes are *not equally likely.*

$$P(\text{sum } 2) = \tfrac{1}{36} \text{ but } P(\text{sum } 3) = \tfrac{2}{36}$$

The possible sums from rolling a pair of number cubes are 2, 3, 4, 5, 6, 7, 8, 9, 10, 11, and 12. If x represents these numbers, you can say that x is a **random variable** and assign to it the probability of each sum. A **probability distribution** represents the values of the variable and corresponding probabilities.

Note

Notice that not all probabilities are equal, but that the sum of the probabilities equals 1.

x	2	3	4	5	6	7	8	9	10	11	12
$P(x)$	$\tfrac{1}{36}$	$\tfrac{2}{36}$	$\tfrac{3}{36}$	$\tfrac{4}{36}$	$\tfrac{5}{36}$	$\tfrac{6}{36}$	$\tfrac{5}{36}$	$\tfrac{4}{36}$	$\tfrac{3}{36}$	$\tfrac{2}{36}$	$\tfrac{1}{36}$

EXAMPLE 6   Making a probability distribution

Go Online
PHSchool.com
Visit: PHSchool.com
Web Code: ayp-0675

6 A bag contains marbles identical in every way but color. The bag contains 1 red, 2 blue, 3 green, and 4 orange marbles. Make a probability distribution that represents the probabilities of choosing each color of marble from the bag. Write the probabilities as fractions and as decimals.

■ SOLUTION

Find the total number of outcomes. $1 + 2 + 3 + 4 = 10$
Make a table of ratios as shown.

color	red	blue	green	orange
probability	$\tfrac{1}{10} = 0.1$	$\tfrac{2}{10} = 0.2$	$\tfrac{3}{10} = 0.3$	$\tfrac{4}{10} = 0.4$

The **complement** of an event E is the set of outcomes in the sample space *not* in E. You can find the probability of the complement by subtracting the $P(E)$ from 1. For example, there is a 25% chance that your birth month is January, February, or March, so the probability of the complement, that your birth month is *not* in January, February, or March, is $1 - 0.25 = 0.75$ or 75%.

Characteristics of Probabilities

If E is impossible, $P(E) = 0$.	The number of favorable outcomes equals 0.
If E is certain, $P(E) = 1$.	The number of favorable outcomes equals the total number of outcomes.
Otherwise, $0 < P(E) < 1$.	The number of favorable outcomes is less than the total number of outcomes.
$P(\text{not } E) = 1 - P(E)$	The number of favorable outcomes is the difference of the unfavorable outcomes and 1.
$\sum P(E) = 1$	The sum of the probabilities of all of the events of an experiment is equal to 1.

Choose the letter preceding the word or expression that best completes the statement or answers the question.

1 If the probability of an event is 0, then

    A. it is certain.

    B. it is impossible.

    C. it is probable but not certain.

    D. it is probable but not impossible.

2 Which completes this probability distribution?

B	4	2	6	8
P(B)	0.2	0.1	0.3	

    A. 0.2   **B.** 0.05   **C.** 0.4   **D.** 0.6

3 The probability that the sun will set in the west is

    A. 0.   **B.** 1.   **C.** −1.   **D.** $\frac{1}{2}$.

4 A box contains five cutouts of the same triangle differing only in color. If one cutout is drawn at random, what is the probability of choosing a specific color?

    A. $\frac{1}{5}$ **B.** $\frac{5}{5}$ **C.** $\frac{2}{5}$ **D.** $\frac{3}{5}$

5 In a local district, there are 2,000 Democratic, 1,700 Republican, and 300 Independent voters registered. If a voter is selected at random, which is the probability that the voter selected is not an Independent?

    A. $1 - \frac{3}{40}$ **C.** $\frac{17}{40}$

    B. $1 - \frac{37}{40}$ **D.** $1 - \frac{17}{40}$

6 A bag contains 7 red, 6 green, and 7 white marbles, all identical but for color. The probability of randomly choosing a red marble is

    A. $\frac{7}{20}$.   **B.** $\frac{13}{20}$.   **C.** $\frac{3}{10}$.   **D.** $1 - \frac{7}{20}$.

In Exercises 7–10, solve the problem.

7 Which is more likely, an event with probability 0.36 or an event with probability 0.6?

8 In an algebra class, 5 students wear contact lenses, 4 students wear glasses, and 13 students wear neither contact lenses nor glasses. If a student is chosen at random, what is the probability that the student wears contact lenses?

9 A weather forecaster predicts that there is a 45% probability of snow today. What is the probability that it will not snow?

10 For the pair of spinners below, make a tree diagram showing all of the outcomes spinning the two spinners. Calculate the probability of having the pointer land on light gray in spinner 1 and on light blue in spinner 2.

    spinner 1   spinner 2

In Exercises 11–14, refer to the table of outcomes for rolling a pair of number cubes. Find each probability as a fraction in lowest terms.

11 P(sum equals 8)   **12** P(numbers unequal)

13 P(sum equals 11)   **14** P(sum equals 13)

In Exercises 15–16, use the given data to make a probability distribution for the selection of one object or person at random.

15 A bag contains 8 blue slips of paper, 9 brown slips of paper, and 8 green slips of paper, all identical but for color. The values of a random variable are 1 for blue, 2 for brown, and 3 for green.

16 The science club consists of 13 first-year students, 12 second-year students, 13 third-year students, and 10 fourth-year students. The values of the random variable are 1, 2, 3, and 4 for the class year.

8.2 Using Probability Formulas

New Jersey Standards

4.4.B.3 Solve problems involving probability

There are situations when two events cannot occur at the same time. For example, the following statements about integers cannot both be true at the same time.

An integer is even.   The same integer is odd.

You can say that these outcomes are *mutually exclusive*. Two events are **mutually exclusive** if there are no outcomes common to both events.

EXAMPLE 1   **Identifying mutually exclusive events**

1 Which events are mutually exclusive?

A. selecting a baseball card showing a Yankee and also a pitcher
B. scoring above 80 on a test and scoring above 90 on the same test
C. rolling a prime number that is also an even number
D. rolling a multiple of 2 that is also a 17

■ **SOLUTION**

Seventeen is not a multiple of 2, so the outcomes in choice **D** are mutually exclusive. The correct choice is D.

To find the probability of two mutually exclusive events, you add the probabilities of each event. Consider the following problem.

What is the probability of drawing a 7 or a Queen when drawing a card from a standard deck of playing cards? There are 52 possible outcomes; four of them are 7s and four of them are Queens. Since there is no card that is both a 7 and a Queen, these events are mutually exclusive. Therefore,

$$P(7 \text{ or } Q) = P(7) + (Q) = \frac{4}{52} + \frac{4}{52} = \frac{8}{52} = \frac{2}{13}.$$

Note

A standard deck of 52 playing cards consists of 13 red hearts, 13 black clubs, 13 red diamonds, and 13 black spades. Each suit has an ace, a king, a queen, a jack, and the numbers 2 through 10.

Probability Involving Mutually Exclusive Events

If A and B are mutually exclusive events, then $P(A \text{ or } B) = P(A) + P(B)$.

EXAMPLE 2   **Using the formula for the probability of mutually exclusive events**

Go Online
PHSchool.com
Visit: PHSchool.com
Web Code: ayp-0643

2 Suppose you roll a pair of number cubes. Find the probability that the numbers showing are the same or that their sum is 11.

■ **SOLUTION**

The events are mutually exclusive since a sum of 11 cannot occur at the same time two number cubes are showing the same number.

Count the outcomes in which the numbers showing are equal.   There are six.
Count the outcomes in which the sum of the numbers showing is 11.   There are two.

$P(\text{numbers equal or sum is 11}) = P(\text{numbers equal}) + P(\text{sum is 11})$

$$= \frac{6}{36} + \frac{2}{36} = \frac{8}{36}, \text{ or } \frac{2}{9}$$

There are also situations when two events can occur at the same time. These events are not mutually exclusive. Consider the following problem.

What is the probability of drawing a red card or a card showing a queen from a standard deck of 52 playing cards?

26 red cards	26 black cards
2 red queens	2 black queens

The diagram at the right shows that these events are not mutually exclusive because there are two cards that show queen and are also red.

You can calculate the probability P(red card or queen) as follows.

$$P\text{(red card or queen)} = \frac{26 + 2}{52} = \frac{28}{52} \qquad \frac{28}{52} = \overset{\substack{\text{number of} \\ \text{red cards}}}{\underset{\downarrow}{\frac{26}{52}}} + \overset{\substack{\text{number of} \\ \text{queens}}}{\underset{\downarrow}{\frac{4}{52}}} - \overset{\substack{\text{number of} \\ \text{red queens}}}{\underset{\downarrow}{\frac{2}{52}}}$$

To determine the probability of events that are *not* mutually exclusive, you add the probabilities of each event and then subtract the probability of both occurring at the same time.

> ### Probability of Events Involving Or
>
> If A and B are events in a sample space, $P(A \text{ or } B) = P(A) + P(B) - P(A \text{ and } B)$.

Note

If A and B are mutually exclusive, $P(A \text{ and } B) = 0$.

EXAMPLES 3 and 4   Finding probability of events that are not mutually exclusive

 Of the 200 seniors at Southside High School, 98 are boys, 34 are on the track team, and 20 are boys on the track team. Find the probability that a student chosen at random is a boy or is on the track team.

■ SOLUTION

Sketch a Venn diagram that shows the sets and relationships.

$$P(\text{boy or track}) = P(\text{boy}) + P(\text{track}) - P(\text{boy and track})$$
$$= \frac{98}{200} + \frac{34}{200} - \frac{20}{200}$$
$$= \frac{98 + 34 - 20}{200}$$
$$= \frac{112}{200}$$
$$= 0.56$$

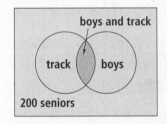

The probability that a student chosen is a boy or is on the track team is 0.56, or 56%.

 What is the probability that either of two number cubes tossed simultaneously shows a 3?

■ SOLUTION

$$P(3 \text{ or } 3) = P(3) + P(3) - P(\text{both cubes show } 3)$$
$$= \frac{6}{36} + \frac{6}{36} - \frac{1}{36}$$
$$= \frac{11}{36}$$

The probability that either of the two cubes shows a 3 is $\frac{11}{36}$.

You can use given information to solve many probability problems.

In Examples 5 through 16, use the information about the Sun City Council. Each council member is identified by gender and party. Parties are indicated by D for Democrat, R for Republican, I for Independent, and C for Conservative. Find each probability that a council member fits the criteria specified.

Name	Gender	Party	Name	Gender	Party
B. Green	M	D	M. Adams	M	I
B. White	F	D	R. Jones	M	C
C. Washington	F	D	T. Black	M	D
S. Brown	F	R	D. Jackson	M	I
L. Smith	M	R	N. Goodman	F	R
R. Jackson	M	R			

5 $P(D)$

■ SOLUTION

$P(D) = \frac{4}{11}$ ← four Democrats

6 $P(\text{not } I)$

■ SOLUTION

$P(\text{not } I) = 1 - \frac{2}{11}$ ← two Independents

$= \frac{9}{11}$

7 $P(F \text{ or } R)$

■ SOLUTION

$P(F \text{ or } R) = \frac{4}{11} + \frac{4}{11} - \frac{2}{11}$ ← two female Republicans

$= \frac{6}{11}$

8 $P(D \text{ or } C)$

■ SOLUTION

$P(D \text{ or } C) = \frac{4}{11} + \frac{1}{11}$ ← 4 Democrats 1 Conservative

$= \frac{5}{11}$

9 $P(R \text{ and } D)$

■ SOLUTION

$P(R \text{ and } D) = 0$ ← impossible event

10 $P(M \text{ or } D)$

■ SOLUTION

$P(M \text{ or } D) = \frac{7}{11} + \frac{4}{11} - \frac{2}{11}$

$= \frac{9}{11}$

11 $P(M \text{ or } I)$

■ SOLUTION

$P(M \text{ or } I) = \frac{7}{11} + \frac{2}{11} - \frac{2}{11}$

$= \frac{7}{11}$

12 $P(F \text{ or } C)$

■ SOLUTION

$P(F \text{ or } C) = \frac{4}{11} + \frac{1}{11} - \frac{0}{11}$

$= \frac{5}{11}$

13 $P(F \text{ and } C)$

■ SOLUTION

$P(F \text{ and } C) = 0$

14 $P(M \text{ or } D)$

■ SOLUTION

$P(M \text{ and } D) = \frac{2}{11}$

15 $P(I \text{ and } F)$

■ SOLUTION

$P(I \text{ and } F) = 0$

16 $P(I \text{ or } F)$

■ SOLUTION

$P(I \text{ or } F) = \frac{2}{11} + \frac{4}{11} - \frac{0}{11}$

$= \frac{6}{11}$

Practice

Choose the letter preceding the word or expression that best completes the statement or answers the question.

1 Two events, A and B, each having at least one outcome, are mutually exclusive. Which of these statements is true?

   A. $P(A \text{ or } B) = 0$

   B. $P(A) = 0$

   C. $P(B) = 0$

   D. $P(A \text{ and } B) = 0$

2 Which events are mutually exclusive?

   A. Bill and Elizabeth both won when they played racquetball against one another.

   B. Bill lost and Elizabeth won when they played racquetball against one another.

   C. The national average age of high school seniors is 17 and for sophomores it is 16.

   D. In one year, the Yankees won the World Series and the Mets won the National League Pennant.

3 A box contains cards, each having exactly one different number from 1 to 19 inclusive on it. Which gives the probability of drawing a card with an odd number on it or a multiple of 3 on it?

   A. $P(\text{odd}) \times P(\text{multiple of } 3)$

   B. $P(\text{odd}) + P(\text{multiple of } 3)$

   C. $P(\text{odd}) + P(\text{multiple of } 3)$ $- P(\text{odd multiple of } 3)$

   D. $P(\text{odd}) \times P(\text{multiple of } 3)$ $- P(\text{odd multiple of } 3)$

4 Mikki has 7 different shirts, 8 different pairs of pants, and 8 different pairs of shoes. How many outfits can she make?

   A. $7 + 8 + 8$ **C.** $7 \times 8 \times 8$

   B. $7^3 + 8^3 + 8^3$ **D.** $3(7 + 8 + 8)$

In Exercises 5–8, suppose you select a card at random from a standard deck of cards. Find each probability as a fraction in lowest terms.

5 $P(\text{queen or diamond})$

6 $P(\text{king or black card})$

7 $P(\text{heart or 5 of clubs})$

8 $P(\text{even number or clubs})$

In Exercises 9–12, suppose you roll a pair of number cubes. Find each probability as a fraction in lowest terms.

9 $P(\text{equal numbers or sum of } 7)$

10 $P(\text{equal numbers or even sum})$

11 $P(\text{equal numbers or odd sum})$

12 $P(\text{sum less than } 4)$

In Exercises 13–15, each card in a bag has exactly one of the numbers 3, $\frac{2}{3}$, −4, $\sqrt{25}$, π, $\sqrt{6}$, 15, 17, or 64 written on it. Find each probability as a fraction in lowest terms.

13 $P(\text{perfect square or even number})$

14 $P(\text{irrational number or negative})$

15 $P(\text{divisible by 3 or by 5})$

16 In a certain area, 104 houses are for sale. Fifty-two houses have garages but not swimming pools, 13 houses have swimming pools but not garages, and 8 houses have both garages and swimming pools. Find the probability that a house for sale has a garage or swimming pool, but not both.

8.3 Independent and Dependent Events

New Jersey Standards

4.4.B.4.1 Find conditional probabilities

4.4.B.4.3 Find probabilities of dependent/ independent events

4.4C.2 Apply the counting principle

4.4.C.3 Justify counting problems

Sometimes you need to determine the size of a rather large sample space. Suppose that Maggie has 5 pairs of jeans and 6 T-shirts. How many outfits consisting of one pair of jeans and one T-shirt does she have available to her? You could make a tree diagram to count the different outfits; however, there is a simpler way to find the answer.

Since Maggie has 5 choices for jeans and 6 T-shirt choices, she has 5×6, or 30 choices, altogether. You can generalize this discussion to state the *Fundamental Counting Principle*.

Fundamental Counting Principle

If there are m ways to make a selection and n ways to make a second selection, then there are mn ways to make the pair of selections.

If there are m ways to make a selection, n ways to make a second selection, and p ways to make a third selection, then there are mnp ways to make the three selections.

Go Online
PHSchool.com

Visit: PHSchool.com
Web Code: ayp-0120

EXAMPLES 1 and 2   Applying the Fundamental Counting Principle

1 How many seven-digit telephone numbers are possible if the first three digits are 268 in that order, the fourth digit is not 0, and the seventh digit is not 9?

■ **SOLUTION**

Sketch a diagram showing how many digits are possible for each slot.

$$268 - \underset{\substack{\uparrow \\ 9 \text{ digits}}}{\text{not 0}} \quad \underset{\substack{\uparrow \\ 10 \text{ digits}}}{\text{any digit}} \quad \underset{\substack{\uparrow \\ 10 \text{ digits}}}{\text{any digit}} \quad \underset{\substack{\uparrow \\ 9 \text{ digits}}}{\text{not 9}}$$

In all, there are $9 \times 10 \times 10 \times 9$, or **8,100**, possible telephone numbers.

2 Bag A contains 5 red marbles, 6 green marbles, and 7 purple marbles. Bag B contains 12 black marbles, 18 blue marbles, and 10 orange marbles. A marble is chosen at random from each bag. Find the probability of selecting a red marble from Bag A and a black marble from Bag B.

■ **SOLUTION**

There are 18×40, or 720, pairs of choices (Bag A, Bag B).

There are 5×12, or 60, pairs of choices (red, black).

$$P(red, then\ black) = \frac{60}{720}, or\ \frac{1}{12}$$

Two events are **independent** if the occurrence of one event does not affect the occurrence of the other event.

EXAMPLES 3 and 4 **Identifying and finding probabilities of independent events**

3 For which is the occurrence of one event dependent on that of the other event?

    A. flipping heads on a coin toss and rolling 6 on a number cube
    B. drawing a jack from a standard deck of cards and rolling a 6 on a number cube
    C. drawing a jack and, without replacing the card, drawing a second jack
    D. drawing a jack and, after replacing the card, drawing a second jack

▪ **SOLUTION**

In choice **C,** the card is not replaced. So, the sample space for the second draw has only 51 members. The second event is dependent on the first. The correct choice is C.

4 A card is drawn from a standard deck of playing cards, replaced, and a second card is drawn. What is the probability that the second card drawn is a spade?

▪ **SOLUTION**

In this situation the probability of drawing the second spade is $\frac{13}{52}$ since after replacement there are still 13 spades out of 52 cards.

The counting principle for independent events says that if $P(A)$ is the probability of event A and $P(B)$ is the probability of event B, then you can find the probability of both A and B occurring by multiplying $P(A) \cdot P(B)$.

EXAMPLES 5 through 7 **Solving problems involving two independent events**

Suppose that you flip a coin and spin a spinner with a 50% red region, 25% blue region, and 25% green region. Find each probability.

5 P(heads and green)

▪ **SOLUTION**

P(heads and green) = P(heads) × P(green)
                 = 0.5 × 0.25 = 0.125

6 P(heads and not green)

▪ **SOLUTION**

P(heads and not green) = P(heads) × P(not green)
                     = P(heads) × (1 − P(green))
                     = 0.5 × (1 − 0.25) = 0.375

7 P(tails and red)

▪ **SOLUTION**

P(tails and red) = P(tails) × P(red)
             = 0.5 × 0.5 = 0.25

Consider this next example.

- A card is drawn from a standard deck of playing cards, without replacement, a second card is drawn. What is the probability that the second card drawn is a spade?

In this situation the probability of drawing the second spade is $\frac{12}{51}$ since there are now 12 spades out of the remaining 51 cards.

The events of this situation are **dependent** because the occurrence of one event affects the probability of the other.

EXAMPLES 8 and 9   **Finding probabilities of dependent events**

A bag contains 3 red marbles and 5 blue marbles. Samuel draws a marble from the bag without looking, puts it into his pocket, and then draws a second marble without looking.

8 Find the probability that both marbles Samuel drew from the bag are red.

■ SOLUTION

Make a tree diagram showing the selections. Label the probabilities.

8 marbles in the bag   7 marbles in the bag

red marble drawn $\frac{3}{8}$

     red marble drawn $\frac{2}{7}$ Only 2 red marbles remain.

     blue marble drawn $\frac{5}{7}$ All 5 blue marbles remain.

blue marble drawn $\frac{5}{8}$

     red marble drawn $\frac{3}{7}$ All 3 red marbles remain.

     blue marble drawn $\frac{4}{7}$ Only 4 blue marbles remain.

$P(\text{red, then red})\ \frac{3}{8} \cdot \frac{2}{7} = \frac{3}{28}$

9 Find the probability that both marbles that Samuel drew at random are the same color.

■ SOLUTION

Refer to the tree diagram in the solution to Example 8.

$P(\text{both marbles the same color}) = P(\text{red, then red}) + P(\text{blue, then blue})$

$$= \frac{3}{8} \cdot \frac{2}{7} + \frac{5}{8} \cdot \frac{4}{7}$$

$P(\text{both marbles the same color}) = \frac{26}{56} = \frac{13}{28}$

Independent and Dependent Events

If events A and B are independent, then $P(A, \text{then } B) = P(A) \cdot P(B)$.

If events A and B are dependent, then $P(A, \text{then } B) = P(A) \cdot P(B \text{ given } A)$.

Find each probability.

10 A spade is randomly drawn from a standard deck of playing cards on two successive draws, given that the card is replaced.

■ **SOLUTION**

Number of (spade, spade) cards → 13 × 13
Total number of cards   → 52 × 52

$P(\text{spade, then spade}) = \frac{13 \times 13}{52 \times 52}$

$= \frac{1}{4} \times \frac{1}{4} = \frac{1}{16}$

11 A spade is randomly drawn from a standard deck of playing cards on two successive draws, given that the card is not replaced.

■ **SOLUTION**

Number of (spade, spade) cards → 13 × 12
Total number of cards   → 52 × 51

$P(\text{spade, then spade}) = \frac{13 \times 12}{52 \times 51}$

$= \frac{1}{17}$

The probability of an event occurring given that some other event has already occurred is called **conditional probability**. The conditional probability that an event A occurs, given that event B occurs, can be denoted as $P(A \mid B)$.

EXAMPLE 12   **Finding conditional probability**

12 High school students were asked to identify their most likely after-school activity. The data is shown below.

Class	Sports Activity	Club Meetings	Homework	Watch TV	Total
Freshman	68	55	22	30	175
Sophomore	56	48	29	27	160
Junior	72	50	20	20	162
Senior	60	45	25	25	155
Total	256	198	96	102	652

Given that the student is a junior, what is the probability that the student's most likely after-school activity is a sports activity?

■ **SOLUTION 1**

Use the formula.

$P(\text{sports} \mid \text{junior})$

$= \dfrac{P(\text{junior and chose sports})}{P(\text{junior})}$

$= \dfrac{\frac{72}{652}}{\frac{162}{652}} = \frac{72}{162} = 0.44$

■ **SOLUTION 2**

Intuitively, the condition is that you are a junior, so our total sample space is now made up of just juniors (162). The probability that sports are a junior student's most likely after-school activity is

$\frac{72}{162} = 0.44.$

Conditional Probability

The conditional probability of event A, given event B, is

$$P(A \mid B) = \frac{P(A \text{ and } B)}{P(B)}, P(B) \neq 0.$$

A coin is *fair* if the probability of heads is the same as the probability of tails. A coin is *unfair* if one of these probabilities does not equal the other. You can apply this to the coin problem in Example 13.

EXAMPLE 13 Finding probabilities involving successive independent events

 A fair coin is tossed three times. Find P(heads, then heads, then heads).

■ SOLUTION

P(heads, heads, heads) $= \frac{1}{2} \cdot \frac{1}{2} \cdot \frac{1}{2} = \left(\frac{1}{2}\right)^3 = \frac{1}{8}$ ← three independent events with P(heads) $= \frac{1}{2}$

Just as one event can be dependent on a second event, a third event can be dependent on the two events preceding it.

EXAMPLE 14 Finding probabilities involving successive dependent events

 A student council sends 4 boys and 6 girls to the local school board meeting. Three of the students will be interviewed. Find the probability that all three students interviewed are girls.

■ SOLUTION

Sketch a diagram showing the three successive selections.

first selection

6 girls of 10 students

second selection

5 girls of 9 students
one student already selected
one girl already selected

third selection

4 girls of 8 students
two students already selected
two girls already selected

P(girl, girl, girl) $= \frac{\overset{3}{6}}{10_5} \times \frac{5}{9} \times \frac{\overset{1}{4}}{8_2} = \frac{3^1}{5_1} \times \frac{5^1}{9_3} \times \frac{1}{2} = \frac{1}{6}$

Practice

Choose the letter preceding the word or expression that best completes the statement or answers the question.

1 A fair coin is flipped four times. If the coin lands heads up on the first three tosses, what is the probability that it will land heads up on the fourth toss?

A. $\frac{1}{2}$ B. $\left(\frac{1}{2}\right)^4$ C. $4 \cdot \frac{1}{2}$ D. $\frac{1}{4 \cdot 2}$

2 Which is the probability of a coin landing heads up each time on three tosses of a fair coin?

A. $\frac{1}{2}$ B. $\left(\frac{1}{2}\right)^3$ C. $3 \cdot \frac{1}{2}$ D. $\frac{1}{3 \cdot 2}$

3 A marble is randomly selected from among 5 red and 4 blue marbles, kept, and then a second marble is drawn at random. What is the probability that both marbles drawn will be red?

A. $\frac{5}{9} \cdot \frac{4}{9}$ B. $\frac{5}{9} + \frac{4}{9}$ C. $\frac{5}{9} \cdot \frac{4}{8}$ D. $\frac{5}{9} + \frac{3}{8}$

4 A marble is randomly selected from among 5 red and 4 blue marbles, replaced, and then a second marble is drawn at random. What is the probability of selecting red both times?

A. $\frac{5}{9} \cdot \frac{5}{9}$ B. $\frac{5}{9} + \frac{4}{9}$ C. $\frac{5}{9} \cdot \frac{3}{8}$ D. $\frac{5}{9} + \frac{3}{8}$

5 A coin is tossed and the arrow on the spinner shown here is spun. What is the probability of heads showing and the arrow landing in the light gray region?

A. $\frac{1}{2} \cdot \frac{1}{4}$ **C.** $\frac{1}{2} \cdot \frac{1}{2}$

B. $\frac{1}{2} + \frac{1}{4}$ **D.** $\frac{1}{2} \cdot \left(1 - \frac{1}{4}\right)$

In Exercises 6–11, a bag contains 3 red, 4 blue, and 5 green marbles, identical but for color. Find each probability given the specified condition.

6 P(red, then red); with replacement

7 P(green, then blue); with replacement

8 P(red, then green); without replacement

9 P(blue, then blue); without replacement

10 P(neither is green); with replacement

11 P(neither is green); without replacement

In Exercises 12–15, find the probability that a family having three children has the indicated number of boys or girls. Use this tree diagram.

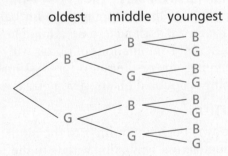

12 All three children are boys.

13 The family has one boy and two girls.

14 The family has at least one girl.

15 The youngest is a boy given that the oldest is a girl.

In Exercises 16–19, teachers send 7 boys and 8 girls to the local science fair. The first three students leaving the fair at lunch time are interviewed. Find each probability.

16 All students interviewed are boys.

17 Exactly two girls are interviewed.

18 A girl is interviewed, then a boy is interviewed, and then a girl is interviewed.

19 A boy is interviewed, given that a boy is interviewed first.

In Exercises 20–23, use the spinners below to find the probability of the situation described. Assume the spinners are fair.

spinner 1   spinner 2   spinner 3

20 The arrow lands in region I, lands in the red region, and lands in region A.

21 The arrow lands in region I or II, lands in the tan region, and lands in region B.

22 The arrow lands in region III, lands in the tan or red region, and lands in region E.

23 The arrow lands in region II, lands in the blue region, and lands in regions A, B, or C.

In Exercise 24, solve the problem. Clearly show all necessary work.

24 Among Jan's 5 sweaters is a red one and a blue one. Among her 5 blouses is a white one and a yellow one. Among her 5 skirts is a green one and a black one. What is the probability that she chooses a red or blue sweater, a white or yellow blouse, and a green or black skirt?

8.4 Combinations

New Jersey Standards

4.4.C.1 Calculate combinations

A **combination** is an arrangement of objects in which the order of the objects is not important. A combination is similar to a permutation in that it can also be used to determine the number of combinations that can be made from a group of items or objects. However, unlike a permutation, order does not matter in a combination. For example, groups ABC, ACB, BAC, BCA, CAB, and CBA are considered one combination because they all have the same three members.

Combinations

The number of combinations of n items taken r at a time is given by

$$_nC_r = \frac{_nP_r}{r!}$$

Another way to determine the number of outcomes in a combination situation is to use an array of numbers known as **Pascal's triangle.** Each entry in this triangle is obtained by adding the two entries above it.

Each entry in the triangle represents the number of combinations possible given the total number of items in a group and the number of items in the combination. The row represents the total items being considered. The diagonal position represents the number of items in the combination. Notice that the first row and the first diagonal in each row is counted as zero.

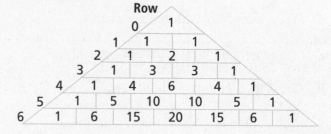

Go Online
PHSchool.com
Visit: PHSchool.com
Web Code: ayp-0124

 EXAMPLES 1 and 2   Evaluating combinations

1 How many different 3 letter combinations can be made from the 26 letters in the alphabet?

- **SOLUTION**

$$_{26}C_3 = \frac{26 \times 25 \times 24}{3 \times 2 \times 1} \quad \leftarrow \text{ Substitute.}$$

$$_{26}C_3 = \frac{15600}{6} = 2,600 \quad \leftarrow \begin{array}{l}\text{Multiply.}\\ \text{Then divide.}\end{array}$$

There are **2,600** different three-letter combinations in the alphabet.

2 The local pizzeria offers a selection of 9 different pizza toppings. The Friday Nite Special is a large three topping pizza for half-price. Use Pascal's triangle to determine how many different combinations of pizzas with three toppings the restaurant offers. Assume no topping is doubled on any given pizza.

- **SOLUTION**

Count down, beginning with 0, to the ninth row. Count across, beginning with 0, to the third diagonal position.

There are **84** possible combinations of pizzas with three toppings.

It is also possible to join two sets of combinations. In this case, each possible combination is considered separately, then the two values are multiplied together. The product represents the total number of combinations for both groups together.

EXAMPLE 3   Joining combinations

3 There are 12 members of the student council, 7 girls and 5 boys. A subcommittee of 5 student ambassadors, 3 girls and 2 boys, will be chosen to welcome foreign exchange students. How many possible combinations of committee members are there?

■ **SOLUTION**

Using Pascal's triangle, there are **35** possible combinations of girls and 10 possible combinations of boys.

$$35 \cdot 10 = 350 \text{ combinations of committee members}$$

The same solution can be found using the combination formula.

$$_7C_3 \cdot {}_5C_2 = \frac{7 \times 6 \times 5}{3 \times 2 \times 1} \times \frac{5 \times 4}{2 \times 1}$$

$$= \frac{210}{6} \times \frac{20}{2}$$

$$= 35 \times 10 = 350 \text{ combinations of committee members}$$

Practice

Choose the letter preceding the word or expression that best completes the sentence or answers the question.

1 Suppose there are six people attending a meeting and each person will shake hands with each of the other attendees only once. How many handshakes will there be?

   A. 720   **B.** 360   **C.** 30   **D.** 15

2 The art teacher has 6 colors of paint, 5 colors of construction paper, and 12 types stickers. Each student is instructed to choose 2 colors of paint, 2 colors of construction paper, and 4 stickers for their project. How many possible combinations of supplies are there for the students to choose from?

   A. 45   **B.** 495   **C.** 7425   **D.** 74,250

3 A 4-digit personal identification number (PIN) is needed to access a debit card account. If no digit is repeated in the sequence, how many PIN combinations are possible?

   A. 126   **C.** 15,120

   B. 210   **D.** 151,200

In Exercises 4–5, solve each problem. Clearly show all necessary work.

4 The local library's book van travels around the county to loan books to children living outside the city limits. The van holds an assortment of 150 books for the children to choose from. Each child is allowed to borrow 3 books at a time. How many different combinations of books can the first child on the route choose? Assuming each child chooses the three books allowed, how many different combinations of books can the 25th child choose? Assuming each child chooses the three books allowed, how many different combinations of books can the 50th child choose?

5 Radio stations are assigned call letters that begin with either a K or a W and are a total of four letters long. How many combinations of call letters are there if no letter is repeated in any one call number. How many combinations will there be if the five vowels are removed from the list of available letters?

8.5 Using Counting Methods with Probability

New Jersey Standards

4.4.C.1 Calculate combinations

4.4.C.3 Justify counting problems

In how many different ways can the letters in the word **MATH** be arranged?

4 letters for first choice	**3** letters for second choice	**2** letters for third choice	**1** letter for fourth choice
M A T or H	M̶ A T or H	M̶ A̶ T or H	M̶ A̶ T̶ or H
For example: M	For example: A	For example: T	For example: H

Using the Fundamental Counting Principle, there are $4 \times 3 \times 2 \times 1$, or 24, different arrangements. Each of these arrangements is called a *permutation* of the letters in **MATH**. A **permutation** of the members in a set of objects is any arrangement of those objects in a specific order.

MATH and **AMTH** are different permutations.

EXAMPLE 1   **Counting simple arrangements**

 How many different arrangements of the letters in **EIGHT** are there if all the letters are used exactly once?

    A. 1   **B.** 5   **C.** 20   **D.** 120

    ■ **SOLUTION**

    There are 5 choices for the first letter, 4 choices for the second, and so on. There are $5 \times 4 \times 3 \times 2 \times 1$, or 120 arrangements. The correct choice is D.

Each of the products below can be abbreviated using **factorial notation**.

$$4 \times 3 \times 2 \times 1 = 4! \qquad\qquad 5 \times 4 \times 3 \times 2 \times 1 = 5!$$

In general, $n \times (n - 1) \times (n - 2) \times \cdots \times 2 \times 1 = n!$. By definition, $0! = 1$.

EXAMPLES 2 and 3   **Evaluating expressions involving $n!$**

Evaluate each expression.

   $\dfrac{5!}{3!}$

    ■ **SOLUTION**

    $\dfrac{5!}{3!} = \dfrac{5 \times 4 \times 3 \times 2 \times 1}{3 \times 2 \times 1}$

    $= \dfrac{5 \times 4 \times \cancel{3 \times 2 \times 1}}{\cancel{3 \times 2 \times 1}} = 20$

3 $\dfrac{7!}{3!2!}$

    ■ **SOLUTION**

    $\dfrac{7!}{3!2!} = \dfrac{7 \times 6 \times 5 \times 4 \times 3 \times 2 \times 1}{3 \times 2 \times 1 \times 2 \times 1}$

    $= \dfrac{7 \times 6 \times 5 \times 4 \times \cancel{3 \times 2 \times 1}}{\cancel{3 \times 2 \times 1} \times 2 \times 1} = 420$

There is a formula that you can use to count the permutations of n objects taken n at a time.

Permutations of n Objects Taken n at a Time

The number of permutations of n objects taken n at a time, denoted $_nP_n$, is given by $_nP_n = n!$.

How many four-letter arrangements can be made from the letters in **HERMIT**? The diagram below suggests that there are $6 \times 5 \times 4 \times 3$ arrangements.

6 letters for first choice	5 letters for second choice	4 letters for third choice	3 letters for fourth choice
HERMIT	~~H~~ERMIT	~~HE~~RMIT	~~HER~~MIT
For example: H	For example: E	For example: R	For example: M

Notice that $6 \times 5 \times 4 \times 3 = \frac{6 \times 5 \times 4 \times 3 \times 2 \times 1}{2 \times 1} = \frac{6!}{(6-4)!}$. In general, you can state and use the following formula for counting permutations of n objects taken r at a time.

Permutations of n Objects Taken r at a Time

Let n and r be natural numbers with $r \leq n$.

The number of permutations of n objects taken r at a time is $_nP_r = \dfrac{n!}{(n-r)!}$.

EXAMPLE 4   **Counting permutations of n objects taken r at a time**

 A student may select a four-digit sequence with no repetition of digits for a lock on his or her locker. How many such sequences are possible?

■ **SOLUTION**

Calculate $_{10}P_4$. In $_{10}P_4$, $n = 10$ and $r = 4$.

$$_{10}P_4 = \frac{10!}{(10-4)!} = \frac{10!}{6!}$$
$$= \frac{10 \times 9 \times 8 \times 7 \times 6!}{6!}$$
$$= 5040$$

The student may choose from **5040** four-digit sequences.

If you list and count the permutations of the letters in **SEE**, you will find 6 permutations. This happens because **E** and **E** are considered distinguishable. If you consider color to be unimportant, permutations 1 and 4, 2 and 5, and 3 and 6 become the same. Then there are only 3 distinguishable permutations.

1	2	3
SEE	ESE	EES

4	5	6
SEE	ESE	EES

Evaluate $\frac{3!}{2!}$ to get the number of distinguishable permutations of **S, E, E**. In general, you can use the following formula.

Permutations of n Objects With Repetition

The number of permutations of n objects with r of them the same is given by $\frac{n!}{r!}$. If r of the n objects are the same and s of the n objects are the same, the number of distinguishable permutations is given by $\frac{n!}{r!s!}$.

In the word **BANANA**, **N** occurs twice and **A** occurs 3 times. The total number of distinguishable permutations of all the letters is given by $\frac{6!}{2!3!}$, or 60.

The permutations of the letters in the word **MATH** taken two letters at a time are shown in the table below. Notice there are 12 such permutations.

MA	MT	MH	AM	AT	AH
TM	TA	TH	HM	HA	HT

Notice that **MA** and **AM** are different permutations that contain the same letters.

Counting permutations plays an important role in solving many probability problems.

Go Online
PHSchool.com
Visit: PHSchool.com
Web Code: ayp-0582

EXAMPLES 5 and 6   **Solving probability problems using permutations**

 5 The student council at Bradville High School consists of the following students. Three members are to be chosen at random as leader, assistant, and record keeper. Find the probability that R. Jones is the leader.

R. Jones	M. White	J. Green	L. Smith	W. Jackson
B. Brown	E. Schwartz	S. Washington	J. Aaron	C. Pike

■ **SOLUTION**

Step 1 Since order is important, the groups below are different.
  R. Jones (leader)   M. White (assistant)   J. Green (record keeper)
  M. White (leader)   R. Jones (assistant)   J. Green (record keeper)
  Therefore, this problem involves permutations.

Step 2 Count favorable outcomes and total outcomes.
  Find how many three-member groups there are with R. Jones as leader.
  R. Jones (leader) × 9 for assistant × 8 for record keeper → 72 groups favorable

  Find how many groups there are with leader, assistant, and record keeper. In all, there are $_{10}P_3$ groups of three students in the specified order.

Step 3 Calculate $\frac{72}{_{10}P_3}$.

$$\frac{72}{_{10}P_3} = \frac{72}{\frac{10!}{(10-3)!}} = 72 \times \frac{(10-3)!}{10!} = \frac{72}{10 \times 9 \times 8} = \frac{1}{10}$$

6 A mathematics teacher places an algebra book, a geometry book, and an algebra II book on a shelf. What is the probability that the geometry book is placed first?

■ **SOLUTION**

Step 1 Calculate how many ways the books can be arranged if the Geometry book is placed first.
$$1 \cdot 2 \cdot 1 = 2$$

Step 2 Calculate the total number of ways the books can be arranged on the shelf.
$$_3P_3 = 3! = 3 \cdot 2 \cdot 1 = 6$$

Step 3 Calculate the probability.
$$\frac{2}{6} = \frac{1}{3}$$

Some calculators enable you to calculate a permutation by using functions built into the calculator. This display shows the calculations of $_{10}P_4$. To get the results shown here, enter 10, then choose $_nP_r$, and then enter 4.

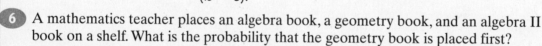

```
10 nPr 4
              5040
```

Practice

Choose the letter preceding the word or expression that best completes the statement or answers the question.

1 The number of distinct arrangements in a specific order using the letters in **APPLE** is given by

   A. $5!$ **C.** $\frac{5!}{2!}$

   B. $_5P_5$ **D.** $\frac{5!}{3!}$

2 In how many ways can 100 people sit in 100 seats on an airplane?

   A. $100!$ **C.** $\frac{100!}{100!}$

   B. $_{100}P_{10}$ **D.** 100

3 A social security number has the form below.

   three digits - two digits - four digits

   If the first digit in each block is 1, and the other digits are taken from 0, 1, 2, 3, 4, 5, 6, 7, 8, and 9, how many such social security numbers are possible?

   A. $10!$ **C.** 9^{10}

   B. $9!$ **D.** $10^2 \times 10^1 \times 10^3$

4 How many distinguishable permutations are possible using all the letters in **LETTER**?

   A. $6!$ **C.** $6! \times 2! \times 3!$

   B. $\frac{6!}{2! \times 2!}$ **D.** $\frac{6!}{2 \times 3}$

5 A drawer contains twelve T-shirts. A second drawer contains six pairs of slacks. If two T-shirts are white and two pairs of slacks are black, which is the probability of choosing a white T-shirt and a black pair of slacks?

   A. $\frac{2+2}{12+6}$ **C.** $\frac{2}{12} \cdot \frac{2}{6}$

   B. $\frac{12!}{2!} \cdot \frac{6!}{2!}$ **D.** $\frac{2!}{12!} \cdot \frac{2!}{6!}$

In Exercises 6–11, evaluate each expression.

6 $\frac{6!}{4!}$

7 $\frac{6!}{(6-3)!}$

8 $\frac{8!}{3!(8-3)!}$

9 $\frac{7!}{3!2!}$

10 $\frac{11!}{2!(11-2)!}$

11 $_4P_2 \times {}_5P_3$

In Exercises 12–18, find the number of specified permutations.

12 How many different seven-digit phone numbers are available if the first three digits are 7, 3, and 4 in that order?

13 permutations of all the letters in **SQUARE**

14 permutations of the letters in **SQUARE** using all letters with the first letter a vowel

15 permutations of the letters in **SQUARE** using all letters with the last letter being **R**

16 permutations of the letters in **SQUARE** using all letters and given that the first letter is **Q** and the last letter is **U**

17 Ten points are scattered around a circle. How many triangles can be formed?

18 A four-digit number consists only of even digits, each used exactly once.

In Exercises 19–22, a bag contains 5 red, 6 blue, and 9 green marbles. Three marbles are drawn at random in one scoop. Find the probability of each outcome as a decimal to the nearest hundredth.

19 All 3 marbles are red.

20 All 3 marbles are blue.

21 Two marbles are red and 1 is blue.

22 Two marbles are blue and 1 is green.

8.6 Expected Value and the Law of Large Numbers

New Jersey Standards

4.4.B.6 Use the law of large numbers

4.4.B.3 Model probability simulations

The **expected value** of an experiment is the average of the possible outcomes in a sample space. This probably will not be the value you always obtain; it is just a mean of the possible values. You can find expected value by multiplying each outcome by its probability and then find the sum over all the possible outcomes. The formula for expected value is

$$E(x) = \sum [x \cdot P(x)]$$

where $P(x)$ is the probability of landing on x or earning x points in a game.

EXAMPLE 1 Calculating expected value

1 An evenly divided spinner is numbered 1 through 8. A game is played where the number of points you can earn is equal to the value of the space the spinner lands. What is the expected value of the points that can be earned from this game?

Note

The expected value of an experiment may be a value that is not even possible to earn from any event.

■ SOLUTION

The probability of the spinner landing on any given space, or $P(x)$, is $\frac{1}{8}$. The values of x are 1, 2, 3, 4, 5, 6, 7, and 8. So, the sum of all the possible outcomes is:

$$E(x) = 1 \cdot \frac{1}{8} + 2 \cdot \frac{1}{8} + 3 \cdot \frac{1}{8} + 4 \cdot \frac{1}{8} + 5 \cdot \frac{1}{8} + 6 \cdot \frac{1}{8} + 7 \cdot \frac{1}{8} + 8 \cdot \frac{1}{8} = 4.5$$

The expected value of the points that can be earned by spinning this spinner is **4.5**.

When an experiment is repeated many times the proportion of each possible outcome will be close to its theoretical probability. This is called **the law of large numbers.**

EXAMPLE 2 Applying the law of large numbers

2 Joseph rolled a number cube 1000 times. About how many times do you think he recorded rolling a 4 if you apply the law of large numbers?

■ SOLUTION

Because you do not have Joseph's actual results you can use the law of large numbers. Since the theoretical probability of rolling a 4 is $\frac{1}{6}$, you can multiply $1000 \times \frac{1}{6}$. **Therefore, Joseph rolled a 4 about 167 times.**

The law of large numbers is applied to games of chance. It is also applied in the insurance industry. For example, life insurance companies can calculate the average life expectancy for individuals based on the population. They can determine the probability that a policy holder may live to a certain age. The company sets its rates based on these numbers to make sure it has enough to cover claims as they occur.

 EXAMPLE 3 **Using the law of large numbers**

3 Kevin tossed a four-sided game piece 100 times. What can you expect to be the average value of his observed outcomes?

- **SOLUTION**

Because the expected value of the points that can be earned tossing a number cube is $E(x) = 1 \cdot \frac{1}{4} + 2 \cdot \frac{1}{4} + 3 \cdot \frac{1}{4} + 4 \cdot \frac{1}{4} = 2.5$ by the law of large numbers, tossing the piece 100 times will yield the same average as the expected value. *Therefore, the average is likely to be 2.5.*

Practice

In Exercises 1–3, select the answer choice that is best for each case.

1 A game is played where a number cube is tossed and players move the number of spaces they roll. What is the expected value of the number of spaces a person will move?

    A. 2.5   **B.** 3   **C.** 3.5   **D.** 4

2 A game is set up at the carnival where a coin is tossed to earn points. Heads is assigned the value of 2, and tails is assigned the value of 1. If you get at least 3 points in 2 tries you get a prize. What is the expected value of the points that can be earned with each toss of the coin?

    A. 2   **B.** 1.5   **C.** 1   **D.** 0.5

3 Cora wants to determine if a game spinner that is divided into four equal parts and numbered 1 through 4 is a fair spinner. She decides to spin the spinner 100 times. Based on the law of large numbers, how many times is it expected that the spinner lands on 3?

    A. 25   **B.** 50   **C.** 60   **D.** 75

In Exercises 4–5, solve the problem. Clearly show all necessary work.

4 Ms. Rosa has students choose a number tile from a bag to see what prize they will get when they play a game. Thomas wants to know if this is fair so he tests this at home. He puts 6 number tiles in a bag as Ms. Rosa does and chooses a tile. He replaces the tile and chooses again. Thomas does this 100 times. What will he most likely find to be the probability of choosing a 4? Explain your reasoning.

5 A spinner numbered 1 through 10 is used to determine how many spaces one will move in a board game. What is the expected value of spaces that one will move? Is this a possible number of spaces to move? Explain these results. Another game spinner is numbered 1 through 5. What is the expected value for the number of spaces this spinner will allow you to move? Explain the differences you notice.

227

DIRECTIONS FOR QUESTIONS 1–25: For each of the questions below, select the answer choice that is best for each case.

1 Which represents the probability of randomly drawing a card showing 7 or a card showing 5 from a standard deck of 52 cards?

A. $\frac{4}{52} + \frac{4}{52}$ C. $\frac{4}{52} \cdot \frac{4}{52}$

B. $1 - \left(\frac{4}{52} + \frac{4}{52}\right)$ D. $\frac{5}{52} + \frac{7}{52}$

2 Which event is impossible?

A. choosing a number between 20 and 30 that is also a prime number

B. rolling a 6 on a number cube and flipping heads on a coin

C. choosing a rational number between 2.1 and 3.9 that is an even number

D. getting a perfect score on a mathematics test and passing that test

3 In how many ways can 5 books be placed on a shelf in any order?

A. 5   B. 25   C. 15   D. 120

4 A bag contains 7 red, 7 blue, and 7 green marbles. Which represents the probability that a red marble will be randomly drawn from the bag and then a green marble will be randomly drawn from the bag given that the first marble drawn is not replaced?

A. $\frac{7}{21} \cdot \frac{6}{20}$ C. $\frac{7}{21} \cdot \frac{7}{20}$

B. $\frac{7}{21} \cdot \frac{7}{21}$ D. $\frac{7}{21} \cdot \frac{6}{21}$

5 On a bookshelf, there are 5 red books, 7 green books, and 10 brown books. If a book is picked at random, to the nearest whole percent, what is the probability that it is green?

A. 7%   B. 23%   C. 32%   D. 45%

6 A weather forecaster predicts that there is a 25% probability of rain today. What is the probability that it will not rain?

A. 65%   C. 75%

B. 5%   D. 45%

7 A container holds 6 red balls and 3 green balls. One green ball is drawn randomly and set aside. What is the probability the second ball drawn is green?

A. $\frac{1}{4}$ C. $\frac{1}{3}$

B. $\frac{2}{3}$ D. $\frac{3}{4}$

8 How many four-digit numbers can be made using only the even digits 0, 2, 4, 6, and 8?

A. 500   C. 625

B. 120   D. 20

In Exercises 9–12, refer to a table of outcomes for rolling a pair of number cubes. Find each probability to the nearest whole percent.

9 P(you roll two 5s)

A. 3%   B. 17%   C. 33%   D. 6%

10 P(sum equals 1)

A. 31%   B. 0%   C. 3%   D. 17%

11 P(sum is not 4)

A. 16%   B. 8%   C. 3%   D. 92%

12 P(sum is even)

A. 25%   C. 10%

B. 50%   D. 75%

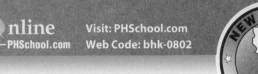
In Exercises 13–14, the Big Dipper Ice Cream Shop has 8 flavors of ice cream, 4 flavors of syrup, and 3 different toppings.

13 How many different ice cream dishes can be made with one flavor of ice cream, one syrup, and one topping?

   A. 15   B. 3   C. 36   D. 96

14 If vanilla and chocolate are two of the available flavors of ice cream, what is the probability that vanilla or chocolate ice cream will be chosen at random?

   A. $\frac{2}{15}$ B. $\frac{1}{3}$ C. $\frac{1}{8}$ D. $\frac{1}{4}$

15 Bag A contains 10 marbles and Bag B contains 24 marbles. If Bag A contains 2 red marbles and Bag B contains 2 red marbles, what is the probability of randomly drawing a red marble from each bag?

   A. $\frac{17}{60}$ B. $\frac{1}{60}$ C. $\frac{1}{55}$ D. $\frac{1}{120}$

16 There are 3 up escalators and one elevator to take shoppers from the first floor to the second floor. There are 3 down escalators and the same elevator to take shoppers from the second floor to the first floor. In how many ways can a shopper go from the first floor to the second floor and back?

   A. 4   B. 9   C. 16   D. 6

17 For which is the occurrence of one event not dependent on that of the other event?

   A. Drawing a 6 out of a deck of cards, and then drawing an 8 without replacing the 6.

   B. Flipping tails on one coin, and then flipping heads on a second coin.

   C. Drawing a king out of a deck of cards, leaving the king out, and then drawing another king.

   D. Randomly choosing a penny and then a nickel out of a bag of coins without replacing the first coin.

18 Find the probability of choosing two aces from a deck of cards on successive draws, given that the card is replaced.

   A. $\frac{1}{169}$ B. $\frac{1}{26}$ C. $\frac{2}{13}$ D. $\frac{4}{13}$

In Exercises 19–21, a bag contains 4 white, 3 silver, and 9 red paperclips identical in size. Find the probability of each event given the specified condition.

19 P(white, then silver); with replacement

   A. $\frac{7}{16}$ B. $\frac{1}{12}$ C. $\frac{3}{64}$ D. $\frac{7}{12}$

20 P(red, then red); without replacement

   A. $\frac{3}{10}$ B. $\frac{81}{256}$ C. $\frac{2}{9}$ D. $\frac{1}{72}$

21 P(neither is silver); without replacement

   A. $\frac{2}{13}$ B. $\frac{169}{256}$ C. $\frac{1}{156}$ D. $\frac{13}{20}$

22 How many different arrangements of the letters in the word **GOAL** are there if all the letters are used exactly once?

   A. 16   B. 24   C. 1   D. 10

23 Evaluate the expression $\frac{6!}{4!2!}$.

   A. 1   B. 15   C. $\frac{21}{13}$ D. $\frac{1}{8}$

24 In how many ways can 50 students sit in 50 seats on a school bus?

   A. $_{50}P_5$ B. $\frac{50!}{50!}$ C. 50!   D. 50

25 A fair spinner has 8 sections numbered 1–8. If the spinner is spun once, what is the probability that it lands on 2?

   A. $\frac{1}{8}$ B. $\frac{1}{2}$ C. $\frac{1}{4}$ D. $\frac{7}{8}$

26 In a local district, there are 9,800 Democratic, 11,000 Republican, and 1,200 Independent registered voters. A voter from the district is selected at random.

- Find the probability that the voter is from any of the three parties.

- Find the probability that the voter is a Democrat.

- Find the probability that the voter is a Republican.

27 On a team with 11 members, there are three captains, voted on by the players.

- Construct Pascal's triangle and explain how to use it to find how many combinations of captains are possible.

- How many combinations are possible on a team with 20 players?

- How many combinations of 2 captains are possible on a team of 25 players?

28 A card is drawn from a standard deck of 52 cards and a number cube is rolled.

- Find the probability that a spade is drawn and a 1 is rolled.

- Find the probability that a king or a queen is drawn and a 6 is rolled.

- Find the probability that a red card is drawn and a number greater than or equal to 3 is rolled.

9 Data Analysis

NEW JERSEY

Discovering New Jersey

Salt Water Taffy

Atlantic City, New Jersey, is known as the home of salt water taffy. Although the exact origin of taffy is unknown, it is commonly accepted that salt water taffy was first made in Atlantic City in 1883.

According to a local legend, a man by the name of David Bradley was selling taffy at his candy stand on the boardwalk in Atlantic City. A northeastern storm (called a "Nor'easter) caused ocean waves to spray saltwater on Bradley's taffy. A young girl came to his stand and asked for some taffy, and Mr. Bradley offered her "salt water" taffy. Hence, a legend and a popular candy was born!

Today, salt water taffy is manufactured mostly on the eastern coast of the United States. It is a favorite souvenir for many who visit the beaches along the Atlantic Ocean.

9.1 Measures of Central Tendency

New Jersey Standards

4.4.A.2   Evaluate and use data

4.4.A.5.1   Analyze data

Statistics is the mathematical study of **data,** its gathering, organization, analysis, representation, and interpretation. You can consider the scores on a mathematics test recorded at the right as data. The entire class in this example is called the **population.** Any subset of the population is called a **sample** of the population.

The **arithmetic mean** (mean) or **average** of a set of values is the sum of all of the values divided by the number of values in the set. If the sum of 32 test scores is 2,543, then the average score, to the nearest tenth, is $\frac{2543}{32} \approx 79.5$.

56	97	97	96	95	92	90	89
81	80	78	78	76	75	74	73
89	89	86	85	85	84	83	83
72	70	70	68	67	65	62	58

EXAMPLE 1   **Calculating the mean of a data set**

Visit: PHSchool.com
Web Code: ayp-0796

 Find the mean of the test scores below.

$$\{84, 80, 78, 73, 71, 95, 74, 93\}$$

■ **SOLUTION**

Step 1 Calculate the sum of the scores.
$$84 + 80 + 78 + 73 + 71 + 95 + 74 + 93 = 648$$

Step 2 Divide the total by 8.
$$\frac{648}{8} = 81$$

The mean of the test scores is 81. (A calculator solution is also shown.)

```
84+80+78+73+71+
95+74+93
                648
Ans/8
                 81
```

When values in a data set repeat, you can organize them in a *frequency table.* The **frequency** represents the number of times a particular value appears in the data set.

EXAMPLE 2   **Using data frequencies find the mean**

 Find the mean of the data in this table.

Data value	3.5	3.4	3.7	3.8	4.0
Frequency	6	3	2	3	1

■ **SOLUTION**

Step 1 Calculate the sum of the products of data values and frequencies.
$$6(3.5) + 3(3.4) + 2(3.7) + 3(3.8) + 4.0 = 54$$

Step 2 Divide by the sum of the frequencies, which is 15.
$$\frac{54}{15} = 3.6$$

Sometimes it is helpful to write an equation to solve a problem involving the mean.

EXAMPLE 3 **Using an equation to solve a data problem with the mean**

3 Jasmine earns scores of 80, 78, 85, and 82 on four successive history tests. What score must she earn on her fifth test to have a mean (average) of 80?

- **SOLUTION**

Let x represent the needed score. Solve the equation below.

$$\frac{\text{sum of scores}}{\text{number of scores}} \rightarrow \frac{80 + 78 + 85 + 82 + x}{5} = 80 \leftarrow \text{mean}$$

$$325 + x = 400$$
$$x = 75$$

Jasmine needs to get a **75** to have a mean score of 80.

Check: $\frac{80 + 78 + 85 + 82 + 75}{5} = \frac{400}{5} = 80$ ✔

The **mode** of a set of data is the value that has the greatest frequency.

$\{2, 3, 4, 5, 4, 5, 7, 8, 5, 9\}$ The value 5 occurs three times.   It has the greatest frequency.   The mode is 5.

$\{5, 3, 6, 4, \mathbf{8}, 6, \mathbf{8}, 9, 7, 10, 11\}$ Both 6 and 8 occur twice.   There are two modes, 6 and 8.

> **Note**
>
> Data sets with one mode, two modes, and three modes are called unimodal, bimodal, and trimodal, respectively.

If each data value has a frequency of 1 or if the frequencies of all of the data values are the same, then you can say that the data set has no mode.

The **median** of a data set is the middle value in an ordered data set. If there is an even number of data values, the median is the average of the two middle values.

EXAMPLES 4 and 5 **Finding the median of a data set**

Find the median of each data set.

 $\{3, 6, 7, 2, 4, 8, 3\}$

- **SOLUTION**

Arrange in order from least to greatest. Identify the middle number.

2 3 3 **4** 6 7 8

middle number

The median is 4.

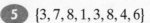 $\{3, 7, 8, 1, 3, 8, 4, 6\}$

- **SOLUTION**

Arrange in order from least to greatest. Identify the middle numbers.

1 3 3 **4** **6** 7 8 8

middle numbers

The median is $\frac{4 + 6}{2}$, or 5.

The mean, median, and mode are referred to as the **measures of central tendency.** These statistics provide an idea of the value around which the set of data is centered.

Sometimes one measure of central tendency is more representative than another for describing the "center" of a data set. Although the values of the mode and median are not generally affected by the other data values, the mean can be significantly affected by extreme values in a data set. You can analyze the data along with the measures of central tendency to determine which measure is the most representative of the data.

EXAMPLES 6 and 7   **Finding the most appropriate measure of central tendency**

 A real estate agent sells homes for $85,000, $93,000, $110,000, and $220,000. Which measure of central tendency best describes the cost of the homes sold? Explain your answer.

■ SOLUTION

The mean is $127,000 and the median is $101,500. The mean is not representative of the home prices because it is affected by the one higher priced home. *The median is a more representative measure of central tendency for this set of data because it seems to represent the data and is not affected by the higher priced home.*

 A head manager earns $250,000 each year. The department manager earns $55,000, and two assistant managers earn $40,000 each. Which is the most appropriate measure of the salaries associated with the managers of the business?

■ SOLUTION

The mean, $96,222, is not a representative measure of the typical manager's salary because it is significantly affected by the huge salary of the head manager. The mode is $40,000 and represents only the lowest-paid of the managers. *The median is $47,500 and best represents the typical salary of the managers of this business.*

Practice

Choose the letter preceding the word or expression that best completes the statement or answers the question.

1 Which value of x will make the mean of the data set below equal to 6?

$$\{3, 3, 4, 5, 6, 7, 8, x\}$$

A. 8   **B.** 12   **C.** 40   **D.** 48

2 Which value is the mean of the data set below?

$$\{1, 4, 4, 5, 6, 7, 8, 9\}$$

A. 4   **B.** 9   **C.** 1   **D.** 5.5

3 Which data set has 54 as its median?

A. $\{10, 30, 40, 45, 50, 58, 60, 65, 75, 90\}$

B. $\{25, 25, 30, 35, 50, 56, 65, 70, 75, 80\}$

C. $\{30, 40, 45, 47, 54, 55, 60, 65, 75, 85\}$

D. $\{10, 20, 30, 40, 50, 54, 60, 70, 80, 90\}$

4 Which expression does not represent the mean of the data set below?

$$\{2, 2, 5, 7, 8, 8, 8\}$$

A. $\dfrac{2(2) + 5 + 7 + 3(8)}{7}$

B. $\dfrac{2 + 2 + 5 + 7 + 8 + 8 + 8}{7}$

C. $\dfrac{40}{7}$

D. $\dfrac{7}{2 + 2 + 5 + 7 + 8 + 8 + 8}$

5 Which statement is always true?

A. The median is a value in the data set.

B. The median is also the maximum.

C. The median and the mean are the same.

D. Fifty percent of the data is at or below the median.

In Exercises 6–16, solve the following problems. Clearly show all necessary work.

6 Find the mean of the data set in this table.

Data Value	Frequency
6	//
4	////
8	///
11	/

7 Find the median of this data set.

Plant Height	
9	3 6 7 8 9 9
8	2 4 6 8 9
7	4 6 8
6	2 5
5	3 6
4	4
3	3
2	1

Key: 2 | 1 means 2.1 cm

8 The mean of a number and 6 equals the mean of twice the number and 1. What is the number?

9 Which interval contains the median?

Interval	Frequency
14–16	2
17–19	6
20–22	9
23–25	8

10 Gina earns scores of 65, 78, 85, and 82 on four tests. What grade must she earn on the next test to have an average of 80?

11 If n represents the smallest of four consecutive integers, write an expression for the mean of the numbers.

12 For the data set $\{11, 13, 15, 15, 16, 17, 18, 19, 19, 20\}$ which is greater, the mean or the median?

13 Boxes weighing 12.5 pounds, 12.4 pounds, 12.5 pounds, and 13.6 pounds have the same average weight as 3 packages of equal weight. How much does each of the equal packages weigh?

14 A set of data contains 200 elements. Explain how to find the median of the data.

15 For which value of a will 2, 3, 5, a, 10, and 12 arranged in order from least to greatest have a median of 5.5?

16 A survey taker forgot to write the frequency n for the data value 6 in the frequency table below, but noted a mean of 6.6. What was the frequency of the data value 6?

Data Value	Frequency
5	//
6	n
8	////

9.2 Representing Data Graphically

New Jersey Standards

4.4.A.2 Evaluate and use data

4.4.A.5.1 Analyze data

Once again, consider the scores on a mathematics test shown in the table below.

56	97	97	96	95	92	90	89
81	80	78	78	76	75	74	73
89	89	86	85	85	84	83	83
72	70	70	68	67	65	62	58

The lowest score is 56 and the highest score is 97. A simple representation of the data is shown in the **bar graph** below. Vertical bars are used to represent the totals of the scores in each of 5 specific groups. The groups are students with scores in the 50s, 60s, 70s, 80s, and 90s. Specific scores are not indicated.

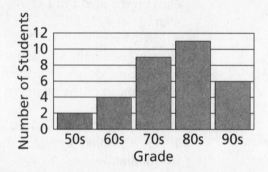

EXAMPLE 1   **Interpreting and analyzing bar-graph data**

 The bar graph shows company profit over the first six months of last year. What percent of the profit did the company earn in the first three months of that year? Describe how the profit earned in the first three months compares to that earned in the months of April, May, and June.

Profit
(in thousands of dollars)

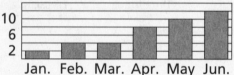

- **SOLUTION**

Calculate profits.

First three months $2000 + 4000 + 4000 = 10,000$

All six months $2000 + 4000 + 4000 + 8000 + 10,000 + 12,000 = 40,000$

Calculate the ratio involving profits. $\frac{10,000}{40,000} = \frac{1}{4} = 0.25 = 25\%$

The bar graph indicates that the company's profits were significantly higher in April, May, and June.

If you want to record the test scores in the table above in such a way that individual scores in the intervals 50s, 60s, 70s, 80s, and 90s are also shown, you can use a **stem-and-leaf plot** like the one shown at the right. To the left of the vertical line are the tens digits in the five intervals. To the right of the vertical line are the units digits for each of the scores in each interval. The numbers to the left of the vertical line are called the *stems*. The numbers to the right of the vertical line are called the *leaves*.

Test scores	
9	0 2 5 6 7 7
8	0 1 3 3 4 5 5 6 9 9 9
7	0 0 2 3 4 5 6 8 8
6	2 5 7 8
5	6 8

Key: 5 | 6 means 56

EXAMPLE 2 **Interpreting and analyzing a stem-and-leaf plot**

 The stem-and-leaf plot below records completion times for runners in one race. What percentage of the runners finished the race in less than 6.5 minutes? Analyze the plot to describe the running times in general.

■ **SOLUTION**

Step 1 Find the total number of competitors.
The total equals the number of leaves.
$$6 + 11 + 9 + 9 + 6 + 4 = 45$$

Step 2 Find the total number of competitors whose completion times are less than 6.5 minutes. The greatest completion time less than 6.5 minutes is 6.4 minutes.
$$2 + 6 + 4 = 12$$

Step 3 Calculate the ratio of 12 to 45. $\frac{12}{45} = \frac{4}{15} \approx 0.27$

About **27%** of the competitors finished in less than 6.5 minutes.

This percentage is reasonable because the plot indicates that most runners completed the race in 7 to 10 minutes.

Running Times	
10	0 0 0 1 3 4
8	0 1 3 3 3 4 5 6 8 8 9
7	0 0 3 3 4 6 6 8 8
6	1 4 5 6 7 6 8 9 9
5	6 6 6 6 7 7
4	0 0 1 3

Key: 4 | 0 means 4.0 min

Certain types of data can also be displayed in a circle graph. Circle graphs are used to compare part of a whole. You can analyze and interpret data displayed in a circle graph.

 Voters are asked how they intend to vote on a local issue. The circle graph at the right represents the results of the survey of 500 voters. How many voters are uncertain which way to vote on the issue? In general, describe how the number of 'Yes' voters compares with 'No' and 'Do not know' voters.

Voter Survey

■ **SOLUTION**

Calculate the degree measure of the slice corresponding to the uncertain voters.

$$360° - (174° + 86°) = 100°$$

Calculate the product: $\frac{100}{360} \times 500 \approx 139$

Of the 500 voters, **139 voters** are uncertain which way to vote.

In general, the same number of people intend to vote yes as those that intend to vote no and those that are undecided combined.

 The circle graph at the right represents the top 5 countries of origin of international visitors to New York City in 2005. The fewest international visitors come from which country? Which country accounts for about 40% of all international visitors to New York City in 2005?

Top 5 Countries of Origin of International Visitors to NYC

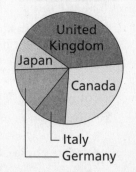

■ **SOLUTION**

A circle graph displays data as parts of a whole. Therefore, of the top 5 countries, the fewest international visitors come from **Italy and Japan** because those pieces of the graph are equally small. The **United Kingdom** accounts for about 40% of the international visitors from the top 5 countries in 2005.

During a 7-day period, a student records the noon temperature in degrees Fahrenheit each day. A **line graph,** or **broken-line graph,** is used to display data representing change over time. In this line graph, the Day is displayed on the horizontal axis and the Temperature at noon is recorded on the vertical axis.

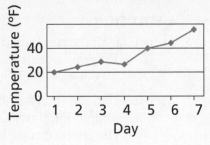

Temperature at Noon

Day	1	2	3	4	5	6	7
Temperature (°F)	20	25	30	27	40	45	57

This line graph illustrates a *trend* over time. In general, the midday temperature increases over the 7 days.

EXAMPLES 5 and 6 Interpreting line graphs

The line graph at the right represents a person's weight during a weight-loss program.

5 What relationship between time and weight does the graph show?

■ SOLUTION

The graph shows that the individual lost weight over the entire 6-week weight-loss program. The individual lost a total of 9 pounds during the program.

6 Describe the individual's weight loss between week 2 and week 5.

■ SOLUTION

The slope of the line is the same, so weight loss was consistent. During each week, the individual lost 3 pounds. Over that 3-week period, the individual lost 9 pounds.

In many cases, there may be more than one appropriate display for a given data set. Here are some guidelines for choosing an appropriate display.

Choosing an Appropriate Statistical Display

■ If the data are numerical, such as test scores, then a stem-and-leaf plot can show how the data compare, given specific ranges for the data. A histogram is also a suitable choice.

■ If numerical data are given for a set of nonnumerical categories and you want to know how the data for each category compare with the whole, then a circle graph is an appropriate choice. You can use a bar graph if you want to know how the data in each category compare with one another.

■ If continuous numerical data are given for a period of time and you want to know what trend the data may show, then a line graph is an appropriate choice.

Choose the letter preceding the word or expression that best completes the statement or answers the question.

1 Which conclusion may you not infer from the stem-and-leaf plot below?

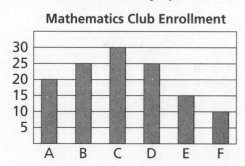

```
           Plant Height
        6  | 0 9
        5  | 3 3 3 4 6 6 6 7
        4  | 0 4 5 6 8 8 9
        3  | 2 3 4 5 5
        2  | 0 0 1 8
        1  | 2 3
      Key: 1 | 2 means 1.2 cm
```

A. There are 8 values between 5.0 and 5.9.

B. Fifty percent of the data values are larger than 4.5.

C. All the data values are less than 7.0 and greater than 1.0.

D. All 28 plants are healthy.

2 This bar graph shows enrollments in the mathematics clubs in the six high schools in one school district. Which statement may you not infer from the display?

Mathematics Club Enrollment

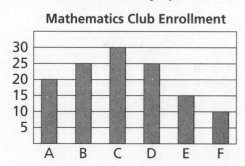

A. School C has the highest enrollment in the club.

B. Schools B and D have the same enrollment in the club.

C. School F has the smallest total student enrollment.

D. The club at school A has 5 members more than the club at school E.

In Exercises 3–4, solve the problem. Clearly show all necessary work.

3 What percentage of those interviewed preferred the three most popular teams?

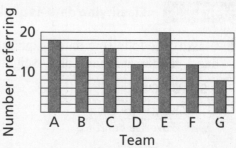

4 What percentage of those interviewed prefer a color other than red or blue?

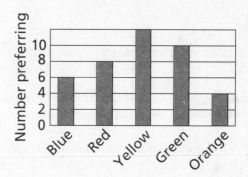

In Exercises 5–6, use the line graph below that shows the closing price of one share of stock in XYZ Company at the end of each week of trading for seven weeks.

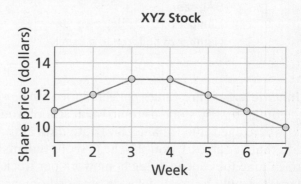

5 How does the share price at the end of week 7 compare with that at the end of week 1?

6 How does the trend of the share price over weeks 1 through 3 compare with that over the weeks 4 through 7?

Data Types, Data Collection, and Bias
9.3

New Jersey Standards

4.4.A.1.1 Determine advantages/ disadvantages of sampling techniques

4.4.A.2.2 Evaluate bias

4.4.A.2.3 Evaluate statistical claims

Data may be of two general types, *qualitative* and *quantitative*. **Qualitative** data may be words or numbers. **Quantitative** data are represented by numerical values.

 EXAMPLE 1   **Classifying data as qualitative or quantitative**

1. Classify the following data as qualitative or quantitative: favorite band, gender, age, hair color, weight, test grade, zip code.

   ■ **SOLUTION**

Qualitative data	Quantitative data
Favorite band	Age
Gender	Weight
Hair color	Test grade
Zip code	

Quantitative data can be classified as *discrete* or *continuous*. A **discrete** variable is one that can take on a finite number of values. **Continuous** variables can take on all the values of a continuous scale.

 EXAMPLE 2   **Classifying quantitative data as discrete or continuous**

Go Online
PHSchool.com

Visit: PHSchool.com
Web Code: ayp-0192

2. Classify the following quantitative data as discrete or continuous: time to complete homework, SAT score, blood pressure, weight, number of DVDs you own, height, number of children in a family.

   ■ **SOLUTION**

   Quantitative Data

Discrete	Continuous
SAT score	Time to complete homework
Number of DVDs you own	Blood Pressure
Number of children in a family	Weight or Height

Univariate data are values collected for a single variable. For example, the age of the first 50 students to arrive at school would create a univariate data set where age is the variable. **Bivariate data** are values collected for two different variables. If you ask the first 50 students who arrive at school how much time they spend doing homework per week and their GPA, a bivariate data set would be created where time on homework is one variable and GPA is the second variable.

You can use data to give a statistical analysis of a population. Sometimes it is impossible or impractical to study an entire population, so only a sample of the population is considered. A sample must be representative of the entire population in order to gather reliable data and assume that the characteristics of the sample accurately reflect those of the entire population.

In order to collect reliable data, you have to determine what data to collect and how to collect it. Among the most common data collection methods, or sampling techniques, are *convenience sampling, voluntary response sampling,* and *random sampling.* **Convenience sampling** uses a sample because it is convenient. **Voluntary response sampling** depends on voluntary respondents to generate a sample of the population. **Random sampling** is usually the most representative of the populations since each member of the population has an equal chance of being part of the sample.

Some advantages and disadvantages of each sampling technique are described in the table below.

Sampling Techniques					
Convenience Sampling		Voluntary Response Sampling		Random Sampling	
Advantages	Disadvantages	Advantages	Disadvantages	Advantages	Disadvantages
Easy and convenient	Limited useful applications	Easy and convenient	More costly and time consuming	Most common	Expensive and not feasible for large population
Accurate results when the members of the population are the same	Sample not typically representative of target population, which leads to bias	Mail survey format is not intrusive and allows respondents to complete at their convenience	Only those who feel strongly may respond, while the majority of sample does not respond; this leads to strong bias of the data and unreliable data.	Each member of a population has an equal chance of being selected, a fact that eliminates or limits bias.	Supplementary information important to the population is not used to determine the sample; sample is completely random.
Inexpensive	Data unreliable	Familiar to population	Interviews "interrupt" lives of respondents	Analysis of this reliable data is well established.	Often impossible to identify every member of a population

You can use a *random sample* to gather data from a group that is representative of the target population. Remember that random sampling requires that each member of the population has an equal chance of being selected.

EXAMPLE 3 **Choosing a random sample**

3 You want to determine which prom is most popular among senior class members. There are 547 students in the senior class. Describe how you would determine a random sample of 60 seniors to poll.

■ SOLUTION

Step 1 Assign each senior student a distinct number from 1 to 547.

Step 2 Generate a random selection of 60 integers from 1 to 547. Use the *randInt* function on a graphing calculator to generate this list. The screen shows the first six random integers generated by the calculator.

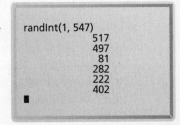

```
randInt(1, 547)
              517
              497
               81
              282
              222
              402
■
```

Step 3 Compile a list of the 60 students that correspond to the 60 integers generated in Step 2.

Bias is an influence that affects the reliability of a statistical measurement in some way. Biased samples result in unreliable data.

EXAMPLE 4   Analyzing biased data

 Suppose that a basketball coach wants to determine the average weight of the members of his team. The players' weights, in pounds, are 125, 132, 128, 145, and 138. While the coach weighs each player, he inadvertently places his foot on the scale, resulting in his recording the following weights; 130, 137, 133, 150, and 143.

- **SOLUTION 1**

$$\text{true mean} = \frac{125 + 132 + 128 + 145 + 138}{5} = 133.6 \text{ lbs}$$

$$\text{biased mean} = \frac{130 + 137 + 133 + 150 + 143}{5} = 138.6 \text{ lbs}$$

- **SOLUTION 2**

You can use a graphing calculator to find the mean of a set of data. Enter the data by pressing `STAT` and then choose 1: Edit. Next, press `STAT`, `CALC`, 1: 1 − Var Stats. The statistics will show on the screen. $\overline{x}$ is the mean.

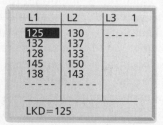

This bias increases each of the weights by exactly 5 pounds and so increases the true mean by exactly 5 pounds also.

Samples that are not representative of the population are another common source of bias.

EXAMPLE 5   Classifying a sample as biased or unbiased

 A researcher intends to gather data in order to determine the likelihood that the citizens of the city of Springwood will support a new indoor football team. Which of the following data collection methods would result in an unbiased sample?

A. Polling fans as they leave a big league football game
B. A telephone poll conducted every afternoon throughout the week
C. A written survey mailed to all Springwood residents
D. Polling every 5 shoppers at the local shopping mall

- **SOLUTION**

Choice **A** is biased because it limits the sample to only football fans. Choice **B** is biased because it limits the sample to residents who are at home and able to answer the telephone during the specified time. Choice **C** is biased because it is a voluntary response sample. Choice **D** is not biased to any specific population and so is the best choice for an unbiased sample.

> **Note**
> A group is **random** if each member has the same chance of being in the group.

> **Note**
> You cannot detect bias after collecting data, so you must be careful to avoid bias in the data collection.

Practice

In Exercises 1–4, identify the following components for the situations given, if possible

    a. Population   **c.** The data of interest

    b. Sample   **d.** Potential for bias

1 A sports magazine mailed a questionnaire to NFL players and received responses from 25% of the players. Those responding reported that they did not use steroids as part of their training.

2 Researchers waited outside a local library. The researchers stopped every tenth person who left the library and asked whether that person believed that reading to young children is important.

3 The Environmental Safety Organization took air samples at 20 locations in the school and checked for evidence of poor air quality. They found no readings that resulted in designating the air quality as poor.

4 The mayor wants to know whether the residents of Mytown support a tax imposed to raise money that will be used to update the city's parks and recreational areas. One hundred residents are surveyed as they enter the local parks.

In Examples 5–7, clearly answer the questions asked.

5 The California poll sometimes conducts preelection surveys by telephone. Could this practice bias the results? How?

6 Suppose that a pollster asks, "What kind of sweet toppings do you like on fruit salad?" Is this question biased?

7 To determine whether the production process is satisfactory, a factory samples the first 30 items of each day's production. Is this a good sampling procedure?

In Exercises 8–13, determine whether the data is quantitative or qualitative. If it is quantitative, determine whether it is discrete or continuous.

8 The number of dollar bills in your wallet

9 Your favorite brand of jeans

10 Your waist size

11 Your area code

12 Number of students in each of your classes

13 Air pressure in your bike tire

In Exercises 14–17, determine whether the data being collected is univariate or bivariate.

14 A student's grade in mathematics

15 A car's weight and its miles per gallon rating

16 A person's age and the number of televisions in his or her home

17 A person's heart rate and the amount of calories being burned

In Exercises 18–21, identify the type of sample described and tell whether the sample is biased or unbiased.

18 A high school baseball coach asks coaches in the Mid-City League if they would prefer that, in their state, the baseball season be held during the fall rather than in the spring.

19 A local newspaper editor wants to know whether customers are satisfied with the newspaper's delivery service. A written survey is mailed to each customer.

20 A history teacher decides to determine the order of the class presentations by writing the names of the students on individual sheets of paper, placing them in a container, and randomly drawing the names.

21 Sam wants to learn how often high school students use the Internet as a tool when completing homework assignments. An Internet survey is sent to each person in Sam's address book.

In Exercise 22, solve the problem. Clearly show all necessary work.

22 You wish to determine the average age of all of the families with students attending your school. Describe how you would gather the data. Collect the data as you described and determine from your data the average age of a family with students attending your school.

9.4 Frequencies and Histograms

New Jersey Standards

4.4.A.2 Evaluate and use data

4.4.A.5.1 Analyze data

In many situations, a set of data will contain many of the same data values. Remember that the frequency of a data value is the number of times it occurs in the data set. In the data set below, the frequency of the data value **1.3** is 4.

$$\{1.1, 0.9, 0.8, 1.1, 1.1, 0.8, 1.5, \mathbf{1.3}, \mathbf{1.3}, 1.7, \mathbf{1.3}, \mathbf{1.3}\}$$

EXAMPLE 1 — Working with data frequencies

 Which statement about the data set below is false?

$$\{0, 2, 2, 4, 3, 3, 6, 7, 3, 2, 6, 5, 2, 3, 7, 7, 8, 1, 0, 2\}$$

A. The data value 3 occurs less often than the data value 2.
B. Every data value occurs more than once.
C. Of the 20 values, 2 and 3 occur almost 50% of the time.
D. 35% of the data are greater than 4.

■ SOLUTION

The second statement is false because the data values 1, 4, 5, and 8 occur only once. The correct choice is B.

To represent data frequency, you can construct a **frequency table** using *tally marks*. Again, consider this data set:

$$\{1.1, 0.9, 0.8, 1.1, 1.1, 0.8, 1.5, 1.3, 1.3, 1.7, 1.3, 1.3\}$$

Each time a data value occurs, write one tally mark, /, to the right of the data value in the table. For example, because the data value 1.3 occurs four times, make 4 tally marks and record 4 as its frequency. When all data are counted, write the frequency of each data value as a number.

Data value	Tally	Frequency
0.8	//	2
0.9	/	1
1.1	///	3
1.3	////	4
1.5	/	1
1.7	/	1

EXAMPLE 2 — Constructing a frequency table

 Construct a frequency table for the data below.

14	14	14	15	15	17	16	16	16	16
18	20	17	16	16	17	15	20	17	15
17	17	17	17	18	18	18	17	18	15

■ SOLUTION

Step 1 Enter the different data values in the left column of a three-column table.

Step 2 Write tally marks in the middle column of the table to count each different data value.

Step 3 Write the frequency from each tally in the right column.

> **Note**
>
> A slash through 4 tally marks indicates a collection of 5 data values.

Data value	Tally	Frequency
14	///	3
15	⅏	5
16	⅏ /	6
17	⅏ ////	9
18	⅏	5
20	//	2

244

You can use a frequency table to interpret and analyze data.

EXAMPLE 3 **Interpreting a frequency table**

3 The frequency table at the right shows completion times for the contestants in a race. What percentage of contestants finishing the race completed it in less than 23 minutes?

Interval (min.)	Frequency
14–16	2
17–19	6
20–22	10
23–25	9
26–28	8
29–31	5

■ **SOLUTION**

Two runners finished in 14–16 minutes, 6 in 17–19 minutes, and 10 finished in 20–22 minutes. Add the frequencies 2, 6, and 10.

$$2 + 6 + 10 = 18$$

Since 40 is the total of the frequencies, 18 runners of the 40 finished in less than 23 minutes.

$$18 \text{ out of } 40 \rightarrow \frac{18}{40} = 0.45$$

Thus, **45%** of the runners finished in less than 23 minutes.

A **histogram** is a visual representation of data from a frequency table. A histogram is a special type of bar graph in which the height of each bar represents the frequency of the interval indicated. You usually use a histogram to represent data organized by intervals.

Go Online
PHSchool.com
Visit: PHSchool.com
Web Code: ayp-0117

EXAMPLES 4 and 5 **Using a frequency table or a set of data to construct a histogram**

4 Represent the data in the frequency table in Example 2 as a histogram.

■ **SOLUTION**

Step 1 Write the intervals for completion times in order on the horizontal axis and frequencies (number of runners) on the vertical axis.

Step 2 For each interval, construct a bar whose height equals frequency for that interval.

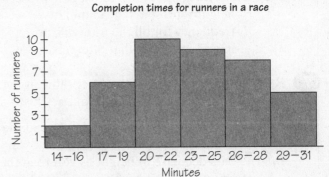

Completion times for runners in a race

5 Represent {3, 5, 5, 6, 7, 6, 4, 5, 6, 3, 3, 3, 4, 2, 2, 3, 6, 7} in a histogram.

■ **SOLUTION**

Step 1 Make a frequency table.

Data value	Frequency
2	2
3	5
4	2
5	3
6	4
7	2

Step 2 Use the table to make the histogram.

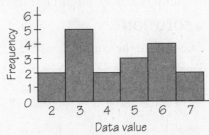

A variation of the frequency table is the **cumulative frequency table.** The graphical display related to a cumulative frequency table is the **cumulative frequency histogram.**

Constructing and interpreting cumulative frequency tables and histograms

 6 A survey was conducted to find out how many hours students spent on schoolwork each week. One hundred students were interviewed. Represent these data in a cumulative frequency table and histogram.

Hours	1–5	6–10	11–15	16–20	21–25	26–30
Frequency	23	25	18	17	10	7

■ **SOLUTION**

Step 1 Add a third row to the table that contains the cumulative frequencies. For example, under the interval 6–10, write the sum of the frequencies for the intervals 1–5 and 6–10.

Hours	1–5	6–10	11–15	16–20	21–25	26–30
Frequency	23	25	18	17	10	7
Cum. Freq.	23	23 + 25 = 48	48 + 18 = 66	66 + 17 = 83	83 + 10 = 93	93 + 7 = 100

Step 2 Locate the data intervals in order along the horizontal axis. Choose a scale for the vertical axis. Since the greatest cumulative frequency is 100, mark the vertical scale in increments of 20 from 0 to 100.

Step 3 For each interval, make a bar whose height represents the cumulative frequency for all the intervals up to and including that interval.

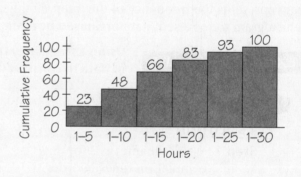

7 Refer to the cumulative frequency table at the right. Which statement about the related cumulative frequency histogram is true?

A. The bars increase in height as you read the histogram left to right.

B. The bars decrease in height as you read the histogram left to right.

C. The bars increase in height and then decrease in height as you read left to right.

D. The bars decrease in height and then increase in height as you read left to right.

Interval	Frequency	Cumulative Frequency
14–16	2	2
17–19	6	8
20–22	9	17
23–25	8	25
26–28	7	32
29–31	4	36

■ **SOLUTION**

The bars in the cumulative frequency histogram will have heights 2, 8, 17, 25, 32, and 36 units as you read left to right. Therefore, the correct choice is **A**.

Choose the letter preceding the word or expression that best completes the statement or answers the question.

1 14 is what percentage of the data shown?

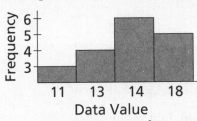

Data Value

A. 6%   **B.** 14%   **C.** $33\frac{1}{3}$%   **D.** 40%

2 What percentage of the dogs in the sample weigh more than 20 pounds?

| 17 | 16 | 16 | 18 | 17 | 18 | 22 | 22 | 19 | 21 |
| 17 | 18 | 20 | 20 | 21 | 19 | 19 | 20 | 21 | 17 |

A. 5%   **B.** 25%   **C.** 40%   **D.** 60%

3 The table represents test scores for one class of students on one mathematics test. Which statement is false?

| C | C | C | B | D | B | A | C | C | B |
| C | A | B | C | C | C | C | D | D | B |

A. Fifty percent of the students earned a **C** and 15% of the students earned a **D.**

B. The total percentages for all grades is 100%.

C. The total number of students who earned a **B** is 25% of the total number of test scores.

D. The number of students earning **A, B,** or **D** was more than 50% of the class.

In Exercises 4–5, use the table of quiz scores shown below.

| 11 | 17 | 33 | 22 | 44 | 48 | 37 | 31 | 40 | 19 |
| 17 | 32 | 38 | 45 | 12 | 41 | 29 | 15 | 49 | 21 |

4 Complete a frequency table for the data.

5 What percent of the scores are above 31?

In Exercises 6–9, solve the problem. Clearly show all necessary work.

6 Construct a histogram for these data.

Score	Frequency
1–10	8
11–20	12
21–30	9
31–40	10

7 Citizens monitored the number of random acts of kindness portrayed on TV in forty randomly selected hours in one week. Construct a cumulative frequency histogram for the data.

Number of random acts of kindness	Frequency
0–9	6
10–19	12
20–29	12
30–39	10

8 The total weight of all boxes represented in this frequency table is 76.3 pounds. How many boxes weigh 5.2 pounds?

Weight (pounds)	Frequency
4.9	//
5.0	////
5.1	///
5.2	m

9 The total weight of all boxes represented in this frequency table is 30.2 pounds. What is the weight of the box with frequency 4?

Weight (pounds)	Frequency
3.2	///
w	////
3.5	//

9.5 Box-and-Whisker Plots

New Jersey Standards
4.4.A.2 Evaluate data
4.4.A.5.1 Analyze data

When you calculate the median, the first quartile, and the third quartile, you can construct and interpret a **box-and-whisker plot**.

In a box-and-whisker plot, one box is divided into two parts. The line segments to the left and to the right of the box are called the whiskers.

To make a box-and-whisker plot to display data, you need to use five important statistical measures. The measures are shown below.

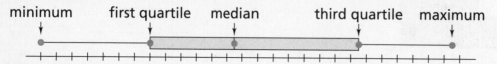

The **range** of a set of data is the difference between the **minimum** data value and the **maximum** data value.

Go Online
PHSchool.com
Visit: PHSchool.com
Web Code: ayp-0118

EXAMPLE 1 Constructing a box-and-whisker plot

1 Construct a box-and-whisker plot for the data below.

99	97	95	92	90	88	88	87	86
85	82	80	78	74	74	73	72	71

■ **SOLUTION**

Step 1 Identify the minimum and the maximum.
minimum: 71 maximum: 99

Step 2 Find the median.

71 72 73 74 74 78 80 82 85 86 87 88 88 90 92 95 97 99
⬆
85.5

Step 3 Find the first and third quartiles.

71 72 73 74 74 78 80 82 85 | 86 87 88 88 90 92 95 97 99
          ⬆   ⬆   ⬆
    first quartile   median   third quartile

Step 4 Draw the box-and-whisker plot. Indicate the minimum, first quartile, median, third quartile, and maximum.

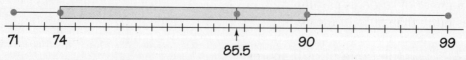

Since the first quartile, median, and third quartile divide the data into four equal groups of data, 50% of the data is between the first quartile and the third quartile. The difference between the third quartile and first quartile is called the **interquartile range**.

Note

This diagram shows the data separated into 4 equal groups.

25% 25% 25% 25%

To interpret a box-and-whisker plot, remember the meaning of minimum, first quartile, median, third quartile, and maximum.

Go Online
PHSchool.com
Visit: PHSchool.com
Web Code: ayp-0119

EXAMPLE 2 **Interpreting a box-and-whisker plot**

2 Which statement best describes the box-and-whisker plot below?

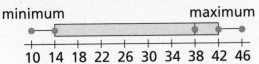

A. Most of the data are between 10 and 46 inclusive.
B. Fifty percent of the data are between 14 and 38 inclusive.
C. All of the data are between 10 and 46 inclusive, and 50% of the data are between 14 and 42 inclusive.
D. None of the data are between 10 and 46.

■ SOLUTION

The correct choice is C because all data must be within the minimum and maximum values, and the first and third quartiles bound 50% of the data.

You can also solve problems by using a box-and-whisker plot.

EXAMPLE 3 **Using a box-and-whisker plot to solve a problem**

3 The heights, in inches, of 20 high school students are shown in the table below. Use a box-and-whisker plot to determine which of the heights represent students who are taller than 75% of the others.

74	73	72	70	69	68	68	68	67	67
66	64	64	64	63	63	62	60	60	59

■ SOLUTION

Step 1 Identify the minimum and the maximum.
minimum: 59   maximum: 74

Step 2 Find the median and first and third quartiles.

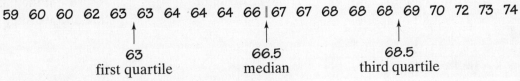

Step 3 Draw the box-and-whisker plot. Indicate the minimum, first quartile, median, third quartile, and maximum.

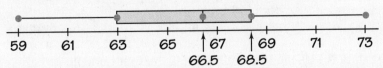

Since 25% of the data lie above the third quartile, the students whose heights are *69, 70, 72, 73, and 74 inches* are taller than 75% of the others.

Box-and-whisker plots are helpful when comparing sets of data.

EXAMPLE 4 Using box-and-whisker plots to compare data

④ The data in Example 1 represent the test scores of 18 students and the set
of data below represents the scores of another class taking the same test.
Construct a box-and-whisker plot for each set of data and compare the scores.

Class 1

99	97	95	92	90	88	88	87	86
85	82	80	78	74	74	73	72	71

Class 2

97	97	94	93	92	92	91	90	88
86	84	84	84	83	82	80	79	72

▪ SOLUTION 1

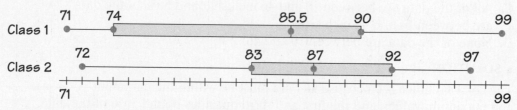

If the box-and-whisker plots for the two classes are placed one above the
other, you can see that the scores in Class 2 are more tightly packed.

You can also use a graphing calculator to analyze and represent the data.

EXAMPLE 5 Construct a box-and-whisker plot on a graphing calculator

⑤ Use a graphing calculator to construct a box-and-whisker plot. Identify the
5 statistics used to construct the plot, and make a general statement about
the data.

Heights of Children, in centimeters

120	122	125	119	123	121	120	132
140	145	147	120	149	160	110	150

▪ SOLUTION

Step 1
Enter the data.

Step 2
Analyze the data.

Step 3
Represent the data as a
box-and-whisker plot.

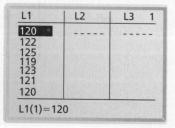

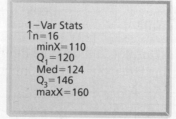

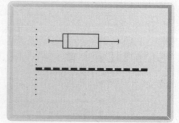

The minimum of the data is 110, the maximum is 160, the first quartile is
120, the third quartile is 146, and the median is 124. The box-and-whisker
plot shows that the majority of the heights fall between the median and the
third quartile, 124 cm and 146 cm.

Practice

Choose the letter preceding the word or expression that best completes the statement or answers the question.

1 Which statement best describes the box-and-whisker plot shown below?

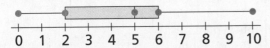

- **A.** All of the data values lie between 2 and 6 inclusive.
- **B.** Fifty percent of the data values are at or above 7.
- **C.** The number 5 is a data value.
- **D.** Fifty percent of the data values lie between 2 and 6 inclusive, and all data lie between 0 and 10 inclusive.

In Exercises 2–4, use the five-statistic summary given below.

$$Min = 50$$
$$Q_1 = 70$$
$$Median = 83$$
$$Q_3 = 88$$
$$Max = 99$$

2 What is the interquartile range?

A. 18   **B.** 49   **C.** 83   **D.** 20

3 What is the range of the data?

A. 18   **B.** 49   **C.** 83   **D.** 20

4 Which of the following scores would be an outlier for this data set?

A. 83   **B.** 110   **C.** 40   **D.** 100

In Exercises 5–8, represent each data set in a box-and-whisker-plot.

5 {2, 2, 5, 5, 5, 6, 8, 5, 8, 9, 10, 11, 12, 7, 8}

6 {1.2, 1.2, 1.3, 1.1, 1.4, 1.5, 1.5, 1.5, 1.6}

7 {71, 81, 82, 80, 74, 76, 76, 76, 73, 73, 74}

8 minimum: 50; first quartile: 70; median: 83; third quartile: 88; maximum: 100

In Exercises 9–14, use the graph below, showing the box-and-whisker plots for data sets A and B.

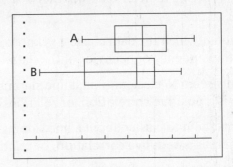

9 Which set of data has the greater range?

10 Which set of data has the lesser median?

11 Which set of data has the greater interquartile range?

12 *True* or *False.* The minimum of set B is the lesser value in the two sets.

13 *True* or *False.* The third quartile of set B is less than the third quartile of set A.

14 *True* or *False.* The first quartile of set A is greater than the median of set B.

In Exercises 15–20, use the box-and-whisker plot below.

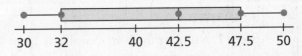

15 What is the minimum of the data set?

16 What is the maximum of the data set?

17 What is the median?

18 What is the first quartile?

19 What is the third quartile?

20 Fifty percent of the data lie between which two values?

9.6 Scatter Plots and Trend Lines

New Jersey Standards

4.4.A.2 Evaluate and use data

4.4.A.5.1 Analyze data

A **scatter plot** is a display of bivariate data. Each data value in one set of data is paired with a data value in the other set of data. These ordered pairs are plotted on a grid. After you have plotted all of the data pairs, look at the clustering of points to determine whether one set of data is related to another.

The line about which the data clusters is known as a **trend line.** This line indicates the tendency or behavior of the data.

If the points seem to cluster about a line sloping up to the right, you can say that there is a **positive correlation,** or relationship, between the variables.

If the points seem to cluster about a line sloping down to the right, you can say that there is a **negative correlation,** or relationship, between the data sets.

If the points are scattered and do not seem to cluster around a line, you can say that there is little or **no correlation** between the data sets.

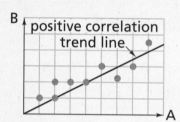
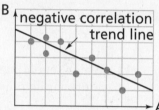
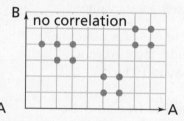

EXAMPLE 1 Constructing a scatter plot

A student asks 15 classmates how many hours they spent studying for a test and how many incorrect answers they gave.

Number of Hours	1	5	6	9	10	8	5	4	10	4	10	7	9	2	8
Incorrect Answers	8	5	3	1	0	3	6	6	2	8	1	4	2	7	2

Represent the relationship between the two variables in a scatter plot.

Go Online
PHSchool.com

Visit: PHSchool.com
Web Code: ayp-0920

■ **SOLUTION**

Step 1 Number the horizontal axis from 1 to 10 to represent hours spent studying. Number the vertical axis from 1 to 8 to represent the numbers of incorrect answers.

Step 2 Plot the pairs of data points in the table. For example, for the student who spent 1 hour studying and gave 8 incorrect answers, plot the ordered pair (1, 8).

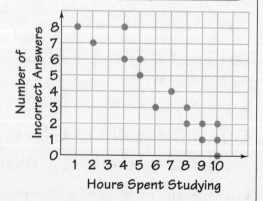

You can model the data displayed in a scatter plot by finding the equation of a trend line.

 EXAMPLE 2   **Finding the equation of a trend line**

2 Use the data from Example 1 to determine an equation for a trend line.

■ **SOLUTION**

Step 1 Draw a line that includes as many points as possible.

Step 2 Choose 2 points on the line, $(4, 6)$ and $(10, 1)$, to find the slope.

$$m = \frac{(6 - 1)}{(4 - 10)} = -\frac{5}{6}$$

Step 2 Find the y-intercept of the line. Substitute the slope and the coordinates of a point in the equation $y = mx + b$.

$$6 = -\frac{5}{6}(4) + b$$

$$\frac{56}{6} = b$$

The equation of the trend line can be written as $y = -\frac{5}{6}x + \frac{56}{6}$. (Note that other lines could have been drawn.)

Using the trend line that you have drawn, you can make **predictions** about the data. You can predict the number of incorrect answers that a person who studied for 3 hours would give by substituting 3 for x in the equation.

$$y = -\frac{5}{6}(3) + \frac{56}{6} = \frac{41}{6} \approx 7$$

To the nearest integer, you can expect a student who studied for 3 hours to answer 7 questions incorrectly.

You can also find the trend line by using a calculator. By plotting the data with the window settings shown, you can determine a **manual** line of best fit. If you use the same two points as before, $(4, 6)$ and $(10, 1)$, your calculator result will be the same as the one you found by using hand calculations.

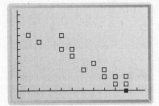  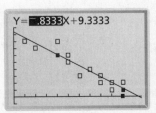

The **least squares line of best fit** is the trend line that shows the relationship between two sets of data most accurately. You can use linear regression on a calculator or computer to determine the equation of this line.

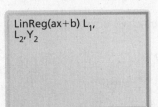 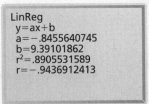

253

The line $y = -0.83333x + 9.3333$ found in Example 2 $\left(y = -\frac{5}{6}x + \frac{56}{6}\right)$ is a very good estimate for the least squares line of best fit.

$$y = -0.84556x + 9.391001$$

Note that two data sets or variables may show a correlation; however, this correlation does not necessarily mean that a cause-and-effect relationship exists between the two variables. Consider this example. *Correlation does not guarantee causation.* A man takes the bus to work each day. When he steps off the bus, he hears the bells in the town hall tower ring. If this happens every day, there is a strong positive correlation between the two events. However, you cannot say that stepping off the bus causes the bells to ring. It is more likely that the man takes the same bus to work each day, arriving at the bus stop at the same time the bells ring.

Note

Correlation measures association, but association is not the same as causation.

EXAMPLE 3   **Problems involving correlation and causation**

3 A real estate professional collects data on a number of home sales during each month of the year. He finds a negative correlation between the last three months of the year and the number of home sales. Can the real estate professional accurately conclude that home sales will be down because it is the month of November?

■ **SOLUTION**

The real estate professional cannot accurately conclude that fewer homes will be sold in November. The fact that a correlation is shown does not prove that slowing of home sales will always occur in November.

Practice

Choose the letter preceding the word or expression that best completes the statement or answers the question.

1 Which of the following statements is true of the scatter plot below?

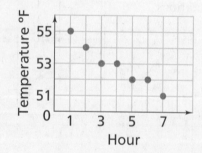

A. The data have a negative correlation.

B. The data have a positive correlation.

C. The data have no correlation.

D. The correlation cannot be determined.

2 Which of the following statements is true of the scatter plot below?

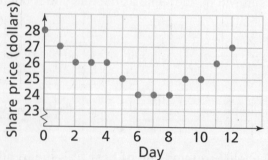

A. The data have a negative correlation.

B. The data have a positive correlation.

C. The data have no correlation.

D. The correlation cannot be determined.

3 Which data set is shown in the scatter plot below?

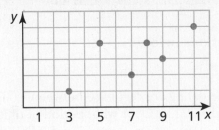

A.

x	3	5	7	8	9	11
y	1	4	2	4	3	5

B.

x	1	4	2	4	3	5
y	3	5	7	8	9	11

C.

x	1	5	2	8	3	11
y	3	4	7	4	9	5

D.

x	3	4	7	4	9	5
y	1	5	2	8	3	11

4 A math teacher records the number of hours a student sleeps the night before a test and the grade the student earns on the test. A scatter plot of the data shows a positive correlation between the hours of sleep and the test grade. Which of the following is a true statement?

A. A student sleeping more hours will earn a higher test grade.

B. A student sleeping fewer hours will earn a lower test grade.

C. A student who earns a higher test grade must sleep more hours than a student who earned a lower test grade.

D. A student may or may not earn a higher test grade by sleeping more hours the night before the test.

In Exercises 5–8, represent each relationship between x and y in a scatter plot with x on the horizontal axis and y on the vertical axis.

5

x	23	24	25	26	27	28
y	2.8	3.0	3.2	3.0	3.4	3.4

6

x	3	4	5	6	7	8
y	7	6	3	5	4	3

7

x	0	1	2	3	4	5
y	7	6	4	6	7	8

8

x	0	1	2	3	4	5
y	1	3	5	7	9	11

In Exercises 9–11, solve the following problems. Clearly show all necessary work.

9 The weight and fuel consumption of different vehicles are given in the accompanying table. Construct a scatter plot of these data and find an equation of a trend line for the data. Use the equation to predict the fuel consumption for a vehicle that weighs 4,800 pounds. Also, predict the weight of a vehicle that gets 18 miles per gallon (mpg).

Weight (in 100 lbs)	27	45	30	47	22	40	34	50
mpg	30	16	24	15	29	20	22	13

10 The table below shows the respiration and heart rates for adult males. Construct a scatter plot of these data and determine a trend line. Use the equation of the line to predict the heart rate of a man with a respiration of 32 breaths per minute.

Respiration (breaths/min)	50	30	25	20	18	16	14
Heart Rate (beats/min)	200	150	140	130	120	110	100

11 Using this scatter plot, find the mean temperature of those recorded between noon and 7:00 P.M.

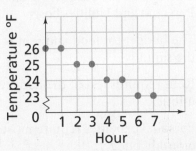

Preparing for the New Jersey HSPA

DIRECTIONS FOR QUESTIONS 1–17: For each of the questions below, select the answer choice that is best for each case.

1 What is the mean of the data set below?

$$\{4, 4, 5, 3, 4, 8, 6, 4, 8, 7, 9, 10, 2, 1, 9\}$$

A. 4   B. 5.6   C. 15   D. 84

2 Which statement is always true for a given data set?

A. The mean is greater than the median.

B. The mode is greater than the mean.

C. The third quartile is greater than or equal to the median.

D. The mean and the median are equal.

3 Which of the following represents the mean of the data?

Data Value	Frequency
5	4
6	7
8	3

A. $4 + 7 + 3$

B. $\dfrac{5 + 6 + 8}{4 + 7 + 3}$

C. $4(5) + 7(6) + 3(8)$

D. $\dfrac{4(5) + 7(6) + 3(8)}{4 + 7 + 3}$

4 Analyze the circle graph shown below. Which statement is correct?

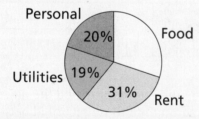

A. One half of the budget is spent on Personal and Utilities costs.

B. The budget for food and rent is about the same.

C. Rent requires less of the budget than utilities.

D. Personal expenses require most of the monthly budget.

5 The data were recorded between 1:00 P.M. and 7:00 P.M. Over what period of time was the temperature at or below 53°F?

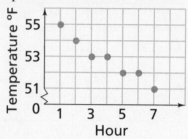

A. Between 1:00 P.M. and 7:00 P.M.

B. Between 3:00 P.M. and 7:00 P.M.

C. Between 1:00 P.M. and 6:00 P.M.

D. Between 3:00 P.M. and 5:00 P.M.

6 A list arranged in order from least to greatest is 25, 30, 44, x, 51, 60, 75, 80. If the median is 50, what does x equal?

A. 49   B. 47.5   C. 35   D. 47

7 To be on the merit roll, Jerry must have an 85 average. If Jerry has grades of 78, 93, 88, 77, and 84, what must he earn on the next test in order to be on the merit roll?

A. 86   B. 85   C. 95   D. 90

8 One number is represented by $3x + 5$ and another is represented by $7x - 3$. What is the average of these numbers in terms of x?

A. $10x + 1$ C. $5x + 1$

B. $\dfrac{10x + 8}{2}$ D. $5x$

9 Find the mean temperature of those recorded between 3:00 A.M. and 10:00 A.M.

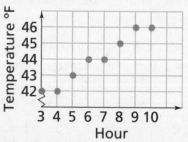

A. 46°F   B. 44°F   C. 42°F   D. 45.5°F

10 Analyze the circle graph shown below. Estimate the percentage of the total spent on food.

Expenses

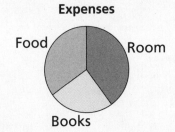

Food
Room
Books

A. 126%

C. 40%

B. 60%

D. 90%

11 To the nearest cent, find the mean share price over the period of time shown in this graph.

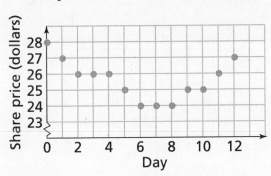

A. $26.00

C. $25.62

B. $26.50

D. $27.75

12 Which of the following can be used to predict the value of a variable?

A. box-and-whisker plot

B. median

C. trend line

D. scatter plot

13 Grocery bags weighing 3.5 pounds, 4.2 pounds, 1.8 pounds, 2.7 pounds, and 3.3 pounds have the same average weight as two grocery bags of equal weight. To the nearest tenth of a pound, what do each of the equal grocery bags weigh?

A. 3.3 pounds

C. 1.8 pounds

B. 3.1 pounds

D. 3.0 pounds

14 Find the mean of the data in this table to the nearest hundredth.

Data Value	Frequency
3	////
−2	/
6	//
10	///
−1	////

A. 3.43   B. 6.00   C. 3.20   D. 3.00

15 Which set of data has a median of 58 and a 70th percentile value of 70?

A. {10, 20, 30, 40, 50, 60, 70, 80, 90, 100}

B. {5, 20, 25, 34, 53, 55, 65, 69, 75, 90}

C. {10, 20, 30, 44, 50, 58, 62, 66, 74, 85}

D. {25, 34, 46, 50, 54, 62, 70, 80, 80, 95}

16 Shameka recorded the daily temperatures for the past week. Her records show 72°, 78°, 80°, 85°, 80°, 73°, and 77°. Which of the following statements is true for these data?

A. The mean is greater than the mode.

B. The mode is less than the median.

C. The mean is greater than the median.

D. The mode is greater than the mean.

17 The combined weight of the luggage in an elevator is 224 pounds. What is the weight of the suitcase with frequency 3?

Weight (pounds)	Frequency
w	///
22	//
50	/
15	/
20	//

A. 25 pounds

C. 21 pounds

B. 117 pounds

D. 27 pounds

DIRECTIONS FOR 18–20: Solve each problem and show your work.

18 The ages of the first 50 people to come to a basketball game are shown.

Age	Frequency
0–9	10
10–19	9
20–29	8
30–39	13
40–49	5
50–59	3
60–69	2

- What is the median age of a person at the basketball game?
- Does the median describe the data? Explain your reasoning.
- Construct a cumulative frequency histogram for the ages.

19 The following table shows the salaries of employees in an office.

$25,500	$45,500	$46,800	$32,300
$34,000	$45,500	$56,000	$42,250
$52,000	$48,900	$44,600	$51,700

- What is the mean salary?
- What is the median salary?
- If each salary is increased by $1,000, how does this affect the mean and the median?

20 A restaurant wants to estimate how many customers they would have if they began to serve breakfast. They ask all of the customers at lunch one day if they would consider coming to the restaurant for breakfast.

- Identify the population.
- Identify the type of sample.
- Is this sample biased? Explain your reasoning.

10 Basic Geometry in the Plane

NEW JERSEY

The Atlantic City Boardwalk

The Atlantic City Boardwalk in Atlantic City, New Jersey, was the first boardwalk built in the world. Dr. Jonathan Pitney and Richard Osborne, the developers of the boardwalk, began working on the area located on Absecon Island in 1850.

Alexander Boardman, a railroad conductor, came up with the idea of building a wooden walkway from the beach to the hotels. Some twenty years later, on June 26, 1870, the first section of the boardwalk opened.

The original boardwalk was eight feet wide and one mile long. Today, the boardwalk is 40 feet wide, over 4 miles long, and lined with shops, restaurants, casinos, and hotels. It also is well known for its many tourist attractions.

10.1 Points, Lines, Planes, and Segments

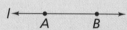
New Jersey Standards

4.2.A.3 Apply properties of geometric shapes

The foundation of geometry begins with three undefined terms: **point**, **line**, and **plane**. After these terms have been described, all other terms can be defined by using them.

Undefined Terms

A **point** can be described as a location in space. It has no length, width, or height. All geometric figures consist of points. **Space** consists of the infinite set of points. The physical representation of a point is a **dot**. A capital letter next to the dot is used to name the point.

A.   point *A*

A **line** is a set of points extending in opposite directions without end. A line indicates direction and has one dimension, length. A line is named by any 2 points on the line, in any order, or by a single lowercase letter. The line at the right can be named line *l*, line *AB* ($\overleftrightarrow{AB}$), or line *BA* ($\overleftrightarrow{BA}$).

A **plane** is a flat surface extending in every direction without end. It has two dimensions, length and width. A single letter or at least three points in the plane can name a plane. The plane at the right is called plane *P* or plane *ABC*.

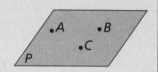

Points and lines that lie in the same plane are **coplanar**. Any three points are always coplanar. If two lines intersect, then they are coplanar. Lines that do not lie in the same plane are **skew** lines.

Collinear points are points that lie on the same line. Two points are always collinear. Points that do not lie on the same line are **noncollinear**.

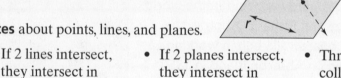

Lines *m* and *n* are intersecting lines.

Lines *r* and *s* are skew lines.

Here are four basic **postulates** about points, lines, and planes.

- Through any 2 points, there is exactly one line. (Any two points determine a line.)

- If 2 lines intersect, they intersect in exactly one point.

- If 2 planes intersect, they intersect in exactly one line.

- Through any 3 non-collinear points, there is exactly one plane.

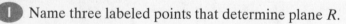

EXAMPLES 1 and 2   Using the basic postulates for points, lines, and planes

1   Name three labeled points that determine plane *R*.

■ SOLUTION

Because three points determine a plane, three points that determine plane *R* are *points X, Y, and Z.*

2   Name the intersection of plane *R* and plane *S*.

■ SOLUTION

The intersection of two planes is a line. The intersection of plane *R* and plane *S* is $\overleftrightarrow{XY}$.

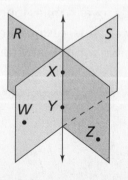

Recall that a *number line* is a line whose points have been placed in one-to-one correspondence with the set of real numbers. This pairing between the points of a line and the real numbers is a fundamental postulate of geometry.

Ruler Postulate

The points of a line can be paired with the real numbers one-to-one so that any two points on the line can be paired with 0 and 1. The real number that corresponds to a point is called the **coordinate** of that point. The **distance** between two points of the line is equal to the absolute value of the difference of their coordinates.

The distance between point A and point B is denoted AB or BA.

EXAMPLE 3 **Using the Ruler Postulate**

3 Find AB on the number line at the right.

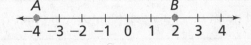

■ **SOLUTION**

The coordinate of A is -4. The coordinate of B is 2. Subtract the coordinates in any order, and then find the absolute value of the difference.

$$AB = |-4 - 2| = |-6| = 6 \quad \text{or} \quad BA = |2 - (-4)| = |6| = 6$$

The Ruler Postulate provides a basis for the following definitions.

Definitions Related to Segments

A **line segment**, or **segment**, is part of a line that begins at one point and ends at another. The points are called the **endpoints of the segment.** You name a segment by its endpoints.

$$J \bullet\!\!-\!\!\!-\!\!\!-\!\!\bullet K \qquad \text{segment } JK \ (\overline{JK})$$

The **length of a segment** is the distance between its endpoints.

Segments that are equal in length are called **congruent segments.** You indicate congruent segments by marking them with an equal number of tick marks. The symbol for congruence is $\cong$.

$$\overline{CD} \cong \overline{EF}$$

The **midpoint** of a segment is the point that divides the segment into two congruent segments.

$$P \bullet\!\!-\!\!|\!-\!\bullet\!-\!|\!-\!\!\bullet Q$$
$$\overline{PM} \cong \overline{QM}$$
$$M \text{ is the midpoint of } \overline{PQ}.$$

If the endpoints of a segment on a number line have coordinates x and y, you can find the coordinate of the midpoint by simplifying the expression $\frac{x + y}{2}$.

EXAMPLE 4 **Finding the midpoint of a segment on a number line**

 Find the coordinate of the midpoint of $\overline{XY}$.

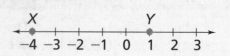

■ SOLUTION

The coordinate of X is -4. The coordinate of Y is 1.

The coordinate of the midpoint is $\frac{-4 + 1}{2} = \frac{-3}{2} = -1\frac{1}{2}$.

On a number line, a point C is **between** point A and point B if the coordinate of point C is between the coordinates of points A and B. This leads to an important postulate concerning segments.

Segment Addition Postulate

If point C is between point A and point B, then $AC + CB = AB$.

EXAMPLE 5 **Using the Segment Addition Postulate**

 In the figure at the right, point U is between point V and point W, and $VW = 31$. Find UW.

■ SOLUTION

$$\begin{aligned}
VU + UW &= VW \quad \leftarrow \text{Apply the Segment Addition Postulate.} \\
3t - 9 + 2t + 5 &= 31 \quad \leftarrow \text{Substitute.} \\
5t - 4 &= 31 \quad \leftarrow \text{Combine like terms.} \\
5t &= 35 \quad \leftarrow \text{Solve.} \\
t &= 7
\end{aligned}$$

Therefore: $UW = 2t + 5 \rightarrow 2(7) + 5 = 19$

Practice

Choose the letter preceding the word or expression that best completes the statement or answers the question.

1 Three noncollinear points determine a

    A. plane.

    B. line.

    C. segment.

    D. midpoint.

2 Consider: *If three points are coplanar, then they are collinear.* Which is true?

    A. The statement is true and its converse is false.

    B. The statement is false and its converse is true.

    C. Both the statement and its converse are true.

    D. Both the statement and its converse are false.

3 On a number line, the coordinate of point A is m and the coordinate of point B is n. Which expression represents the length of $\overline{AB}$?

  A. $n - m$ **C.** $m + n$

  B. $|m - n|$ **D.** $\dfrac{m + n}{2}$

4 Given that point R is the midpoint of $\overline{PQ}$, which statement is false?

  A. $PR = QR$ **C.** $PR = 2PQ$

  B. $QR = \frac{1}{2}PQ$ **D.** $PR + RQ = PQ$

In Exercises 5–14, refer to the figure below.

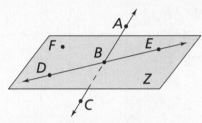

Are the points collinear? Write *Yes* or *No*.

5 B, E, A **6** D, B, E

7 A, B, D **8** A, C, B

Are the points coplanar? Write *Yes* or *No*.

9 C, B, A, E **10** E, F, B, D

11 D, B, F, A **12** D, B, F, C

13 Use the labeled points to name plane Z in three different ways.

14 Name the intersection of $\overleftrightarrow{AC}$ and $\overleftrightarrow{ED}$.

In Exercises 15–20, refer to the figure below. Use the labeled points to answer each question.

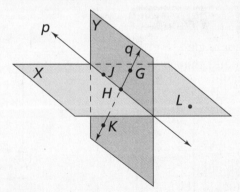

15 Name two points that determine line p.

16 Name three points that determine plane X.

17 Name the intersection of line p and line q.

18 Name line q in three different ways.

19 Name the intersection of planes X and Y.

20 Name the intersection of line q and plane X.

In Exercises 21–24, refer to the number line below. Find each length.

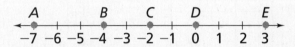

21 AC **22** BD **23** CB **24** AE

In Exercises 25–28, refer to the number line below.

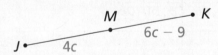

Give the letter that names the midpoint of each segment.

25 $\overline{QS}$ **26** $\overline{SW}$ **27** $\overline{VZ}$ **28** $\overline{RZ}$

In Exercises 29–30, use the figure below. Point M is the midpoint of $\overline{JK}$.

29 Find c.

30 Find JM and JK.

31 The towns of Ames, Bradley, and Carlton lie along the same straight road. Ames is 45 miles due east of Bradley, and Carlton is 10 miles due west of Ames. Which town is between the other two? Draw a diagram to illustrate your answer.

10.2 Rays and Angles

Another set of definitions and postulates is associated with the concept of a *ray*.

Definitions Related to Rays

A **ray** is part of a line that begins at one point and extends without end in one direction. The point is called the **endpoint of the ray.** You name a ray by its endpoint and one other point on it.

ray RS ($\overrightarrow{RS}$)

On a line, if point B is between point A and point C, then $\overrightarrow{BA}$ and $\overrightarrow{BC}$ are **opposite rays.**

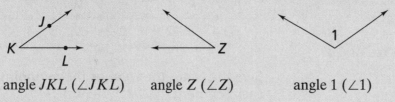

opposite rays $\overrightarrow{BA}$ and $\overrightarrow{BC}$

An **angle** is the figure formed by two rays with a common endpoint. Each ray is a **side** of the angle, and the endpoint is the **vertex** of the angle. The symbol for angle is $\angle$. There are several ways to name an angle.

angle JKL ($\angle JKL$)   angle Z ($\angle Z$)   angle 1 ($\angle 1$)

EXAMPLE 1   **Identifying rays**

1 Identify all the rays in the figure.

   ■ SOLUTION
   $\overrightarrow{CA}, \overrightarrow{CD}, \overrightarrow{CB}, \overrightarrow{BD}, \overrightarrow{DB}$

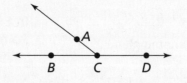

Angles are classified according to their degree measure.

Definitions Related to Angle Measure

An **acute angle** is an angle whose measure is greater than 0° and less than 90°.

An **obtuse angle** is an angle whose measure is greater than 90° and less than 180°.

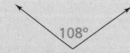

A **right angle** is an angle whose measure is equal to 90°.

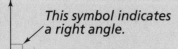
This symbol indicates a right angle.

A **straight angle** is an angle whose measure is equal to 180°.

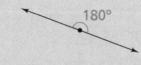

Definitions Relating to Angle Relationships

Congruent angles are two angles that have the same degree measure.

This is written as $m\angle A = m\angle B$; read *the measure of $\angle A$ is equal to the measure of $\angle B$*, or $\angle A \cong \angle B$, read *$\angle A$ is congruent to $\angle B$.*

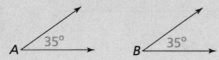

An **angle bisector** is a ray that divides an angle into two congruent angles. $\overrightarrow{CE}$ bisects $\angle DCF$.

Adjacent angles are two angles that share a common side and the same vertex.

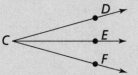

In the diagram on the left, $\angle DCE$ is also adjacent to $\angle FCE$.
$\angle DCE \cong \angle FCE$

Complementary angles are two angles that have a sum of 90°. In the diagram at the right, $\angle 1$ and $\angle 2$ are complementary.

Supplementary angles are two angles that have a sum of 180°. Supplementary angles form a **linear pair.** $\angle 3$ and $\angle 4$ are supplementary.

You can use these definitions to identify the angle relationships in a given figure.

EXAMPLES 2 and 3   **Identifying angle relationships**

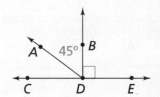

2 Use the figure to identify at least one of each of the following:

Angle bisector	Congruent angles
Adjacent angles	Complementary angles
Linear pair	Supplementary angles

■ SOLUTION

Angle bisector: $\overrightarrow{DA}$ bisects $\angle CDB$ and $\overrightarrow{DB}$ bisects $\angle CDE$

Adjacent angles: $\angle CDA$ and $\angle ADB$ or $\angle ADB$ and $\angle BDE$

Linear pair: $\angle CDA$ and $\angle ADE$ or $\angle CDB$ and $\angle BDE$

Congruent angles: $\angle CDA \cong \angle ADB$ or $\angle CDB \cong \angle BDE$

Complementary angles: $\angle CDA$ and $\angle ADB$

Supplementary angles: $\angle CDB$ and $\angle BDE$

3 Find $m\angle ADC$.

■ SOLUTION

$\overleftrightarrow{CE}$ forms a straight angle with measure 180°. You are given that $m\angle ADB = 45°$ and $m\angle BDE = 90°$. Therefore, $m\angle ADC = 180 - 45 - 90 = 45°$. The angles $\angle ADC$ and $\angle ADB$ are complementary angles.

An angle separates a plane into three sets of points: the angle itself, the points in the *interior* of the angle, and the points in the *exterior* of the angle.

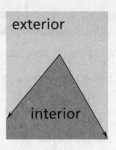
exterior

interior

Angle Addition Postulate

If point B is in the interior of $\angle AOC$, then $m\angle AOB + m\angle BOC = m\angle AOC$.

EXAMPLE 4   **Using the Angle Addition Postulate**

 In the figure, $m\angle AOB = 74°$ and $m\angle AOC = 106°$. Find $m\angle BOC$.

■ **SOLUTION**

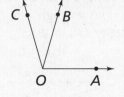

$$
\begin{aligned}
m\angle AOB + m\angle BOC &= m\angle AOC \quad &\leftarrow \text{Apply the Angle Addition Postulate.} \\
74° + m\angle BOC &= 106° \quad &\leftarrow \text{Substitute.} \\
m\angle BOC &= 32° \quad &\leftarrow \text{Solve.}
\end{aligned}
$$

Practice

Choose the letter preceding the word or expression that best completes the statement or answers the question.

1 The measure of a straight angle is

   A. less than 90°.   **C.** exactly 90°.

   B. less than 180°.   **D.** exactly 180°.

2 The supplement of an acute angle is

   A. an acute angle.

   B. an obtuse angle.

   C. a right angle.

   D. a straight angle.

3 Which is the most reasonable estimate of the measure of $\angle QRS$?

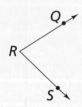

   A. about 115°   **C.** about 75°

   B. about 95°   **D.** about 15°

4 In the figure below, $\overrightarrow{AX}$ and $\overrightarrow{AZ}$ are opposite rays, and $\angle XAY$ is a right angle. Which statement is false?

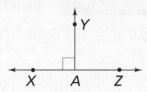

   A. $\angle YAZ$ is the complement of $\angle XAY$.

   B. $\angle YAZ$ is adjacent to $\angle XAY$.

   C. $\angle YAZ$ is congruent to $\angle XAY$.

   D. $\angle XAY$ and $\angle YAZ$ are a linear pair.

5 If $\angle 1$ is supplementary to $\angle 2$ and $\angle 2$ is supplementary to $\angle 3$, which statement is always true?

   A. $\angle 1$ is supplementary to $\angle 3$.

   B. $\angle 1$ is complementary to $\angle 3$.

   C. $\angle 1$ is congruent to $\angle 3$.

   D. $\angle 1$ is adjacent to $\angle 3$.

6 Two acute angles can be which of the following?

  I. congruent   III. complementary
  II. adjacent   IV. supplementary

  A. I and II   **C.** I, II, and III

  B. I and III   **D.** I, II, and IV

7 $\overrightarrow{OF}$ bisects $\angle EOG$. Which of the following is not true?

  A. $m\angle EOF = m\angle FOG$

  B. $m\angle FOG = m\angle EOG - m\angle EOF$

  C. $m\angle EOF \cong m\angle EOG$

  D. $m\angle FOG = \frac{1}{2}m\angle EOG$

8 $\angle YXZ$ is adjacent to $\angle ZXW$. If they are supplementary angles and $m\angle YXZ = 37°$, what is $m\angle ZXW$?

  A. 143°   **C.** 53°

  B. 37°   **D.** unknown

9 What is the measure of the angle formed by opposite rays?

  A. 90°   **C.** 180°

  B. 360°   **D.** unknown

10 $\angle AZB$ and $\angle CZB$ are supplementary. The $m\angle AZB = 2x - 4$ and $m\angle CZB = 8x + 4$. What is the measure of each angle?

  A. $m\angle AZB = 32°$ and $m\angle CZB = 148°$

  B. $m\angle AZB = 12°$ and $m\angle CZB = 76°$

  C. $m\angle AZB = 43°$ and $m\angle CZB = 22°$

  D. $m\angle AZB = 68°$ and $m\angle CZB = 292°$

In Exercises 11–13, give the measure of the complement of an angle of the given measure.

11 56°   **12** 12.5°   **13** $x°$

In Exercises 14–16, give the measure of the supplement of an angle of the given measure.

14 113°   **15** 41.5°   **16** $y°$

In Exercises 17–18, $\overrightarrow{OA}$ and $\overrightarrow{OB}$ are opposite rays. Find $m\angle AOC$.

17   **18**

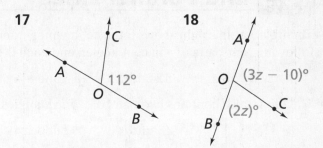

In Exercises 19–20, $\angle PZR$ is a right angle. Find $m\angle PZQ$.

19   **20**

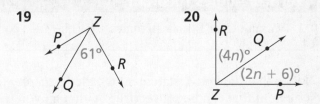

In Exercises 21–24, answer *true* or *false*.

21 Complementary angles are always adjacent.

22 The angles of a linear pair are always adjacent.

23 If $\overrightarrow{PQ}$ and $\overrightarrow{PR}$ are names for the same ray, then Q and R are names for the same point.

24 If the union of two rays is a line, then the rays are opposite rays.

In Exercises 25–28, solve the problem.

25 The measure of an angle is equal to the measure of its complement. Find the measure of each angle.

26 The measure of an angle is equal to the measure of its supplement. Find the measure of each angle.

27 The measure of an angle is twice the measure of its supplement. Find the measure of the larger angle.

28 The measure of an angle is fourteen degrees less than the measure of its complement. Find the measure of the smaller angle.

Intersecting, Perpendicular,
10.3 and Parallel Lines

New Jersey Standards

4.2.A.3 Apply properties of geometric shapes

4.2.C.1 Represent and verify properties of lines

The figure at the right shows intersecting lines ℓ and m. The lines form the following four pairs of adjacent angles, and each is a linear pair.

$\angle 1$ and $\angle 2$ $\angle 2$ and $\angle 3$ $\angle 3$ and $\angle 4$ $\angle 4$ and $\angle 1$

The figure also contains two pairs of *vertical* angles.

$\angle 1$ and $\angle 3$ $\angle 2$ and $\angle 4$

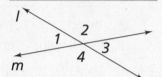

Vertical angles are two angles whose sides form two pairs of opposite rays. There is a special relationship between vertical angles, stated as follows.

Vertical Angles Theorem

If two angles are vertical angles, then they are congruent.

Note
A **postulate** is a statement that is accepted as true without proof.

Notice that the above statement is called a *theorem*. A **theorem** is a statement that can be proved true. Although you will not be asked to prove theorems in this book, you should understand the meaning of the term.

 EXAMPLE 1   **Using the Vertical Angles Theorem**

1 In the figure at the right, lines s and t intersect at point P, $m\angle 1 = (3n - 14)°$, and $m\angle 3 = (2n + 17)°$. Find $m\angle 2$.

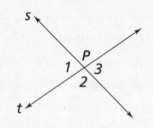

■ **SOLUTION**

$m\angle 1 = m\angle 3$	← Apply the Vertical Angles Theorem.
$3n - 14 = 2n + 17$	← Substitute.
$n - 14 = 17$	← Solve.
$n = 31$	

Therefore: $m\angle 1 = (3n - 14)° \rightarrow (3[31] - 14)° = 79°$

Because $\angle 1$ and $\angle 2$ are a linear pair, $m\angle 2 = 180° - m\angle 1 = 180° - 79° = 101°$.

Perpendicular lines are two lines that intersect to form right angles. The symbol for perpendicular is $\perp$.

$\overleftrightarrow{EF}$ is perpendicular to $\overleftrightarrow{GH}$, denoted $\overleftrightarrow{EF} \perp \overleftrightarrow{GH}$.

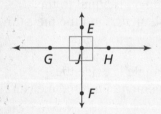

Because $\overleftrightarrow{EF} \perp \overleftrightarrow{GH}$, $\angle EJG$, $\angle GJF$, $\angle EJH$, and $\angle HJF$ are right angles and each measures 90°.

Note
A small square at the intersection of two lines denotes a right angle.

EXAMPLE 2   **Working with perpendicular lines**

2 In the figure, $\overleftrightarrow{AB} \perp \overleftrightarrow{CD}$ and $m\angle EZD = 53°$. Find $m\angle AZE$.

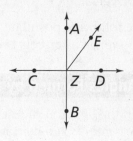

■ SOLUTION

Because $\overleftrightarrow{AB} \perp \overleftrightarrow{CD}$, $\angle AZD$ is a right angle and $m\angle AZD = 90°$.

$m\angle AZE + m\angle EZD = m\angle AZD$ ← **Apply the Angle Addition Postulate.**
$m\angle AZE + \quad 53° \quad = 90°$ ← **Substitute.**
$\qquad\qquad m\angle AZE = 37°$ ← **Solve.**

Coplanar lines that do not intersect are called **parallel lines**.
In the diagram at the right, lines p and q are parallel, denoted $p \parallel q$.

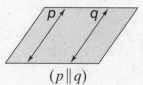

$(p \parallel q)$

Parallel Postulate

Through a point not on a line, there is exactly one line parallel to the given line.

Parallel lines are equidistant; that is, they are the same distance apart at every point.

$\overleftrightarrow{AB} \parallel \overleftrightarrow{CD}$ is illustrated by the diagram at the right.

The lines are parallel if they are the same distance apart at every point.
If $\overleftrightarrow{AC} \perp \overleftrightarrow{CD}$, $\overleftrightarrow{BD} \perp \overleftrightarrow{CD}$, and $\overline{AC} \cong \overline{BD}$, then $\overleftrightarrow{AB} \parallel \overleftrightarrow{CD}$.

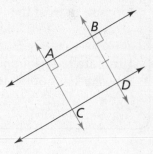

EXAMPLE 3   **Working with parallel lines**

3 According to the diagram, if $\overline{WZ} \cong \overline{XY}$, which of the following statements must be true?

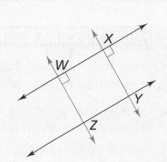

(I) $\overleftrightarrow{XY} \parallel \overleftrightarrow{YZ}$ (III) $\overleftrightarrow{WZ} \parallel \overleftrightarrow{XY}$
(II) $\overleftrightarrow{XW} \parallel \overleftrightarrow{ZY}$ (IV) $\overleftrightarrow{XY} \parallel \overleftrightarrow{WX}$

A. I and III   **C.** II and III
B. I, II, and IV   **D.** I, III, and IV

■ SOLUTION

Because $\overline{WZ} \cong \overline{XY}$ and the segments form right angles with $\overleftrightarrow{WX}$,
$\overleftrightarrow{WZ} \perp \overleftrightarrow{WX}$, $\overleftrightarrow{XY} \perp \overleftrightarrow{WX}$, $\overleftrightarrow{WZ} \perp \overleftrightarrow{ZY}$, and $\overleftrightarrow{XY} \perp \overleftrightarrow{ZY}$. Therefore,
$\overleftrightarrow{WZ} \parallel \overleftrightarrow{XY}$ and $\overleftrightarrow{WX} \parallel \overleftrightarrow{ZY}$.
Therefore, the correct choice is *C*.

A line that intersects two or more coplanar lines at different points is called a **transversal.**

The following postulate and theorems apply to the angles formed when a transversal intersects two parallel lines.

Angles Formed by a Transversal

In the figure at the right, lines a and b are intersected by transversal t.

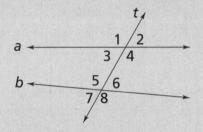

The **interior angles** are:
$\angle 3, \angle 4, \angle 5,$ and $\angle 6$

The **exterior angles** are:
$\angle 1, \angle 2, \angle 7,$ and $\angle 8$

Corresponding angles are a pair of nonadjacent angles, one interior and one exterior, that are both on the same side of the transversal. In the figure above, these are the pairs of corresponding angles.

$\angle 1$ and $\angle 5$ $\qquad$ $\angle 2$ and $\angle 6$ $\qquad$ $\angle 3$ and $\angle 7$ $\qquad$ $\angle 4$ and $\angle 8$

Alternate interior angles are a pair of nonadjacent interior angles on opposite sides of the transversal. The alternate interior angles are:

$\angle 3$ and $\angle 6$ $\qquad$ $\angle 4$ and $\angle 5$

Alternate exterior angles are a pair of nonadjacent exterior angles on opposite sides of the transversal. The alternate exterior angles are:

$\angle 1$ and $\angle 8$ $\qquad$ $\angle 2$ and $\angle 7$

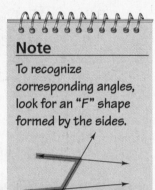

When a transversal intersects parallel lines, the pairs of angles have special relationships. These are summarized by the following postulate and theorems.

Parallel Lines and Related Angles

Corresponding Angles Postulate If two parallel lines are cut by a transversal, then corresponding angles are congruent.

Alternate Interior Angles Theorem If two parallel lines are cut by a transversal, then alternate interior angles are congruent.

Alternate Exterior Angles Theorem If two parallel lines are cut by a transversal, then alternate exterior angles are congruent.

Same-Side Interior Angles Theorem If two parallel lines are cut by a transversal, then interior angles on the same side of the transversal are supplementary.

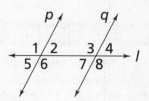

4 $p\|q$ and $m\angle 1 = 118°$. Find $m\angle 7$.

  ■ **SOLUTION**

  Step 1 $m\angle 8 = m\angle 1$ ← Use the Alternate Exterior Angles Theorem.
  $m\angle 8 = 118°$ ← Substitute.

  Step 2 $m\angle 7 + m\angle 8 = 180°$ ← Apply the definition of linear pair.
  $m\angle 7 + 118° = 180°$ ← Substitute.
  $m\angle 7 = 62°$ ← Solve.

5 $m\angle 3 = 24(n + 1)$ and $m\angle 5 = 15n$.
Find the value of n and the measure of both angles.

  ■ **SOLUTION**

  Step 1 Identify the relationship between $\angle 3$ and $\angle 5$.
  $\angle 3 + \angle 2 = 180°$ ← Use the Same-Side Interior Angle Theorem.
  $\angle 2 \cong \angle 5$ ← Use the Vertical Angle Theorem.
  Therefore, $\angle 3 + \angle 5 = 180°$. ← Substitute.

  Step 2 Solve for n.
  $24(n + 1) + 15n = 180°$ ← Substitute.
  $24n + 24 + 15n = 180°$ ← Use the Distributive Property.
  $39n + 24 = 180°$ ← Solve.
  $39n = 156°$
  $n = 4°$

  Step 3 Find the measure of both angles.
  $m\angle 3 = 24(n + 1)$ and $m\angle 5 = 15n$ ← Given.
  $m\angle 3 = 24(4 + 1)$ $m\angle 5 = 15(4)$ ← Substitute.
  $m\angle 3 = 120°$ $m\angle 5 = 60°$ ← Solve.

  Therefore, the value of $n = 4$, $m\angle 3 = 120°$, and $m\angle 5 = 60°$.

Perpendicular Transversal Theorem

If a transversal is perpendicular to one of two parallel lines, then it is
perpendicular to the other.

EXAMPLE 6   **Applying the Perpendicular Transversal Theorem**

6 In the figure at the right, $a \perp c, c \parallel d$, $m\angle 1 = (7x - 8)°$, and $m\angle 2 = (4x)°$. Find $m\angle 2$.

  ■ **SOLUTION**

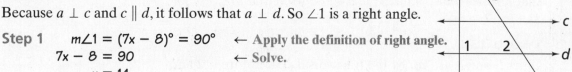

  Because $a \perp c$ and $c \parallel d$, it follows that $a \perp d$. So $\angle 1$ is a right angle.

  Step 1 $m\angle 1 = (7x - 8)° = 90°$ ← Apply the definition of right angle.
  $7x - 8 = 90$ ← Solve.
  $x = 14$

  Step 2 $m\angle 2 = (4x)°$
  $m\angle 2 = (4[14])°$ ← Substitute.
  $m\angle 2 = 56°$ ← Simplify.

You can use the following postulates and theorems to show that two lines are parallel.

Showing That Lines Are Parallel

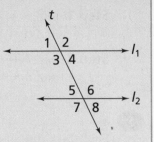

Converse of Corresponding Angles Postulate If two lines are cut by a transversal so that a pair of corresponding angles are congruent, then the lines are parallel.

If $\angle 1 \cong \angle 5$, then $l_1 \parallel l_2$.

Converse of Alternate Interior Angles Theorem If two lines are cut by a transversal so that a pair of alternate interior angles are congruent, then the lines are parallel.

If $\angle 4 \cong \angle 5$, then $l_1 \parallel l_2$.

Converse of Alternate Exterior Angles Theorem If two lines are cut by a transversal so that a pair of alternate exterior angles are congruent, then the lines are parallel.

If $\angle 1 \cong \angle 8$, then $l_1 \parallel l_2$.

Converse of Same-Side Interior Angles Theorem If two lines are cut by a transversal so that a pair of same side interior angles are supplementary, then the lines are parallel.

If $\angle 3$ and $\angle 5$ are supplementary, then $l_1 \parallel l_2$.

EXAMPLES 7 and 8 Justifying a statement that lines are parallel

7 Given the figure at the right, state the postulate or theorem that justifies the conclusion $\overleftrightarrow{AB} \parallel \overleftrightarrow{CD}$.

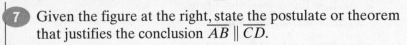

■ SOLUTION

The segments $\overline{AB}$ and $\overline{CD}$ are parts of two lines, $\overleftrightarrow{AB}$ and $\overleftrightarrow{CD}$, that are cut by transversal $\overleftrightarrow{BC}$. You may find it helpful to copy the figure and extend the lines as shown at the right.

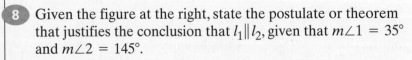

The labeled angles, $\angle ABC$ and $\angle DCB$, are a pair of alternate interior angles. Because these angles are congruent, $\overleftrightarrow{AB} \parallel \overleftrightarrow{CD}$.

The justification is that **the Converse of the Alternate Interior Angles Theorem applies.**

8 Given the figure at the right, state the postulate or theorem that justifies the conclusion that $l_1 \parallel l_2$, given that $m\angle 1 = 35°$ and $m\angle 2 = 145°$.

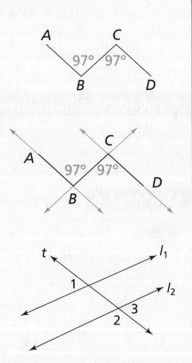

■ SOLUTION

Lines l_1 and l_2 are cut by the transversal t. Therefore, $\angle 2$ and $\angle 3$ are supplementary and $m\angle 3 = 180 - 145 = 35°$. Therefore, $\angle 1 \cong \angle 3$ and $l_1 \parallel l_2$.

The justification is that **the Converse of the Alternate Interior Angles Theorem applies.**

Choose the letter preceding the word or expression that best completes the statement or answers the question.

1 If two lines are each parallel to a third line, then

    A. they are parallel to each other.

    B. they are perpendicular to each other.

    C. they are a pair of skew lines.

    D. their relationship cannot be determined.

2 Given the figure below, which statement is true?

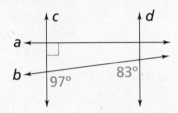

    A. $a \parallel b$ **C.** $a \perp d$

    B. $a \parallel d$ **D.** $b \perp d$

3 If two lines are coplanar, then they cannot be

    A. intersecting.   **C.** perpendicular.

    B. parallel.   **D.** skew.

In Exercises 4–6, refer to the figure below. Find each angle measure.

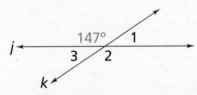

  4 $m\angle 1$ **5** $m\angle 2$ **6** $m\angle 3$

In Exercises 7–12, refer to the figure below. Given $r \parallel s$, find each angle measure.

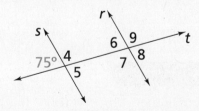

  7 $m\angle 4$ **8** $m\angle 5$ **9** $m\angle 6$

10 $m\angle 7$ **11** $m\angle 8$ **12** $m\angle 9$

In Exercises 13–18, refer to the figure below. Given $\overleftrightarrow{BE} \perp \overleftrightarrow{FC}$, find each angle measure.

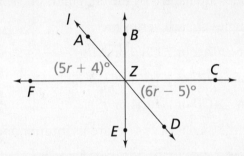

13 $m\angle CZD$ **14** $m\angle AZB$ **15** $m\angle BZC$

16 $m\angle DZE$ **17** $m\angle AZC$ **18** $m\angle AZE$

In Exercises 19–24, refer to the figure below. Given $l \parallel m$, find each angle measure.

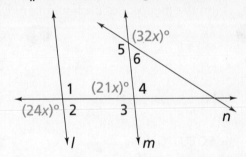

19 $m\angle 1$ **20** $m\angle 2$ **21** $m\angle 3$

22 $m\angle 4$ **23** $m\angle 5$ **24** $m\angle 6$

In Exercises 25–26, state the postulate or theorem that justifies the conclusion $\overline{AB} \parallel \overline{DC}$.

25

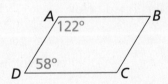

26

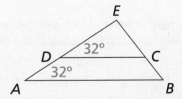

10.4 Triangles

New Jersey Standards

4.2.A.3 Apply properties of geometric shapes

4.2.E.1 Use techniques of indirect measurement

Recall that a triangle is a closed plane figure with three line segments or sides, containing three angles.

The sides are named by the endpoints of each segment: $\overline{AB}$, $\overline{AC}$, $\overline{BC}$.

The angles at each vertex are

$\angle A$ or $\angle BAC$ or $\angle CAB$ or $\angle 1$

$\angle B$ or $\angle ABC$ or $\angle CBA$ or $\angle 2$

$\angle C$ or $\angle ACB$ or $\angle BCA$ or $\angle 3$

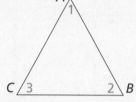

The three angles of $\triangle ABC$ are its **interior angles.**

> **Note**
>
> The angles of a triangle can be named three ways: by the letter of the vertex, by three endpoints, or by a designated number inside the angle.

Triangle Angle-Sum Theorem

> The sum of the measures of the angles of a triangle is 180°.

Therefore, in the triangle above, $m\angle A + m\angle B + m\angle C = 180°$.

EXAMPLES 1 through 3   Finding the measures of interior angles

Find the measure of each numbered angle.

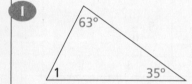

1

■ **SOLUTION**

$m\angle 1 + 63° + 35° = 180°$
$m\angle 1 + 98° = 180°$
$m\angle 1 = 82°$

2

■ **SOLUTION**

$m\angle 2 + 110° + 45° = 180°$
$m\angle 2 + 155° = 180°$
$m\angle 2 = 25°$

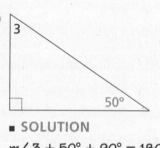

3

■ **SOLUTION**

$m\angle 3 + 50° + 90° = 180°$
$m\angle 3 + 140° = 180°$
$m\angle 3 = 40°$

A triangle has three exterior angles. When a side of a triangle is extended, the angle formed outside the triangle is called an **exterior angle.**

An exterior angle of a triangle is supplementary to its **adjacent interior** angle, as illustrated below.

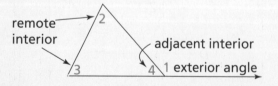

$m\angle 1 + m\angle 4 = 180°$
$m\angle 1 = m\angle 2 + m\angle 3$

Exterior Angle Theorem

> The measure of an exterior angle of a triangle is equal to the sum of the measures of the two nonadjacent angles, called the **remote interior angles** of the triangle.

274

EXAMPLES 4 through 6 **Finding the measures of exterior angles**

Find the measure of each numbered angle.

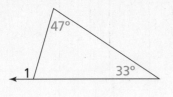

4

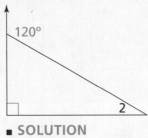

5

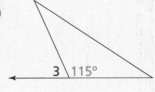

6

■ SOLUTION

$m\angle 1 = 47° + 33°$
$m\angle 1 = 80°$

■ SOLUTION

$120° = 90° + m\angle 2$
$30° = m\angle 2$

■ SOLUTION

$m\angle 3 + 115° = 180°$
$m\angle 3 = 65°$

When we consider an exterior angle and any one remote interior angle, we find the following statement also to be true.

Exterior Angle Inequality Theorem

The measure of an exterior angle of a triangle is greater than the measures of either of its remote interior angles.

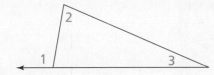

$$m\angle 1 > m\angle 2 \quad \text{and} \quad m\angle 1 > m\angle 3$$

The **altitude,** or height, of a triangle is the length of the segment from any vertex of a triangle perpendicular to the opposite side.

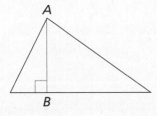

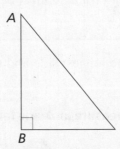

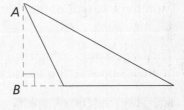

$\overline{AB}$ is inside the $\triangle$.

$\overline{AB}$ is the side of the right $\triangle$.

$\overline{AB}$ is outside the $\triangle$.

A triangle has three altitudes. The altitudes of a triangle are concurrent.

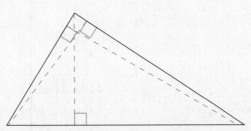

Note

Concurrent lines intersect at one unique point.

275

A **median** is a line segment that starts at any vertex of a triangle and extends to the midpoint of the opposite side.

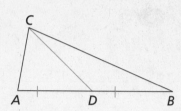

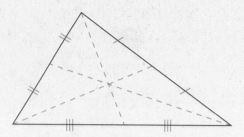

If $\overline{CD}$ is the median, then D is the midpoint of $\overline{AB}$ and $\overline{AD} \cong \overline{DB}$.

A triangle has three medians. The medians of a triangle are concurrent.

An **angle bisector** is a ray that starts at any vertex and divides the angle into two congruent angles.

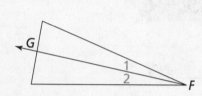

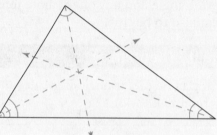

$\overrightarrow{FG}$ bisects the angle so that $\angle 1 \cong \angle 2$.

A triangle has three angle bisectors. The angle bisectors of a triangle are concurrent.

Triangle Inequality Theorem

The sum of the lengths of any two sides of a triangle must be greater than the length of the third side.

The largest angle of a triangle is opposite the longest side and the smallest angle is opposite the shortest side.

EXAMPLES 7 and 8   Using angle measure and side length

7 Which is the shortest side?

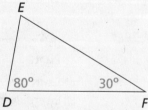

■ SOLUTION

$\angle F$ is the smallest angle, so $\overline{ED}$ is the shortest side.

8 Which is the largest angle?

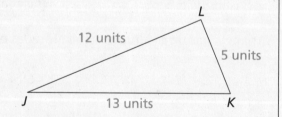

■ SOLUTION

$\overline{JK}$ is the longest side, so $\angle L$ is the largest angle.

If a triangle has at least two congruent sides, it is an **isosceles triangle** and the following theorems apply.

Isosceles Triangle Theorems

If two sides of a triangle are congruent, then the angles opposite those sides are also congruent.

If $\overline{AB} \cong \overline{BC}$, then $\angle A \cong \angle C$.

If two angles of a triangle are congruent, then the sides opposite the angles are also congruent.

If $\angle A \cong \angle C$, then $\overline{AB} \cong \overline{BC}$.

The bisector of the **vertex angle,** the angle opposite the base of an isosceles triangle, is the perpendicular bisector of the base.

If $\overline{AB} \cong \overline{BC}$ and $\overline{BD}$ bisects $\angle ABC$,
then $\overline{BD} \perp \overline{AC}$ and $\overline{BD}$ bisects $\overline{AC}$
so that $\overline{AD} \cong \overline{DC}$.

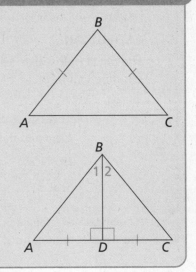

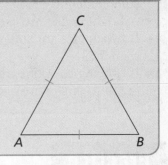

If a triangle has three congruent sides, it is an **equilateral triangle** and the following corollaries apply.

Equilateral Triangle Corollaries

If a triangle is **equilateral,** then it is also **equiangular.**

If $\overline{AB} \cong \overline{BC} \cong \overline{AC}$, then $\angle A \cong \angle B \cong \angle C$.

If a triangle is **equiangular,** then it is also **equilateral.**

If $\angle A \cong \angle B \cong \angle C$, then $\overline{AB} \cong \overline{BC} \cong \overline{AC}$.

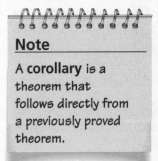

A triangle can be classified by its sides or by its angles. Triangles can be right, obtuse, or acute when classified by angles and equilateral, isosceles, or scalene when classified by sides.

Note

A **corollary** is a theorem that follows directly from a previously proved theorem.

Classification by Sides			Classification by Angles	
Triangle	Description of Sides	Angle Properties	Triangle	Description of Angles
Equilateral Triangle	All three sides are congruent.	All three angles are congruent and measure 60°.	Acute Triangle	All angles are acute.
Isoceles Triangle	Two sides are congruent.	The angles opposite the congruent sides are congruent.	Right Triangle	One angle is a right angle and the other two are acute.
Scalene Triangle	No sides are congruent.	No angles are congruent.	Obtuse Triangle	One angle is a obtuse and the other two are acute.

EXAMPLE 9   Applying triangle classifications

9 Which of the three types of triangles cannot have a right angle?
Which of the three types of triangles cannot have an obtuse angle?
Explain why or why not.

■ **SOLUTION**

The chart below lists all the possible types of angles each type of
triangle can have.

	Acute	Right	Obtuse
Equilateral	YES	NO	NO
Isosceles	YES	YES	YES
Scalene	YES	YES	YES

An **equilateral triangle** is also equiangular. Each angle measures 60°,
and therefore, it cannot contain a right angle or an obtuse angle.

Additional Theorems About Angles in Triangles

- If a triangle is a right triangle, then the acute angles are
  complementary.
- All right angles are congruent.
- If two angles are both congruent and supplementary, then they are
  right angles.
- If two angles of one triangle are congruent to two angles of another,
  the third angles are congruent.

Practice

**Choose the letter preceding the word or expression that best
completes the statement or answers the question.**

1 Which pair of terms best describes the
triangle below?

A. acute, isosceles

B. right, isosceles

C. right, equilateral

D. obtuse, scalene

2 In the figure below, two sides of $\triangle JKL$
are extended as shown. Which is a true
statement?

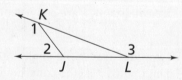

A. $m\angle 1 + m\angle 2 = m\angle 3$

B. $m\angle 1 + m\angle 2 = m\angle KLJ$

C. $m\angle 1 + m\angle 3 = m\angle KJL$

D. $m\angle JKL + m\angle KJL = m\angle 3$

3 The degree measures of the angles of a triangle are represented by the expressions $2a + 10, 4a$, and $5a + 5$. What are the measures of the angles?

   A. $45°, 50°, 85°$

   B. $40°, 60°, 80°$

   C. $30°, 40°, 110°$

   D. $20°, 70°, 90°$

4 Given $\triangle ABC$ below, what is $m\angle CBD$?

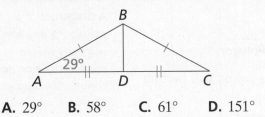

   A. $29°$ **B.** $58°$ **C.** $61°$ **D.** $151°$

In Exercises 5–10, determine whether the statement is true or false.

5 All isosceles triangles are equilateral.

6 All acute triangles contain three acute angles.

7 A right triangle has three right angles.

8 A scalene triangle can have an obtuse angle.

9 The median of a triangle bisects the vertex angle.

10 An altitude of a triangle always lies inside the triangle.

In Exercises 11–12, information is given about the measures of the angles of $\triangle XYZ$. List the measures of the three angles.

11 $m\angle X = 43°$
   $\angle Z$ is a right angle.

12 $m\angle X = 24°$
   $m\angle Y = 5(m\angle Z)$

In Exercises 13–15, one side of $\triangle LMN$ is extended as shown. Find each angle measure.

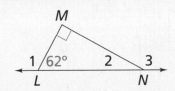

13 $m\angle 1$ **14** $m\angle 2$ **15** $m\angle 3$

In Exercises 16–17, identify the longest side and the shortest side of the triangle.

16 In $\triangle JKL, m\angle J = 65°$ and $m\angle K = 68°$.

17 In $\triangle RST, m\angle S = 28°$ and $\angle T$ is a right angle.

In Exercises 18–19, identify the largest angle and the smallest angle of the triangle.

18 In $\triangle GHJ, GH = 6, HJ = 8$, and $GJ = 9$.

19 In $\triangle PQR, PQ = 5, QR = \sqrt{21}$, and $PR = \sqrt{43}$.

In Exercises 20–21, determine whether the given measures could be the lengths of the sides of a triangle. Write *Yes* or *No*.

20 $6, 10, 17$ **21** $11, 12, 13$

In Exercises 22–24, refer to $\triangle PRS$. Find each angle measure.

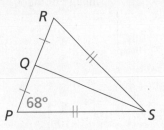

22 $m\angle PRS$ **23** $m\angle RQS$ **24** $m\angle PSQ$

25 In $\triangle UVW$ below, find $m\angle W$.

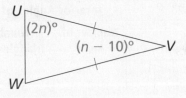

26 In $\triangle DEF$ below, find EF.

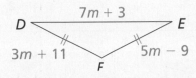

10.5 Quadrilaterals and Other Polygons

New Jersey Standards

New Jersey Standards

4.2.A.3 Apply properties of geometric shapes

4.2.E.1 Use techniques of indirect measurement

Recall that a **polygon** is a closed plane figure with at least three sides.

All closed plane figures can be classified as either *convex* or *concave*. In a **convex polygon,** no point on any diagonal lies outside the figure. In a **concave polygon,** at least one diagonal will contain points that lie outside the figure.

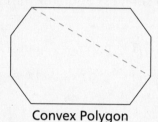

Convex Polygon

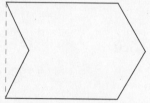

Concave Polygon

The properties, theorems, and postulates discussed in this lesson will pertain to convex polygons.

You can classify any polygon by its number of sides. The following table lists names for the most common polygons.

Note

A **diagonal** of a polygon is any line segment whose endpoints lie on non-consecutive vertices.

Classifying a Polygon by the Number of Sides	
Number of Sides	**Name**
3	triangle
4	quadrilateral
5	pentagon
6	hexagon
8	octagon
9	nonagon
10	decagon
12	dodecagon

Note

If a polygon has *n* sides, you call it an *n*-gon. For example, a 16-sided polygon is called a 16-gon.

The following table shows how you can find the sum of the interior angles of a convex polygon by drawing all the diagonals from one vertex.

Interior Angles of a Polygon			
Polygon	**Number of Sides**	**Number of Triangles Formed**	**Sum of the Measures of the Interior Angles**
(triangle)	3	$3 - 2 = 1$	$1 \cdot 180° = 180°$
(quadrilateral)	4	$4 - 2 = 2$	$2 \cdot 180° = 360°$
(pentagon)	5	$5 - 2 = 3$	$3 \cdot 180° = 540°$
(octagon)	8	$8 - 2 = 6$	$6 \cdot 180° = 1080°$

Note

The number of triangles found in the interior of any polygon is always two fewer than the number of sides.

The relationship between the number of sides and the number of interior triangles of any polygon leads to the following theorem.

Polygon Interior Angle-Sum Theorem

The sum of the measures of the interior angles of a convex polygon with n sides is $(n - 2)180°$.

 EXAMPLE 1   **Using the Polygon Interior Angle-Sum Theorem**

1   Find the sum of the measures of the interior angles of a dodecagon.

   ■ **SOLUTION**

   A dodecagon is a polygon that has 12 sides. Use the Polygon Interior Angle-Sum Theorem with $n = 12$.

$$\text{sum of measures of interior angles} = (n - 2)180°$$
$$= (12 - 2)180°$$
$$= (10)180° = 1800°$$

The sum of the exterior angles of a polygon is consistent, regardless of the number of sides of a given figure.

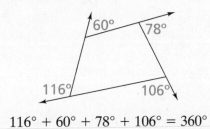

$$116° + 60° + 78° + 106° = 360°$$

> **Note**
>
> An **exterior angle of a convex polygon** is an angle that forms a linear pair with one of its interior angles.

Polygon Exterior Angle-Sum Theorem

The sum of the measures of the exterior angles of a convex polygon, one at each vertex, is 360°.

EXAMPLE 2   **Using the Polygon Exterior Angle-Sum Theorem**

2   Find the $m\angle A$.

   ■ **SOLUTION**

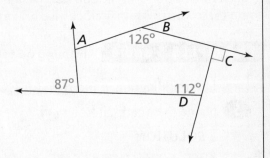

$m\angle A + m\angle B + m\angle C + m\angle D + 87°$ ← Use the
$= 360°$ Polygon Exterior Angle-Sum Theorem.

$m\angle B + 126° = 180°$ ← Use the Linear Pair Postulate.
$\quad\quad m\angle B = 54°$

$m\angle C = 90°$

$m\angle D + 112° = 180°$
$\quad\quad m\angle D = 68°$

$m\angle A + 54° + 90° + 68° + 87° = 360°$ ← Substitute.
$\quad\quad\quad\quad m\angle A + 299° = 360°$ ← Solve.

Therefore, $m\angle A = 61°$.

An **equilateral polygon** is a polygon in which all sides are congruent. An **equiangular polygon** is a polygon in which all angles are congruent. A **regular polygon** is both equilateral and equiangular. There is a relationship between the number of sides and the angle measure of regular polygons.

Corollaries for Regular Polygons

The measure of each interior angle of a regular n-gon is $\dfrac{(n-2)180°}{n}$.

The measure of each exterior angle of a regular n-gon is $\dfrac{360°}{n}$.

EXAMPLES 3 and 4 — **Using the corollaries for regular polygons**

3 Find the measure of each interior angle of the polygon shown at the right.

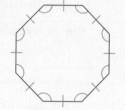

- **SOLUTION**

All sides are congruent and all angles are congruent, so the figure is a regular polygon. Use the first corollary with $n = 8$.

measure of each interior angle $= \dfrac{(n-2)180°}{n}$

$$= \dfrac{(8-2)180°}{8} = \dfrac{(6)180°}{8} = \dfrac{1080°}{8} = 135°$$

4 The measure of each exterior angle of a regular polygon is 40°. Find the number of sides.

measure of each exterior angle $= \dfrac{360°}{n}$

$$40° = \dfrac{360°}{n}$$

$$n = 9$$

The polygon has 9 sides.

A **quadrilateral** is a 4-sided polygon. To name a quadrilateral, start at any vertex and list the other **vertices** consecutively. **Consecutive** vertices are next to each other and form the consecutive angles of the quadrilateral. You can name these vertices either clockwise or counterclockwise.

> **Note**
>
> Nonconsecutive vertices of a quadrilateral are opposite angles.

EXAMPLES 5 and 6 — **Naming quadrilaterals**

Use the diagram at the right for Examples 5 and 6.

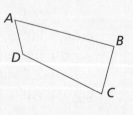

5 Name the quadrilateral.

- **SOLUTION**

ABCD, BCDA, CDAB, or DABC

6 Name each angle of the quadrilateral.

- **SOLUTION**

∠A, ∠B, ∠C, ∠D
or ∠DAB, ∠ABC, ∠BCD, ∠CDA
or ∠BAD, ∠CBA, ∠DCB, ∠ADC

All quadrilaterals have four sides, four angles, and a sum of the angles equal to 360°. Quadrilaterals can be further classified according to specific unique relationships between the sides and the angles of a figure. These unique relationships form a subcategory known as **special quadrilaterals.**

Special Quadrilaterals	
Quadrilateral	**Special Vocabulary and Properties**
A **parallelogram** has two pairs of parallel sides.	If a quadrilateral is a parallelogram, then • its opposite sides are congruent; • its opposite angles are congruent; • its consecutive angles are supplementary; and • its diagonals bisect each other.
A **rhombus** has four congruent sides.	If a quadrilateral is a rhombus, then it has all the properties of a parallelogram, plus • each diagonal bisects a pair of opposite angles; and • its diagonals are perpendicular.
A **rectangle** has four right angles.	If a quadrilateral is a rectangle, then it has all the properties of a parallelogram, plus • its diagonals are congruent.
A **square** has four congruent sides and four right angles.	If a quadrilateral is a square, then it has all the properties of a parallelogram, plus • each diagonal bisects a pair of opposite angles; • its diagonals are perpendicular; and • its diagonals are congruent.
A **trapezoid** has exactly one pair of parallel sides.	The parallel sides of a trapezoid are called its **bases.** Two angles whose vertices are the endpoints of a single base form a pair of **base angles.** The nonparallel sides of a trapezoid are its **legs.** If a quadrilateral is a trapezoid, then • two consecutive angles whose vertices are endpoints of different bases are supplementary.
An **isosceles trapezoid** has legs that are congruent.	If a quadrilateral is an isosceles trapezoid, then it has all the properties of a trapezoid, plus • its base angles are congruent; and • its diagonals are congruent.
A **kite** has two distinct pairs of consecutive sides that are congruent.	In a kite, the common endpoint of a pair of congruent sides is called an **endpoint of the kite.** If a quadrilateral is a kite, then • its diagonals are perpendicular; and • one diagonal bisects the angles whose vertices are the endpoints of the kite.

You can use these properties to solve problems involving quadrilaterals.

EXAMPLES 7 through 10   **Using the properties of quadrilaterals**

7 In the figure at the right, *WXYZ* is a parallelogram.
Find $m\angle X$.

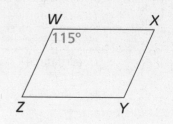

- **SOLUTION**

Consecutive angles of a parallelogram are supplementary.
Therefore: $m\angle X = 180° - 115° = 65°$

8 Given that *ABCD* is an isosceles trapezoid, find $m\angle D$.

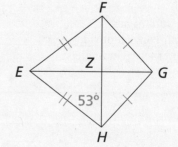

- **SOLUTION**

*In a trapezoid, two consecutive angles whose vertices are
endpoints of different bases are supplementary.*
Therefore:
$$m\angle A \quad + \quad m\angle B \quad = \quad 180°$$
$$(2n + 17)° + (5n + 9)° = 180°$$
$$7n + 26 = 180$$
$$n = 22$$

Base angles of an isosceles trapezoid are congruent.
Therefore: $m\angle D = m\angle A = (2n + 17)° \rightarrow m\angle D = (2[22] + 17)° = 61°$

9 In the figure at the right, *EFGH* is a kite with congruent
sides as marked. Find $m\angle FEH$.

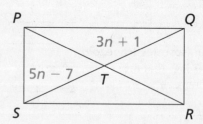

- **SOLUTION**

The diagonals of a kite are perpendicular.
Therefore, in $\triangle EZH$: $m\angle EZH = 90°$

The sum of the measures of the angles of a triangle is 180°.
Therefore, in $\triangle EZH$: $m\angle ZEH = 180° - (53° + 90°) = 37°$

*In a kite, one diagonal bisects the angles whose vertices are the
endpoints of the kite.*
Therefore, in kite *EFGH*: $m\angle FEH = 2(m\angle ZEH) = 2(37°) = 74°$

10 In the figure at the right, *PQRS* is a rectangle with
diagonals $\overline{PR}$ and $\overline{QS}$. Find *PR* and *QS*.

- **SOLUTION**

A rectangle is a type of parallelogram.

The diagonals of a parallelogram bisect each other.
Therefore: $5n - 7 = 3n + 1 \rightarrow n = 4$
$$QS = (5n - 7) + (3n + 1)$$
$$= (5[4] - 7) + (3[4] + 1) = 26$$

The diagonals of a rectangle are congruent.
Therefore: $PR = QS = 26$

Choose the letter preceding the word or expression that best completes the statement or answers the question.

1 Four interior angles of a pentagon each have measure 110°. What is the measure of the fifth interior angle?

A. 72°   **B.** 100°   **C.** 108°   **D.** 110°

2 What is the measure of each exterior angle of a regular decagon?

A. 30°   **B.** 36°   **C.** 72°   **D.** 144°

3 Which expression represents the measure of each interior angle of a regular n-gon?

A. $(180n)°$

B. $\frac{360°}{n}$

C. $(n-2)180°$

D. $\frac{(n-2)180°}{n}$

4 The measure of each interior angle of a regular polygon is 144°. How many sides does the polygon have?

A. 6   **B.** 7   **C.** 8   **D.** 10

5 In the figure below, one side of polygon $RSTU$ has been extended as shown. What is $m\angle S$?

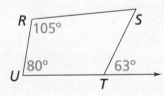

A. 58°   **C.** 75°

B. 63°   **D.** 112°

6 Which conditions will not guarantee that quadrilateral $QUAD$ is a parallelogram?

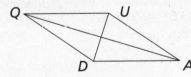

A. $\overline{QD} \cong \overline{QU}$ and $\overline{AD} \cong \overline{AU}$

B. $\overline{QD} \cong \overline{AU}$ and $\overline{QU} \cong \overline{AD}$

C. $\overline{QD} \cong \overline{AU}$ and $\overline{QD} \parallel \overline{AU}$

D. $\overline{QU} \parallel \overline{AD}$ and $\overline{QD} \parallel \overline{AU}$

7 In quadrilateral $PQRS$, find $m\angle P, m\angle Q$, and $m\angle R$.

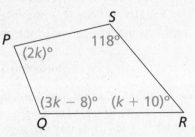

8 Given that $MATH$ is a rhombus, find MA, AT, TH, and HM.

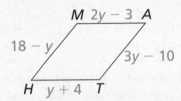

9 The measures of four interior angles of a pentagon are 115°, 92°, 107°, and 83°. Find the measure of the fifth interior angle.

In Exercises 10–12, the sum of the measures of the interior angles of a polygon is given. Find the number of sides.

10 180°   **11** 900°   **12** 2700°

In Exercises 13–15, the measure of an exterior angle of a regular polygon is given. Find the number of sides.

13 120°   **14** 72°   **15** 18°

In Exercises 16–17, classify the polygon by its number of sides. Then find the value of a.

16

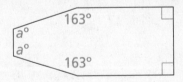

17

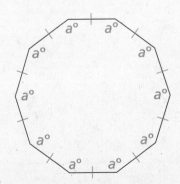

10.6 Congruence and Similarity

New Jersey Standards

4.2.A.3 Properties of geometric shapes

4.2.E.1 Techniques of indirect measurement

Congruent polygons are polygons whose sides and angles can be placed in a correspondence so that corresponding sides are congruent and corresponding angles are congruent. Remember that congruent segments are equal in length and congruent angles are equal in measure. There are five concise methods used to prove triangular congruence.

Showing That Triangles Are Congruent		
Side-Side-Side (SSS) Congruence Postulate If three sides of one triangle are congruent to three sides of another triangle, then the triangles are congruent.	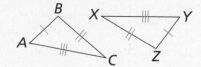	$\triangle ABC \cong \triangle YZX$
Side-Angle-Side (SAS) Congruence Postulate If two sides and the included angle of one triangle are congruent to two sides and the included angle of another triangle, then the triangles are congruent.	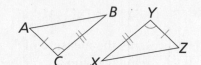	$\triangle ABC \cong \triangle ZXY$
Angle-Side-Angle (ASA) Congruence Postulate If two angles and the included side of one triangle are congruent to two angles and the included side of another triangle, then the triangles are congruent.	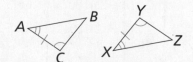	$\triangle ABC \cong \triangle XZY$
Angle-Angle-Side (AAS) Congruence Theorem If two angles and the nonincluded side of one triangle are congruent to two angles and the nonincluded side of another triangle, then the triangles are congruent.	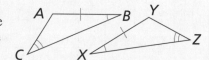	$\triangle ABC \cong \triangle YXZ$
Hypotenuse-Leg (HL) Congruence Theorem If the hypotenuse and one leg of a right triangle are congruent to the hypotenuse and one leg of another right triangle, then the triangles are congruent.	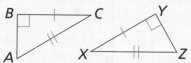	$\triangle ABC \cong \triangle ZYX$

EXAMPLES 1 and 2   Showing that triangles are congruent

Write a congruence statement for each pair of triangles. Identify the postulate or theorem that justifies the congruence statement.

1

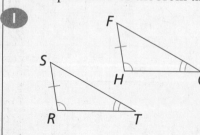

- **SOLUTION**

These congruences are marked.

$\angle R \cong \angle H$ $\angle T \cong \angle G$ $\overline{RS} \cong \overline{HF}$

Congruence statement: $\triangle RST = \triangle HFG$
Justification: AAS Congruence Theorem

2

- **SOLUTION**

These congruences are marked.

$\overline{MZ} \cong \overline{NZ}$ $\overline{SZ} \cong \overline{TZ}$ $\angle MZS \cong \angle NZT$

Congruence statement: $\triangle MZS = \triangle NZT$
Justification: SAS Congruence Postulate

Note

When stating the congruence between figures, name the vertices of each figure in the order of correspondence.

$\triangle GHJ$ and $\triangle KLM$ have a special relationship: they are *similar*.
Similar polygons are polygons whose sides and angles can be placed in a correspondence so that corresponding angles are congruent and corresponding sides are in proportion. The ratio of the lengths of corresponding sides is called the **similarity ratio,** or the **scale factor.**

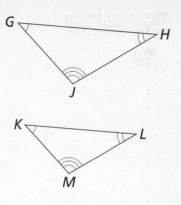

For instance, the markings in the quadrilaterals below indicate the relationships listed.

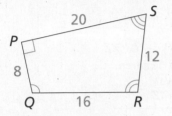 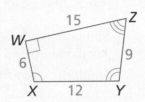

$\angle P \cong \angle W$	$\frac{PQ}{WX} = \frac{8}{6} = \frac{4}{3}$	$\angle R \cong \angle Y$	$\frac{RS}{YZ} = \frac{12}{9} = \frac{4}{3}$
$\angle Q \cong \angle X$	$\frac{QR}{XY} = \frac{16}{12} = \frac{4}{3}$	$\angle S \cong \angle Z$	$\frac{SP}{ZW} = \frac{20}{15} = \frac{4}{3}$

Corresponding angles are congruent, and the similarity ratio of the sides of $PQRS$ to the sides of $WXYZ$ is $\frac{4}{3}$. Therefore, the quadrilaterals are similar, and the vertices correspond in the following order.

$$P \leftrightarrow W \qquad Q \leftrightarrow X \qquad R \leftrightarrow Y \qquad S \leftrightarrow Z$$

The symbol for similarity is $\sim$. So to state the similarity between the quadrilaterals, you use this symbol and name the vertices in the same order as the above correspondence: $PQRS \sim WXYZ$.

Just as there are postulates and theorems that you can use to show two triangles congruent, there also are postulates and theorems for triangle similarity. These are summarized in the table below.

Showing That Triangles Are Similar		
Angle-Angle (AA) Similarity Postulate If two angles of one triangle are congruent to two angles of another triangle, then the triangles are similar.	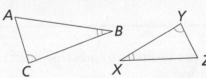	$\triangle ABC \sim \triangle ZXY$
Side-Side-Side (SSS) Similarity Theorem If corresponding sides of two triangles are in proportion, then the triangles are similar.		$\frac{AB}{XZ} = \frac{BC}{ZY} = \frac{CA}{YX}$ $\triangle ABC \sim \triangle XZY$
Side-Angle-Side (SAS) Similarity Theorem If an angle of one triangle is congruent to an angle of another triangle, and the lengths of the sides including these angles are in proportion, then the triangles are similar.	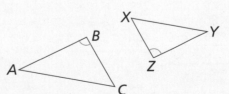 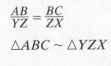	$\frac{AB}{YZ} = \frac{BC}{ZX}$ $\triangle ABC \sim \triangle YZX$

EXAMPLE 3   **Showing that triangles are similar**

 Write a similarity statement for each pair of triangles. Identify the postulate or theorem that justifies the similarity statement. If possible, write the similarity ratio.

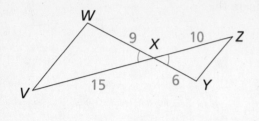

■ SOLUTION

$\angle WXV \cong \angle YXZ$ ← This congruence is marked.

$\dfrac{XW}{XY} = \dfrac{XV}{XZ}$ ← $\dfrac{XW}{XY} = \dfrac{9}{6} = \dfrac{3}{2}; \dfrac{XV}{XZ} = \dfrac{15}{10} = \dfrac{3}{2}$

Similarity statement: $\triangle WXV \sim \triangle YXZ$
Justification: SAS Similarity Theorem
Similarity ratio: $\dfrac{\text{sides of } \triangle WXV}{\text{sides of } \triangle YXZ} = \dfrac{3}{2}$

Ratios and proportions are useful when establishing the similarity of overlapping figures.

EXAMPLE 4   **Working with similar overlapping triangles**

> **Note**
> Congruent figures have the same shape and size. **Similar figures** have the same shape, but not necessarily the same size.

4 Write a similarity statement for the overlapping triangles. Identify the postulate or theorem that justifies the similarity statement, and identify the similarity ratio.

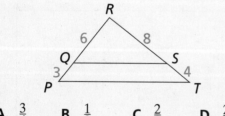

■ SOLUTION

$\dfrac{AB}{AC} = \dfrac{AE}{AD}$ ← $\dfrac{AB}{AC} = \dfrac{6}{6+2} = \dfrac{3}{4}; \dfrac{AE}{AD} = \dfrac{9}{9+3} = \dfrac{3}{4}$

$\angle A \cong \angle A$ ← An angle is congruent to itself.

Similarity statement: $\triangle ABE \sim \triangle ACD$
Justification: SAS Similarity Theorem
Similarity ratio: $\dfrac{\text{sides of } \triangle ABE}{\text{sides of } \triangle ACD} = \dfrac{3}{4}$

Practice

Choose the letter preceding the word or expression that best completes the statement or answers the question.

1 In the figure below, what is the similarity ratio of the sides of $\triangle RQS$ to the sides of $\triangle RPT$?

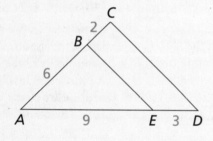

A. $\dfrac{3}{4}$ **B.** $\dfrac{1}{2}$ **C.** $\dfrac{2}{3}$ **D.** $\dfrac{2}{1}$

2 In the figure below, $\triangle ABC \cong \triangle DEC$. Which statement cannot be justified?

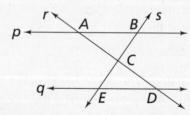

A. $\overline{AB} \cong \overline{DE}$ **C.** $r \perp s$

B. $p \parallel q$ **D.** Point C is the midpoint of $\overline{AD}$.

3 Which of the following justifies the conclusion $\triangle ABC \cong \triangle XYZ$?

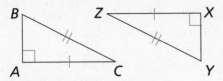

    A. HL Congruence Theorem

    B. SAS Congruence Postulate

    C. AAS Congruence Theorem

    D. definition of congruent polygons

4 The figure below shows rhombus $KLMN$ with diagonals $\overline{KM}$ and $\overline{LN}$. Which statement is not necessarily true?

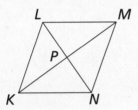

    A. $\triangle LKN \cong \triangle NML$

    B. $\triangle MKN \cong \triangle LNK$

    C. $\triangle MPN \cong \triangle KPL$

    D. $\triangle LMP \cong \triangle NKP$

In Exercises 5–7, write a congruence statement for each pair of triangles. Identify the postulate or theorem that justifies the congruence statement.

5

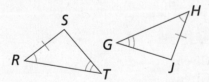

6

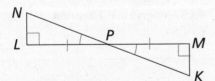

7

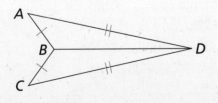

In Exercises 8–10, write a similarity statement for each pair of triangles. Identify the postulate or theorem that justifies the similarity statement. If possible, write the similarity ratio.

8

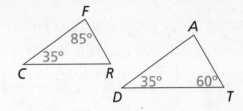

9

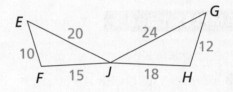

10

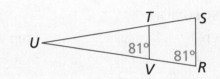

In Exercises 11–16, given that $\triangle JKM \cong \triangle LKN$, name the angle or side that is congruent to the given angle or side.

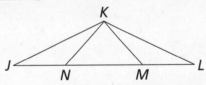

11 $\overline{LK}$ **12** $\overline{NK}$ **13** $\overline{JM}$

14 $\angle J$ **15** $\angle KNL$ **16** $\angle LKN$

17 In the figure below, find $m\angle WZY$. Explain your reasoning.

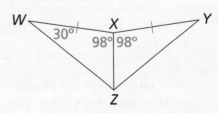

10.7 Proofs and Counterexamples

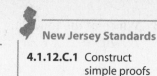
New Jersey Standards

4.1.12.C.1 Construct simple proofs

You use the triangle congruence theorems to prove that three parts of one triangle are congruent to the corresponding parts of another triangle. You can use the Corresponding Parts of Congruent Triangles are Congruent (CPCTC) postulate to *prove* that the other 3 parts are also congruent.

Recall the theorems you can use to prove that triangles are congruent.

You can use a simple two-column format to show all of the steps of a proof, or you can use a short paragraph to clearly explain the logic of a proof. Remember that you must verify each step or statement with a postulate or theorem.

SAS	Side-Angle-Side
SSS	Side-Side-Side
ASA	Angle-Side-Angle
AAS	Angle-Angle-Side
HL	Hypotenuse-Leg

Go Online
PHSchool.com

Visit: PHSchool.com
Web Code: ayp-0397

EXAMPLES 1 and 2   **Writing two-column proofs**

Complete a two-column proof.

1 **Given:** $\triangle ABC$ with $\overline{AB} \cong \overline{AC}$
Prove: $\angle B \cong \angle C$

■ SOLUTION

Step 1 Make a plan.
Draw $\overline{AD}$ bisecting $\angle A$ to prove that $\triangle ABD \cong \triangle ACD$, and then all corresponding parts are congruent by CPCTC.

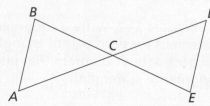

Step 2 Complete the proof.

Statements	Reasons
$\overline{AB} \cong \overline{AC}$	Given
$\angle 1 \cong \angle 2$	Definition of angle bisector
$\overline{AD} \cong \overline{AD}$	Reflexive property
$\triangle ABD \cong \triangle ACD$	SAS Congruence Theorem
$\angle B \cong \angle C$	CPCTC

2 **Given:** $\overline{BC} \cong \overline{EC}$
$\overline{AC} \cong \overline{DC}$
Prove: $\overline{BA} \cong \overline{ED}$

■ SOLUTION

Step 1 Make a plan.
Prove that $\triangle BCA \cong \triangle ECD$, and then all corresponding parts are congruent by CPCTC.

Step 2 Complete the proof.

Statements	Reasons
$\overline{BC} \cong \overline{EC}$	Given
$\overline{AC} \cong \overline{DC}$	Given
$\angle BCA \cong \angle ECD$	Vertical angles are congruent.
$\triangle BCA \cong \triangle ECD$	SAS Congruence Theorem
$\overline{BA} \cong \overline{ED}$	CPCTC

If a statement is false and therefore cannot be proved, you can simply provide a **counterexample**. A counterexample is an actual example or situation where the given is true but the desired proof is not true.

Is it possible to prove that two triangles are congruent if two adjacent sides and a nonincluded angle of one triangle are congruent to the corresponding two sides and nonincluded angle of the other triangle?

EXAMPLE 3   **Proving triangles *not* congruent by SSA**

Complete a two-column proof.

3 **Given:** $\triangle ABC$ with $\overline{AB} \cong \overline{AC}$
Prove: $\triangle ABD$ is not congruent to $\triangle ACD$.

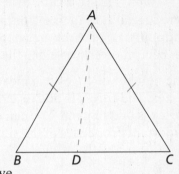

■ SOLUTION

Step 1 Make a plan.
Draw $\overline{AD}$ where D is any point on $\overline{BC}$.

Step 2 Complete the proof.
You are given that $\overline{AB} \cong \overline{AC}$. $\overline{AD} \cong \overline{AD}$ by the Reflexive Property, and $\angle B \cong \angle C$ because they are base angles of an isosceles triangle. Although the two triangles have corresponding adjacent sides and a nonincluded angle (*SSA*) congruent, $\triangle ABD$ is *not* congruent to $\triangle ACD$ because $BD \neq CD$.

Practice

Choose the letter preceding the word or expression that best completes the statement or answers the question.

1 Which of the following statements can be proved by the given information?
Given: $\angle H \cong \angle L$; $\overline{HJ} \cong \overline{JL}$; $\angle IJH \cong \angle KJL$

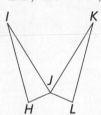

A. $\triangle HIJ \cong \triangle LKJ$ by ASA

B. $\triangle HIJ \cong \triangle JLK$ by SAS

C. $\triangle HIJ \cong \triangle JLK$ by ASA

D. $\triangle HIJ \cong \triangle LKJ$ by SAS

2 Which theorem or postulate proves that $\triangle ABD \cong \triangle CBD$?

A. AAS

B. ASA

C. SAS

D. All of the above

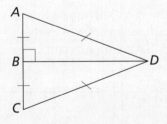

In Exercises 3–5, complete the proof.

3 **Given:** Parallelogram $PRTS$
$\angle PSR \cong \angle TRS$
$\angle PRS \cong \angle TSR$

Prove: $\triangle PRS \cong \triangle TSR$

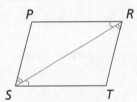

4 **Given:** Rhombus $GHJK$
$\angle G \cong \angle J$

Prove: $\angle K \cong \angle H$

5 **Given:** $\triangle XYZ$ is an equilateral triangle.
A is the midpoint of $\overline{YZ}$.

Prove: $\angle XYA \cong \angle XZA$

10.8 Vertex-Edge Graphs

New Jersey Standards

4.4.D.1 Use vertex-edge graphs

One special type of graph or map is a **network** or a **vertex-edge graph.** The **endpoints** or **vertices** are connected by **segments** called **edges.** A **path** connects the vertices along the edges.

The number of edges that meet at a vertex determines the **degree** of the vertex. The vertex is **odd** or **even,** depending on whether the degree of the vertex is odd or even. You can count the edges and vertices to determine important properties of the vertex-edge graph.

Note

The edges of a network can be straight line segments or curves.

EXAMPLE 1   **Counting vertices and edges of a vertex-edge graph**

1 Find the number of vertices and edges of the vertex-edge graph. Determine the degrees of vertices A and B.

■ **SOLUTION**

The graph has 4 vertices represented by the points in the four corners. There is a total of 7 edges. The diagonals of the square represent only two edges because there is no vertex at the center of the square. There are 3 edges meeting at vertex A, so vertex A has degree 3 and is odd. Vertex B has degree 4 and is even because there are 4 edges meeting at vertex B.

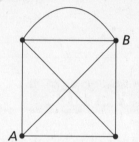

You can travel along the edges of the vertex-edge graph to determine paths from one vertex to another. A network has an **Euler path** if you can place your pencil at one vertex and trace all of the edges of the graph exactly once without lifting your pencil. This graph is also said to be **traversable.**

A vertex-edge graph has an Euler path if and only if it has exactly 0 or 2 odd vertices. When every vertex of the network is even (0 odd vertices), the Euler path forms a **circuit.** An **Euler circuit** begins and ends at the same vertex.

Note

If a network has 2 odd vertices, the Euler path must begin at one odd vertex and end at the other odd vertex.

EXAMPLE 2   **Mapping a route**

2 Draw a vertex-edge graph to represent the mapping of 5 towns where there are at least 2 roads to each town and you can follow an Euler circuit through all of the towns.

■ **SOLUTION**

There are 5 towns, so there are 5 vertices in the graph. Because there is an Euler circuit, you know that the degree of each vertex is even. Each vertex of the simplest graph has degree 2. An Euler circuit is *ABCDEA.*

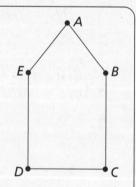

You can use vertex-edge graphs to solve practical, real-world problems involving finding the optimal road or airway routes for trucks, buses, mail carriers, airplanes, and so on. You can also use networks to organize and plan a tournament or competition.

EXAMPLE 3 **Solving a real-world problem with a vertex-edge graph**

 Five high schools within a league compete during the spring term. At the end of the term, each team will have played the others exactly once.

a) How many games must the teams play?
b) Draw a network to represent this situation.
c) What is the degree of each vertex? Describe why.

■ **SOLUTION**

a) *The teams will play 10 games.*

b)

c) *Each vertex is of degree 4 because each team must play the other 4 teams once.*

Practice

In Exercises 1–2, use the following vertex-edge graph to find the answer choice that is best for each case.

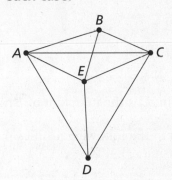

1 How many more edges than vertices does the vertex-edge graph have?

A. 8   **B.** 5   **C.** 4   **D.** 2

2 Which is an Euler path of the vertex-edge graph?

A. *ADCBEABCA*

B. *ABCDAEC*

C. *BACBADCAD*

D. *BECBACDAED*

In Exercise 3, select the answer choice that is best.

3 You want to make a graph to represent 8 people in a room, where each person knows 4 other people. How many vertices would the graph have?

A. 4   **B.** 8   **C.** 16   **D.** 32

In Exercises 4–5, solve each problem and clearly show all necessary work.

4 A simple maze is shown below.

	1	
2	3	4
5	6	7
8	9	10

Draw a vertex-edge graph that represents the maze with vertices 1 through 10 and an edge for each doorway between each section of the maze. Is it possible to go through each doorway exactly once? Explain your answer.

5 A vertex-edge graph has four vertices. What is the minimum number of edges the graph can have if it has an Euler circuit? Explain your answer and give an example.

DIRECTIONS FOR QUESTIONS 1–21: For each of the questions below, select the answer choice that is best for each case.

1 If two planes intersect, then they intersect in exactly

A. one line.   C. one point.

B. one plane.   D. two points.

2 Which is a possible relationship between two acute angles?

  I vertical   III complementary

II adjacent   IV supplementary

A. I and II only   C. I, II, and III only

B. I and III only   D. I, II, III, and IV

3 In the figure below, $\ell \parallel m$ and $m\angle 1 = 48°$. Which other numbered angles have a measure of 48°?

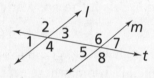

A. $\angle 2, \angle 4,$ and $\angle 8$

B. $\angle 2, \angle 4, \angle 6,$ and $\angle 8$

C. $\angle 3, \angle 5,$ and $\angle 7$

D. $\angle 3, \angle 4, \angle 5,$ and $\angle 6$

4 The lengths of two sides of a triangle are 5 and 8. Which is not a possible length for the third side?

A. 5   B. 8   C. 12   D. 13

5 Given that $\overrightarrow{KM}$ bisects $\angle JKL$ and $m\angle JKM = 74°$, then $m\angle JKL =$

A. 26°   C. 106°

B. 37°   D. 148°

6 If both pairs of opposite sides of a quadrilateral are congruent, then the quadrilateral must be a

A. rectangle.   C. parallelogram.

B. square.   D. trapezoid.

7 Quadrilateral $PQRS$ is an isosceles trapezoid with bases $\overline{PQ}$ and $\overline{SR}$. Given that $m\angle S = 118°$, what is $m\angle R$?

A. 59°   C. 118°

B. 62°   D. 121°

8 What is the measure of each exterior angle of a regular hexagon?

A. 45°   C. 72°

B. 60°   D. 120°

9 In the figure below, it is given that $\overline{AD}$ and $\overline{BE}$ intersect at point C and that $\overline{AC} \cong \overline{DC}$. Which additional information would not help you show that $\triangle ABC \cong \triangle DCE$?

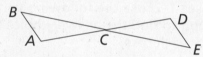

A. $\overline{AB} \cong \overline{DE}$

B. $\overline{AB} \parallel \overline{DE}$

C. $\angle CBA \cong \angle CED$

D. Point C is the midpoint of $\overline{BE}$.

10 Which of the following justifies the conclusion $\triangle VWZ \sim \triangle VXY$?

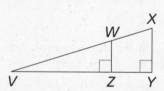

A. AA Similarity Postulate

B. SSS Similarity Theorem

C. SAS Similarity Theorem

D. definition of similar polygons

11 In which type of quadrilateral are the diagonals not necessarily perpendicular?

A. rectangle   C. kite

B. square   D. rhombus

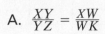

12 This figure is a trapezoid with congruent sides as marked. Which statement is false?

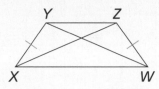

A. $\overline{YZ} \cong \overline{XW}$

B. $\overline{XZ} \cong \overline{WY}$

C. $m\angle XYZ = m\angle WZY$

D. $m\angle XYZ + m\angle YXW = 180°$

13 Find x.

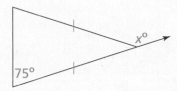

A. 75°   C. 150°

B. 30°   D. 105°

14 Identify the largest angle of $\triangle ABC$.

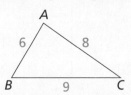

A. $\angle C$ C. $\angle B$

B. $\angle A$ D. All angles are equal in measure.

15 Using only the markings shown, the triangles below are congruent by which postulate or theorem?

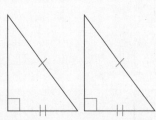

A. HL   C. HAL

B. SSA   D. CPCTC

16 Which proportion is not true for the figure?

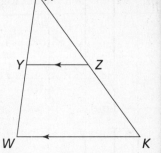

A. $\dfrac{XY}{YZ} = \dfrac{XW}{WK}$

B. $\dfrac{WY}{KZ} = \dfrac{XY}{XZ}$

C. $\dfrac{XY}{XZ} = \dfrac{ZK}{YW}$

D. $\dfrac{XY}{XW} = \dfrac{YZ}{WK}$

17 If all sides of a quadrilateral are congruent and opposite sides are parallel, the figure must be a

A. rhombus.   C. rectangle.

B. parallelogram.   D. trapezoid.

18 The lengths of two sides of a triangle are 5 inches and 8 inches. Which can be the length of the third side?

A. 2 in.   B. 13 in.   C. 15 in.   D. 7 in.

19 The figure to the right is a regular hexagon. Find the value of x.

A. 120°   C. 45°

B. 60°   D. 135°

20 The length of a side of a regular decagon is 11 centimeters. What is the perimeter of the decagon?

A. 132 cm   C. 110 cm

B. 220 cm   D. 55 cm

21 Given the triangle below, which is the range of all possible values of y?

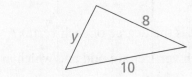

A. $2 < y < 18$ C. $2 < y < 10$

B. $8 < y < 10$ D. $y > 18$

DIRECTIONS FOR 22–24: Solve each problem and show your work.

22 *ABCD* is a parallelogram.

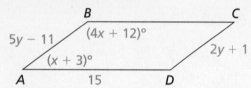

- Find *x*.

- Find *y*.

- Find *AB* and *CD*.

- Find $m\angle A$ and $m\angle B$.

23 $\triangle JKM$ is an isosceles triangle with base $\overline{KM}$. $\overline{JL}$ bisects $\angle KJM$ and $\angle K = 71°$.

- Find $m\angle JLK$.

- Find $m\angle M$.

- Find $m\angle KJM$.

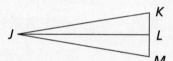

24 Consider the following vertex-edge graph.

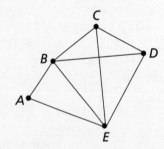

- Describe a situation that could be represented by the vertex-edge graph.

- What is the degree of each vertex?

- Which vertices are odd and which are even?

- Does the vertex-edge graph have a Euler path? Explain.

11 Geometry and Measurement

NEW JERSEY

Kingda Ka

In 2005, the Kingda Ka roller coaster in Jackson, New Jersey opened to delight thrill-seekers from around the world. With a maximum height of 456 feet, it is one of the tallest and fastest roller coasters in the world. It travels at a top speed of 128 miles per hour.

The steel coaster uses a hydraulic launch mechanism to quickly accelerate the speed of the train. The train goes from 0 to 128 miles per hour in 3.3 seconds. At the end of the launch track, the train climbs a 90-degree vertical hill and then plunges vertically in a three-quarter spiral.

The coaster then goes up a 129-foot hill before returning to the station. Employing more recent technology, Kingda Ka uses a magnetic braking system, which provides a high degree of safety for its riders.

11.1 Measurement and Error

New Jersey Standards

4.1.C.1 Assessing amount of error

4.2.D.2.1 Degree of accuracy

There are two systems of measurement. The **metric system** is used in almost all of the countries in the world, but in the United States the **Customary** or **English system** is used.

The chart below shows common metric and customary (English) units of measure.

Measure	Metric	Customary
Length	10 millimeters (mm) = 1 centimeter (cm) 100 cm = 1 meter (m) 1000 m = 1 kilometer (km)	12 inches (in.) = 1 foot (ft) 3 feet (ft) = 1 yard (yd) 36 in. = 1 yd 5280 ft =1 mile (mi) 1760 yd = 1 mi
Area	100 square millimeters (mm^2) = 1 sq. cm (cm^2) 10,000 cm^2 = 1 sq. meter (m^2)	144 sq. in. ($in.^2$) = 1 sq. ft (ft^2) 9 ft^2 = 1 sq. yd = (yd^2) 4,840 yd^2 = 1 acre
Volume	10,000 cubic millimeters (mm^3) = 1 cubic cm (cm^3) 1,000,000 cm^3 = 1 cubic meter (m^3)	1,728 cubic in. ($in.^3$) = 1 cubic ft (ft^3) 27 ft^3 = 1 cubic yd (yd^3)
Mass or Weight	1000 milligrams (mg) = 1 gram (g) 1000 g = 1 kilogram (kg) 1000 kg = 1 metric ton	16 ounces (oz) = 1 pound (lb) 2000 lb = 1 ton (t)
Liquid Volume (Capacity)	1000 milliliters (mL) = 1 liter (L)	8 fluid ounces (fl oz) = 1 cup (c) 2 cups =1 pint (pt) 2 pt = 1 quart (qt) 4 qt = 1 gallon (gal)

Go Online
PHSchool.com

Visit: PHSchool.com
Web Code: ayp-0767

It is important that you have an idea of the relative size of the different measurements in both the metric and customary systems of measurement. Although it is not usually recommended that you convert a metric unit to a customary unit, it helps to understand how the measurements in each system compare. For example, 1 inch is approximately the same as 2.5 centimeters, and 1 meter is just a little bit longer than 1 yard.

When you measure an object, you should choose an appropriate unit with which to measure. A long distance should be measured in miles or kilometers rather than inches or centimeters. A small object would be measured in inches or centimeters rather than miles or kilometers.

Note

For example, the distance from New York to California should be measured in miles or kilometers. The length of a pencil should be measured in inches or centimeters.

Often it is necessary to convert within the same system. To change a given measurement from one unit to another, you can use a process called **dimensional analysis.** This process involves multiplying the given measurement by a conversion factor. A **conversion factor** is a ratio of two measurements that is equal to 1.

For example, 12 in. = 1 ft, so $\frac{12 \text{ in.}}{1 \text{ ft}} = 1$.

Since a conversion factor is equal to 1, the value of the measurement does not change. The following examples show how to use dimensional analysis to convert various measurements.

Go Online
PHSchool.com
Visit: PHSchool.com
Web Code: ayp-0049

EXAMPLES 1 and 2 **Using dimensional analysis to convert measurements**

1 Use dimensional analysis to convert 15 quarts to gallons.

■ SOLUTION

$15 \text{ qt} = \frac{15 \text{ qt}}{1} \cdot \frac{1 \text{ gal}}{4 \text{ qt}}$ ← Use the conversion factor for changing quarts to gallons, $\frac{1 \text{ gal}}{4 \text{ qt}}$.

$= \frac{15 \text{ qt} \cdot 1 \text{ gal}}{1 \cdot 4 \text{ qt}}$ ← Divide the common units.

$= \frac{15}{4} \text{ gal} = 3\frac{3}{4} \text{ gal}$ ← Simplify.

2 How many kilometers are in 20,000 meters?

■ SOLUTION

$20{,}000 \text{ m} = \frac{20{,}000 \text{ m}}{1} \cdot \frac{1 \text{ km}}{1{,}000 \text{ m}}$ ← Use the conversion factor for changing meters to kilometers, $\frac{1 \text{ km}}{1{,}000 \text{ m}}$.

$= \frac{20{,}000 \text{ m} \cdot 1 \text{ km}}{1{,}000 \text{ m}}$ ← Divide the common factors and units.

$= 20 \text{ km}$ ← Simplify.

All measurements are approximations. If you measure a paper clip with a ruler that is calibrated in $\frac{1}{4}$ inches, it will not be as precise as measuring the same paper clip with a ruler calibrated in millimeters. The paper clip is too small to measure precisely in $\frac{1}{4}$ inches.

Precision in measurement is how exact the measurement is. When comparing measurements, the one that uses the smallest unit of measure is the more precise measurement.

Go Online
PHSchool.com
Visit: PHSchool.com
Web Code: ayp-0815

EXAMPLES 3 through 5 **Choosing the more precise measurement**

Choose the more precise measurement.

3 10 oz or 1 cup

■ SOLUTION

An ounce is a smaller unit than a cup, so **10 oz** is more precise than 1 cup.

4 10.6 kg or 140 g

■ SOLUTION

A gram is a smaller unit than a kilogram, so **140 g** is more precise than 10.6 kg.

5 $30\frac{1}{3}$ yd or 45 yd

■ SOLUTION

Both are measured in yards, so neither is more precise.

The difference between a measurement and its actual value is called the **error** of the measurement. The **greatest possible error** that occurs in measurement is always one-half of the unit of measure used. For example, if you measure a distance in miles, the greatest possible error in measurement is $\frac{1}{2}$ mile shorter or longer than the distance. If the same distance is measured more precisely in feet, then the greatest possible error is $\pm\frac{1}{2}$ foot.

The greatest possible error only tells you the error in the units of your measure. If you wish to find the *percent of error,* you have to compare the greatest possible error to the total measurement.

$$\text{percent of error} = \frac{\text{greatest possible error}}{\text{total measurement}}$$

Go Online
PHSchool.com
Visit: PHSchool.com
Web Code: ayp-0291

Note

When the total measurement is large, the percent of error will be small.

EXAMPLE 6   **Finding the percent of error in a measurement**

 Find the percent of error in a measurement of 200 mi.

■ SOLUTION

The greatest possible error $= \frac{1}{2}$ mi or **0.5 mi**

The percent of error $= \frac{0.5}{200} =$ **0.25%**

Errors in measurement can greatly affect computations in measurement. The less precise the measurement, the greater the percent of error will be in the calculations.

EXAMPLE 7   **Finding percent of error**

 Find the percent of error in calculating the perimeter of a square with side length 6 in. to the nearest tenth of a percent.

■ SOLUTION

Step 1 Calculate the perimeter without error.
$4s = 4(6) = 24$ in.

Step 2 The greatest possible error is **0.5 in.** Therefore,

Maximum possible perimeter = 4(6.5) or **26 in.**
Minimum possible perimeter = 4(5.5) or **22 in.**

Step 3 The amount of error will be the difference between the maximum possible perimeter and the perimeter without error.

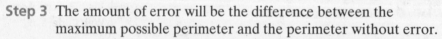

Therefore, the percent of error $= \dfrac{\text{maximum possible perimeter} - \text{perimeter without error}}{\text{perimeter without error}}$

$= \dfrac{26 \text{ in.} - 24 \text{ in.}}{24 \text{ in.}}$

$= \dfrac{2}{24} =$ **8.3%**

6 in.

Choose the letter preceding the word or expression that best completes the statement or answers the question.

1 How many milligrams are equal to 0.5 g?

   A. 0.005   **B.** 500   **C.** 5,000   **D.** 5

2 Which unit is most appropriate when measuring the length of a pencil?

   A. cm   **B.** m   **C.** L   **D.** g

3 Which measure would you consider most precise?

   A. inches   **C.** feet

   B. centimeters   **D.** meters

4 Find the greatest possible error for a measurement of $1\frac{1}{4}$ in.

   A. $\frac{1}{2}$ in.   **B.** $\frac{3}{4}$ in.   **C.** $\frac{1}{8}$ in.   **D.** $\frac{1}{16}$ in.

5 The greatest possible percent of error in a measurement of 15.3 m is

   A. $\frac{1}{2}$%   **C.** 2%

   B. 0.33%   **D.** 3%

6 Which represents the greatest possible error in a length measured to the nearest quarter-inch?

   A. $\frac{1}{2}$ in.   **B.** $\frac{3}{4}$ in.   **C.** $\frac{1}{8}$ in.   **D.** $\frac{1}{16}$ in.

7 The length and width of a rectangle have been measured to the nearest foot. The calculated perimeter is 20 ft. Which is the percent of error?

   A. 10%   **B.** 2.5%   **C.** 0.1%   **D.** 0.025%

8 Which represents 1.6 miles in feet?

   A. $1.6 \times \frac{5280}{1}$ **C.** $1.6 \times \frac{1760}{1}$

   B. $1.6 \times \frac{1}{5280}$ **D.** $5280 \times \frac{1}{1.6}$

9 Which represents the perimeter in yards of a square with sides of length 6 ft?

   A. 8 yd   **C.** 24 yd

   B. 18 yd   **D.** 72 yd

In Exercises 10–15, use dimensional analysis to find each value.

10 340 in. = ? ft   **11** 23 qt = ? gal

12 $5\frac{1}{2}$ qt = ? pt   **13** 5 km = ? m

14 6,000 ft = ? mi   **15** 355 ml = ? L

In Exercises 16–20, choose the more precise measurement.

16 15 in. or $11\frac{3}{4}$ in.   **17** 23 L or 35 mL

18 6 months or 2 years

19 10 cm or 100 mm

20 2 qt or 32 oz

In Exercises 21–26, write the given measurement in the specified unit of measure. Give answers to the nearest tenth of a unit as necessary.

21 340 in.; yards   **22** 640 yd; feet

23 245 ft; yards   **24** 2.5 miles; feet

25 7392 ft; miles   **26** 2816 yd; miles

In Exercises 27–28, use the following information.

You are riding your bike on a 3 mile trail. A sign says you have completed 1,500 ft.

27 How many feet do you have left to bike?

28 Approximately how many miles do you have left to bike?

11.2 Perimeter and Circumference

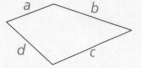
New Jersey Standards

4.2.E.2.3 Perimeter and circumuference of plane figures

The **perimeter** of a plane figure is the distance around it. The perimeter of a polygon is the sum of the lengths of its sides. For the quadrilateral below the perimeter is given by the sum $a + b + c + d$.

Perimeter of Rectangles and Regular Polygons

The perimeter P of a rectangle with length l and width w is given by either $P = 2l + 2w$, or $P = 2(l + w)$.

The perimeter P of a regular polygon with n sides each side s units long is given by $P = ns$.

In particular, the perimeter P of a square whose sides are each s units long is given by $P = 4s$. Since the sides of a rhombus are equal in length, the perimeter of a rhombus whose sides are each s units long is also given by $4s$.

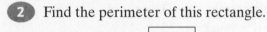

EXAMPLES 1 through 4   **Finding the perimeter of a polygon**

1 Find the perimeter of this polygon.

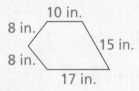

- **SOLUTION**
Perimeter: $(8 + 8 + 10 + 15 + 17)$ in. = 58 in.

2 Find the perimeter of this rectangle.

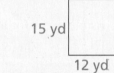

- **SOLUTION**
Perimeter: $2(12 + 15)$ yd = 54 yd

3 Find the perimeter of a rhombus whose sides are each 7 m long.

- **SOLUTION**
Perimeter: $4(7)$ m = 28 m

4 Find the perimeter of a regular hexagon whose sides are each 9 units long.

- **SOLUTION**
Perimeter: $6(9)$ units = 54 units

A circle is the set of all points in a plane that are a fixed distance from a fixed point in the plane called its **center.** Any segment whose endpoints are the center and a point of the circle is called a **radius.** A **diameter** is a segment that contains the center and whose endpoints are points of the circle.

Note

The diameter d of a given circle is twice its radius r; that is, $d = 2r$.

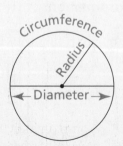

The **circumference** of a circle is the distance around the outside of the circle. It can also be called the perimeter of a circle. The circumference is measured in linear units.

Circumference of a Circle

The circumference C of a circle with radius r and diameter d is given by $C = 2\pi r$, or $C = \pi d$.

Go Online
PHSchool.com
Visit: PHSchool.com
Web Code: ayp-0089

EXAMPLE 5   Finding the circumference of a circle

5   Find the circumference of a circle with radius of 7 units. Use $\pi = 3.14$.

■ SOLUTION

Since the radius is given, use $C = 2\pi r$.

$$2(\pi)7 = 14\pi = 43.96$$

If you use a calculator, you might see a display like the one shown here. To the nearest hundredth, the circumference is **43.96 units**.

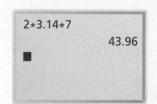

2*3.14*7
                43.96
■

The following examples show how you can apply the concepts of perimeter and circumference to solve problems.

EXAMPLES 6 and 7   Solving problems involving perimeter and circumference

6   The perimeter of a pentagon is 144 ft. Two of its sides are congruent. The other three sides have lengths 25 ft, 40 ft, and 30 ft. What is the length of each of the congruent sides?

■ SOLUTION

Let x represent the length of one of the congruent sides. Use an equation.

$$25 + 40 + 30 + x + x = 144 \rightarrow x = 24.5$$

The length of each of the congruent sides is **24.5 ft**.

7   Using $\pi = 3.14$ estimate the radius and diameter of a circle whose circumference is 220 yd.

■ SOLUTION

Use the formula for circumference.

$$220 = \pi \times d \qquad \leftarrow \text{Use } C = \pi d.$$
$$d = 220 \div \pi$$

$$d = \frac{220}{\pi}$$

The diameter is **about 70 yd** and the radius is **about 35 yd**.

Note

The relationship $d = 2r$ can be written as $r = \frac{d}{2}$ by solving for r in terms of d.

When you solve problems involving perimeters of irregular-shaped geometric figures, be careful to only add the lengths of sides around the outside of the figure.

EXAMPLE 8   **Solving problems with perimeter and multiple polygons**

 In the diagram at the right, four regular hexagons are arranged so that sides coincide as shown. Dashed segments show where the hexagons join. The lengths of all sides are 2 units. Which represents the perimeter of the single polygon formed by these hexagons?

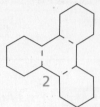

A. 36 units   **B.** 45 units   **C.** 48 units   **D.** 56 units

■ **SOLUTION**

The perimeter of one hexagon is 6(2) units, or 12 units. The total perimeter of the four hexagons is 4(12) units, or 48 units. Since six sides are not part of the perimeter, and each side is 2 units long, subtract 6(2) units, or 12 units. The correct choice is A.

Sometimes you must first convert units of measurement before solving a problem.

EXAMPLE 9   **Finding perimeter or circumference in different units of measure**

 A garden is shaped like three semicircles arranged along the sides of an equilateral triangle whose sides are 6 ft long. To the nearest tenth of a yard, how much fencing is needed for the perimeter of this garden?

■ **SOLUTION**

A semicircle is half of a circle. The three semicircles together make 1.5 circles with diameter 6 ft.

Step 1 Write 6 ft as a number of yards. $6ft \cdot \frac{1\,yd}{3\,ft} \rightarrow 2\,yd$

Step 2 Use the formula $C = \pi d$.
Find the total length of $1.5 \times \pi \times 2 = 3\pi$
1.5 semicircles with diameter 2 yd.

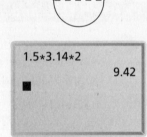

To the nearest tenth of a yard: *9.4 yd of fencing will be needed.*
(A calculator solution is also shown.)

Practice

Choose the letter preceding the word or expression that best completes the statement or answers the question.

1 Which represents the side length of an equilateral triangle with a perimeter of 7.5 cm?

A. 2.25 cm   **C.** 2.5 cm

B. 7.5 cm   **D.** 22.5 cm

2 Given $P = 2l + 2w$, which expression represents w?

A. $P - 2l$ **C.** $P - 2w$

B. $\frac{P - 2l}{2}$ **D.** $\frac{P - 2w}{2}$

3 Which represents the circumference of a circle with a radius of 15 cm?

   A. 2×15 **C.** $15 \times \pi$

   B. $2 \times 15 \times \pi$ **D.** $\frac{2 \times 15}{\pi}$

4 A garden is in the shape of a regular pentagon with side lengths of 13 ft. Which represents the perimeter of the garden in feet?

   A. 5×13 **C.** 13^2

   B. 3×13 **D.** 5×13^2

In Exercises 5–8, find the perimeter of each rectangle.

5 length: 7 cm; width: 6 cm

6 length: 11 m; width: 9 m

7 length: 17 cm; width: 3 cm

8 length: 4 ft; width: 10.5 ft

In Exercises 9–12, find the circumference of each circle in terms of π and to the nearest hundredth of a unit.

9 radius: 8 cm

10 diameter: 1.7 m

11 diameter: 0.9 m

12 radius: 2.1 m

In Exercises 13–19, solve the problem. Clearly show all necessary work.

13 In the figure below, all angles are right angles. Find the perimeter of the polygon.

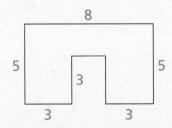

14 Find the perimeter of a regular hexagon whose sides are 4 units long.

15 The circumference of a circle is 26π. Find the radius and the diameter of the circle.

16 To the nearest tenth of a unit, what is the radius of a circle whose circumference is 10 units?

17 By how much does the circumference of a circle with a radius of 31 in. exceed that of a circle with a radius of 22 in.?

18 What is the perimeter in yards of a square whose sides are 4 feet long?

19 The width of a rectangle is 6 m and the perimeter is 24 m. What is the area of the rectangle?

In Exercises 20–22, find the value of the variable.

20 The perimeter of the rectangle is 16 units.

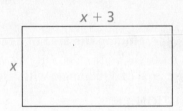

21 The perimeter of the regular pentagon is 54 units.

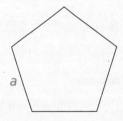

22 The perimeter of the figure is 60 units. Not drawn to scale.

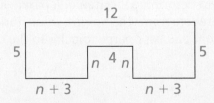

305

11.3 Area

The **area** of any plane geometric figure or polygon is the number of non-overlapping square units enclosed by the figure.

For example, to find the **area of a square** with 4 units on one side, you can draw a diagram to represent the figure and count the squares.

If you count the squares you can see the area will contain 16 square units. The same result can be obtained by multiplying the length of a side of the square by itself. Therefore, the formula for the area of a square is $s \times s$ or s^2.

Note

Lengths are measured in units, while areas are measured in square units.

$$A_{square} = s^2$$

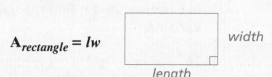

If you look at a rectangle, its length and width are perpendicular to each other just as in a square. Therefore, the length and width are used in the formula for area. Note that in the figure below, the length is the *base* of the rectangle and the width is the *height* of the rectangle. Therefore, the formula for the area of a rectangle is *lw*.

$$A_{rectangle} = lw$$

width

length

Go Online
PHSchool.com

Visit: PHSchool.com
Web Code: ayp-0363

 EXAMPLE 1   **Finding the area of a rectangle**

Find the area of a rectangle with a length of 3.5 ft and a width of 6 in.

■ **SOLUTION 1**	■ **SOLUTION 2**
Use dimensional analysis so that the units agree.	Use dimensional analysis so that the units agree.
Convert 6 inches to feet.	Convert 3.5 feet to inches.

$6 \text{ in.} \times \frac{1 \text{ ft}}{12 \text{ in.}} = \frac{6}{12} \text{ ft} = \frac{1}{2} \text{ ft}$ $\qquad$ $3.5 \text{ in.} \times \frac{12 \text{ in.}}{1 \text{ ft}} = 42 \text{ in.}$

Therefore, $l = 3.5$ ft and $w = \frac{1}{2}$ ft $\qquad$ Therefore, $l = 42$ in. and $w = 6$ in.

Since $A_{rectangle} = lw$, $\qquad$ Since $A_{rectangle} = lw$,

$A_{rectangle} = 3.5\left(\frac{1}{2}\right)\text{ft}^2 = 1.75 \text{ ft}^2$ $\qquad$ $A_{rectangle} = 42(6) = 252 \text{ in.}^2$

In order to determine the area of a parallelogram, you must know the height of the parallelogram. The **height,** or **altitude,** is the length of a segment drawn from one base perpendicular to the other base.

In the figures below, you can see that the sides of this parallelogram are *not* perpendicular to each other.

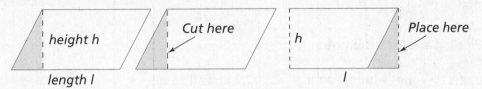

You can see how the parallelogram on the left becomes the rectangle on the right. Then the area of a parallelogram = *base* × *height*.

$$A_{parallelogram} = bh$$

EXAMPLES 2 and 3   **Finding areas of simple polygons**

 Find the area of a square with side length 6.4 cm.

■ **SOLUTION**
$A = 6.4^2 = 40.96$

The area is 40.96 cm².

 Find the area of a parallelogram with base 17 units and height 12 units.

■ **SOLUTION**
$A = (17)(12) = 204$

The area is 204 units².

Recall that a trapezoid is a quadrilateral with one pair of parallel sides. These sides are the bases of the trapezoid. The height of the trapezoid is the perpendicular distance between the bases. The figure at the right shows two congruent trapezoids, side by side, forming a parallelogram. The height of the trapezoid is the same as the height of the parallelogram.

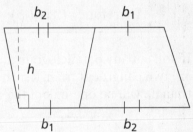

The area of the entire parallelogram is the height h times the sum of the bases $b_1 + b_2$ or $h(b_1 + b_2)$. The area of each trapezoid is one-half of the area of the parallelogram. Therefore, the $A_{trapezoid} = \frac{1}{2} h(b_1 + b_2)$ or

$$A_{trapezoid} = \frac{h(b_1 + b_2)}{2}.$$

You can use area formulas to help solve problems involving multiple polygons.

EXAMPLE 4   **Finding an area when more than one polygon is involved**

 In the figure at the right, $\overline{BD} \parallel \overline{AE}$. Find the area of trapezoid *CDEA*.

■ **SOLUTION**

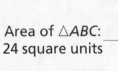

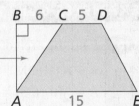

Area of △ABC: 24 square units

The bases of trapezoid *CDEA* are $\overline{AE}$ and $\overline{CD}$. Its height is *AB*. Use the area formula for a triangle to find *AB*.

$$\frac{1}{2} \cdot 6 \cdot (AB) = 24 \rightarrow AB = 8$$

Use the area formula for a trapezoid to find the area of *CDEA*.

$$A = \frac{1}{2} \times 8 \times (5 + 15) = 80$$

The area of trapezoid *CDEA* is 80 square units.

The area of a rhombus can be calculated by finding one-half of the product of its diagonals.

$$A_{rhombus} = \tfrac{1}{2}d_1 \cdot d_2$$

EXAMPLE 5   **Finding area of a rhombus**

5 Find the area of a rhombus whose diagonals are 12.4 in. and 15 in.

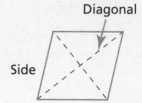

■ **SOLUTION**

Step 1 Estimate the area of the rhombus.

$$A_{rhombus} = \tfrac{1}{2}d_1 \cdot d_2$$

$$\approx \tfrac{1}{2}(12)(10 + 5)$$

$$\approx \tfrac{1}{2}(120 + 60)$$

$$\approx \tfrac{1}{2}(180) \approx 90 \text{ in.}^2$$

Step 2 Calculate the area of the rhombus.

$$A_{rhombus} = \tfrac{1}{2}d_1 \cdot d_2$$

Therefore, $\tfrac{1}{2}(12.4)(15) = 93$ in.^{2}

If you cut any parallelogram along one of its diagonals, the figures formed are two congruent triangles. Therefore, the formula for the area of each triangle will be one-half of the area of the parallelogram.

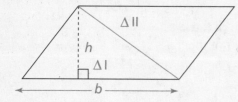   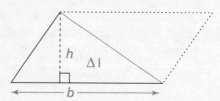

Since area of $\triangle$I + $\triangle$II = Area of the parallelogram,
and $A_{\textbf{parallelogram}} = \textbf{\textit{bh}}$, then $A_{\textbf{triangle}} = \frac{bh}{2}$ or $\frac{1}{2}\textbf{\textit{bh}}$.

You can find the area of an equilateral triangle given the length of a side.

Note

An alternate area formula can be used in an equilateral triangle if only one side is known.

$A_{\substack{equilateral \\ triangle}} = \frac{s^2\sqrt{3}}{4}$.

EXAMPLES 6 and 7   **Finding area of triangles**

6 Find the area of a triangle with base 9 and height 6.3.

■ **SOLUTION**

$A = \tfrac{1}{2}(9)(6.3) = 28.35$

The area is 28.35 units^2.

7 Find the area (to the nearest tenth) of an equilateral triangle whose side length is 6 cm.

■ **SOLUTION**

$$A_{equilateral\ triangle} = \frac{s^2\sqrt{3}}{4} \text{ or } \frac{6^2\sqrt{3}}{4} = \frac{36\sqrt{3}}{4} = 9\sqrt{3} \approx 15.6\,cm^2$$

You may need to use an equation to solve an area problem.

  The area of the trapezoid at the right is 144 square units.
Find b, the length of the shorter base.

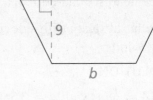

■ **SOLUTION**

Use the formula for the area of a trapezoid. Solve for b.

$$\tfrac{1}{2} \cdot 9(b + 21) = 144$$

$$b + 21 = 144 \cdot \tfrac{2}{9} \qquad \leftarrow \textbf{Multiply each side by } \tfrac{2}{9}.$$

$$b + 21 = 32$$

$$b = 11$$

The shorter base b has length 11 units.

In a regular polygon, the point that is equidistant from all the vertices is called its **center**. A segment drawn from the center to the midpoint of a side is called an **apothem** of the regular polygon. Since all apothems in a given regular polygon are congruent, their common length is called *the* apothem of the polygon.

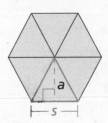

In the regular hexagon at the right, each side is s units long and the hexagon is subdivided into six triangles. The area of one triangle is $\tfrac{1}{2}as$, where a is the apothem represented by the dotted line. The area of the hexagon is given by $A = 6\left(\tfrac{1}{2}as\right) = \tfrac{1}{2} \times a \times (6s)$. If the polygon has n sides, the equation for area becomes what is shown below.

$$A = n\left(\tfrac{1}{2}as\right)$$

$$= \tfrac{1}{2} \times a \times (ns)$$

Notice that ns is the perimeter of the n-sided regular polygon. So, the equation above can be written as $A = \tfrac{1}{2}ap$, where p is the perimeter.

In the figure at the right, a circle is *circumscribed* about a regular polygon so that each vertex of the polygon is a point of the circle. If the number of sides of the polygon were increased, then the apothem would get closer to the radius of the circle and the perimeter would get closer and closer to the circumference. Using this reasoning, you can write the following equation for the area of a circle.

$$A = \tfrac{1}{2}r(2\pi r) = \pi r^2$$

Areas of Regular Polygons and Circles

The area A of a regular polygon with n sides each s units long, perimeter p, and apothem a is given by the formulas below.

$$A = \tfrac{1}{2}ans, \text{ or } A = \tfrac{1}{2}ap$$

The area A of a circle with radius r is given by the formula below.

$$A = \pi r^2$$

You can apply these formulas to find the area of all circles and regular polygons.

EXAMPLES 9 and 10   **Finding the area of a regular polygon and a circle**

To the nearest hundredth of a square unit, find the area of each figure.

9 a regular hexagon with sides of length of 7 units and apothem of $3.5\sqrt{3}$ units

■ **SOLUTION**

Use $A = \frac{1}{2}ans$ with $a = 3.5\sqrt{3}$, $n = 6$, and $s = 7$.

$A = 0.5 \times 3.5\sqrt{3} \times 6 \times 7 \approx 127.31$ square units

(A calculator solution is shown at the right.)

> 0.5*3.5*√ (3)*6*7
>   127.3057344
> ■

10 a circle whose diameter is 11 mm

■ **SOLUTION**

Use $A = \pi r^2$ with $r = \frac{11}{2}$.

$A = \pi\left(\frac{11}{2}\right)^2 \approx 94.99$ mm^2

(A calculator solution is shown at the right.)

> 3.14(11/2)^2
>   94.985

A **sector** of a circle is the part of a circle formed by two radii and the arc they intercept; it is a fractional part of a circle. A **segment** of a circle is the part of a circle formed by an arc and the chord it intercepts.

 Sector   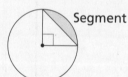 Segment

Note

Be careful not to confuse a segment of a circle with a line segment.

EXAMPLES 11 and 12   **Finding the area of a sector and a segment**

11 Find the area A of the sector. Use $\pi = 3.14$.

■ **SOLUTION**

There are 360° in a circle. So the area of the 60° sector is $\frac{60}{360}$, or $\frac{1}{6}$, the area of the circle.

$A = \frac{1}{6}(\pi \times 15^2) = \frac{225}{6} \times \pi = \frac{75}{2}\pi = 117.75$

The area of the sector is 117.75 cm^2.

12 Find the area A of the segment. Use $\pi = 3.14$.

■ **SOLUTION**

The area of the segment is $\frac{90}{360}$, or $\frac{1}{4}$, the area of the circle, less the area of the triangle.

$A = \frac{1}{4}(\pi \times 5^2) - \frac{1}{2} \times 5 \times 5$

The area is $\frac{25}{4}\pi - \frac{25}{2} = 19.625 - 12.5 = 7.125$.

Practice

Choose the letter preceding the word or expression that best completes the statement or answers the question.

1 A rectangle with perimeter 30 in. has length 10 in. Which is the area of the rectangle?

   A. 15 in.^{2} **C.** 150 in.^{2}

   B. 50 in.^{2} **D.** 300 in.^{2}

2 What is the area of a circle whose diameter is 8 ft?

   A. 12.56 ft^2 **C.** 50.24 ft^2

   B. 25.12 ft^2 **D.** 200.96 ft^2

3 What is the area of the triangle?

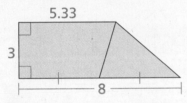

   A. 3 units^2 **C.** 6 units^2

   B. 5 units^2 **D.** 10 units^2

4 Given that the area of the circle is 4π yd^2, what is the area of the shaded region?

   A. 5.024 yd^2 **C.** 2.512 yd^2

   B. 125.6 yd^2 **D.** 12.56 yd^2

5 What is the height of a triangle whose area is 18 in.^{2} and whose base is 6 in.?

   A. 3 in.   **B.** 6 in.   **C.** 9 in.   **D.** 12 in.

6 How much greater is the area of a circle with a radius of 6 ft than the area of a circle with a radius of 2 ft?

   A. 12.56 ft^2 **C.** 100.48 ft^2

   B. 25.12 ft^2 **D.** 125.6 ft^2

In Exercises 7–10, find the area of each figure.

7 a circle with radius 7 in.

8 a circle with diameter 16 ft

9 a parallelogram with base 72 in. and height 2.5 yd

10 a parallelogram with base 20 yd and height 15 ft

In Exercises 11–17, find the area of the shaded region. Round answers to the nearest tenth when necessary.

11

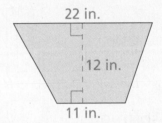

12

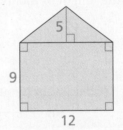

13

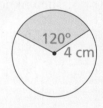

14

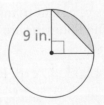

15 square and semicircle

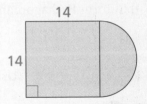

16 regular hexagon

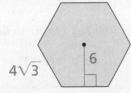

17 quarter-circle in a square

11.4 The Pythagorean Theorem

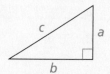
The figure shown is a right triangle with sides a, b, and c. The side opposite the right angle, called the **hypotenuse,** is the longest side. Each of the sides, a and b, that form the right angle, is called a **leg** of the right triangle.

You can use the Pythagorean Theorem to find an unknown side length of a right triangle.

The Pythagorean Theorem

In any right triangle, the sum of the squares of the lengths of the legs is equal to the square of the length of the hypotenuse. That is, $a^2 + b^2 = c^2$.

EXAMPLES 1 and 2 Finding lengths of sides in a right triangle by using the Pythagorean Theorem

Find the unknown to the nearest hundredth.

1 Find n in the right triangle below.

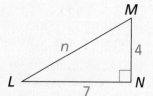

2 Find z in the right triangle below.

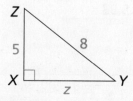

■ SOLUTION

The unknown n is the length of the hypotenuse.

$$n^2 = 7^2 + 4^2$$
$$n^2 = 65$$
$$n = \pm\sqrt{65} \approx \pm 8.06$$
$$n = \sqrt{65} \text{ units, or about } 8.06 \text{ units}$$

■ SOLUTION

The unknown z is the length of a leg.

$$8^2 = z^2 + 5^2$$
$$39 = z^2$$
$$z = \pm\sqrt{39} \approx \pm 6.24$$
$$z = \sqrt{39} \text{ units, or about } 6.24 \text{ units}$$

If the lengths of all three sides of a right triangle are counting numbers, they form a **Pythagorean Triple.** The following are some examples of side lengths that form Pythagorean Triples.

a) 3, 4, 5   b) 5, 12, 13   c) 8, 15, 17   d) 7, 24, 25

Go Online
PHSchool.com
Visit: PHSchool.com
Web Code: ayp-0852

EXAMPLE 3 Using Pythagorean Triples ratios

3 Find the hypotenuse of a right triangle whose legs are 60 and 144.

■ SOLUTION

$$\frac{60}{144} = \frac{12(5)}{12(12)} = \frac{5}{12}$$ 60 and 144 are in the ratio of 5 to 12.

Therefore, the hypotenuse = 12(13) or 156.

312

The Converse of the Pythagorean Theorem

If a, b, and c are the lengths of the sides of a triangle such that $a^2 + b^2 = c^2$, then the triangle is a right triangle with hypotenuse of length c.

Since the hypotenuse is always the longest side of a right triangle, you can use the Converse of the Pythagorean Theorem to find out if a triangle is a right triangle.

EXAMPLE 4 **Determining if three positive numbers determine a right triangle**

 Do 5, 12, and 14 determine a right triangle?

■ **SOLUTION**

Since the hypotenuse of a right triangle must be the longest side, check to see if $5^2 + 12^2$ equals 14^2.

$$5^2 + 12^2 = 169 \qquad 14^2 = 196$$

Since $169 \neq 196$, these numbers *do not determine a right triangle.*

The next example shows how you can use the Pythagorean Theorem to solve problems.

Visit: PHSchool.com
Web Code: ayp-0431

EXAMPLE 5 **Solving problems involving the Pythagorean Theorem**

5 A ladder is placed against the side of a building. To climb the ladder safely, the ladder must be placed against the building at a height that is three times the distance from the foot of the ladder to the base of the building. To the nearest tenth of a foot, how far from the base of a building should the foot of a 24-foot ladder be placed to match safety recommendations?

■ **SOLUTION**

Step 1 Draw a sketch. Let x represent the distance from the foot of the ladder to the base of the building.

Step 2 Use the Pythagorean Theorem to solve for x.

$$x^2 + (3x)^2 = 24^2$$
$$10x^2 = 576$$
$$x^2 = 57.6$$
$$x \approx 7.6$$

The foot of the ladder should be placed about 7.6 feet from the base of the building.

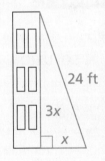

To apply the Pythagorean Theorem, you must know the lengths of two sides of a right triangle. However, if you are only given the length of one side of a right triangle, you can find the other side by knowing the values of its complementary angles.

Certain right triangles have special properties that make it easier to find the length of a side. You can use formulas based on these special properties to find the leg and hypotenuse of triangles with angle measures 45°-45°-90° and 30°-60°-90°.

An isosceles right triangle with each base angle of 45° is called a 45°-45°-90° triangle. Since both of its base angles are congruent, both of its legs are also congruent.

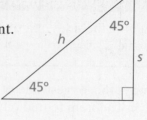

Let each leg = s.
Then
$$h^2 = s^2 + s^2$$
$$h^2 = 2s^2$$
$$\sqrt{h^2} = \sqrt{2s^2}$$
$$h = s\sqrt{2}$$

In a 45°-45°-90° triangle, the length of the hypotenuse is the length of the leg times $\sqrt{2}$. **hypotenuse = leg · $\sqrt{2}$; $h = s · \sqrt{2}$**

Note

If you know the hypotenuse, solving for s gives $s = \frac{1}{2}h\sqrt{2}$.

EXAMPLE 6   **Finding lengths in a 45°-45°-90° triangle**

6 Find the length of the hypotenuse of the given right triangle with side length 7.5.

■ **SOLUTION**

Since $h = s\sqrt{2}$, then $h = 7.5\sqrt{2} \approx 10.6$.

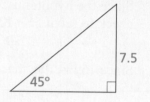

An easy way to work with a 30°-60°-90° right triangle is to make it a part of an equilateral triangle with sides $2x$ and altitude a. The altitude a bisects the vertex angle and the base. Therefore, the side opposite the 30° angle = $\frac{1}{2}(2x) = x$.

The length of the hypotenuse is two times the length of the side opposite the 30° angle (the shorter side). Therefore, $h = 2x$.

The length of the side opposite the 60° angle (the longer side) is $\sqrt{3}$ times the length of the side opposite the 30° angle. Therefore, $a = x\sqrt{3}$.

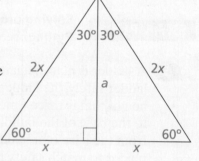

EXAMPLE 7   **Finding lengths in a 30°-60°-90° triangle**

7 Find the missing lengths in the given right triangle with hypotenuse 14 units.

■ **SOLUTION**

x = length of shorter leg = $\frac{1}{2}h$

$x = \frac{1}{2}(14) = 7$

y = length of longer leg = length of shorter leg $\sqrt{3}$
$y = 7\sqrt{3} \approx 12.1$ units

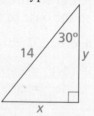

Right Triangle Theorems

45°-45°-90° Triangles
The hypotenuse of a 45°-45°-90° triangle with side length s and hypotenuse h is given by $h = \sqrt{2}s$.

30°-60°-90° Triangles
The side opposite the 30° angle (the shorter side) = $\frac{1}{2}$ hypotenuse, or the hypotenuse = 2 times the shorter leg. The side opposite the 60° angle is $\frac{1}{2}$ hypotenuse times $\sqrt{3}$, or the longer leg = shorter leg times $\sqrt{3}$.

Practice

Choose the letter preceding the word or expression that best completes the statement or answers the question.

1 Which of the following is the measure of the side of a square whose diagonal is 14?

A. 7   **B.** $7\sqrt{2}$ **C.** 14   **D.** $7\sqrt{3}$

2 What is the length of a diagonal of a square whose sides are 5 units long?

A. 5   **C.** $5\sqrt{3}$

B. $5\sqrt{2}$ **D.** 50

3 Which three lengths do not determine a right triangle?

A. 6, 8, and 10

B. 5, 12, and 13

C. 3, 4, and 7

D. 7, 24, and 25

4 Find the altitude of an equilateral triangle with side length 9 to the nearest tenth.

A. 9   **C.** 6.4

B. 4.5   **D.** 7.8

5 Find the perimeter of a right triangle whose leg lengths are 5 and 12 units.

A. 40   **B.** 34   **C.** 30   **D.** 17

6 Which represents x in this right triangle?

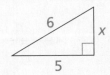

A. $6 - 5$

B. $6^2 - 5^2$

C. $\sqrt{6^2 - 5^2}$

D. $\sqrt{6^2 + 5^2}$

In Exercises 7–9, *ABC* is a right triangle with hypotenuse of length *c* and legs of lengths *a* and *b*. Find the unknown length exactly and round to the nearest tenth as necessary.

7 $a = 10$ and $b = 12$

8 $a = 12$ and $c = 13$

9 $a = 5\sqrt{3}$ and $c = 10\sqrt{3}$

In Exercises 10–13, find the missing value to solve the problem.

10 A garden is in the shape of a right triangle. One leg of the triangle is 6 feet long and the hypotenuse is 12 feet long. To the nearest tenth of a foot, how long is the third side?

11 In an isosceles right triangle, the length of the hypotenuse is 10 units. How long is each leg? Give an exact answer.

12 In a right triangle, the acute angles measure 30° and 60°. The shortest side is 6 ft long. Find the lengths of the other sides to the nearest tenth of a foot.

13 In a rhombus, the sides are 14 in. long. Two intersecting sides form a 60° angle. What is the length of each diagonal? What is the area of the rhombus? Give exact answers.

In Exercises 14–17, find the value of the variable(s). Give exact answers.

14 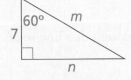   **15**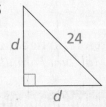

16 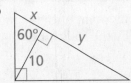   **17**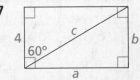

315

11.5 Distance and Midpoint

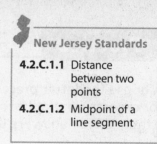

New Jersey Standards

4.2.C.1.1 Distance between two points

4.2.C.1.2 Midpoint of a line segment

You can use the Pythagorean Theorem to find the distance between any two points in the coordinate plane. If you graph any two points in the coordinate plane such that the line that connects them is not parallel to either axis, you can form a right triangle. The distance between the two points will be the length of the line segment joining those points.

In the figure at the right, you can see that if the coordinates of P are (x_1, y_1) and the coordinates of Q are (x_2, y_2), then the coordinates of R will be (x_2, y_1). With these coordinates known, you can determine the length of PR and QR by finding the difference in the x and y values.

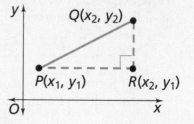

Using the Pythagorean theorem, you can then find the distance between P and Q. This is called the *Distance Formula*.

The Distance Formula

The distance PQ between $P(x_1, y_1)$ and $Q(x_2, y_2)$ is given by the formula below.

$$PQ = \sqrt{(x_2 - x_1)^2 + (y_2 - y_1)^2}$$

Go Online
PHSchool.com

Visit: PHSchool.com
Web Code: ayp-0360

EXAMPLE 1 | **Finding the distance between two points in the coordinate plane**

 Find the distance between $A(4, -1)$ and $B(-3, 5)$. Give an exact answer and an answer rounded to the nearest hundredth.

■ **SOLUTION**

$$AB = \sqrt{(-3 - 4)^2 + (5 - [-1])^2} = \sqrt{(-7)^2 + (6)^2} = \sqrt{85} \approx 9.22$$

The distance between A and B is $\sqrt{85}$, or about 9.22.

A midpoint of a segment in the coordinate plane is the point halfway between the endpoints of the segment. You can use the coordinates of the endpoints to find the midpoint. In the diagram at the right, the coordinates of P are (x_2, y_2), and the coordinates of Q are (x_1, y_1). The coordinates of the midpoint, M, are found by calculating the average of the x-values $\frac{x_1 + x_2}{2}$, and the average of the y-values $\frac{y_1 + y_2}{2}$.

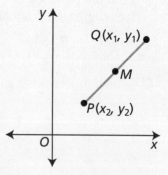

Therefore, to find the midpoint of a line segment in the coordinate plane, use the *Midpoint Formula*.

The Midpoint Formula

The coordinates of the midpoint of the segment with endpoints $P(x_1, y_1)$ and $Q(x_2, y_2)$ are given by the following.

$$\left(\frac{x_1 + x_2}{2}, \frac{y_1 + y_2}{2}\right)$$

2 Find the coordinates of the midpoint of the segment whose endpoints are $A(-2, -3)$ and $B(5, 4)$.

▪ SOLUTION

$$(x, y) = \left(\frac{-2 + 5}{2}, \frac{-3 + 4}{2}\right)$$

$$= \left(\frac{3}{2}, \frac{1}{2}\right)$$

3 The point $Z(3, -5)$ is the midpoint of the segment with endpoints $K(4, 6)$ and $P(x, y)$. Find x and y.

▪ SOLUTION

$$(3, -5) = \left(\frac{4 + x}{2}, \frac{6 + y}{2}\right)$$

$$3 = \frac{4 + x}{2} \text{ and } -5 = \frac{6 + y}{2}$$

$$x = 2 \text{ and } y = -16$$

Practice

Choose the letter preceding the word or expression that best completes the statement or answers the question.

1 Find the midpoint of a segment with endpoints $(-1, 5)$ and $(6, -3)$.

A. $\left(3\frac{1}{2}, 4\right)$ **C.** $\left(-3\frac{1}{2}, -4\right)$

B. $\left(2\frac{1}{2}, 1\right)$ **D.** $\left(-2\frac{1}{2}, -1\right)$

2 If the midpoint of a segment is $(2, 8)$, and an endpoint is $(-4, 0)$, the other endpoint is

A. $(-1, 4)$.   **C.** $(8, 16)$.

B. $(4, 8)$.   **D.** $(3, 4)$.

3 Which pair of points has $(3.5, -9)$ as the midpoint of the segment joining them?

A. $(6, -2)$ and $(10, 11)$

B. $(0, -4)$ and $(-7, 5)$

C. $(-2, -3)$ and $(9, 15)$

D. $(-1, -7)$ and $(8, -11)$

4 Which represents the midpoint of the segment with endpoints $(4, 8)$ and $(-2, 1)$?

A. $(3, 3.5)$ **C.** $(6, -0.5)$

B. $(3, 4.5)$ **D.** $(1, 4.5)$

5 Which represents the length of the segment with endpoints $(1, 3)$ and $(4, 5)$?

A. $\sqrt{13}$ **B.** 5   **C.** 13   **D.** 25

In Exercises 6–9, find the coordinates of the midpoint and the length of the segment whose endpoints are given.

6 $A(3, -2)$ and $B(5, -4)$

7 $X(9, 15)$ and $Y(-6, -2)$

8 $P(1, 2)$ and $Q(4, 6)$

9 $M(3, -4)$ and $N(8, 6)$

In Exercises 10–15, give the distance between each pair of points. Round to the nearest hundredth as necessary.

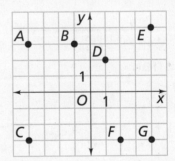

10 A and F

11 E and C

12 C and G

13 E and G

14 B and D

15 D and G

11.6 Using Geometric Models to Solve Problems

The formulas you learn in geometry can be applied to real-world situations. In the construction industry, architects and engineers use these formulas everyday. For example, if you need to know if an object will fit into a specific container, you can draw a 2-dimensional model to represent the situation. Then you can visualize the problem, making it easier to determine how to find the solution.

When modeling real-world situations, perpendicular lines will often create situations involving right triangles. In these cases, you can use the Pythagorean Theorem (or its converse) to determine the length of an unknown side of a right triangle.

Note

A scale drawing is drawn *to scale* when the objects in the model are proportionally identical in size to the objects being represented.

EXAMPLES 1 and 2   **Applying the Pythagorean Theorem**

1 To alleviate traffic, the city decides to pave a new road that connects Route 19 to Main Street, as shown in the diagram below. The construction cost has been estimated at $100 per foot. To the nearest dollar, estimate the cost for building the street. (Hint: 1 mile = 5,280 ft.)

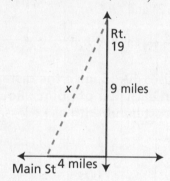

■ **SOLUTION**

Step 1

$x^2 = 9^2 + 4^2$
$x^2 = 81 + 16 = 97$
$x = \sqrt{97} \approx 9.85$ miles

Step 2

1 mile = 5,280 ft
9.85 miles = (9.85) · (5280) = 52,008 ft

Find the cost of 52,008 ft at $100 per foot
Total Cost = (5280) · (100) = $5,200,800

2 The location of Chicago and San Diego are placed on the coordinate plane with Chicago at the point (6, 5) and San Diego at the point (−2, 3). A major airline plans a route that will fly directly from Chicago to San Diego. What distance represents the flight path on the coordinate grid?

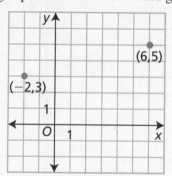

■ **SOLUTION**

You can use the Distance Formula to find the distance between the two cities.

$$d = \sqrt{(6-(-2))^2 + (5-3)^2}$$
$$= \sqrt{64 + 4} = \sqrt{68} \approx 8.25$$

Therefore, the distance that represents the flight path on the coordinate grid is 8.25 units.

The Pythagorean Theorem also applies to finding missing lengths of triangles formed in 3-dimensional figures. Often the diagonal of a rectangular face of a prism is the hypotenuse of a right triangle completed by two sides of the prism.

EXAMPLE 3   Applying the Pythagorean Theorem to a 3-dimensional problem

3 The box below is a rectangular solid. Its length is 21 in., its width is 28 in., and its height is 40 in. What is the length of the longest tube that fits into the box?

■ SOLUTION

The longest tube fits along the diagonal d_2 of the box. To find the length d_2, first find the length of a diagonal d_1 of the face.

Step 1

$d_1 = \sqrt{21^2 + 28^2}$

$\quad = \sqrt{441 + 784} = \sqrt{1225} = 35$

Step 2

$d_2 = \sqrt{35^2 + 40^2}$

$\quad = \sqrt{1224 + 1600}$

$\quad = \sqrt{2835} = 53.1$ in.

The longest tube that can fit into the box has a length of 53.1 in.

You can also model circular objects. Recall that if you know the circle's diameter or radius you can find its circumference and area, and vice versa.

EXAMPLES 4 and 5   Applying circumference and area formulas

4 The circumference around the equator of Mars is estimated to be 6800π kilometers. What is the radius of the cross section of the planet at its equator?

■ SOLUTION

You can use the formula for circumference to find the radius. Since $6800\pi = 2\pi r$,

$r = \dfrac{6800\pi}{2\pi} = 3400$ km.

5 In science class, a team of students marks the side of a wheel with a piece of chalk and then rolls the wheel in a straight line until the chalk mark returns to the same position. The team measures the distance the wheel rolls and finds that it is 35 cm. To the nearest tenth, what is the area of the wheel?

■ SOLUTION

Step 1

$\dfrac{C}{2\pi} = r$ ← Use $C = 2\pi r$ and solve for r.

$r = \dfrac{35}{2(3.14)}$ ← Substitute $C = 35$.

$\quad = \dfrac{35}{6.28}$

$\quad = 5.57$ cm

Step 2

$A = \pi r^2$

$A = 3.14(5.57)^2$ ← Use $r = 5.7$ cm from Step 1.

$\quad = 3.14(31.06)$

$\quad = 97.53 \approx 97.5$ cm^2

You can use what you know about the properties of geometric figures to compare their measurements. For example, if you know the dimensions of a rectangular prism, you can determine whether another object can fit inside the prism.

EXAMPLE 6 **Applying the circumference formula**

6 The diameter of a basketball rim is 18 in. A standard basketball has a circumference of 30 in. What is the distance between the ball and the rim in a shot in which the basketball moves through the basketball hoop exactly at the center of the rim?

basketball

■ SOLUTION

Step 1

$C = 2\pi r$ ← Find the radius of

$30 = 2(3.14)r$ the basketball.

$r = \dfrac{35}{6.28}$

$r = 4.8$ in.

Step 2

Because the diameter of the basketball rim is 18 in., its radius is 9 in.

Therefore, $9 - 4.8 = 4.2$ in.

You can also model and solve real-world problems that involve area, perimeter, and volume.

EXAMPLES 7 and 8 **Applying area and volume formulas**

7 Justin wants to use 70 ft of fencing to enclose the greatest possible area for a square garden. What dimensions should he use? What will be the area of the garden in square feet?

■ SOLUTION

Step 1

The 70 ft of fencing that Justin uses is the *perimeter* of the garden, so the length of each side s is:

$s = \dfrac{70}{4}$ ft or $s = 17.5$ ft

Each side of the garden measures 17.5 ft.

Step 2

The area of the garden is $A = s^2$

$= (17.5)^2$ or 306.25 ft^2

8 Ricardo is wrapping a gift to take to a party and needs a box for the gift. The only box he has measures 4 in. × 7 in. × 5 in. He needs a box with dimensions that have double the lengths of the box he has. What is the volume of the box Ricardo needs? How does the volume needed compare to that of the box he already has?

■ SOLUTION

Step 1

$V_{new\ box} = 8(14)(10) = 1120$ in.^{3}

Step 2

The volume of the original box is $V = 4(7)(5) = 140$ in.^{3}
Since $\frac{1120}{140} = 8$, the box is 8 times larger than the original.

Therefore, **the box Ricardo needs is 8 times that of the box he has now.**

Choose the letter preceding the word or expression that best completes the statement or answers the question.

1 The formula for the lateral area of a cone is $S.A. = \pi r \sqrt{r^2 + h^2}$. What is the lateral area of the cone pictured?

A. 86.1 cm^2

B. 347.6 cm^2

C. 429.4 cm^2

D. 6988.7 cm^2

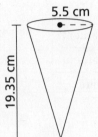

5.5 cm

19.35 cm

2 In a cube with side length x, what is the length of the indicated diagonal?

A. $2x$

B. $x\sqrt{2}$

C. $x\sqrt{3}$

D. $2x\sqrt{2}$

x

3 A pizza with a diameter of 22 in. is cut into 8 equal pieces. What is the area of each piece of pizza, approximated to the nearest tenth?

A. 17.3 in.^{3}

B. 47.5 in.^{2}

C. 138.2 in.^{2}

D. 380.1 in.^{2}

In Exercises 4–5, solve each problem. Clearly show all necessary work.

4 A circle has a circumference of 160.14 cm. What is the volume of a sphere with the same radius? (Hint: the formula for the volume of a sphere is $V = \frac{4}{3}\pi r^3$.)

5 A restaurant serves paella, a traditional Spanish dish, in large circular dishes that come in two sizes. One dish has an area of 78.5 in.^{2}, and the other has a circumference of 42.4 in. What is the difference in diameter between the two dishes?

In Exercises 6–7, use the situation described below.

In 1969, Major League Baseball decided to lower the pitcher's mound to lessen the advantage the pitcher has over the batter by appearing to tower over the batter. The old height was 15 in., and the new mound height is 10 in. The distance from home plate to the pitcher remained 60 ft., 6 in. A visual model of this situation is shown below.

—60.5 ft—

old height 15 in.

new height 10 in.

6 For a pitcher who stood 6 ft tall, how much farther did he have to pitch the ball to reach the plate in 1969 than he did previously?

7 Who has to throw the ball farther to reach the plate: A 5' 11'' pitcher in 1967 or a 6' 2'' pitcher in 1970?

In Exercises 8–9, use the situation described below.

The telephone company needs to connect a 41-ft wire from the phone box on the side of a house to a telephone pole on the street that has not yet been built. The box must be placed 35 ft up on the pole.

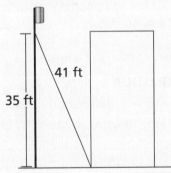

41 ft

35 ft

8 How far away from the house must the telephone company place the pole?

9 If the phone box needs to be only half as high up the pole as originally required and the length of the wire remains the same, how will this affect the distance between the pole and the house? What is the new distance? Is it double what it was in the first part? Explain.

11.7 Segments Joining Two Sides of a Triangle

New Jersey Standards

4.2.A.3.2b Applying the properties of triangles

Recall that if $\overline{DE} \parallel \overline{BC}$ in $\triangle ABC$, then $\triangle ADE$ and $\triangle ABC$ are similar. The proof is shown below.

Statement	Justification
1. $\overline{DE} \parallel \overline{BC}$	Given
2. $\angle A = \angle A$	Identity
3. $\angle D \cong \angle B$	Corresponding angles are congruent
4. $\angle E \cong \angle C$	Corresponding angles are congruent
5. $\triangle ABC \sim \triangle ADE$	Angle-Angle Similarity Postulate

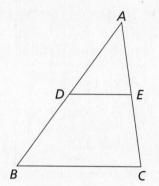

You know that the side lengths of similar triangles are proportional. For example, in $\triangle ADE$ at the right, $\frac{AD}{AB} = \frac{AE}{AC}$.

This leads to the following theorem; If a line is parallel to one side of a triangle and intersects the other two sides, then it divides those sides proportionally.

You can use what you know about the sides of similar triangles to find side lengths of similar triangles.

Go Online
PHSchool.com
Visit: PHSchool.com
Web Code: ayp-0426

EXAMPLES 1 and 2   **Finding side lengths of similar triangles**

In $\triangle ADE$ and $\triangle ABC$ above, $AB = 15$, $AE = 3$, $AC = 9$.

1 Find AD.

- **SOLUTION**

Let $AD = x$. Then the proportion of sides gives $\frac{x}{15} = \frac{3}{9}$; therefore $9x = 45$, and $x = AD = 5$.

2 If $\overline{BC}$ is twice the length of $\overline{AE}$, find DE.

- **SOLUTION**

Let $DE = y$. Since $AE = 3$, $BC = 2(3) = 6$. The proportion of the side lengths using AD and AB gives $\frac{y}{6} = \frac{5}{15}$; therefore $15y = 30$, and $y = DE = 2$.

If the segment joining the two sides of a triangle intersects the sides at their midpoints, the following theorem applies.

Triangle Midsegment Theorem

If a segment joins the midpoints of two sides of a triangle, then it is parallel to the third side and one half its length. That is, in $\triangle ABC$, if D is the midpoint of AB and E is the midpoint of AC, then

$$\overline{DE} \parallel \overline{BC} \text{ and } DE = \tfrac{1}{2}BC.$$

EXAMPLE 3 **Applying the Midsegment Theorem**

3 *T* is the midpoint of *QR*. *U* is the midpoint of *QS*. *RS* = 36 and *m∠QUT* = 85°. Find *TU* and *m∠QSR*.

■ **SOLUTION**

By the Triangle Midsegment Theorem, *TU* = 18 and $\overline{TU} \parallel \overline{RS}$. Therefore, *m∠QSR* = 85° by the Corresponding Angles Postulate.

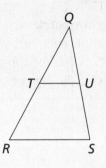

Practice

Choose the letter preceding the word or expression that best completes the statement or answers the question.

1 What is the name of the segment inside the large triangle?

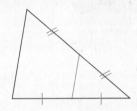

A. perpendicular bisector

B. midsegment

C. median

D. altitude

2 A triangular side of the Transamerica Building in San Francisco, California, is 149 feet at its base. If the distance from a base corner of the building to its peak is 859 feet, how wide is the triangle halfway to the top?

A. 74.5 ft   **C.** 298 ft

B. 149 ft   **D.** 429.5 ft

Transamerica Pyramid

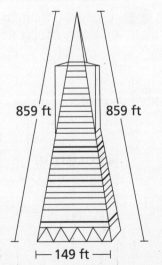

3 Find the length of the midsegment.

A. 12

B. 24

C. 42

D. 84

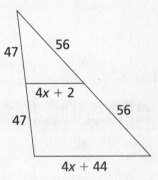

In Exercises 4–5, solve the problem. Clearly show all necessary work.

4 Identify all pairs of parallel line segments in the following diagram.

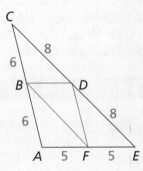

5 *B* is the midpoint of $\overline{AC}$ and *D* is the midpoint of $\overline{CE}$. Solve for *x*, given *BD* = 5*x* + 3 and *AE* = 4*x* + 18.

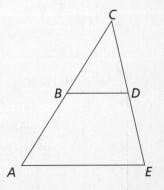

323

Right-Triangle Trigonometry

New Jersey Standards

4.3.E.1.3 Right triangle geometry

In a right triangle below, the sides of the triangle have names relative to an acute angle such as $\angle A$. In the diagram below, $\overline{AC}$ is the leg adjacent to $\angle A$ and $\overline{BC}$ is the leg opposite $\angle A$. Relative to $\angle B$, $\overline{BC}$ is the leg adjacent to $\angle B$ and $\overline{AC}$ is the leg opposite $\angle B$.

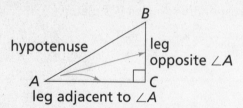

The diagram at the right shows three right triangles, $\triangle ABC$, $\triangle ADE$, and $\triangle AFG$, nesting inside one another. All three triangles are similar to one another. So, the ratios below are equal.

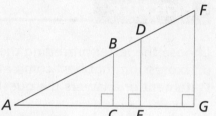

$$\frac{BC}{AC} = \frac{DE}{AE} = \frac{FG}{AG}$$

Notice each ratio represents the length of the leg opposite $\angle A$ to the length of the leg adjacent to $\angle A$ and that these ratios are equal.

The Tangent Ratio

In any right triangle $\triangle ABC$ with right angle at C, the ratio of the length of the leg opposite an acute angle such as $\angle A$ to the length of the leg adjacent to that angle is a constant called the **tangent** of $\angle A$, denoted tan A.

$$\text{tangent of } \angle A = \frac{\text{length of leg opposite } \angle A}{\text{length of leg adjacent to } \angle A}$$

You can use a calculator when working with the tangent ratio. The display at the right shows the tan 75° and the measure of the angle whose tangent is 0.75. Notice that, on many calculators, when you press [2nd] then [TAN] the display shows tan^{-1}.

```
tan(75)
        3.732050808
tan⁻¹(0.75)
        36.86989765
```

EXAMPLES 1 and 2   **Using the tangent ratio**

① Using the triangle below, find LM to the nearest hundredth.

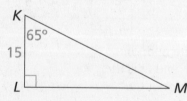

■ SOLUTION

$$\tan 65° = \frac{LM}{LK}$$
$$\tan 65° = \frac{LM}{15}$$
$$15 \tan 65° = LM$$
$$32.17 \approx LM$$

② Using the triangle below, find the measure of $\angle A$ to the nearest degree.

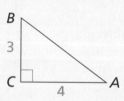

■ SOLUTION

$$\tan A = \frac{3}{4}$$
$$m\angle A = \tan^{-1}\left(\frac{3}{4}\right)$$
$$m\angle A \approx 37°$$

The tangent ratio is the ratio of the lengths of the opposite leg to the adjacent leg. Other trigonometric ratios use the ratio of the length of a leg and the length of the hypotenuse. Use the same diagram from the previous page, since the triangles are similar, to set up other equal ratios.

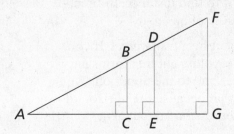

These proportions lead to the following definitions.

The Sine and Cosine Ratios

In any right triangle $\triangle ABC$ with right angle at C:

$$\text{sine of } \angle A = \frac{\text{length of leg opposite } \angle A}{\text{length of hypotenuse}}$$

$$\text{cosine of } \angle A = \frac{\text{length of leg adjacent to } \angle A}{\text{length of hypotenuse}}$$

The sine of $\angle A$ is denoted $\sin A$.
The cosine of $\angle A$ is denoted $\cos A$.

Note

An acronym for remembering the correct ratios is SOHCAHTOA. For example, the SOH would mean

$$\sin e = \frac{\text{Opposite}}{\text{hypotenuse}}.$$

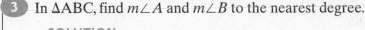

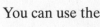 **EXAMPLE 3** **Using trigonometric ratios to find angles**

3 In $\triangle ABC$, find $m\angle A$ and $m\angle B$ to the nearest degree.

■ **SOLUTION**

You can use the sine ratio to find $m\angle A$.

$$\sin \angle A = \frac{\text{opposite}}{\text{hypotenuse}}$$

$$= \frac{5}{13} = 0.384615384$$

Then $m\angle A = \sin^{-1}(0.384615384) = 22.61986495 \approx 23°$

To find the $m\angle B$, use the fact that $\sin \angle A = \cos \angle B$.

Therefore, $\cos \angle B = \frac{\text{adjacent}}{\text{hypotenuse}} = \frac{5}{13} = 0.384615384$.

Then $m\angle B = \cos^{-1}(0.384615384) = 67.38013505 = 67°$

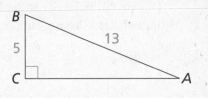

There are alternate methods for finding the measure of the second angle. Once you have found the measure of the acute angle $\angle A$, you can subtract it from its complement. Therefore, $\angle B = 90° - \angle A$, so $\angle B = 90° - 23 = 67°$. You can also use the Pythagorean Theorem to find side b (Pythagorean Triple 5, 12, 13), then use $\sin \angle B = \frac{\text{opposite}}{\text{hypotenuse}} = \frac{12}{13}$, and proceed from there.

If you use a ruler or tape measure to find the distance between two points on a flat surface, you are using **direct measurement.** If the points are far apart or you cannot easily get from one point to another, you may be able to find the distance indirectly. Trigonometric ratios may enable you to calculate distance and thereby use **indirect measurement** to find distance. Indirect measurement can also be used to find the measure of an angle.

The diagram below shows two horizontal lines cut by a transversal. If you look down from the upper line to the lower one, your sight line forms an **angle of depression.** If you sight from the lower line to the upper one, your sight line forms an **angle of elevation.** Notice that because the horizontal lines are parallel, the angles of elevation and depression are equal in measure.

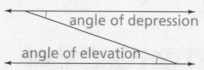

angle of depression

angle of elevation

Go Online
PHSchool.com

Visit: PHSchool.com
Web Code: ayp-0321

EXAMPLES 4 and 5 **Solving problems involving angles of elevation and depression**

4 A steel cable extends from the top of a building to a point on the ground that is 1000 ft from the base of the building. At the point where the cable is anchored to the ground, it is determined that the measure of its angle of elevation is 42°. To the nearest foot, how tall is the building?

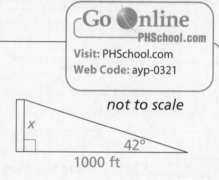

not to scale

x

42°

1000 ft

■ **SOLUTION**

This problem involves the leg adjacent to the 42° angle and the leg opposite it. Choose the tangent ratio.

$$\tan 42° = \frac{x}{1000}$$
$$x = 1000 \tan 42°$$
$$x \approx 900$$

The building is *about 900 feet* tall.

5 Rose is flying a kite and has let out 300 feet of string. The kite is 120 feet above the ground and Rose is 5 feet tall. To the nearest tenth of a degree, at what angle of elevation does she sight the kite?

■ **SOLUTION**

First sketch a diagram showing what is known and what is unknown. If Rose is 5 feet tall and the kite is 120 feet above the ground, then the height of the right triangle shown is 115 ft.

To find the angle of elevation, use the sine ratio.

$$\sin x° = \frac{115}{300}$$
$$x \approx 22.5$$

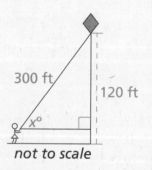

300 ft

120 ft

x°

not to scale

She sights the kite along a line making an angle of *about 22.5°* with the horizontal.

Practice

Choose the letter preceding the word or expression that best completes the statement or answers the question.

1 What is sin B?

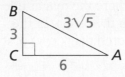

   A. $5\sqrt{5}$ **C.** $\frac{3\sqrt{5}}{5}$

   B. 3 **D.** $\frac{2\sqrt{5}}{5}$

2 Which equation can be used to find the height of this building?

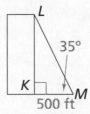

  A. $\sin M = \frac{LK}{500}$

  B. $\tan M = \frac{LK}{500}$

  C. $\cos M = \frac{500}{LM}$

  D. $\tan M = \frac{500}{LK}$

3 Which represents $m\angle X$ to the nearest whole number?

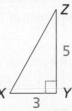

  A. $31°$ **C.** $45°$

  B. $41°$ **D.** $59°$

4 To the nearest tenth, which represents the length of the diagonal $\overline{AC}$ in the rectangle below?

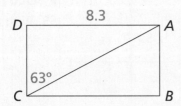

  A. 7.4   **B.** 9.3   **C.** 16.3   **D.** 18.3

In Exercises 5–7, find the value of each variable. Give answers to the nearest tenth.

5

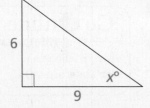

6

7

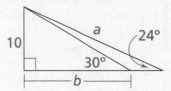

In Exercises 8–12, find the missing value to solve the problem.

8 The captain of a ship spots the top of a lighthouse at a 6° angle of elevation. The lighthouse is on the edge of the shore and is 50 ft tall. To the nearest foot, how far is the ship from shore?

9 An airplane pilot can see the top of a traffic control tower at a 20° angle of depression. The straight-line distance between the plane and the top of the tower is 5,000 feet. To the nearest foot, how far above the tower is the plane?

10 A forest ranger looking out from a ranger's station can see a forest fire at a 35° angle of depression. The ranger's position is 100 ft above the ground. To the nearest foot, how far is it from the base of the ranger's station to the fire on level ground with it?

11 To the nearest whole number, find the measures of the angles in $\triangle PQR$.

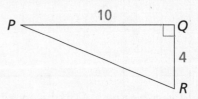

12 Find a to the nearest whole number.

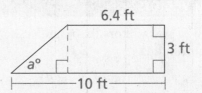

11.9 Vectors

New Jersey Standards

4.2.C.2 Use vectors in the coordinate plane

A **vector** is any quantity that has *magnitude* (size) and *direction*. You can represent a vector by using an arrow that starts at one point, the *initial* point, and ends at another point, the *terminal* point. The *magnitude* is the distance from the initial point to the terminal point of the vector.

Vectors can be described using the coordinate plane where the magnitude and direction would be the distance and direction from the origin. In the coordinate plane, a vector can be described by the ordered pair $\langle x, y \rangle$ of its terminal point.

> **Note**
>
> If the initial point of the vector is O and the terminal point is P, you write the vector as $\overrightarrow{OP}$.

EXAMPLE 1   Describing a vector using a coordinate grid

 Find the initial point and terminal point of $\overrightarrow{OD}$.

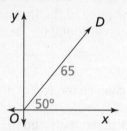

■ **SOLUTION**   Use the sine and cosine ratios to find $D = (x, y)$.

$$\cos 50° = \frac{x}{65}$$
$$x = 65(\cos 50°) \approx 41.8$$

$$\sin 50° = \frac{y}{65}$$
$$y = 65(\sin 50°) \approx 49.8$$

Therefore, **the terminal point of $\overrightarrow{OD} \approx$ (41.8, 49.8). The initial point of $\overrightarrow{OD}$ is (0, 0).**

Directions of vectors are often described using compass directions of north, south, east, and west.

EXAMPLES 2 and 3   Describing a vector direction

Use compass directions to describe the direction of each vector

2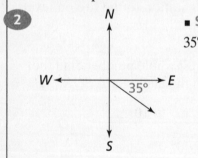

■ **SOLUTION**
35° South of East

3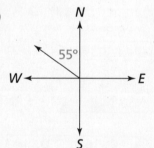

■ **SOLUTION**
55° West of North

You can add vectors that are on the coordinate plane that have their initial point at the origin.

Adding vectors

The sum of two vectors $\langle a, b \rangle$ and $\langle c, d \rangle$ is found by taking the sum of their coordinates.

$$\langle a, b \rangle + \langle c, d \rangle = \langle a + c, b + d \rangle$$

Go Online
PHSchool.com
Visit: PHSchool.com
Web Code: ayp-0436

You can solve problems using vectors.

EXAMPLE 4   Solving problems using vectors

 Sammy drives from his home 23 miles due East and then 47 miles due South to reach his aunt's home. How many miles would he travel if he drove in a direct path from his starting point to his aunt's home? What would his direction be?

■ **SOLUTION**

Step 1
Find the distance.
$23^2 + 47^2 = 529 + 2209 = 2738$
$\sqrt{2738} \approx 52.3$ miles if he drove in a direct path

Step 2
Find the direction.
$\tan x° = \frac{47}{23} = 2.0435 \approx 64°$
He is 64° South of East.

Practice

Choose the letter preceding the word or expression that best completes the statement or answers the question.

1 A small airplane lands 300 mi. East and 400 mi. North from where it took off. Find the approximate direction of its flight.

  A. 23° East of North

  B. 36° North of East

  C. 53° East of North

  D. 53° North of East

2 From his home, Johnny's mom drives him 2 miles due West and then 6 miles due North to get to school. How many miles is it in a straight line from Johnny's home to his school? Round to the nearest tenth.

  A. 4   **B.** 5.2   **C.** 6.3   **D.** 5.7

3 Write the sum of the vectors $\langle 6, 1 \rangle$ and $\langle 0, -5 \rangle$ as an ordered pair.

  A. $\langle 3, -2 \rangle$

  B. $\langle 5, -5 \rangle$

  C. $\langle 6, -4 \rangle$

  D. $\langle 0, -5 \rangle$

In Exercises 4–6, solve each problem and show your work.

4 To the nearest tenth, give the coordinates of vector $\overrightarrow{OT}$.

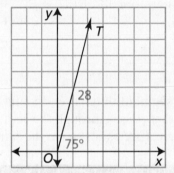

In Exercises 5–6, use compass directions to describe the direction of each vector.

5

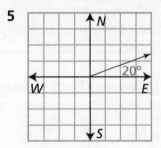

6

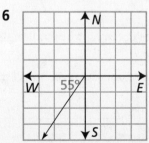

329

11.10 Circles—Arcs, Angles, Chords, and Tangents

New Jersey Standards

4.2.12.A.3 Applying the properties of circles

Recall that a circle is a set of points a fixed distance from a point called the center. A line that intersects the circle in exactly one point is **tangent** to the circle. If a line is tangent to a circle, then the line is perpendicular to the radius drawn to the point of tangency. Consider $\odot O$ at the right. $\overline{AB} \perp \overline{OP}$; therefore, $\angle APO = 90°$.

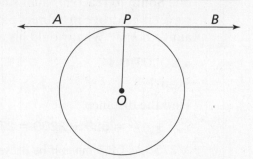

Another tangent segment theorem states that if 2 tangents are drawn to a circle from the same point outside the circle, then the 2 segments are congruent.

EXAMPLE 1   **Applying the tangent theorem**

 Two tangents are drawn to $\odot O$. If $m\angle O = 111°$, find x.

■ **SOLUTION**

Because the figure formed by the two tangents and two radii is a quadrilateral, the sum of the 4 angles is 360°.

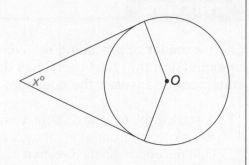

Therefore, $111° + 90° + 90° + x° = 360°$

$$291° + x° = 360°$$
$$x = 69°$$

Any line segment that has endpoints on the circle is a **chord** of the circle. A chord that passes through the center of the circle is called the **diameter** of the circle. Circles that have the same diameter are congruent.

Chords, Arcs, and Central Angles Theorems

- Congruent central angles intercept congruent chords.
- Congruent chords intercept congruent arcs.
- Congruent arcs intercept congruent central angles.

Note

Recall that a central angle must have its vertex at the center of the circle.

EXAMPLE 2   **Applying chords, arcs, and central angles theorems**

 If $\odot O \cong \odot P$ and $\angle O \cong \angle P$, what can you conclude about $\overline{AB}$ and $\overline{CD}$ and $\overset{\frown}{AB}$ and $\overset{\frown}{CD}$?

■ **SOLUTION**

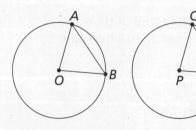

$\overline{AB} \cong \overline{CD}$ because congruent central angles intercept congruent chords.

$\overset{\frown}{AB} \cong \overset{\frown}{CD}$ because congruent chords intercept congruent arcs.

Chords that are equidistant from the center are congruent. For example, in $\odot O$, $\overline{AB} \perp \overline{OP}$, $\overline{CD} \perp \overline{OQ}$ and $OP = OQ$. Therefore, $\overline{AB} \cong \overline{CD}$.

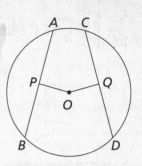

More Chords and Arcs Theorems

A diameter of a circle that is perpendicular to a chord bisects the chord and its arcs. The perpendicular bisector of a chord is a diameter.

You can use these theorems to solve problems that involve circles.

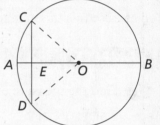

Go Online
PHSchool.com
Visit: PHSchool.com
Web Code: ayp-0475

EXAMPLE 3 Solving problems involving circles

3 In $\odot O$, $\overline{AB}$ is a diameter, $\overline{AB} \perp \overline{CD}$, and $m\widehat{AD} = 40°$. Find $m\angle CDO$.

■ SOLUTION
Look at $\triangle EDO$. $\overline{AB} \perp \overline{CD}$ is given, so $m\angle OED = 90°$.

Since $m\widehat{AD} = 40° = \frac{m\widehat{AC}}{2}$, $m\angle AOD = 40°$.

Note that $\angle CDO \cong \angle EDO$, therefore
$m\angle CDO = 180° - 90° - 40° = 50°$.

Practice

Choose the letter preceding the word or expression that best completes the statement or answers the question.

1 $\overleftrightarrow{AB}$ is tangent to $\odot O$, and $\overline{AC}$ is a diameter. Find x.

A. 46°

B. 90°

C. 44°

D. 30°

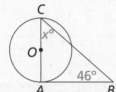

2 $\overline{JK}$, $\overline{KL}$, and $\overline{LJ}$ are all tangent to $\odot O$. $JA = 9$, $AL = 10$, and $CK = 14$. Find the perimeter of $\triangle JKL$.

A. 66 **C.** 46

B. 38 **D.** 33

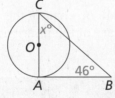

In Exercises 3–4, solve each problem. Clearly show all necessary work.

3 $AB = 7$, $OB = 3.75$, and $AO = 8$. Determine whether $\overline{AB}$ is tangent to the circle. Explain your reasoning.

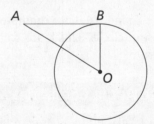

4 Find x.

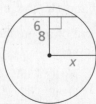

11.11 Circles—Inscribed Angles

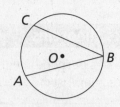

New Jersey Standards

4.2.A.3.4 Applying the properties of circles

In the diagram to the right, $\angle B$ is on Circle O. The sides of $\angle B$ are the chords $\overline{AB}$ and $\overline{CB}$ of the circle. $\angle B$ is an *inscribed angle*, and its *intercepted arc* is $\overset{\frown}{AC}$.

Inscribed Angle Theorem

The measure of an inscribed angle is half the measure of its intercepted arc.

$$m\angle B = \frac{m\overset{\frown}{AC}}{2}$$

Go Online
PHSchool.com
Visit: PHSchool.com
Web Code: ayp-0773

You can use this theorem to find angle measures in circles.

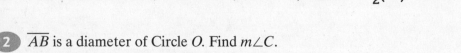

EXAMPLES 1 and 2   **Finding measures of inscribed angles**

1 Find the measure of $\angle BAC$.

- **SOLUTION**
Since $m\angle BOC = 57°$, $m\overset{\frown}{BC} = 57°$; therefore, $m\angle BAC = \frac{1}{2}(57) = 28.5°$.

2 $\overline{AB}$ is a diameter of Circle O. Find $m\angle C$.

- **SOLUTION**
Since $\overline{AB}$ is a diameter, $m\overset{\frown}{AB} = 180°$.

Therefore, $m\angle C = \frac{1}{2}(180) = 90°$.

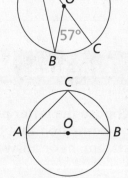

In Example 2 since $\overline{AB}$ is a diameter of circle O, then $\overset{\frown}{ACB}$ is half of the circle or a **semicircle**. This leads to the following corollary of the inscribed angle theorem:

Inscribed Angle Corollaries

An angle inscribed in a semicircle is a right angle.

In the diagram at the right, $\angle B$ is on Circle O. The sides of $\angle B$ are chord $\overline{AB}$ and $\overrightarrow{BD}$ tangent to Circle O and its intercepted arc is $\overset{\frown}{ACB}$.

The measure of an angle formed by a tangent and chord is half its intercepted arc.

$$m\angle B = \frac{1}{2}\overset{\frown}{ACB}$$

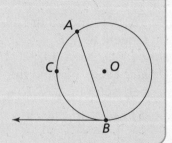

EXAMPLE 3   **Finding angle measures formed by a chord and tangent**

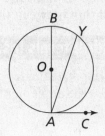

3 If $m\overset{\frown}{BY} = 40°$, what is $m\angle YAC$?

■ **SOLUTION**

If $\overline{AB}$ is the diameter, then $m\overset{\frown}{AB} = 180°$, and $m\angle BAC = \frac{180°}{2}$ or 90°.

Given $m\overset{\frown}{BY} = 40°$, then $m\angle BAY = 20°$.

Therefore, $m\angle YAC = 90° - 20° = 70°$.

A **secant** is a line, ray, or segment that intersects a circle at two points. You can find the measure of an angle formed by two secants. How you measure the angle depends on where the secants intersect.

Secants That Intersect Inside a Circle

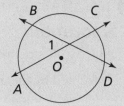

The measure of an angle formed by two secants that intersect inside a circle is half the measure of the sum of its intercepted arcs.

$$m\angle 1 = \frac{\overset{\frown}{AB} + \overset{\frown}{CD}}{2}$$

Two secants can also intersect outside the circle. You find the angle formed by the intersection by using a different theorem.

Secants Intersecting Outside a Circle

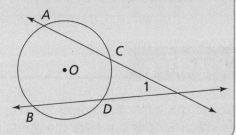

The measure of an angle formed by two secants that intersect outside a circle is half the difference of its intercepted arcs.

$$m\angle 1 = \frac{\overset{\frown}{AB} - \overset{\frown}{CD}}{2}$$

EXAMPLE 4   **Angles formed by intersecting secants**

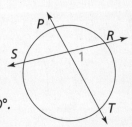

4 The sum of the measures of $\overset{\frown}{PR}$ and $\overset{\frown}{ST}$ is 220°. What is $m\angle 1$?

■ **SOLUTION**

The circle is broken into four arcs by the secants, so the sum of the measures of all the arcs is 360°.

Therefore, $m\overset{\frown}{PS} + m\overset{\frown}{RT} = 360° - (m\overset{\frown}{PR} + m\overset{\frown}{ST}) = 360° - 220° = 140°$.

The angle is half of the sum of its intercepted arcs,

so $m\angle 1 = \frac{140}{2} = 70°$.

When four chords share the same endpoints on a circle, they form a quadrilateral inscribed in a circle. The following describes how the relationship between the angles of the quadrilateral.

Quadrilaterals Inscribed in a Circle

The opposite angles of a quadrilateral inscribed in a circle are supplementary.

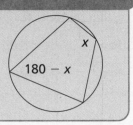

Each vertex of the quadrilateral is an inscribed angle.

EXAMPLES 5 and 6   Angles of an inscribed quadrilateral

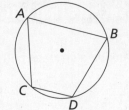

The quadrilateral $ABCD$ is inscribed in a circle with $m\widehat{ABD} = 200°$.

5 If $m\angle A = 70°$, what is $m\widehat{CAB}$?

■ SOLUTION

Since $\angle D$ is opposite of $\angle A$, $m\angle D = 180° - 70° = 110°$. The arc $\widehat{CAB}$ is formed by the inscribed angle $\angle D$, so $m\widehat{CAB} = 2(110) = 220°$.

6 What is $m\angle B$?

■ SOLUTION

You know that $\angle B$ is the supplement of $\angle C$. Since $\widehat{ABD} = 200°$,

$\angle C = \frac{200}{2} = 100°$.

Therefore, $m\angle B = 180 - 100 = 80°$

Practice

Choose the letter preceding the word or expression that best completes the statement or answers the question.

1 $m\angle R = 22°$. Find $m\angle O$. (Note: The figure is not drawn to scale.)

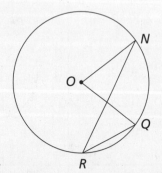

A. 68°   **B.** 22°   **C.** 158°   **D.** 44°

2 $\overline{BA}$ is tangent to Circle O, $m\widehat{BC} = 230°$, and $m\widehat{BD} = 92°$. Find $m\angle A$.

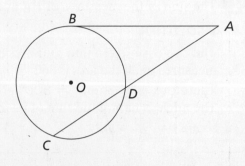

A. 69°   **B.** 161°   **C.** 46°   **D.** 138°

3 Find $m\angle 1$, if $\overset{\frown}{PR} = 40°$ and $\overset{\frown}{ST} = 65°$.

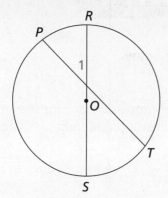

A. 22.5°   **B.** 45°   **C.** 52.5°   **D.** 105°

4 If $m\angle 1 = 20°$ and $m\overset{\frown}{DB} = 30°$, what is $m\overset{\frown}{CA}$?

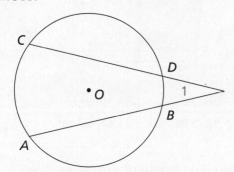

A. 40°   **B.** 70°   **C.** 30°   **D.** 50°

5 $\overline{AB}$ is the diameter, and $\overline{AB} \perp \overline{CD}$. Find $m\overset{\frown}{BD}$ if $m\overset{\frown}{AC} = 43°$.

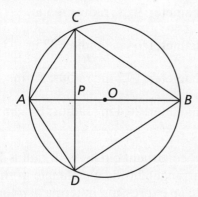

A. 137°   **B.** 133°   **C.** 86°   **D.** 47°

In Exercises 6–7, solve each problem using the following figure. Clearly show all necessary work.

$m\angle A = 40°$ and $m\overset{\frown}{BC} = 170$. (Note: The figure is not drawn to scale)

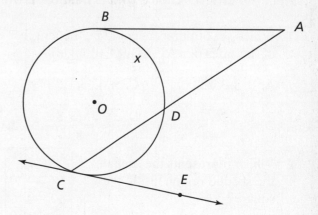

6 Find x.

7 Find $m\angle DCE$.

8 If $ABCD$ is a rectangle inscribed in circle O, do both diagonals contain the center of the circle? Explain your reasoning.

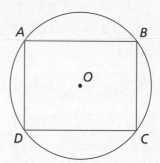

9 Find the measures of $\angle A$, $\angle D$ and $\overset{\frown}{BCD}$.

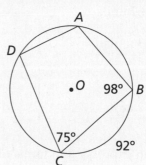

DIRECTIONS FOR QUESTIONS 1–26: For each of the questions below, select the answer choice that is best for each case.

1 Which set of numbers could be the lengths of the sides of a 45°-45°-90° triangle?

A. $3, 3, 3\sqrt{3}$ C. $\frac{1}{2}, 1, \frac{\sqrt{3}}{2}$

B. $2, 2, 2\sqrt{2}$ D. $\frac{\sqrt{3}}{2}, \sqrt{3}, 3$

2 Which represents the area of the shaded region inside the square?

A. $4\pi + 16$ C. $16 - 4\pi$

B. $4\pi - 16$ D. $16\pi - 16$

3 One base of a trapezoid is three times as long as the other base. The height of the trapezoid is the average of the two bases. If the area of the trapezoid is 16 yd², how many yards long is the shorter base?

A. 2 B. 4 C. 12 D. 16

4 The figure at the right consists of four semicircles arranged along the sides of a square as shown. Find the perimeter of the figure.

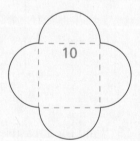

A. 125.67 units

B. 62.83 units

C. 40 units

D. 31.42 units

5 Write an expression in terms of b for the area of a rectangle whose length is $2b - 1$ and whose width is $b + 3$.

A. $2b^2 + 6b - 3$ C. $7b - 3$

B. $3b^2 + 4b - 3$ D. $2b^2 + 5b - 3$

6 Write an expression in z for the area of a circle whose circumference is $24\pi z$.

A. $24z$ C. 144π

B. $144\pi z^2$ D. $12z^2$

7 Find the area of trapezoid $PQRS$.

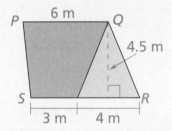

A. 58.5 m² C. 22.5 m²

B. 29.25 m² D. 27 m²

8 A straight length of wire 64 in. long is shaped into a circle with no wire overlapping. What are the diameter and radius of the circle formed? Give your answer to the nearest tenth of an inch.

A. diameter: 9 in.; radius: 4.5 in.

B. diameter: 64 in.; radius: 32 in.

C. diameter: 10.2 in.; radius: 5.1 in.

D. diameter: 20.4 in.; radius: 10.2 in.

9 Eight congruent circles with radius a are arranged inside a rectangle as shown. Write an expression in terms of a for the perimeter of the rectangle.

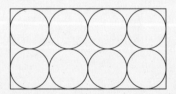

A. $24a$ B. $16a$ C. $32a$ D. $12a$

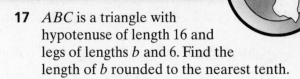

10 Find the total distance along the sides of the square and along the semicircle.

A. 40   C. 45.7

B. 61.4   D. 68.5

11 Find the total distance along the longer sides of the rectangle and along the two semicircles.

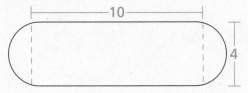

A. 28   B. 26.3   C. 32.6   D. 45.1

12 What is the midpoint of the points $(-5, 2)$ and $(3, -7)$?

A. $(3.5, 5)$ C. $(-1, -2.5)$

B. $(-1.5, -2)$ D. $(4, -4.5)$

13 Which represents the greatest possible error in a length measured to the nearest half-inch?

A. $\frac{1}{2}$ in.   B. $\frac{1}{4}$ in.   C. $\frac{1}{8}$ in.   D. $\frac{1}{16}$ in.

14 Which represents the length of a side of an equilateral triangle whose perimeter is 12.2 cm?

A. 36.6 cm   C. 4.1 cm

B. 9.2 cm   D. 12.2 cm

15 Write the sum of the vectors $\langle 2, -5 \rangle$ and $\langle 10, -3 \rangle$ as an ordered pair.

A. $\langle 6, -4 \rangle$ C. $\langle 8, 2 \rangle$

B. $\langle -3, 7 \rangle$ D. $\langle 12, -8 \rangle$

16 Which of the following is the measure of the side of a square with a diagonal of 24?

A. $12\sqrt{2}$ C. $24\sqrt{2}$

B. 6   D. $21\sqrt{3}$

17 ABC is a triangle with hypotenuse of length 16 and legs of lengths b and 6. Find the length of b rounded to the nearest tenth.

A. 17.1   B. 10   C. 14.8   D. 4.7

18 Which represents $m\angle A$ to the nearest whole degree?

A. 55°

B. 99°

C. 66°

D. 38°

19 In the figure, B is the midpoint of $\overline{AC}$ and D is the midpoint of $\overline{AE}$. If the length of $\overline{CE}$ is 18, what is the length of $\overline{BD}$?

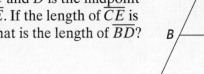

A. 6

B. 9

C. $9\sqrt{2}$

D. 10

20 Find the value of y. Note that the figure is not drawn to scale.

A. 8

B. 12

C. 13

D. 17

21 Find $m\angle R$ given that $m\overarc{ST} = 110°$ and $m\overarc{RS} = 140°$.

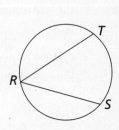

A. 30°

B. 55°

C. 110°

D. 125°

DIRECTIONS FOR 22–24: Solve each problem and show your work.

22 A regular pentagon inscribed in a circle is shown in the figure below.

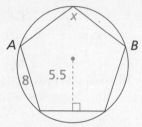

- Find the area of the regular pentagon.

- What is $m\widehat{AB}$? (Hint: remember that this is a regular pentagon.)

- Find $m\angle x$.

23 Two trees are 100 ft apart on level ground. The height of the taller tree is 75 ft. The angle of depression from the top of the taller tree to the top of the shorter tree is 15°.

- Find the height of the shorter tree to the nearest tenth of a foot.

- What is the distance between the tops of the two trees to the nearest tenth of a foot?

- If all of the measurements were taken to the nearest tenth of a foot, what is the percent of error in your answer to the second part?

24 Two diameters go through the center of a spinner, creating four sections.

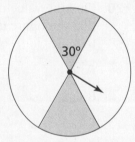

- If the area of one of the shaded sections is 20 in.^{2}, what is the area of the entire circle?

- What percentage of the spinner is shaded?

- If the arc formed by one of the white sections is 16 in. long, what is the length of the arc formed by the other white section? Explain.

12 Surface Area and Volume

New Jersey Rocks!

At the age of 13, Les Paul used a microphone from an old telephone and a needle from a phonograph to build a guitar that amplified its sound. Les Paul went on to become a famous musician and a pioneer in the development of solid body electric guitars and recording techniques.

Les Paul built his first solid body electric guitar around 1941. After many revisions to Paul's original model, *The Les Paul Standard* was first sold by the Gibson Guitar Corporation in 1952. Among the famous guitarists to play a Les Paul Standard are Eric Clapton, Jeff Beck, and Jimmy Page.

Les Paul now resides at his home in Mahwah, New Jersey where he continues to study and refine the technology of the electric guitar.

Lateral and Surface Areas
12.1 of Prisms

New Jersey Standards

4.2.E.1.1 Use Pythagorean Theorem

4.2.E.2.1 Find perimeter, area, and volume

4.3.E.2.3 Estimate perimeter, area, and volume

A **polyhedron** is a three-dimensional figure formed by flat surfaces that are bounded by polygons joined along their sides. Each of the flat surfaces is called a **face** of the polyhedron. A segment that is the intersection of two faces is called an **edge.** A point that is the intersection of three or more edges is a **vertex.**

If all of the faces of a polyhedron are regular polygons that are congruent to each other, the figure is a **regular polyhedron.** In a regular polyhedron, the same number of faces meets at each vertex.

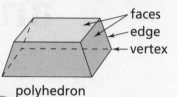

polyhedron

Regular Polyhedrons

- **Tetrahedron-** a polyhedron with 4 congruent faces that are triangles.
- **Hexahedron-** a polyhedron with 6 congruent faces that are squares. (the hexahedron is also called a **cube**)
- **Octahedron-** a polyhedron with 8 congruent faces that are triangles.
- **Dodecahedron-** a polyhedron with 12 congruent faces that are pentagons.
- **Icosahedron-** a polyhedron with 20 congruent faces that are triangles.

A **prism** is a polyhedron with two parallel **bases** bounded by congruent polygons and with **lateral faces** bounded by parallelograms that connect corresponding sides of the bases. The **height** h of a prism is the length of any perpendicular segment drawn from a point on one base to the plane containing the other base.

A prism is a **right prism** if the segments that join corresponding vertices of the bases are perpendicular to the bases. Otherwise, the prism is called *oblique.* You can further classify a prism by the shape of its bases: triangular, square, rectangular, and so on.

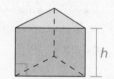

right triangular prism

oblique triangular prism

 EXAMPLE 1   **Classifying a prism**

1   Which best describes the prism at the right? The measure of each interior angle of a base is 108°.

  A. pentagonal prism   **C.** right regular pentagonal prism

  B. regular pentagonal prism   **D.** oblique regular pentagonal prism

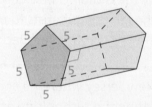

■ SOLUTION

The bases are regular pentagons. The right-angle symbol indicates that the segments joining corresponding vertices are perpendicular to the planes containing the bases. The correct choice is *C.*

The **lateral area of a prism** is the sum of the areas of its lateral faces. If you look at a *net* of a rectangular prism you will see that it is made up of four rectangles laid side by side, all with the same height. The figure below is a **net** of the prism.

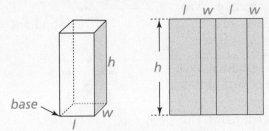

You can calculate the area of a prism if you multiply the height of the figure by the perimeter of its base. The formula for lateral area is *ph*, where *p* is the perimeter of the base and *h* is the height of the figure.

$$\textbf{L.A.} = \textbf{\textit{ph}} \text{ or } \textbf{\textit{h}(2\textit{l} + 2\textit{w})} \text{ or } \textbf{2(\textit{lh} + \textit{hw})}$$

To find the total **surface area of a prism** you add the lateral area and the areas of the two congruent bases. The formula is **Surface Area = L.A. + 2B,** where *B* is the area of the base.

$$\textbf{S.A.} = \textbf{L.A.} + \textbf{2}\textbf{\textit{B}}$$

Since the L.A. = 2(*lh* + *hw*) added to the area of the two bases, 2*B* = 2*lw*, another formula for the surface area can be **S.A. = 2(*lh* + *hw* + *lw*).**

EXAMPLES 2 and 3 **Finding lateral and surface area of a right prism**

2 Find the lateral and surface area of the right triangular prism below.

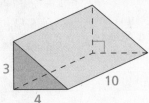

■ SOLUTION

The bases are right triangles. The length of the hypotenuse is 5 by the Pythagorean Theorem.

$$\text{L.A.} = 5 \times 10 + 3 \times 10 + 4 \times 10$$
$$= 120 \text{ square units}$$
$$\text{S.A.} = 120 + 2\left(\frac{1}{2} \times 3 \times 4\right)$$
$$= 132 \text{ square units}$$

3 Find the lateral and surface area of the right rectangular prism below.

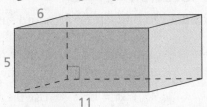

■ SOLUTION

Consider the top and the bottom as the bases of the prism.

$$\text{L.A.} = 2(5 \times 11) + 2(6 \times 5)$$
$$= 170 \text{ square units}$$
$$\text{S.A.} = 170 + 2(6 \times 11)$$
$$= 302 \text{ square units}$$

A **pyramid** is a polyhedron with one base that is bounded by a polygon, a point outside the plane of the base called the **vertex,** and lateral faces that are bounded by triangles connecting the vertex to each side of the base. The **height** h of a pyramid is the length of the perpendicular segment drawn from the vertex to the plane containing the base. Like a prism, a pyramid can be classified by the shape of its base.

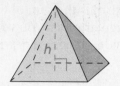 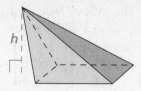

rectangular pyramids

A pyramid is a **regular pyramid** if its base is bounded by a regular polygon and the segment joining the center of this polygon to the vertex is perpendicular to the plane of the base. Its lateral faces are congruent isosceles triangles. The height of one of these triangles is called the **slant height** ℓ of the pyramid.

regular square pyramid

regular pentagonal pyramid

The **lateral area** of a pyramid is the sum of the areas of its lateral faces. The surface area of a pyramid is the sum of the area of the base and the lateral area.

Area Formulas for a Regular Pyramid

If the base of a regular pyramid has n sides each having length s and slant height ℓ, then the lateral area L.A. is given by this formula.

$$\text{L.A.} = n\left[\tfrac{1}{2}s\ell\right] = \tfrac{1}{2}ns\ell$$

The surface area S.A. is given by the following formula.

$$\text{S.A.} = \text{L.A.} + B = \tfrac{1}{2}ns\ell + B, \text{ where } B \text{ is the area of the base}$$

Go Online
PHSchool.com
Visit: PHSchool.com
Web Code: ayp-0911

EXAMPLE 4 | **Finding areas of a regular pyramid given height and slant height**

4 Find the lateral and surface area of a regular square pyramid with a height of 4 in. and a slant height of 5 in.

■ **SOLUTION**

Step 1 To find lateral area and surface area, you need to find the length of a side of the square base. The length of a side of the base is $2x$, where x represents the length shown in the second sketch at the right.

$$4^2 + x^2 = 5^2 \quad \leftarrow \textbf{Use the Pythagorean Theorem.}$$
$$x = 3$$

The length of a side of the base is 2(3) in., or 6 in.

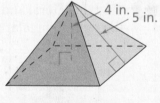

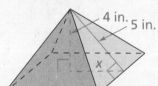

Step 2 Apply the formulas for lateral area and surface area.

$$\text{L.A.} = 4\left[\tfrac{1}{2}(6 \times 5)\right] = 60 \quad \rightarrow \quad 60 \text{ in.}^2$$
$$\text{S.A.} = 60 + 6^2 = 96 \quad \rightarrow \quad 96 \text{ in.}^2$$

You may need to find the slant height of a pyramid before finding the areas.

EXAMPLE 5

Finding areas of a regular pyramid given height and length of one side of the base

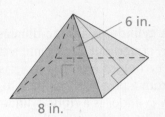

5 Find the lateral and surface area of a regular square pyramid with a height of 6 in. and base with side length 8 in.

- **SOLUTION**

Step 1 To find lateral area and surface area, you need to find the slant height of the pyramid. This is represented by y in the second sketch at the right.

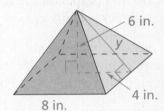

$$4^2 + 6^2 = y^2 \quad \leftarrow \text{Use the Pythagorean Theorem.}$$
$$y = \sqrt{52} = 2\sqrt{13}$$

The slant height is $2\sqrt{13}$ in.

Step 2 Apply the formulas for lateral area and surface area.

$$\text{L.A.} = 4\left[\tfrac{1}{2}(8 \times 2\sqrt{13})\right] = 32\sqrt{13} \quad \rightarrow \quad 32\sqrt{13} \text{ in.}^2, \text{ or about } 115.38 \text{ in.}^2$$

$$\text{S.A.} = 32\sqrt{13} + 8^2 = 64 + 32\sqrt{13} \quad \rightarrow \quad (64 + 32\sqrt{13}) \text{ in.}^2, \text{ or about } 179.38 \text{ in.}^2$$

Practice

Choose the letter preceding the word or expression that best completes the statement or answers the question.

1 What is the surface area of a rectangular prism with length 20 m, width 6 m, and height 7 m?

A. 604 m^2 **C.** 564 m^2

B. 456 m^2 **D.** 744 m^2

2 Which is the lateral area of a regular square pyramid with base length 6 units and height 4 units?

A. 12 units^2 **C.** 84 units^2

B. 60 units^2 **D.** 96 units^2

In Exercises 3–4, find the surface area of each right prism. Round answers to the nearest tenth if necessary.

3
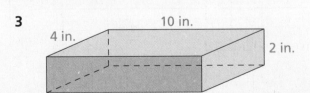

4
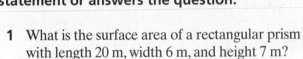

In Exercises 5–7, solve the problem. Clearly show all necessary work.

5 Find the lateral area of a regular pyramid whose base is a square, whose slant height is 5 m, and whose height is 3 m.

6 Find the lateral and surface area of the right rectangular prism whose length is 7.0 cm, width is 5.0 cm, and height is 1.5 cm.

7 Find the lateral and surface area of the regular square pyramid. Give exact answers.

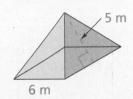

343

Lateral and Surface Areas
12.2 of Cylinders and Cones

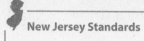

New Jersey Standards

4.2.E.1.1 Use Pythagorean Theorem

4.2.E.2.1 Find perimeter, area, and volume

4.3.E.2.3 Estimate perimeter, area, and volume

A **cylinder** is a three-dimensional figure with two parallel **bases** bounded by congruent circles and a curved **lateral surface** that connects the circles. The **height** h of a cylinder is the length of any perpendicular segment drawn from a point on one base to the plane containing the other base. A cylinder is a **right cylinder** if the segment joining the centers of the bases is perpendicular to the planes of the bases. Otherwise, the cylinder is *oblique*.

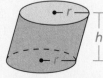

right cylinder   oblique cylinder

To derive area formulas for a right cylinder, imagine its net as shown at the right. Notice that the length of the lateral surface is equal to the circumference of a base.

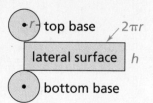

Area Formulas for Cylinders

If a right cylinder has a height h and base with radius r, then the lateral area L.A. is given by this formula.

$$\text{L.A.} = 2\pi rh$$

The surface area S.A. is given by the following formula.

$$\text{S.A.} = \text{L.A.} + 2\pi r^2$$

EXAMPLES 1 and 2   **Finding the surface area of a right cylinder**

① Find the surface area of a right cylinder with a radius of 4.5 ft and height 5 ft. Use $\pi = 3.14$.

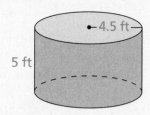

- **SOLUTION**

$$\text{S.A.} = 2\pi(4.5)(5) + 2\pi(4.5)^2$$
$$= 85.5\pi$$
$$\approx 268.47$$

The surface area is 268.47 ft².

② Find the surface area of a right cylinder with a diameter of 11 m and height 6 m. Use $\pi = 3.14$.

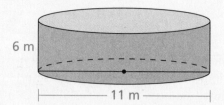

- **SOLUTION**

$$\text{S.A.} = 2\pi(5.5)(6) + 2\pi(5.5)^2 \leftarrow r = \tfrac{11}{2}$$
$$= 126.5\pi$$
$$\approx 397.21$$

The surface area is 397.21 m².

You can also use the formulas to solve problems that involve lateral and surface areas of a cylinder.

EXAMPLE 3   **Solving problems involving the lateral and surface area of a cylinder**

3 The can shown at the right is shaped like a right cylinder with no top base. It has a radius of 5 inches and a height of 7 inches. Estimate the lateral and surface area of the outside of the can.

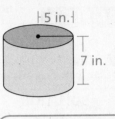

- **SOLUTION**

Step 1 Estimate the lateral area of the can.

$$7(2 \times \pi \times 5) \approx 7(30) \approx 210$$

Step 2 Estimate the surface area of the can. Add the area of the bottom of the can.

$$210 + \pi \times 5^2 = 210 + 75$$
$$= 285$$

The lateral area ≈ 210 in.^{2} and the surface area ≈ 285 in.^{2}.

Go Online
PHSchool.com
Visit: PHSchool.com
Web Code: ayp-0098

A **cone** is a three-dimensional figure with a **base** bounded by a circle, a point outside the plane of the base called the **vertex,** and a curved **lateral surface** connecting the vertex to each point on the boundary of the base. The **height** h of a cone is the length of a perpendicular segment drawn from the vertex to any point in the plane of the base.

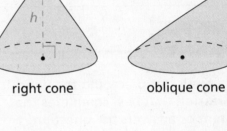

right cone   oblique cone

A cone is a **right cone** if the segment joining the center of the base to the vertex is perpendicular to the plane of the base. Otherwise, the cone is *oblique.*

In a right cone, the distance between the vertex and any point on the boundary of the base is called the **slant height** ℓ of the cone. In the figure at the right, notice that the slant height ℓ, height h, and the radius r of the base form a right triangle. Therefore, the Pythagorean Theorem applies.

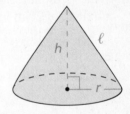

$$h^2 + r^2 = \ell^2$$

This relationship helps derive formulas for the lateral and surface area of a right cone.

Area Formulas for a Right Cone

The lateral area L.A. of a right cone with radius r and slant height ℓ is given by the formula below.

$$\text{L.A.} = \pi r \ell$$

The surface area S.A. is given by the formula below.

$$\text{S.A.} = \pi r \ell + \pi r^2 = \pi r (\ell + r)$$

345

You can use the formulas to find the lateral area and surface area of a right cone.

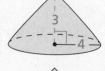

EXAMPLE 4 **Finding areas of a right cone given height and the radius of the base**

4. Find the lateral and surface area of the right cone with height 3 units and the radius of the base 4 units. Use $\pi = 3.14$.

- **SOLUTION**

Step 1 First find the slant height of the cone. This is represented by z in the second sketch at the right.

$$3^2 + 4^2 = z^2 \quad \leftarrow \text{Use the Pythagorean Theorem.}$$
$$z = 5$$

The slant height is 5 units.

Step 2 Apply the formulas for lateral area and surface area.

$$\text{L.A.} = \pi(4)(5) = 20\pi = 62.8$$
$$\text{S.A.} = 20\pi + \pi \times 4^2 = 36\pi = 113.04$$

Therefore, the L.A. = 62.8 square units and the S.A. = 113.04 square units.

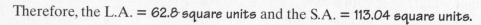

Practice

Choose the letter preceding the word or expression that best completes the statement or answers the question.

1. What is the lateral area of a cylinder with a height of 20 m and a radius of 7 m? Use $\pi = 3.14$.

   A. 879.2 m^2 **C.** 872.92 m^2

   B. 307.72 m^2 **D.** 2373.84 m^2

2. If the radius and height of a cylinder are doubled, the surface area is

   A. quadrupled.   **C.** doubled.

   B. squared.   **D.** tripled.

3. What is the surface area of a cone with radius of 15 cm and a slant height of 25 cm?

   A. 706.65 cm^2 **C.** 1962.5 cm^2

   B. 1884 cm^2 **D.** 1177.5 cm^2

4. Which represents the lateral area of a right cylinder whose radius is 2 ft and whose height is 2 ft?

   A. 12.56 ft^2 **C.** 37.68 ft^2

   B. 25.12 ft^2 **D.** 50.24 ft^2

5. The circumference of the circular base of this cone-shaped funnel is 12π cm. Which gives its lateral area?

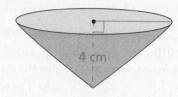

   A. 135.65 cm^2

   B. 339.12 cm^2

   C. 271.3 cm^2

   D. 248.69 cm^2

In Exercises 6–7, find the surface area of each right cylinder. Round your answer to the nearest tenth.

6
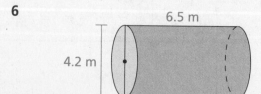

7

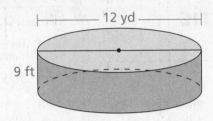

8 One paint roller has length 11 in. and diameter 2 in. A second roller has length 7 in. and diameter 3 in. Which roller can spread more paint in one revolution?

9 One gallon of paint covers 250 ft². How many gallons of paint are needed to paint the top and lateral face of a right cylinder with radius 4.4 ft and height 9 ft? Give your answer to the nearest quarter of a gallon.

In Exercises 10–14, find the lateral and surface area as specified. Give exact answers.

10 the surface area of a right cone with radius 10 cm and height 24 cm

11 the lateral area of a right cone whose radius is 15 cm and whose slant height is 20 cm

12 the lateral area of a right cone with height 12 ft and radius 5 ft

13 the lateral area of a right cylinder with equal radius and height of 10 in.

14 the surface area of a right cylinder with radius 2.8 cm and height 6 cm.

In Exercises 15–18, find the lateral area and surface area of each figure. Show all necessary work.

15

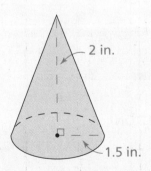

16

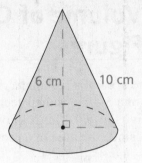

17

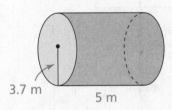

18

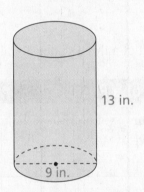

In Exercises 19–20, find the surface area of each figure.

19

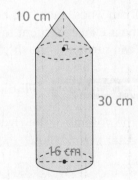

20

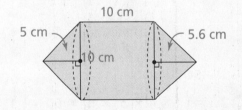

Volume of Other Geometric Figures

12.3

New Jersey Standards

4.2.E.1.1 Use Pythagorean Theorem

4.2.E.2.1 Find perimeter, area, and volume

4.3.E.2.3 Estimate perimeter, area, and volume

Consider the area of a rectangle, $A = lw$, and try to visualize the rectangle as the base of a 3-dimensional rectangle, with identical rectangles stacked on top to give it its *height*. This is known as a rectangular prism. It is easy to deduce that since the area of a rectangle is lw, the volume of a rectangular prism is $V = lwh$.

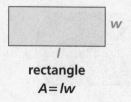

rectangle
$A = lw$

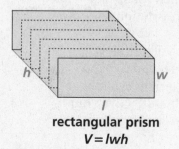

rectangular prism
$V = lwh$

Note

Area is 2-dimensional and is measured in square units. Since volume involves all three dimensions, it is measured in cubic units.

The **volume** of a three-dimensional figure is the amount of space it encloses.

Volume of a Prism

The volume V of a prism is the product of the area B of a base and the height h of the prism.

$$V = Bh$$

In the special case of a right rectangular prism with length l, width w, and height h, you can show that a formula for volume V is $V = (lw)h$, or simply $V = lwh$.

A **cube** is a prism whose faces are bounded by six congruent squares. The edges of a cube are all congruent to each other. For a cube with edges of length e, you can further refine the formula for volume as $V = (e^2)e$, or $V = e^3$.

EXAMPLES 1 and 2   **Finding the volume of a prism**

1 Find the volume of the right triangular prism below.

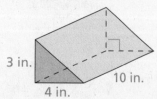

3 in.

10 in.

4 in.

■ SOLUTION

$V = \left(\frac{1}{2} \times 4 \times 3\right) \times 10 = 60 \leftarrow V = Bh$

The volume is 60 in.³.

2 Find the volume of the right rectangular prism below.

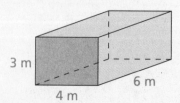

3 m

6 m

4 m

■ SOLUTION

$V = 3 \times 4 \times 6 = 72 \leftarrow V = lwh$

The volume is 72 m³.

The volume of a cylinder is found by multiplying the area of the base of the cylinder by the height of the cylinder. The formula for the volume of a cylinder is similar to the formula for the volume of a prism.

Volume of a Cylinder

The volume V of a cylinder with base of radius r is the product of the area B of a base and the height h of the cylinder.

$$V = Bh, \text{ or } V = \pi r^2 h$$

EXAMPLES 3 through 6   **Finding the volume of a cylinder**

Find the volume of each cylinder. Use $\pi = 3.14$.

3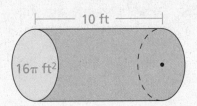

SOLUTION

$V = (16\pi)(10)$ ← $V = Bh$
  $= 160\pi$
  ≈ 502.4

The volume is 502.4 ft^3.

4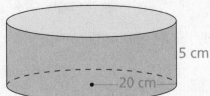

SOLUTION

$V = \pi(20)^2(5)$ ← $V = \pi r^2 h$
  $= 2000\pi$
  ≈ 6280

The volume is 6280 cm^3.

5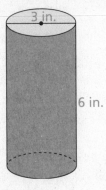

SOLUTION

$V = \pi(1.5)^2(6)$
  $= 13.5\pi$
  $= 42.39$

The volume is 42.39 in.^{3}.

6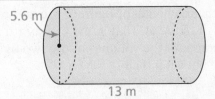

SOLUTION

$V = \pi(5.6)^2(13)$
  $= 407.68\pi$
  $= 1280.12$

The volume area is 1280.12π m^3.

If you compare a cone to a cylinder with the same base and height you find that the cylinder is exactly three times the volume of the cone, or the cone is $\frac{1}{3}$ the volume of the cylinder.

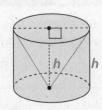

Volume of a Cone

The volume V of a cone with radius of the base r and height h is given by $V = \frac{1}{3}\pi r^2 h$.

Go Online
PHSchool.com
Visit: PHSchool.com
Web Code: ayp-0104

EXAMPLE 7 **Finding the volume of a right cone given radius of the base and slant height**

 7 Find the volume of a right cone whose base has radius 6 cm and whose slant height is 10 cm. Use $\pi = 3.14$.

■ **SOLUTION**

To find the volume of a right cone, find its height h.

$$h^2 + 6^2 = 10^2 \quad \leftarrow h^2 + r^2 = \ell^2$$
$$h = 8$$

Apply the formula for volume.

$$V = \tfrac{1}{3}\pi(6)^2(8) = 96\pi = 301.44$$

The volume is $301.44 \ cm^3$.

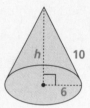

The volume of a pyramid is $\frac{1}{3}$ the volume of a prism with the same base and height. Therefore, the $\boldsymbol{V}_{\text{pyramid}} = \frac{1}{3}\boldsymbol{Bh}$, where $\boldsymbol{B}$ is the area of the base.

If you examine the two right rectangular prisms below, you will see that the length, width, and height of figure B are all 1.5 times the corresponding dimensions of figure A. That is, the prisms are similar, with similarity ratio 1.5. If you compare the volumes of the two figures, you will see a special relationship between them.

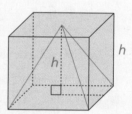

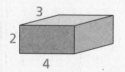

Figure *A*

Volume of Figure *A*
$2 \times 3 \times 4 =$
24 cubic units

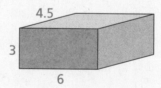

Figure *B*

Volume of Figure *B*
$2(1.5) \times 3(1.5) \times 4(1.5) =$
24×1.5^3 cubic units

Similarity and Volume

If figure B is similar to figure A, and the linear dimensions of figure B are s times the linear dimensions of figure A, then:

$$\text{volume of figure } B = s^3 \times \text{volume of figure } A$$

EXAMPLE 8   Using similarity ratios to determine volume and weight

8 A box in the shape of a right rectangular prism has length 10 in., width 8 in., and height 15 in. When completely filled, the box and its contents weigh 0.05 pounds per cubic inch. A second box has linear dimensions twice those of the corresponding dimensions of the first box. Find the weight of the second box when it is completely filled with contents of the same type.

■ SOLUTION

Step 1 Write an expression for the volume of the second box.

$$V = (10 \times 8 \times 15) \times 2^3 \quad \leftarrow \text{ Use } V = lwh \text{ and multiply by } s^3.$$

Step 2 Multiply by 0.05.

$$\text{weight} = 0.05[(10 \times 8 \times 15) \times 2^3]$$

The larger box and contents weigh 480 pounds.

(A calculator solution is shown at the right.)

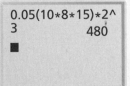

0.05(10*8*15)*2^
3   480
■

Practice

Choose the letter preceding the word or expression that best completes the statement or answers the question.

1 Two figures have a similarity ratio of 2:5. The volume of the smaller figure is 16 cubic inches. Find the volume of the larger figure.

   A. 40 in.^{3} C. 125 in.^{3}

   B. 250 in.^{3} D. 80 in.^{3}

2 Which could be the dimensions of a right rectangular prism that has the same volume as a right rectangular prism with volume 576 cubic units?

   A. length 12, width 8, and height 12

   B. length 12, width 6, and height 10

   C. length 12, width 12, and height 4

   D. length 2, width 2, and height 1.5

3 Which is the volume of a right rectangular prism with length 9, width 2, and height 3?

   A. $2 \times 3 \times 9$

   B. $2(2 \times 2 + 2 \times 9 + 3 \times 9)$

   C. $(2 \times 3 \times 9)^3$

   D. $2(2 + 3 + 9)$

4 The volume of a right rectangular prism is 20 in.^{3} The linear dimensions of a larger prism are 1.5 times those of the original prism. Which is the volume of the larger prism?

   A. 40 in.^{3} C. 30 in.^{3}

   B. 80 in.^{3} D. 67.5 in.^{3}

In Exercises 5–7, solve the problem. Clearly show all necessary work.

5 A small can of soup is shaped like a right cylinder with diameter 7 cm and height 12 cm. A family-size can of the soup has diameter 10 cm and height 15 cm. Which contains more soup, two small cans or one family-size can?

6 What is the volume of a right rectangular prism with length 12 ft, width 15 ft, and height 3 ft? Give your answer to the nearest tenth of a cubic yard.

7 Find the weight of the contents of a right rectangular prism with length 13 ft, width 6 ft, and height 2.5 ft if the contents weigh 0.02 pounds per cubic inch.

12.4 Surface Area and Volume of a Sphere

New Jersey Standards

4.2.E.2.1 Find perimeter, area, and volume

4.3.E.2.3 Estimate perimeter, area, and volume

A **sphere** is the set of all points in space a fixed distance r, the radius, from C, the center. A **great circle** is any circle in the plane that contains the center of the sphere.

The **circumference** of a sphere is the circumference of any great circle of the sphere.

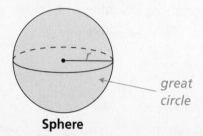

great circle

Sphere

Surface Area and Volume of a Sphere

The surface area S.A. of a sphere with radius r is given by S.A. $= 4\pi r^2$.

The volume V of a sphere with radius r is given by $V = \frac{4}{3}\pi r^3$.

Note

A sphere has only a surface area and no lateral area since it has no base.

EXAMPLE 1   **Finding the surface area of a sphere**

1 Estimate the surface area of the sphere at the right if its radius is 7 cm.

- **SOLUTION**

S.A. $= 4\pi r^2 = 4(\pi)7^2 = 4(49)\pi = 196\pi \approx 200(3) \approx 600 \text{ cm}^2$

You can use this formula to find the volume of a sphere.

Go Online
PHSchool.com

Visit: PHSchool.com
Web Code: ayp-0465

EXAMPLE 2   **Finding surface area and volume of a sphere**

2 Find the surface area and volume of a sphere whose radius is 12 ft. Use $\pi = 3.14$.

- **SOLUTION**

$$S.A. = 4\pi r^2 \rightarrow 4\pi(12)^2 = 576\pi \approx 1808.64$$
$$V = \frac{4}{3}\pi r^3 \rightarrow \frac{4}{3}\pi(12)^3 = 2304\pi \approx 7234.56$$

The surface area is 1808.64 ft^2.
The volume is 7234.56 ft^3.
(A calculator solution is shown at the right.)

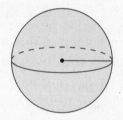

```
4(3.14)12²
         1808.64
(4/3)(3.14)12^3
         7234.56
```

352

The volume of a sphere is completely determined by its radius. Suppose that sphere A has radius r and sphere B has radius $2r$. Then you can compare the volume V_B of sphere B to the volume V_A of sphere A as follows.

$$\frac{V_B}{V_A} = \frac{\frac{4}{3}\pi(2r)^3}{\frac{4}{3}\pi(r)^3} = \frac{(2r)^3}{r^3} = \frac{2^3 r^3}{r^3} = 2^3$$

So, if the radius is doubled, then the volume is multiplied by 2^3.

Similarity and Volume of a Sphere

If the radius r of a sphere is multiplied by a, then the volume of the sphere with radius ra is a^3 times that of the sphere with radius r.

Practice

Choose the letter preceding the word or expression that best completes the statement or answers the question.

1 Find the volume of the sphere shown below.

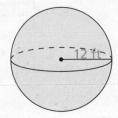

12 ft

A. 7238.23 ft^3 **C.** 3619.11 ft^3

B. 2412.74 ft^3 **D.** 1809.56 ft^3

2 Which has the same volume as a sphere with radius 6?

A. a cylinder with radius 4 and height 16

B. a cone with radius 6 and height 24

C. a cube whose edges are 6

D. a pyramid with base area 36 units^2 and height 6

In Exercises 3–4, find the surface area and volume of each sphere.

3 a sphere whose diameter is 10 in.

4 a sphere with surface area of 144π ft^2

In Exercises 5–7, solve the following problems. Clearly show all necessary work.

5 Find the surface area and volume of the sphere shown here. The circle contains the center of the sphere and its radius is the same as the radius of the sphere. Give exact answers and answers rounded to the nearest tenth of a unit.

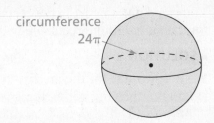

circumference
24π

6 Find the volume of the space inside the cylinder but outside the sphere. Give an exact answer.

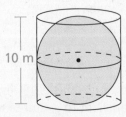

10 m

7 A sphere has a volume of 85.3π cm^3. What is the volume of a sphere with a radius that is 3 times longer?

353

12.5 Maximum and Minimum Values for Geometric Measurements

New Jersey Standards

4.2.E.2 Finding attributes of shapes

You have already learned how to find values such as perimeter and surface area of geometric figures. In this lesson, you will learn how different measurements are related. For example, if you fix the perimeter of a rectangle, you will investigate how to maximize the area.

EXAMPLE 1   **Finding maximum areas by investigation**

1 You have 28 yd of fencing for a rectangular-shaped garden. What are the dimensions of the garden that maximize the area of the garden?

■ **SOLUTION 1**

Draw different rectangles with a perimeter of 28 yd and calculate each area.

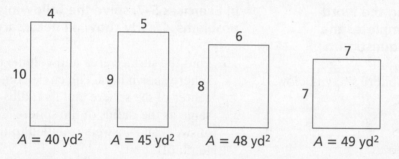

$A = 40$ yd^2 $A = 45$ yd^2 $A = 48$ yd^2 $A = 49$ yd^2

You can determine from the rectangles above that the maximum area for the garden is the rectangle with dimensions 7 yd × 7 yd, a square.

■ **SOLUTION 2**

Write a formula for the area of the garden. If the width is w and the length is l, then the perimeter is $2w + 2l = 28$.

$$2w + 2l = 28 \qquad \leftarrow \textbf{Solve this equation for } l.$$

$$l = \frac{28 - 2w}{2} \qquad \leftarrow \textbf{Subtract } 2w \textbf{ and then divide by 2.}$$

$$l = 14 - w \qquad \leftarrow \textbf{Simplify.}$$

Next, substitute this expression for l in the formula for area of a rectangle, $A = lw$.

$$A = lw$$
$$A = (14 - w)w \qquad \leftarrow \textbf{Substitute } 14 - w \textbf{ for } l.$$
$$A = 14w - w^2 \qquad \leftarrow \textbf{Apply the Distributive Property.}$$

You can use the TABLE function on a graphing calculator or spreadsheet to estimate the area as the dimensions change. Enter the formula for area as $Y = 14X - X^2$. Next, press the TABLE key. You can then analyze the values in the table to find that the maximum area for these values occurs at $X = 7$. Therefore, since the length of the garden is $14 - X$, you can calculate that the maximum area occurs when the width is 7 and the length is 7.

Note

Additional rectangles need not be drawn because the rectangles will begin to duplicate. For example, a garden with a length of 10 yd and a width of 4 yd will have the same area as a garden with a width of 10 yd and a length of 4 yd.

Note

You can also calculate from the table that the minimum area will occur when the width is 1. Therefore, the height is $14 - X = 13$, and the $A = 13$ yd^2.

You can also examine the graph of the function for area $Y = 14X - X^2$ to determine that the maximum value of the graph occurs at approximately $x = 7$.

X	Y_1
1	13
2	24
3	33
4	40
5	45
6	48
7	49
8	48
9	45

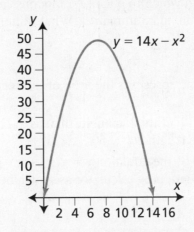

You can use the graphing calculator to explore the surface area and volume of geometric objects. Recall that the volume of a square prism V is the area of the base times the height, $V = Bh = s^2h$. Also recall that the surface area of a square prism is S.A. $= 2s^2h + 4wh$.

EXAMPLE 2　Analyzing surface area of a square prism

2　A square prism has $V = 1000$ cm^3. Analyze the surface area of the prism as the length and width of the base are changed. What dimensions minimize the surface area of the prism? Describe the prism.

■ **SOLUTION**

Let X represent whole number values for the base side length.

Solve $V = s^2h$ for height h.

$$1000 = s^2h$$

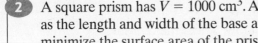

$$h = \frac{1000}{s^2}$$

Therefore, S.A. $= 2s + \frac{4000}{s}$.

Enter the equation for height $h = \frac{1000}{s^2}$ in Y_1 and the equation

for S.A. $= 2s + \frac{4000}{s}$ in Y_2. Press TABLE to view the table.

You can see from the third column on the graphing calculator that the smallest surface area is when $s = h$ or 10; the square prism or cube.

X	Y_1	Y_2
1	1000	4002
2	250	2004
3	111.11	1339.3
4	62.5	1008
5	40	810
6	27.77	678.67
7	20.4	585.43
8	15.6	516
9	12.34	462.44
10	10	420
11	8.26	385.64

You have used whole number values to estimate measurements. You can use a graphing calculator to make more precise measurements.

EXAMPLE 3   **Finding a maximum with a graph**

3 A farmer has 100 ft of fence in which to enclose a rectangular region. He wishes to enclose the maximum area. What dimensions should he use for the rectangle?

■ **SOLUTION**

Step 1 Find the equation that represents the area of the rectangular region and graph it.

If x represents the width of the rectangle, then as in Example 2, you can solve and find that the length is $l = 50 - x$.

The area is then given by the equation $y = x(50 - x)$. This function can be graphed by using a graphing calculator as shown below.

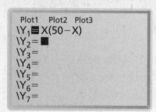 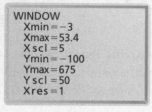 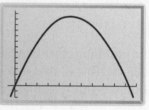

Step 2 Determine the dimensions of the rectangle that encloses the maximum area.

Use the calculator to determine the maximum point (vertex) of this graph. The vertex will correspond to the maximum area of the region.

Press **2nd** **CALC** to view the menu shown below. Select menu item **4: maximum.** Respond to the prompts for a left bound, right bound, and a guess, selecting a point to the left, to the right, and as close to the vertex as possible.

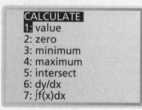 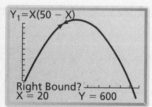 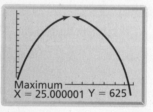

The calculator indicates that the maximum area occurs when the width = 25 ft. Therefore, the rectangle whose perimeter is 100 ft and encloses the maximum area is a square whose side length is 25 ft.

Practice

Choose the letter preceding the word or expression that best completes the statement or answers the question.

1 The perimeter of a rectangle is 120 ft. What dimensions give the maximum area?

A. 25 ft × 35 ft   **C.** 30 ft × 30 ft

B. 20 ft × 40 ft   **D.** 15 ft × 45 ft

2 In Exercise 1, what is the maximum area?

A. 875 ft^2 **C.** 950 ft^2

B. 900 ft^2 **D.** 1000 ft^2

3 If a square prism has a volume of 150 cm³, what dimensions give the smallest surface area?

A. 5 cm × 5 cm × 6 cm

B. 4.17 cm × 6 cm × 6 cm

C. 5.3 cm × 5.3 cm × 5.3 cm

D. 3 cm × 5 cm × 6 cm

4 Determine which cylinder has the greatest surface area.

A. a cylinder with a height of 8 cm and a radius of 3 cm

B. a cylinder with a height of 4 cm and a radius of 8 cm

C. a cylinder with a height of 8 cm and a radius of 4 cm

D. a cylinder with a height of 6 cm and a radius of 3 cm

5 Juan is making a dog pen enclosed by 60 ft of fencing. Which expression could be used to find the maximum possible area of the pen?

A. $A = x(60 - x)$

B. $A = x(30 - x)$

C. $A = 2x + 2(30 - x)$

D. $A = 2x + 2(60 - x)$

6 Nadia buys a rug that has an area of 30 ft². What measurements approximate the minimum possible perimeter of the rug?

A. 15 ft × 2 ft

B. 5 ft × 6 ft

C. 10 ft × 3 ft

D. 30 ft × 1 ft

7 A square prism is twice as tall as its base side length. What expression could be used to find the minimum surface area of the prism?

A. $6h + 8h^2$

B. $8h + 8h^2$

C. $8h^2$

D. $10h^2$

In Exercises 8–11, solve the problem. Clearly show all necessary work.

8 A parking lot has a perimeter of 300 meters. Write an expression for the area of the parking lot in terms of one of its side lengths. Use a table to approximate the dimensions that will maximize the area of the parking lot.

9 You build a deck with an area of 30 m² along the side of your house. You want to minimize the length of railing used on three sides of the deck (you do not need railing for the side of the deck against the house). Write an expression for the perimeter of the deck in terms of one of its side lengths. Use a graphing calculator to approximate the minimum length of railing needed.

10 A triangular prism has an equilateral base and a height that is 3 times longer than one of the sides of the base. If the volume of the prism is 20 cubic units, use a graphing calculator to estimate the maximum possible side length of the base.

11 A projectile is launched into the air from the ground. Its path can be modeled by the equation $y = -x^2 + 16x$. What is the maximum height of the projectile? How long after launch does the projectile reach its maximum height? Explain your reasoning.

12 Barb has 44 ft of fencing to enclose a pen for her pet. Write an equation to maximize the area of the pen. What dimensions maximize the area of the pen?

12.6 Perspective Views of 3D Objects

New Jersey Standards

4.2.A.2 Draw 3D objects on dot paper

Everything you draw on paper is a 2-dimensional (length and width) representation of a 3-dimensional object (length, width, and height). Using isometric dot paper, you can construct an isometric drawing to show the 3 sides of a 3-dimensional figure.

Go Online
PHSchool.com

Visit: PHSchool.com
Web Code: ayp-0348

EXAMPLES 1 through 3　**Constructing isometric drawings**

Construct an isometric drawing of each of the cube structures below.

1

■ SOLUTION

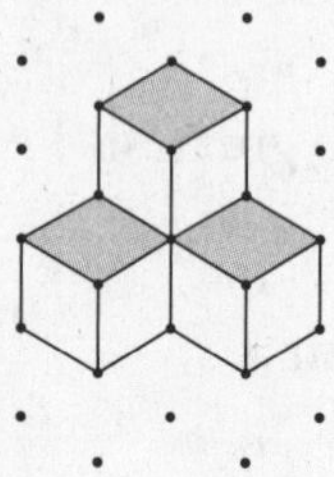

2

■ SOLUTION

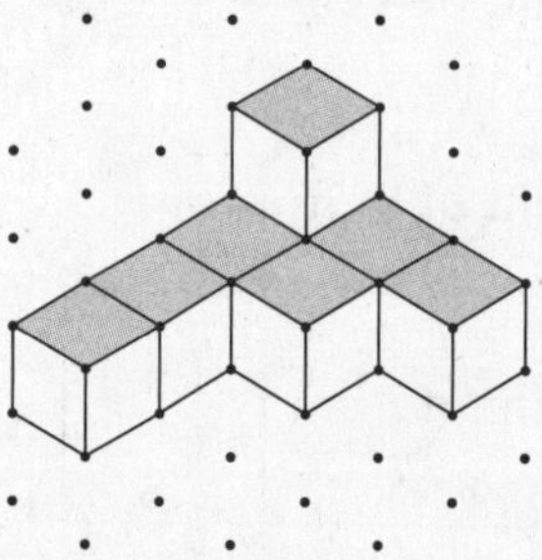

3

■ SOLUTION

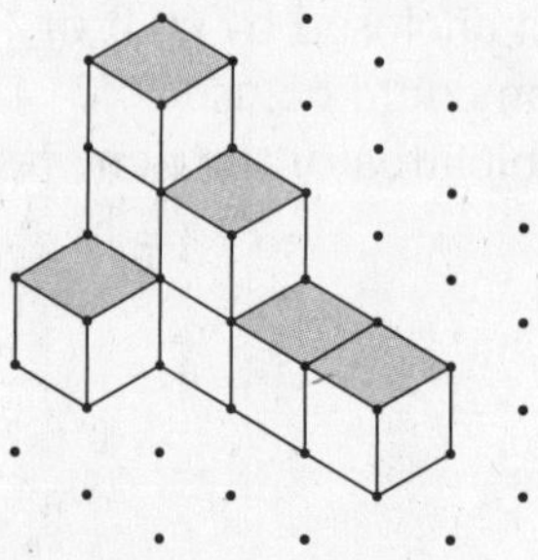

After you have constructed an isometric drawing, you can construct an **orthographic drawing** that shows a top view, a front view, and a right view.

Orthographic drawings show the various depths of an object from a single perspective. In cube constructions, the depth of any given unit of the shape is related to the cube units around it. If the depth of any given cube is the same as that of any adjacent cube, the individual cube units are drawn as a single unit. This notation allows you to interpret the position of any given cube in relation to adjacent cubes.

In the next examples, notice that adjacent cubes of the same depth are drawn as a continuous shape rather than as the individual cube units used in the isometric drawings above.

358

Go Online
PHSchool.com
Visit: PHSchool.com
Web Code: ayp-0349

Construct the top, front, and right views of the figure. Assume that no blocks are hidden from view.

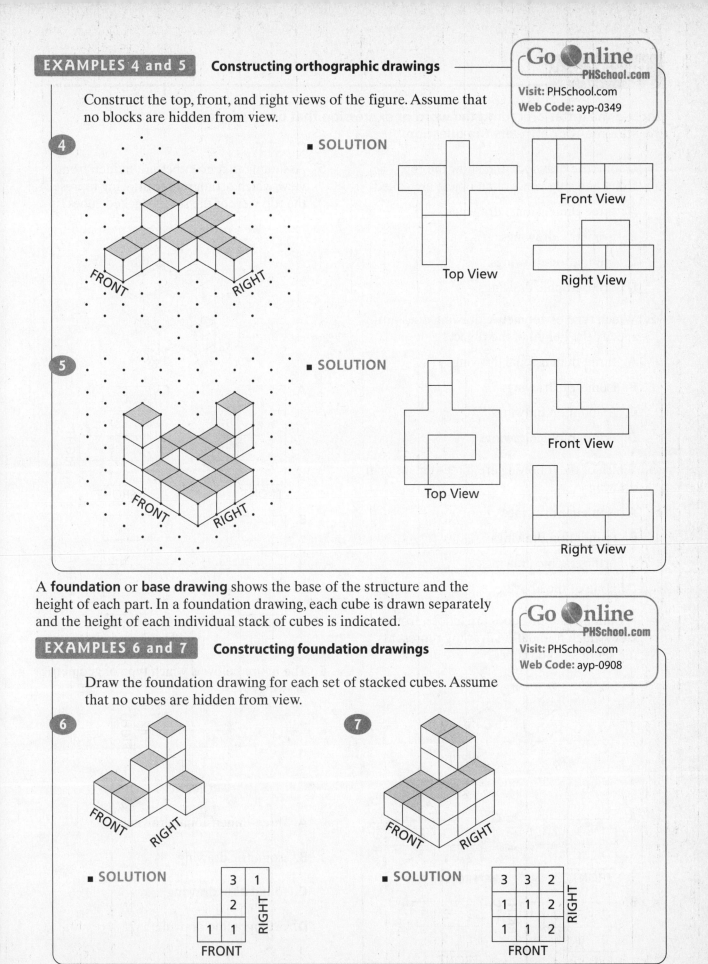

4

FRONT   RIGHT

■ **SOLUTION**

Front View

Top View

Right View

5

FRONT   RIGHT

■ **SOLUTION**

Top View

Front View

Right View

A **foundation** or **base drawing** shows the base of the structure and the height of each part. In a foundation drawing, each cube is drawn separately and the height of each individual stack of cubes is indicated.

Go Online
PHSchool.com
Visit: PHSchool.com
Web Code: ayp-0908

EXAMPLES 6 and 7   **Constructing foundation drawings**

Draw the foundation drawing for each set of stacked cubes. Assume that no cubes are hidden from view.

6

FRONT   RIGHT

■ **SOLUTION**

	3	1
	2	
1	1	

FRONT   RIGHT

7

FRONT   RIGHT

■ **SOLUTION**

3	3	2
1	1	2
1	1	2

FRONT   RIGHT

359

Choose the letter preceding the word or expression that best completes the statement or answers the question.

1 Geometric drawings that show the top, front, and side views of an object are called

    A. three-dimensional drawings.

    B. isometric drawings.

    C. foundation drawings.

    D. orthographic drawings.

2 Which type of geometric drawing does not specify the height of the object?

    A. three-dimensional drawings

    B. isometric drawings

    C. foundation drawings

    D. orthographic drawings

3 Which of the following are three-dimensional drawings?

    A. isometric drawings

    B. foundation drawings

    C. orthographic drawings

    D. none of the above

4 Assuming that no cubes are hidden from view, which foundation drawing represents the set of stacked cubes?

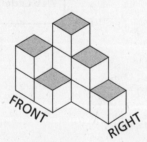

    A.

1	3	2	1
2	1		

FRONT

    B.

2	3	2	1
2	1		

FRONT

    C.

3	2	1
2	1	

FRONT

    D.

3	2	1
2	1	

FRONT

5 Assuming that no cubes are hidden from view, which orthographic drawing represents the top view of the set of stacked cubes?

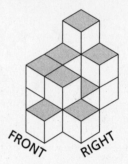

    A.

    C.

    B.

    D.

6 The figure below is which type of geometric drawing?

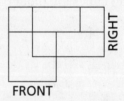

    A. three-dimensional drawing

    B. isometric drawing

    C. foundation drawing

    D. orthographic drawing

7 Which stack of cubes does the orthographic front view represent?

FRONT

A.
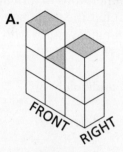

C.
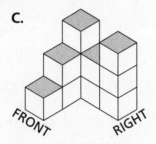

B.
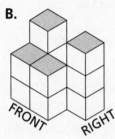

D.
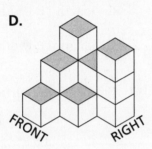

8 Which stack of cubes does the foundation drawing represent?

3	2	3
2	1	
1		

FRONT

A.
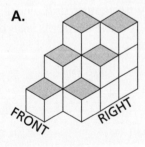

C.
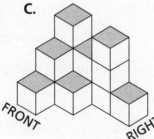

B.
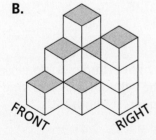

D.
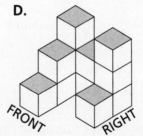

In Exercises 9–11, draw the specified view of the figure. Assume that no cubes are hidden from view.

9 Top view

10 Front view

11 Right view

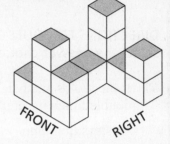

In Exercise 12, construct an isometric drawing of each figure. Assume that no cubes are hidden from view.

12

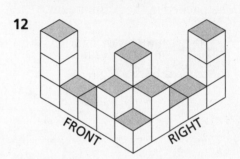

In Exercises 13–14, construct a foundation drawing of each figure. Assume that no cubes are hidden from view.

13   **14**

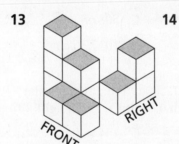 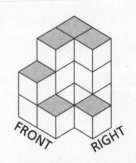

In Exercises 15–16, use the foundation drawing to construct an isometric drawing of each figure. Assume that no cubes are hidden from view.

15

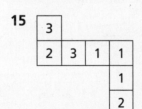

16

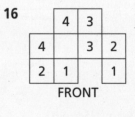

DIRECTIONS FOR QUESTIONS 1–18: For each of the questions below, select the answer choice that is best for each case.

1 If the radius and height of a cylinder are doubled then its lateral area

   A. stays the same.   C. triples.

   B. doubles.   D. quadruples.

2 Find the number of 3 ft × 2 ft × 1 ft boxes that can be packed in the prism below.

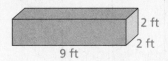

   A. 6   C. 2

   B. 3   D. 4

3 The cone-shaped paper cup has a height 9 cm and a rim with circumference 12π cm. What is the volume of the cup?

   A. 169.56 cm^2 C. 508.68 cm^2

   B. 339.12 cm^2 D. 1017.36 cm^2

4 Which is the surface area of a rectangular prism with length 6, width 5, and height 4?

   A. 120 units^2 C. 154 units^2

   B. 148 units^2 D. 180 units^2

5 Suppose that a spherical scoop of ice cream sets in the cone below so that its great circle is along the circumference of the cone, how much space is left inside the cone?

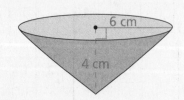

   A. 75.4 cm   C. 150.8 cm

   B. 301.6 cm   D. 226.2 cm

6 Which could be the dimensions of a right rectangular prism that has the same volume as a right rectangular prism with volume 132 cubic units?

   A. length 11, width 2, and height 5

   B. length 12, width 6, and height 2

   C. length 11, width 2, and height 6

   D. length 11, width 2, and height 12

7 Find the total surface area of the cone.

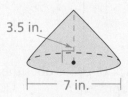

   A. 76.93 in.^{2} C. 92.32 in.^{2}

   B. 75.83 in.^{2} D. 261.56 in.^{2}

8 Find the weight of the contents of a right rectangular prism with length 15 ft, width 3 ft, and height 3.5 ft if the contents weigh 0.25 pounds per cubic ft.

   A. 39.375 pounds

   B. 630 pounds

   C. 33.75 pounds

   D. 540 pounds

9 The volume of a right cylinder is 245 cm^3. If the radius of the cylinder is 5.5 cm, find its height to the nearest hundredth.

   A. 2.08 cm   C. 2.41 cm

   B. 2.58 cm   D. 3.61 cm

10 A rectangle has an area of 504 in.² What is the maximum possible perimeter of the rectangle?

    A. 1000 in.   C. 508 in.

    B. 260 in.   D. 1010 in.

11 A rectangular fish tank has dimensions 2.5 ft × 2 ft × 1.5 ft. It is packed in a 3 ft × 4 ft × 3 ft box. How much filler is needed to securely package the aquarium for shipping?

    A. 2.5 ft³   C. 42 ft³

    B. 4 ft³   D. 28.5 ft³

12 A can has a diameter of 3 inches and a height of 4.5 inches. How much paper will it take to create the label for the can?

    A. 84.78 in.²

    B. 42.39 in.²

    C. 31.79 in.²

    D. 127.17 in.²

13 The length of each side of the Pyramid of Cheops originally measured 756 ft and its slant height was 482 ft. Find the lateral area of the pyramid when it was built.

    A. 926,100 ft²

    B. 728,784 ft²

    C. 927,315 ft²

    D. 730,296 ft²

14 If the lateral area of a right cylinder with a 1 ft radius is 9π ft², what is its height?

    A. 6 ft   C. 4.5 ft

    B. 2.9 ft   D. 0.9 ft

15 Which best describes the prism below?

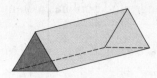

    A. triangular prism

    B. rectangular prism

    C. pentagonal prism

    D. hexagonal prism

16 A cylinder has one lateral face. What is the shape of its face?

    A. circle   C. rectangle

    B. square   D. triangle

17 A right triangular prism has how many lateral faces?

    A. 1   B. 2   C. 3   D. 4

18 Assuming no cubes are hidden from view, which foundation drawing represents the set of stacked cubes?

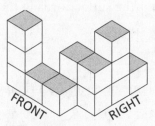

A.

			1
			3
		2	2
3	1	1	

C.

3			
1	2		
1	2	3	1

B.

3			
1	2		
1	2	3	1

D.

	2	3	1
1	2		
1			
3			

DIRECTIONS FOR 19–21: Solve each problem and show your work.

19 A circular aboveground pool has a diameter of 8 ft and stands 5.5 ft off the ground.

- Find the surface area of the pool. (Hint: The top of the pool is not enclosed.)

- If the pool company charges an installation fee of $11 per square ft, how much will the installation cost?

- If the pool is to only be filled to 75% of its maximum capacity, how much water can it hold?

20 Use the figure below.

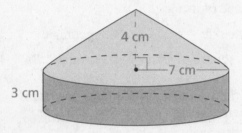

- Find the volume of the right cylinder.

- Find the volume of the right cone.

- Find the volume of the entire figure.

- What is the surface area of the entire figure?

21 A right cone nests inside a right cylinder as shown.

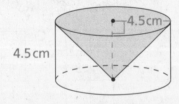

- Find the volume of the inscribed cone.

- Find the volume of the cylinder.

- Find the volume of the space inside the cylinder but outside the cone.

13 Transformational Geometry

NEW JERSEY

The First Baseball Game

For years, baseball has been called our national pastime. The game of baseball we know evolved during the 1840s in Manhattan after an engineer named Alexander Cartwright came up with a set of rules similar to the rules we use today. Cartwright and a group of New York professionals (bankers, brokers, salesmen) began playing ball together, calling themselves the New York Knickerbocker Base Ball Club. With green space becoming scarcer in Manhattan, the club moved across the Hudson River to practice at the Elysian Fields in Hoboken, New Jersey. On June 19, 1846, the Knickerbockers took on the New York Base Ball Club in Hoboken, losing 23–1 in the first organized baseball game between two teams.

New Jersey Standards

4.2.B.1 Transformations
     on a geometric
     object

In geometry, a transformation is a mapping of a figure, called the **preimage**, to a corresponding figure called its **image.** One type of transformation is a line reflection.

In the figure at the right, △ABC, the preimage, is reflected over line m, which results in △$A'B'C'$ (read A prime, B prime, C prime).

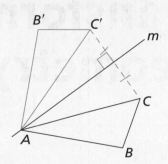

Line m is the line of reflection and acts like a mirror. For example, the image point C' must be the exact same distance from line m as its corresponding preimage point C. Further, the segment that connects the points C and C' must be perpendicular to line m. This reflection maps all of the points of △ABC onto △$A'B'C'$.

Note that because point A lies directly on the line of reflection, it is its own image. A point that is its own image under a transformation is called a **fixed point.**

You can use what you know about reflections to sketch an image of a figure under a reflection.

Go Online
PHSchool.com
Visit: PHSchool.com
Web Code: ayp-0889

EXAMPLE 1 — **Sketching the image of a polygon under a reflection**

1 Sketch the image of a right triangle △ABC reflected in a line not intersecting the triangle.

■ SOLUTION

Step 1	**Step 2**	**Step 3**	**Step 4**
Sketch a right triangle △ABC and line p not intersecting it.	Construct lines through A, B, and C that are perpendicular to p.	Place points A', B', and C' the same distance from p as points A, B, and C are.	Join points A', B', and C' to make △$A'B'C'$, the image of △ABC under the reflection.

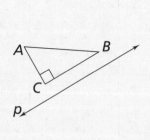
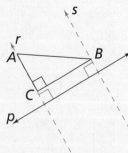
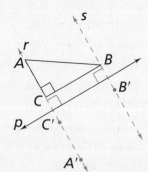
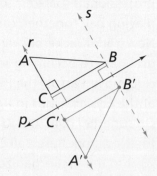

In the coordinate plane, there are three common line reflections.

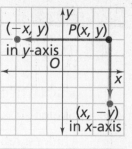

Special Reflections

The image of $P(x, y)$ under a **reflection in the x-axis** is the point $P'(x, -y)$.

$$P(x, y) \qquad \rightarrow \qquad P'(x, -y)$$

The image of $P(x, y)$ under a **reflection in the y-axis** is the point $P'(-x, y)$.

$$P(x, y) \qquad \rightarrow \qquad P'(-x, y)$$

The image of $P(x, y)$ under a **reflection in $y = x$** is the point $P'(y, x)$.

$$P(x, y) \qquad \rightarrow \qquad P'(y, x)$$

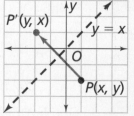

A **reflection in a point** is another type of transformation. In the figure at the right, the image of point P is itself and the image of any other point Q is the point Q' where P is the midpoint of $\overline{QQ'}$. Point P is called the *point of reflection*. This diagram shows $\overline{QR}$ and its image $\overline{Q'R'}$ under a reflection in point P.

EXAMPLE 2   **Sketching the image of a polygon under a reflection in an axis**

 The vertices of $\triangle ABC$ are $A(-3, 3)$, $B(6, 6)$, and $C(4, 1)$. Sketch the image of this triangle after reflection in the x-axis and in the y-axis.

■ **SOLUTION**

Sketch $A(-3, 3)$, $B(6, 6)$, and $C(4, 1)$ and $\triangle ABC$.
Under a reflection in the x-axis, replace y with $-y$.

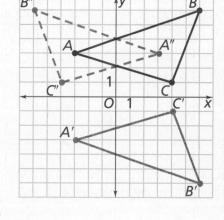

$P(x, y)$	$\rightarrow$	$P'(x, -y)$
$A(-3, 3)$	$\rightarrow$	$A'(-3, -3)$
$B(6, 6)$	$\rightarrow$	$B'(6, -6)$
$C(4, 1)$	$\rightarrow$	$C'(4, -1)$

Graph $A'(-3, -3)$, $B'(6, -6)$, and $C'(4, -1)$. Draw $\triangle A'B'C'$. The image is shown with solid blue segments.

Under a reflection in the y-axis, replace x with $-x$.

$P(x, y)$	$\rightarrow$	$P''(-x, y)$
$A(-3, 3)$	$\rightarrow$	$A''(3, 3)$
$B(6, 6)$	$\rightarrow$	$B''(-6, 6)$
$C(4, 1)$	$\rightarrow$	$C''(-4, 1)$

Graph $A''(3, 3)$, $B''(-6, 6)$, and $C''(-4, 1)$. Draw $\triangle A''B''C''$.
The image is shown with dashed blue segments.

Now consider a special point of reflection in the coordinate plane. Suppose that the point of reflection is the origin. In that case, the coordinates (x, y) of any point in the preimage are reflected to $(-x, -y)$ in the image.

EXAMPLE 3   **Sketching an image under reflection in the origin**

 The vertices of $\triangle ABC$ are $A(-3, 3)$, $B(6, 6)$, and $C(4, 1)$. Sketch the image of this triangle after reflection in the origin.

■ SOLUTION

Sketch $A(-3, 3)$, $B(6, 6)$, and $C(4, 1)$ and $\triangle ABC$.

Under a reflection in the origin, replace x with $-x$ and y with $-y$.

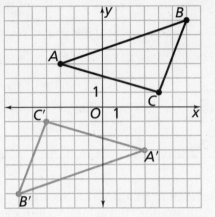

$P(x, y)$	$\rightarrow$	$P'(-x, -y)$
$A(-3, 3)$	$\rightarrow$	$A'(3, -3)$
$B(6, 6)$	$\rightarrow$	$B'(-6, -6)$
$C(4, 1)$	$\rightarrow$	$C'(-4, -1)$

Graph $A'(-3, 3)$, $B'(-6, -6)$, and $C'(-4, -1)$. Draw $\triangle A'B'C'$. The image is shown with solid blue segments.

A figure may be its own image after reflection across a line. For example, if m is a line of reflection, then the image of octagon $ABCDEFGH$ after reflection across line m is the octagon $ABCDEFGH$. A figure in the plane has **line symmetry** if it is its own image after reflection across some line in the plane. The line of reflection is called a **line of symmetry**.

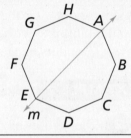

EXAMPLE 4   **Drawing lines of symmetry**

 Sketch all lines of symmetry for a square.

■ SOLUTION

Sketch a square. The diagonals of the square are lines of symmetry. The lines passing through the midpoints of opposite sides are, too.

Go Online
PHSchool.com
Visit: PHSchool.com
Web Code: ayp-0441

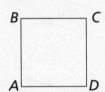 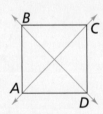 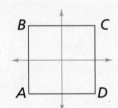

Lines of symmetry can be identified and specifically named when the figure is placed on a coordinate grid.

EXAMPLE 5   **Identifying lines of symmetry**

 Does the figure at the right have line symmetry? Explain.

■ SOLUTION

The line $y = 0$ (the x-axis) and the line $x = 2.5$ are lines of symmetry. The figure is its own image after a reflection over either of those two lines.

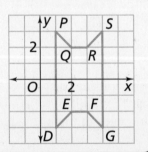

Practice

Choose the letter preceding the word or expression that best completes the statement or answers the question.

1 Which represents the image of $G(4, -3)$ after reflection in the x-axis?

   A. $G'(-4, -3)$ **C.** $G'(-4, 3)$

   B. $G'(4, 3)$ **D.** $G'(-3, 4)$

2 Which represents the image of $X(-3, -7)$ after reflection in the y-axis?

   A. $X'(-3, 7)$ **C.** $X'(3, 7)$

   B. $X'(3, -7)$ **D.** $X'(7, 3)$

3 For which point is $V(3, 2)$ the image of $M(x, y)$ after reflection in the line $y = x$?

   A. $M(-3, -2)$ **C.** $M(-2, 3)$

   B. $M(2, 3)$ **D.** $M(3, -2)$

4 For which point is $A(9, -3)$ the image of $N(x, y)$ after reflection in the origin?

   A. $N(-9, -3)$ **C.** $N(-9, 3)$

   B. $N(9, -3)$ **D.** $N(-3, 9)$

5 Which is the image of $K(3, 1)$ after reflection in the line $y = -1$?

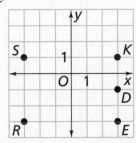

   A. D **B.** E **C.** R **D.** S

6 Which represents the image of $P(x, y)$ after reflection in the line $y = 0$?

   A. $P'(x, -y)$ **C.** $P'(-x, y)$

   B. $P'(-x, -y)$ **D.** $P'(y, -x)$

In Exercise 7, sketch the image of the given figure in the specified line.

7 $\triangle ABC$ in line z

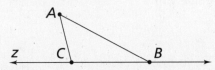

8 Copy this figure. Sketch all lines of symmetry.

In Exercises 9–12, write the coordinates of the image under the specified reflection.

9 $\triangle RST$ with vertices having coordinates $R(1, 1)$, $S(5, 1)$, and $T(5, 3)$ in the x-axis

10 $\triangle NBA$ with vertices having coordinates $N(1, 1)$, $B(5, 1)$, and $A(5, 3)$ in the y-axis

11 quadrilateral $EUDP$ with vertices having coordinates $E(3, 3)$, $U(5, 3)$, $D(1, -1)$, and $P(-1, -1)$ in the origin

12 quadrilateral $EUDP$ with vertices having coordinates $E(3, 3)$, $U(5, 3)$, $D(1, -1)$, and $P(-1, -1)$ in the line $y = x$

In Exercises 13–15, solve the problem. Clearly show all necessary work.

13 One vertex of a quadrilateral is $A(-3, -2)$. Find the coordinates of the other three vertices that complete a quadrilateral symmetric about the x-axis and the y-axis.

14 One vertex of a quadrilateral is $P(4, 2)$. Find the coordinates of the other three vertices that complete a quadrilateral symmetric about the lines $x = 1$ and $y = 1$.

15 Sketch the reflection of the parabola in the line $y = x$.

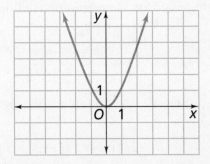

13.2 Translations and Rotations

A **translation** is a transformation of a figure in which each point is moved the same distance in the same direction. The sketch at the right shows the translation of $\triangle ABC$ along the arrows shown in blue. The image of each vertex of $\triangle ABC$ is found by placing a point at the tip of the arrows shown. When you join the vertices, the image is $\triangle A'B'C'$.

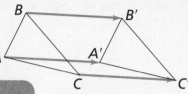

Characteristics of a Translation

If a line segment is translated, the image is a line segment congruent to the original line segment.

If an angle is translated, the image is an angle congruent to the original angle.

The orientation of the image is the same as that of the original object.

Note

A translation is also called a slide.

EXAMPLE 1 **Translating a polygon in the plane**

1 Draw the image of rectangle $WXYZ$ under the translation shown by the arrow.

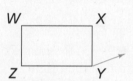

- **SOLUTION**

Step 1 Draw an arrow from each of the three remaining vertices. Make sure that the arrows are the same length, point in the same direction, and are parallel to the original arrow.

Step 2 Draw the rectangle whose vertices are at the tips of the arrows.

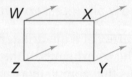 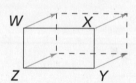

In the coordinate plane, you can represent a translation by specifying how far the object slides horizontally along the x-axis and how far the object slides vertically along the y-axis.

Translations

The image of $P(x, y)$ under a translation a units horizontally and b units vertically is given by:

$$P(x, y) \rightarrow P'(x + a, y + b)$$

If you translate $P(-2, 4)$ 5 units to the right and 3 units down, the image will be as follows:

$$P(-2, 4) \rightarrow P'(-2 + 5, 4 + (-3)) = P'(3, 1)$$

EXAMPLE 2   **Identifying a translation**

2. The point $A(6, 10)$ is translated to $Q(0, 3)$.
    Which statement accurately describes this translation?

    A. 6 units left and 7 units up   **C.** 6 units left and 7 units down
    B. 6 units right and 7 units up   **D.** 6 units right and 7 units down

    ▪ **SOLUTION**

    Let a be the horizontal distance and b be the vertical distance
    $A(6, 10)$ is translated.

    $$0 = 6 + a \quad \text{and} \quad 3 = 10 + b$$
    $$a = -6 \quad \text{and} \quad b = -7$$

    The translation is 6 units left and 7 units down. Choose C.

Note

If $a > 0$, slide right.
If $a < 0$, slide left.
If $b > 0$, slide up.
If $b < 0$, slide down.

You may need to find the coordinates of an image under a specific translation.

EXAMPLE 3   **Finding the coordinates of the image under a translation**

3. The coordinates of the vertices of $\triangle ABC$ are $A(-1, 2)$, $B(4, 6)$, and $C(3, -2)$.
    Find the coordinates of the image, $\triangle A'B'C'$, under a translation 4 units
    to the left and 2 units down.

    ▪ **SOLUTION**

    $$A(-1, 2) \quad \rightarrow \quad A'(-1 + (-4), 2 + (-2)) = A'(-5, 0)$$
    $$B(4, 6) \quad \rightarrow \quad B'(4 + (-4), 6 + (-2)) = B'(0, 4)$$
    $$C(3, -2) \quad \rightarrow \quad C'(3 + (-4), -2 + (-2)) = C'(-1, -4)$$

A translation results when an object is reflected over two parallel lines.

EXAMPLE 4   **Sketching the image of reflections in parallel lines**

4. Sketch the image of $\triangle ABC$ after reflection across m and then n.

    ▪ **SOLUTION**

    Step 1 Copy the
    given figures.

    Step 2 Reflect $\triangle ABC$
    across line
    m to get
    $\triangle A'B'C'$.

    Step 3 Sketch the
    reflection
    of $\triangle A'B'C'$
    across line n
    to get $\triangle A''B''C''$.

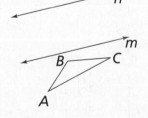

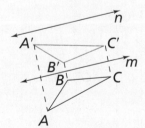

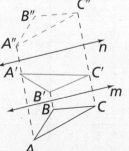

Translations Related to Reflections

If the reflection of A in line m is A' and the reflection of A' over line n parallel to m is A'', then A'' is a translation of A.

Given a translation and the coordinates of the image, you can use equations to find the coordinates of the preimage.

EXAMPLE 5   **Finding the coordinates of a point given its image under a translation**

 After $G(x, y)$ is translated to the right 6 units and down 4 units, the coordinates of the image are $Z(-2, 7)$. Find the coordinates of $G(x, y)$.

■ **SOLUTION**

$$Z(-2, 7) = Z(x + 6, y + (-4))$$
$$-2 = x + 6 \text{ and } 7 = y - 4 \qquad a = 6 \text{ and } b = -4$$
$$x = -8 \text{ and } y = 11$$

Therefore, the coordinates of $G(x, y)$ are $G(-8, 11)$.

When you translate a figure, you slide it to another position in the plane. Under a **rotation** in the plane, you turn a figure using a fixed distance from a fixed point in the plane, called the **center of rotation.** The rotation may be clockwise or counterclockwise. In the diagram at the right, P is rotated counterclockwise 25° about point O to P'.

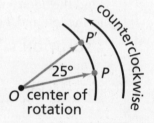

EXAMPLE 6   **Sketching the image of a figure under a rotation**

 Sketch the image of $\triangle PQR$ under a rotation of 90° counterclockwise about O.

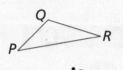

■ **SOLUTION**

Step 1 Copy the given figure. Draw segments joining O to $P, Q,$ and R.

Step 2 Rotate $\overline{OR}, \overline{OQ},$ and $\overline{OP}$ counterclockwise 90°. Use a protractor to measure the 90° angle and a compass to draw $\overline{OR'}, \overline{OQ'},$ and $\overline{OP'}$ equal in length to $\overline{OR}, \overline{OQ},$ and $\overline{OP}$, respectively.

Step 3 Join $P', Q',$ and R' to make $\triangle P'Q'R'$, the image of $\triangle PQR$.

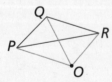 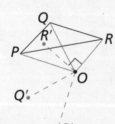 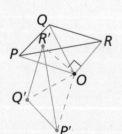

A rotation results when an object is reflected over two intersecting lines. The intersection point of the lines is the center of rotation.

Rotations Related to Reflections

If the reflection of A in line m is A' and the reflection of A' over line n intersecting line m is A'', then A'' is a rotation of A about the point where lines m and n intersect.

Go Online
PHSchool.com
Visit: PHSchool.com
Web Code: ayp-0443

EXAMPLE 7   **Reflecting a figure and its image across intersecting lines**

 Sketch the image of $\triangle ABC$ after a reflection across m and then across n.

■ **SOLUTION**

Step 1   Copy the given figures.

Step 2   Reflect $\triangle ABC$ across line m to get $\triangle A'B'C'$.

Step 3   Sketch the reflection of $\triangle A'B'C'$ across line n to get $\triangle A''B''C''$.

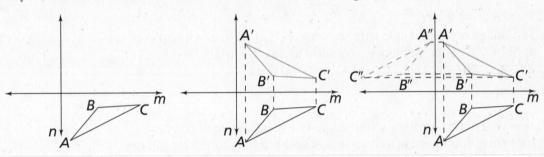

A figure in the plane has **rotational symmetry** if it is its own image after a rotation of 180° or less around some point in the plane. The point is called the **center of symmetry**.

EXAMPLE 8   **Recognizing and identifying rotational symmetry**

 Which figure has rotational symmetry?

   A. square   **B.** letter T   **C.** isosceles trapezoid   **D.** ray

■ **SOLUTION**

Sketch a square and its diagonals. If you rotate the square about the intersection of the diagonals 90° counterclockwise, the image will be the original square. Therefore, a square has rotational symmetry. (A rotation of 90° clockwise about O will also show rotational symmetry.) The correct choice is A.

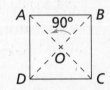

In the coordinate plane, you can rotate a figure 90° counterclockwise about the origin by using the transformation rule on the next page.

90° Counterclockwise Rotation About the Origin

The image of $P(x, y)$ under a 90° counterclockwise rotation about the origin is given by the rule below.

$$P(x, y) \rightarrow P'(-y, x)$$

Go Online
PHSchool.com
Visit: PHSchool.com
Web Code: ayp-0866

EXAMPLE 9 | **Sketching the image of a rotation in the coordinate plane**

9 Sketch the image of the triangle with vertices $A(1, 2)$, $B(5, 3)$, $C(4, 6)$ under a 90° counterclockwise rotation about the origin.

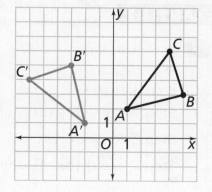

■ **SOLUTION**

Apply the rule for a 90° counterclockwise rotation about the origin.

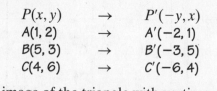

$P(x, y)$	$\rightarrow$	$P'(-y, x)$
$A(1, 2)$	$\rightarrow$	$A'(-2, 1)$
$B(5, 3)$	$\rightarrow$	$B'(-3, 5)$
$C(4, 6)$	$\rightarrow$	$C'(-6, 4)$

The image of the triangle with vertices $A(1, 2)$, $B(5, 3)$, $C(4, 6)$ under a 90° counterclockwise rotation about the origin has $A'(-2, 1)$, $B'(-3, 5)$, and $C'(-6, 4)$ as its vertices.

The rotation of a figure through a 180° angle is a special type of rotation called a **half-turn**. If a figure is its own image under a half-turn, you can say that the figure has **point symmetry**.

180° Rotation About the Origin

The image of $P(x, y)$ under a 180° rotation about the origin is given by:

$$P(x, y) \rightarrow P'(-x, -y)$$

EXAMPLE 10 | **Sketching the image of a half-turn in the coordinate plane**

10 Sketch the image of the triangle with vertices $X(2, 2)$, $Y(5, 3)$, $Z(4, 5)$ under a half-turn about the origin.

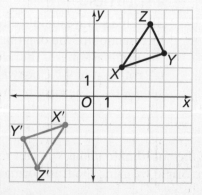

■ **SOLUTION**

Apply the rule for a 180° rotation about the origin.

$P(x, y)$	$\rightarrow$	$P'(-x, -y)$
$X(2, 2)$	$\rightarrow$	$X'(-2, -2)$
$Y(5, 3)$	$\rightarrow$	$Y'(-5, -3)$
$Z(4, 5)$	$\rightarrow$	$Z'(-4, -5)$

The coordinates of the image of $\triangle XYZ$ are $X'(-2, -2)$, $Y'(-5, -3)$, and $Z'(-4, -5)$.

Practice

Choose the letter preceding the word or expression that best completes the statement or answers the question.

1 Under which transformation will $P'(2, -4)$ be the image of $P(1, 1)$?

  A. reflection in the x-axis

  B. translation 1 unit right and 5 units down

  C. rotation of 180° about the origin

  D. translation 1 unit right and 1 unit up

2 What are the coordinates of the image of $A(3, 5)$ under a translation 5 units left and 4 units down?

  A. $A'(-2, 1)$ **C.** $A'(8, 9)$

  B. $A'(-2, 9)$ **D.** $A'(8, 1)$

3 Which transformation is illustrated below?

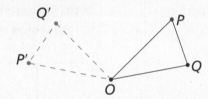

  A. rotation of $\triangle OPQ$ about O

  B. translation of $\triangle OPQ$ along $\overrightarrow{OQ}$

  C. translation of $\triangle OPQ$ along $\overrightarrow{OP}$

  D. reflection of $\triangle OPQ$ across $\overleftrightarrow{PQ}$

4 Which of the following are the coordinates of the image of $G(4, 6)$ under a 90° counterclockwise rotation about the origin?

  A. $G(4, -6)$ **C.** $G(-6, 4)$

  B. $G(-4, 6)$ **D.** $G(-6, -4)$

5 Which represents the translation under which the image of $H(-3, -5)$ is $H'(7, 0)$?

  A. 10 units right and 5 units down

  B. 10 units right and 5 units up

  C. 10 units left and 5 units down

  D. 10 units left and 5 units up

6 If the length of $\overline{LM}$ is 10 units, what is the length of its image under a half-turn?

  A. 5 units   **C.** 20 units

  B. 10 units   **D.** −10 units

In Exercises 7–12, write the coordinates of the image of the given point under the specified transformation.

7 $A(4, 1)$; half-turn about the origin

8 $B(3, 4)$; 90° counterclockwise rotation about the origin

9 $C(-5, 4)$; translation 2 units left and 4 units up

10 $D(-5, 4)$; translation 4 units right and 4 units down

11 $E(3, 2)$; reflection in the x-axis followed by a reflection in the line $y = -3$

12 $F(3, 2)$; reflection in the x-axis followed by a reflection in the y-axis

In Exercises 13–15, graph the given points in the coordinate plane. In the same plane, sketch the image under the specified transformation.

13 quadrilateral $ABCD$ with vertices $A(1, 0)$, $B(4, 7)$, $C(6, 4)$, and $D(5, 0)$; translation 2 units left and 2 units up

14 $\triangle PQR$ with vertices $P(3, 0)$, $Q(0, 4)$, $R(0, 0)$; 90° counterclockwise rotation about the origin

15 $\triangle XYZ$ with vertices $X(4, 0)$, $Y(0, 4)$, and $Z(0, 0)$; half-turn about the origin

In Exercises 16–17, perform the transformation indicated.

16 Sketch the indicated translation of $\triangle CDE$.

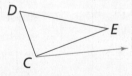

17 Sketch the 90° clockwise rotation of $\triangle LTY$ about T.

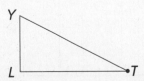

13.3 Dilations

New Jersey Standards

4.2.B.1 Transformations on a geometric object

An **isometry** is a transformation under which the image and preimage are congruent. Reflections, translations, and rotations are all isometries.

A **dilation (similarity transformation)** with center O is a transformation in which a given figure is enlarged or reduced. The measures of the angles in the image equal the measures of the corresponding angles in the preimage. However, the dimensions of the image are n times those of the preimage. The **scale factor** n determines the *enlargement* or *reduction* of the preimage.

In the diagram at the right, you can see a dilation of $\triangle ABC$ with center O and scale factor 1.5. Notice $\triangle ABC \sim \triangle A'B'C'$.

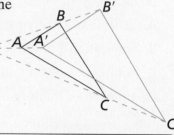

$$\frac{OA'}{OA} = \frac{OB'}{OB} = \frac{OC'}{OC} = 1.5 \text{ and } \frac{A'B'}{AB} = \frac{B'C'}{BC} = \frac{A'C'}{AC} = 1.5$$

EXAMPLE 1   **Identifying a scale factor for a dilation**

1. When $\triangle PQR$ is dilated, its image is $\triangle P'Q'R'$ and $PQ = 2P'Q'$. What is the scale factor?

   A. 2   **B.** 1   **C.** 0.5   **D.** 0.25

   ■ **SOLUTION**

   Under the dilation, the original figure is $\triangle PQR$ and the image is $\triangle P'Q'R'$.

   $$\triangle PQR \quad \rightarrow \quad \triangle P'Q'R'$$

   If $PQ = 2P'Q'$, then $P'Q' = 0.5(PQ)$. So, $\frac{P'Q'}{PQ} = 0.5$.

   The correct choice is C.

> **Note**
>
> The scale factor is the ratio of side lengths in the image to the corresponding lengths in the preimage.

A dilation of any given scale factor can be sketched by multiplying the given scale factor by the distance from the center to any given point on the figure.

EXAMPLE 2   **Sketching a dilation in the plane**

2. Sketch the image of square $WXYZ$ under a dilation with center O and scale factor 0.5.

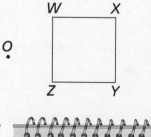

   ■ **SOLUTION**

   Step 1
   Draw lines connecting each vertex of the preimage to the center.

   Step 2
   Multiply the distance from the origin to any vertex by the scale factor. The product represents a vertex of the image. Locate and label all points.

   Step 3
   Connect the image points respectively to create the dilation.

> **Note**
>
> Scale factors less than 1 will result in a reduction of the preimage.
>
> Scale factors greater than 1 will result in an enlargement of the preimage.

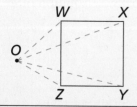
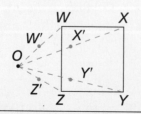
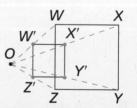

You can perform a dilation in the coordinate plane with the origin as the center of dilation by using a transformation rule.

Dilations in the Coordinate Plane

The image of $P(x, y)$ under a dilation in the coordinate plane with the origin as center of dilation and a scale factor k (k a nonzero real number) is $P'(kx, ky)$.

$$P(x, y) \quad \rightarrow \quad P'(kx, ky)$$

Note that the previous rule applies only when the dilation has center at the origin.

Visit: PHSchool.com
Web Code: ayp-0894

EXAMPLE 3   **Sketching a dilation in the coordinate plane**

3. A triangle has vertices $K(1, 2)$, $L(1, 4)$, and $M(4, 1)$. Sketch the image of $\triangle KLM$ under a dilation with center of dilation at the origin and scale factor 2.

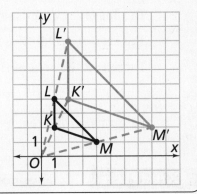

■ **SOLUTION**

Sketch $K(1, 2)$, $L(1, 4)$, and $M(4, 1)$ and $\triangle KLM$.
Under the dilation with the origin as center and scale factor 2:
$K(1, 2) \rightarrow K'(2, 4) \qquad L(1, 4) \rightarrow L'(2, 8) \qquad M(4, 1) \rightarrow M'(8, 2)$

Plot $K'(2, 4)$, $L'(2, 8)$, and $M'(8, 2)$ to form $\triangle K'L'M'$.

Characteristics of a Dilation

Let k represent a positive real number.

If a segment is dilated with a scale factor k, the image is a line segment whose length is k times that of the original.

If an angle is dilated with a scale factor k, the image is an angle congruent to the original angle.

You can use one pair of points to find the scale for the dilation of an entire figure.

EXAMPLE 4   **Finding unknown coordinates under a dilation**

4. Under a dilation with center at the origin, the image of $\triangle ABC$ is $\triangle A'B'C'$. Complete this table of coordinates.

preimage	image	preimage	image	preimage	image
$A(3, 6)$	$A'(4.5, 9)$	$B(-4, 0)$	$B'(\ \ , \ \ )$	$C(\ \ , \ \ )$	$C'(9, -3)$

■ **SOLUTION**

Find the scale. Because $\frac{4.5}{3} = \frac{9}{6} = 1.5$, the scale factor is 1.5.

coordinates of B': $B'(-4 \times 1.5, 0 \times 1.5) = B'(-6, 0)$ ← **Multiply to find the coordinates of the image.**

coordinates of C: $C'(9 \div 1.5, -3 \div 1.5) = C(6, -2)$ ← **Divide to find the coordinates of the original.**

If A is the area of the preimage, then the area of the image A' after a dilation with scale factor k is $A' = k^2A$.

 EXAMPLE 5   **Relating areas of figures under a dilation**

5 A triangle has vertices $P(1, 5)$, $Q(6, 1)$, and $R(1, 1)$. Under a dilation with scale factor 2 and center at the origin, the image of the triangle is $\triangle P'Q'R'$. What is the area of $\triangle P'Q'R'$?

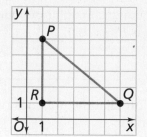

■ **SOLUTION**

Sketch a coordinate diagram and graph $P(1, 5)$, $Q(6, 1)$, and $R(1, 1)$. Find the area of $\triangle PQR$.

$$\text{Area of } \triangle PQR = \tfrac{1}{2}(RQ)(RP) = \tfrac{1}{2}(6 - 1)(5 - 1) = 10$$

The image $\triangle P'Q'R'$ is similar to $\triangle PQR$ and the similarity ratio is $2 : 1$.

The area of $\triangle P'Q'R'$ is four times the area of $\triangle PQR$.

Therefore, the area of $\triangle P'Q'R'$ is 4(10) square units, or 40 square units.

You can perform two different transformations on the same object, one after the other.

EXAMPLE 6   **Composition of transformations**

6 $\triangle RST$ has vertices $R(1, 1)$, $S(0, 4)$, and $T(5, 2)$. Find the coordinates of $\triangle R'S'T'$ under a 90° counterclockwise rotation around the origin and a dilation scale factor 2 with the origin as the center.

■ **SOLUTION**

		90° counterclockwise rotation around the origin		Dilation scale factor 2
$P(x, y)$	$\rightarrow$	$P'(-y', x')$	$\rightarrow$	$P''(2(-y'), 2(x'))$
$R(1, 1)$	$\rightarrow$	$R'(-1, 1)$	$\rightarrow$	$R''(2(-1), 2(1)) = R''(-2, 2)$
$S(0, 4)$	$\rightarrow$	$S'(-4, 0)$	$\rightarrow$	$S''(2(-4), 2(0)) = S''(-8, 0)$
$T(5, 2)$	$\rightarrow$	$T'(-2, 5)$	$\rightarrow$	$T''(2(-2), 2(5)) = T''(-4, 10)$

The coordinates of the final image are $R''(-2, 2)$, $S''(-8, 0)$, and $T''(-4, 10)$.

Practice

Choose the letter preceding the word or expression that best completes the statement or answers the question.

1 Under a dilation with center at $O(0, 0)$, the image of $A(-4, 2)$ is $A'(-2, 1)$. What is the scale factor for the dilation?

   A. 0.5   **C.** 2

   B. 1   **D.** −2

2 Under a dilation with scale factor 0.25 and center at $O(0, 0)$, what is the image of $A(-4, 2)$ after the dilation?

   A. $A'(-1, 8)$ **C.** $A'(-1, 0.25)$

   B. $A'(-1, 0.5)$ **D.** $A'(-100, 50)$

3 Identify the scale factor for this dilation. The image of $\overline{AB}$ is $\overline{A'B'}$.

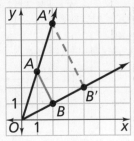

A. 0.5   **B.** 1   **C.** 2   **D.** 3

4 What are the coordinates of a line segment with the endpoints $R(2,2)$ and $S(5,6)$ after a dilation with the origin as the center and a scale factor 2 followed by a dilation with the origin as center and a scale factor of 3?

A. $R''(7,7)$; $S''(11,12)$

B. $R''(10,10)$; $S''(25,30)$

C. $R''(12,12)$; $S''(30,36)$

D. $R''(6,6)$; $S''(15,18)$

5 What are the coordinates of parallelogram $C'D'E'F'$ after $C(-7,2)$, $D(2,2)$, $E(0,-2)$, and $F(-9,-2)$ are dilated with the origin as the center with scale factor 0.5?

A. $C'(-3.5,1)$, $D'(1,1)$, $E'(0,-1)$, $F'(-4.5,-1)$

B. $C'(-3.5,-1)$, $D'(1,1)$, $E'(0,-1)$, $F'(4.5,1)$

C. $C'(-35,-10)$, $D'(10,10)$, $E'(0,-10)$, $F'(45,10)$

D. $C'(-35,10)$, $D'(10,10)$, $E'(0,-10)$, $F'(-45,-10)$

6 Under a dilation with the origin as center and scale factor 4, the image of $\triangle ABC$ is $A'(3,6)$, $B'(7,1)$, $C'(6,6)$. What are the coordinates of A, B, and C?

A. $A(0.75,1.5)$, $B(1.75,0.25)$, $C(1.5,1.5)$

B. $A(7,10)$, $B(11,5)$, $C(10,10)$

C. $A(-1,2)$, $B(3,-3)$, $C(2,2)$

D. $A(12,24)$, $B(28,4)$, $C(24,24)$

7 If the coordinates of $\triangle XYZ$ are $X(-1,5)$, $Y(3,-1)$, $Z(-2,-3)$, and the coordinates of $\triangle X'Y'Z'$ after a dilation with the origin as the center are $X'(-2.5,12.5)$, $Y'(7.5,-2.5)$, $Z'(-5,-7.5)$, what is the scale factor?

A. 1.5   **B.** 4.5   **C.** 2.5   **D.** 4

In Exercises 8–10, sketch the image of each dilation.

8 The center of dilation is X and the scale factor is 0.5.

9 The center of dilation is O and the scale factor is 2.

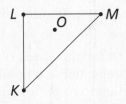

10 Plot the following points of the polygon and then sketch the dilation. The center of dilation is $O(0,0)$. The vertices are $A(-1,1)$, $B(1,2)$, $C(1,-2)$, and $D(-2,-1)$. The scale factor is 1.5.

In Exercises 11–12, write the coordinates of the vertices of the image of each polygon under the dilation with the given scale factor and the origin as center of dilation.

11 $\triangle ABC$ with vertices $A(-2,1)$, $B(3,1)$, and $C(-2,5)$; scale factor 1.5

12 the square $WXYZ$ with vertices $W(-3,3)$, $X(3,3)$, $Y(3,-3)$, and $Z(-3,-3)$; scale factor 4

In Exercises 13–14, find the coordinates of the vertices of the image of the given figure after each pair of transformations.

13 the line segment with endpoints $X(-3,1)$ and $Y(3,4)$ after a translation 4 units right and 2 units down followed by a dilation with the origin as center and scale factor 3

14 the line segment with endpoints $A(0,-2)$ and $T(3,5)$ after a dilation with the origin as center and scale factor 2 followed by a dilation with the origin as center and scale factor 0.5

13.4 Composite Transformations

You know that multiple transformations can be applied to a figure one after the other. In the figure below, $\triangle ABC$ has been translated, resulting in $\triangle A'B'C'$, and then this image is reflected in line m, resulting in $\triangle A''B''C''$. This is called a **composition** of transformations.

The notation for such a combination of transformations—in this case, "a translation of $\triangle ABC$ to $\triangle A'B'C'$ and then a reflection of $\triangle A'B'C'$ over line m"—is $R_m \circ T_{a,b}$. R_m denotes the reflection over line m, and $T_{a,b}$ denotes the translation of a units on the x-axis and b units on the y-axis. Similarly, the notation that denotes a 90° rotation about point N is $Rot_{N,90°}$.

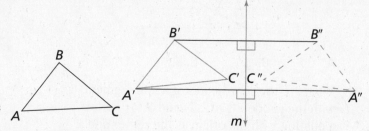

Notice that the translation listed last in the notation is performed first, followed by the reflection. Composite transformation notation lists the first transformation to be performed last. For example, the notation $T_{a,b} \circ Rot_{Q,90°} \circ R_n$ denotes that first the object is to be reflected over line n, then rotated 90° about point Q, and finally translated a units on the x-axis and b units on the y-axis.

You can use transformation notation to determine which transformations to perform and in what order.

EXAMPLE 1   Performing composite transformations

1. Perform the composite transformation $R_m \circ Rot_{P,90°}$ on $\triangle ABC$.

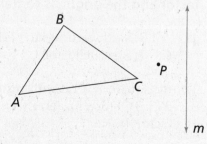

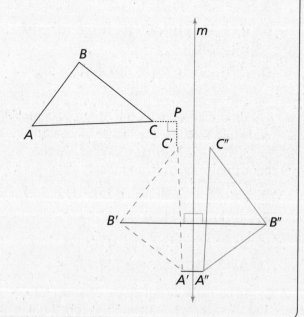

■ SOLUTION

Remember that the transformations are performed right to left. Therefore, the rotation is performed first, resulting in the dashed $\triangle A'B'C'$. Then the reflection over line m is performed, resulting in the image of this composite transformation, $\triangle A''B''C''$.

Choose the letter preceding the word or expression that best completes the statement or answers the question.

1 Which of the following accurately denotes the composition transformation of pentagon ABC to pentagon $A''B''C''$ shown below?

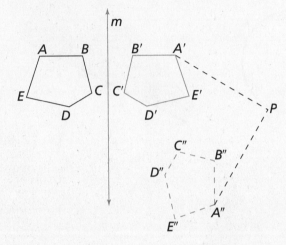

A. $Rm \circ Rot_{P,90°}$

C. $T_{a,b} \circ R_m$

B. $T_{a,b} \circ Rot_{P,90°}$

D. $Rot_{P,90°} \circ R_m$

2 What composite transformation is shown below?

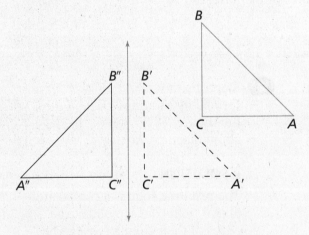

A. a reflection followed by a translation

B. a translation followed by a rotation

C. a dilation followed by a reflection

D. a translation followed by a reflection

3 What transformation is shown first below?

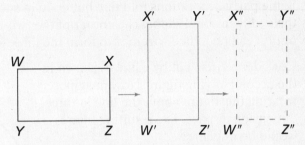

A. rotation of 90° counterclockwise

B. translation

C. rotation of 180° counterclockwise

D. reflection

In Exercises 4–5, use the following diagram.

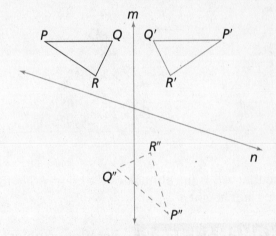

4 Which transformation is performed last in the composition?

A. the reflection of $\triangle PQR$ over line m

B. the reflection of $\triangle PQR$ over line n

C. the reflection of $\triangle P'Q'R'$ over line m

D. the reflection of $\triangle P'Q'R'$ over line n

5 Which denotes the composite transformation shown?

A. $R_m \circ R_n$

B. $R_m \circ Rot_{n,180°}$

C. $R_n \circ R_m$

D. $Rot_{n,180°} \circ R_m$

381

New Jersey Standards

4.2.B.1 Transformations on a geometric object

Some party decorations fold flat, but open in such a way that they form a three-dimensional shape. The corner of the two-dimensional shape is rotated until it can be joined together to form the three-dimensional shape.

Consider a circle cut by a line as shown in the accompanying figure. Now imagine rotating this figure about the line in three-dimensional space. The resulting figure would be a sphere.

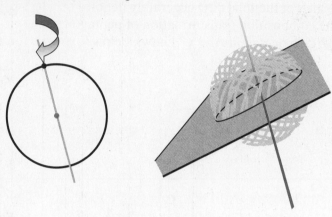

Another example of a solid generated from the rotation of a two-dimensional figure is shown in the sequence of figures below. Triangle *ABC* is rotated 360° about leg *AB*. The solid that results is a right circular cone.

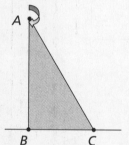 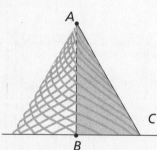 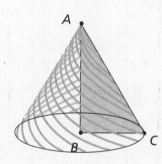

Note that $\overline{AB}$ is the altitude of the cone, $\overline{BC}$ is the radius of the base, and $\overline{AC}$ is the slant height.

EXAMPLES 1 and 2 — Rotating an object from 2D to 3D

 Describe the solid formed by rotating the rectangle *ABCD* 360° about $\overline{AD}$.

■ **SOLUTION**

The resulting solid is a right circular cylinder with height *AD* and radius *DC*.

2 Describe the solid formed by rotating the square *RSTU* 360° about diagonal $\overline{RU}$.

■ **SOLUTION**

The resulting solid is a composite of two right cones joined at the edges of their circular bases. The overall figure has height *RU* and diameter *ST*.

Practice

Choose the letter preceding the word or expression that best completes the statement or answers the question.

1 A triangle is formed by joining the points $A(0,0)$, $B(0,3)$, and $C(4,0)$. Which action on the triangle forms a right circular cone with a height of AC and a base radius of AB?

A. a 360° rotation about the y-axis

B. a 360° rotation about the side AB

C. a 360° rotation about the side BC

D. a 360° rotation about the side AC

2 What solid is formed be rotating the trapezoid in the figure around the y-axis by 360°?

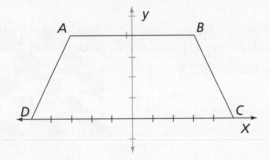

A. sphere

B. flat-topped circular cone

C. cylinder

D. rectangular prism

3 A right circular cone is formed by rotating a right triangle about the y-axis 360°. If one leg of the triangle is 5 in. and the slant height of the cone is 13 in, what is the length of the second leg of the triangle?

A. 5 in.   **C.** 13 in.

B. 12 in.   **D.** $\sqrt{194}$ in.

In Exercises 4–5, use the following information.

A rectangle 20 in. long and 8 in. wide revolves about its short side to form a solid three-dimensional object.

4 Sketch and describe the solid formed by the rotation.

5 Find the volume, lateral area, and surface area of the object.

In Exercises 6–7, use the following information.

An isosceles triangle with altitude 6 in. and base 10 in. revolves about its altitude.

6 Draw and label the object that is formed.

7 What is the volume of the object?

In Exercises 8–9, use the following information.

The right circular cone below has height 7 cm and the radius of the base is 2 cm.

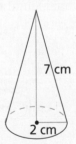

8 What two-dimensional figure could be rotated to form this cone?

9 Describe and trace the rotation.

13.6 Tessellations

A **tessellation** is a covering of the plane with congruent copies of the same region with no holes and no overlaps. Such a covering is also known as a **tiling.** Often walls and floors are tessellated.

In the accompanying figure, the plane has been covered with copies of $\triangle ABC$. $\triangle ABC$ is called the **fundamental region** of the tiling. We say $\triangle ABC$ tessellates the plane.

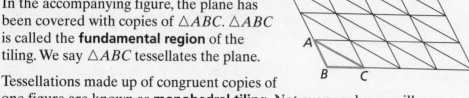

Tessellations made up of congruent copies of one figure are known as **monohedral tiling.** Not every polygon will tessellate the plane. Only three regular polygons will tessellate the plane: the equilateral triangle, the square, and the hexagon.

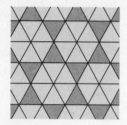

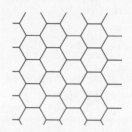

When tessellating the plane, the regular polygons must fill the plane at each vertex. Therefore, the interior angles must be a factor of 360°. The interior angles of the equilateral triangle, square, and hexagon measure 60°, 90°, and 120° respectively, all multiples of 360°.

An infinite number of non regular polygons or abstract shapes can be used to tile the plane. An example is shown at the right.

EXAMPLE 1   **Identifying the fundamental region**

 Trace the fundamental region in the tessellation shown at the right.

■ SOLUTION

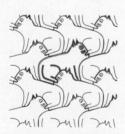

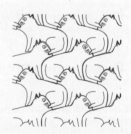

The plane can be tessellated with two or more shapes as long as the sum of the angles at a vertex adds to 360°. A possible tiling that uses equilateral triangles and squares is shown at the right. If two rectangles and three equilateral triangles meet at a vertex, the sum of the interior angles is 360°; 2(90°) + 3(60°) = 360°. A tessellation that uses two different congruent figures is called a **dihedral tiling.**

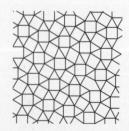

EXAMPLE 2   **Determining tessellation properties**

2   Can the plane be tessellated by using regular octagons and squares?

   ■ **SOLUTION**

The interior angle of a regular octagon is 135°. Because $2(135°) + 90° = 360°$, two regular octagons and a square meeting at each vertex will cover the plane. One such configuration is shown in the figure.

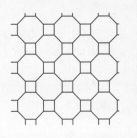

An example of a tessellation that uses three different figures, known as **trihedral tiling,** is shown at the right. This particular tessellation is made up of hexagons, squares, and triangles.

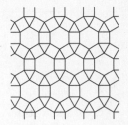

Practice

Choose the letter preceding the word or expression that best completes the statement or answers the question.

1   The covering of the plane with congruent figures with no holes or gaps is known as a

   A. copy.   **C.** covering.

   B. tessellation.   **D.** congruence.

2   When a particular shape tiles the plane, that shape is called

   A. a fundamental region.

   B. a basic region.

   C. an original region.

   D. an essential region.

3   A tessellation made up of dodecagons, hexagons, and squares would be classified as a

   A. monohedral tiling.

   B. dihedral tiling.

   C. trihedral tiling.

   D. quadrahedral tiling.

4   To tile the plane, the sum of the angles that meet at the vertex of the figures used must be

   A. 90°.   **B.** 180°.   **C.** 270°.   **D.** 360°.

5   Which of the following will *not* tessellate the plane?

   A. regular triangle

   B. regular quadrilateral

   C. regular pentagon

   D. regular hexagon

In Exercises 6–7, follow the instructions.

6   Trace the fundamental region in the accompanying tessellation.

7   Verify that the plane could be tiled by using dodecagons and equilateral triangles.

DIRECTIONS FOR QUESTIONS 1–18: For each of the questions below, select the answer choice that is best for each case.

1 What transformation is illustrated in this diagram?

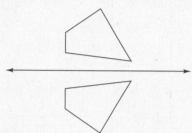

A. reflection   C. rotation

B. translation   D. dilation

2 The vertices of $\triangle ABC$ are $A(0,2)$, $B(0,5)$, and $C(7,2)$. Which point is inside the image of $\triangle ABC$ after it is reflected across the y-axis?

A. $X(-1,-3)$ C. $X(-1,3)$

B. $X(1,-3)$ D. $X(1,3)$

3 Which pair of points M and N could not be the images of the line segment with endpoints $A(3,2)$ and $B(6,4)$ under a translation?

A. $M(4,3)$ and $N(7,5)$

B. $M(2,1)$ and $N(5,3)$

C. $M(7,5)$ and $N(10,8)$

D. $M(-4,8)$ and $N(-1,10)$

4 How many lines of symmetry does the figure below have?

A. 0   B. 2   C. 4   D. 6

5 A polygon $WXYZ$ has four right angles. Two opposite sides have length 6 feet. The other two opposite sides have length 4 feet. How many lines of symmetry does polygon $WXYZ$ have?

A. 0   B. 2   C. 4   D. 6

6 The image of $A(5,-4)$ is $A'(-4,5)$. By which transformation rule is A' the image of A?

A. $P(x,y) \rightarrow P'(x,-y)$

B. $P(x,y) \rightarrow P'(-x,-y)$

C. $P(x,y) \rightarrow P'(-x,y)$

D. $P(x,y) \rightarrow P'(y,x)$

7 Which points A' and B' are the images of the endpoints of $\overline{AB}$ under a 90° counterclockwise rotation about the origin?

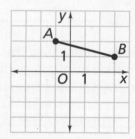

A. $A'(-1,-2)$ and $B'(3,-4)$

B. $A'(2,1)$ and $B'(1,3)$

C. $A'(-2,-1)$ and $B'(-1,3)$

D. $A'(-2,1)$ and $B'(1,-3)$

8 A figure in the plane has point symmetry if it is its own image under which transformation?

A. 90° counterclockwise rotation about the origin

B. half-turn

C. reflection in a line

D. some translation

9 Regular octagons are used to tessellate a plane. What other figure can be used to complete the tessellation?

A. equilateral triangle

B. square

C. isosceles triangle

D. hexagon

10 The quilt pattern shown in the diagram contains pentagons and squares as outlined. What is the measure of the obtuse angles in the pentagons?

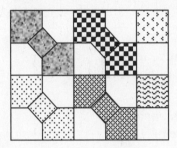

A. 100°   C. 135°

B. 120°   D. 270°

11 $\triangle ABC$ has coordinates of $A(1,6)$, $B(5,2)$, and $C(2,1)$. What are the coordinates of $\triangle A'B'C'$ after a 90° counterclockwise rotation about the origin?

A. $A'(-1,6)$, $B'(-5,2)$, and $C'(-2,1)$

B. $A'(1,-6)$, $B'(5,-2)$, and $C'(2,-1)$

C. $A'(-6,1)$, $B'(-2,5)$, and $C'(-1,2)$

D. $A'(6,-1)$, $B'(2,-5)$, and $C'(1,-2)$

12 Which of the following characteristics of translations are true?

A. A translated line segment is congruent to the original line segment.

B. A translated angle is congruent to the original angle.

C. The orientation of the image is the same as that of the original figure.

D. All of the above.

13 Which figure has rotational symmetry?

A. right triangle

B. equilateral triangle

C. isosceles triangle

D. None of the above.

14 A figure that is dilated with scale factor 1 will be

A. larger than the preimage.

B. smaller than the preimage.

C. the same size as the preimage.

D. none of the above.

15 Which of the following transformations is not an isometry?

A. reflection   C. rotation

B. translation   D. dilation

16 Parallelogram $WXYZ$ lies on the coordinate plane such that $W(-2,2)$, $X(2,1)$, $Y(2,-3)$, and $Z(-2,-2)$. What is the scale factor if $W'(-6,6)$, $X'(6,3)$, $Y'(6,-9)$, and $Z'(-6,-6)$?

A. 2   B. 3   C. 0.5   D. 5

17 Which two consecutive transformations does the figure illustrate?

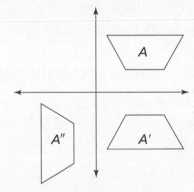

A. translation and reflection

B. rotation and translation

C. reflection and rotation

D. translation and tessellation

18 Find the volume of the cone generated by a triangle with hypotenuse of length 5 ft rotated around a leg of length 4 ft, rounded to the nearest tenth.

A. 12 ft³   C. 37.7 ft³

B. 33.3 ft³   D. 83.7 ft³

DIRECTIONS FOR 19–21: Solve each problem and show your work.

19 The library is located at the origin on the coordinate grid. The locations of three houses are given in terms of blocks east or west and north or south of the library: $A(-4, 3)$, $B(1, 4)$, and $C(1, -2)$.

   • Locate and label the three houses on the coordinate grid.

   • Locate and label three other houses, A', B', and C', relative to the library if they are each 4 blocks east and 2 blocks north of houses A, B, and C.

   • Describe the transformation involved in solving this problem and the effect that the transformation has on the relative distance of A', B', and C' from the library.

20 $\triangle ABC$ lies on the coordinate plane such that $A(-3, 4)$, $B(2, 3)$, and $C(-2, 1)$.

   • What are the coordinates of $\triangle A'B'C'$ when the figure is rotated $180°$ about the origin?

   • What are the coordinates of $\triangle A'B'C'$ when the figure is reflected across the x-axis?

   • What conditions would $\triangle ABC$ have to meet in order for the previous solutions to be identical?

21 Draw a line segment $\overline{AB}$ and complete the following translations.

   • Translate $\overline{AB}$ a distance equal to and perpendicular to $\overline{AB}$. Label the image $\overline{A'B'}$.

   • Translate $\overline{A'B'}$ in the opposite direction, a distance equal to twice the length of $\overline{AB}$ and perpendicular to $\overline{AB}$.

Glossary

GLOSSARY

Abscissa The value of the x-coordinate in an ordered pair.

Absolute value The distance that a number is from zero on a number line. The symbol for the absolute value of a number n is $|n|$.

Acute angle An angle whose measure is greater than $0°$ and less than $90°$.

Acute triangle A triangle that has three acute angles.

Addend One of a set of numbers to be added. In the expression $a + b$, a and b are the addends.

Addition-multiplication method A method used to solve a system of equations in which the equations are added to eliminate one of the variables. In some cases, one or more of the equations must be multiplied by a nonzero constant before the addition can occur. Also called the *elimination method*.

Addition property of equality For all real numbers a, b, and c, if $a = b$, then $a + c = b + c$.

Addition property of inequality For all real numbers a, b, and c,

- If $a < b$, then $a + c < b + c$; and
- If $a > b$, then $a + c > b + c$.

Additive identity Zero. When 0 is added to any given number, the sum is identical to the given number. See also *identity property of addition*.

Additive inverse See *inverse property of addition*.

Adjacent angles Two coplanar angles that share a common side and a common vertex, but have no interior points in common.

Algebraic expression See *variable expression*.

Alternate exterior angles A pair of nonadjacent exterior angles on opposite sides of a transversal.

Alternate Exterior Angles Theorem If two parallel lines are cut by a transversal, then alternate exterior angles are congruent.

Alternate interior angles A pair of nonadjacent interior angles on opposite sides of a transversal.

Alternate Interior Angles Theorem If two parallel lines are cut by a transversal, then alternate interior angles are congruent.

Altitude of a triangle A perpendicular segment from a vertex to the line containing the opposite side.

Angle The figure formed by two rays with a common endpoint.

Angle Addition Postulate If point B is in the interior of $\angle AOC$, then $m\angle AOB + m\angle BOC = m\angle AOC$.

Angle-Angle-Side (AAS) Congruence Theorem If two angles and the nonincluded side of one triangle are congruent to two angles and the nonincluded side of another triangle, then the triangles are congruent.

Angle-Angle (AA) Similarity Postulate If two angles of one triangle are congruent to two angles of another triangle, then the triangles are similar.

Angle bisector The ray that divides a given angle into two congruent angles.

Angle of a convex polygon See *interior angle of a convex polygon*.

Angle of depression An angle whose vertex and horizontal side are level with an observer's eye and whose other side slopes downward from an observer's eye level to an object below.

Angle of elevation An angle whose vertex and horizontal side are level with an observer's eye and whose other side slopes upward from an observer's eye level to an object above.

Angle-Side-Angle (ASA) Congruence Postulate If two angles and the included side of one triangle are congruent to two angles and the included side of another triangle, then the triangles are congruent.

Antecedent See *hypothesis*.

Apothem In a regular polygon, the segment, or the length of the segment, drawn from the center to the midpoint of a side.

Arc An unbroken part of a circle.

Area of a plane figure The number of nonoverlapping square units contained in its interior.

Arithmetic sequence A sequence in which each term differs by a common difference.

Associative property of addition For all real numbers a, b, and c, $a + b + c = (a + b) + c = a + (b + c)$.

Associative property of multiplication For all real numbers a, b, and c, $a \cdot b \cdot c = (a \cdot b) \cdot c = a \cdot (b \cdot c)$.

Average See *mean*.

Axis of symmetry of a parabola The line that divides the parabola into two matching parts. For a parabola with equation $y = ax^2 + bx + c$, $a \neq 0$, the equation of the axis of symmetry is $x = -\frac{b}{2a}$.

Bar graph A statistical display in which data are represented by bars that are determined by two axes; one of these axes is labeled with categories of data, and the other is labeled with a numerical scale.

Base angles See *isosceles triangle*, *trapezoid*.

Base of an isosceles triangle See *isosceles triangle*.

Base of a plane figure See *triangle*, *trapezoid*, *parallelogram*.

Base of a power When a number is written in the exponential form x^n, the number x is the base.

Base of a three-dimensional figure See *prism*, *cylinder*, *pyramid*, *cone*.

Between On a number line, point C is between point A and point B if the coordinate of point C is between the coordinates of points A and B.

Biconditional statement The conjunction of a conditional statement and its converse. The biconditional *If p, then q and If q, then p* is written in abbreviated form as *p if, and only if, q*.

Binomial A polynomial with exactly two terms.

Boundary of a half-plane See *open half-plane*.

Box-and-whisker plot A display of numerical data in which a *box* represents the data from the first to third quartiles, a vertical segment crosses the box at the median, and horizontal *whiskers* extend from the left and right of the box to represent the rest of the data.

Broken-line graph See *line graph*.

Center of a circle See *circle*.

Center of a regular polygon The point that is equidistant from all the vertices of the polygon.

Center of rotation See *rotation*.

Center of a sphere See *sphere*.

Center of symmetry See *rotational symmetry*.

Chord of a circle Any line segment that has endpoints on the circle.

Circle The set of all points in a plane that are a fixed distance from a fixed point in the plane. The fixed point is called the *center of the circle*. The fixed distance is called the *radius of the circle*.

Circle graph A statistical display in which a data set is represented by a circle, and distinct categories of the data are represented by distinct "slices" of the circle; the percent of the circle allotted to each slice is equal to the percent of the data set within that category.

Circuit A path that begins and ends at the same point.

Circumference of a circle The distance around the circle.

Closed half-plane The union of an open half-plane and its boundary.

Closed statement A statement that is either true or false.

Closure property of addition For all real numbers a and b, $a + b$ is a unique real number.

Closure property of multiplication For all real numbers a and b, $a \cdot b$ is a unique real number.

Coefficient of a term The numerical part of a term that contains variables. Also called the *numerical coefficient of a term*.

Collinear points Points that lie on the same line. Points that do not lie on the same line are called *noncollinear points*.

Column matrix An $n \cdot 1$ matrix, meaning there are n number of rows with only one element in each.

Combination A selection of objects from a set without regard to order.

Common difference A fixed number by which all the terms in an arithmetic sequence will differ.

Common ratio A fixed number by which all the terms in a geometric sequence will vary.

Commutative property of addition For all real numbers a and b, $a + b = b + a$.

Commutative property of multiplication For all real numbers a and b, $a \cdot b = b \cdot a$.

Compatible matrices A row matrix and a column matrix having an equal number of elements.

Complement of an event The difference between the set of possible outcomes and the set of actual outcomes of an event.

Complement of a set If E is a subset of a set X, then the set of all members of X that are not in E is the *complement* of E.

Complementary angles Two angles whose measures equal a sum of $90°$. Each angle is the *complement* of the other.

Composite number A natural number greater than 1 that has more than two factors.

Composition When multiple transformations are applied to a figure.

Compound inequality Two inequalities joined by the word *and* or the word *or*.

Compound statement A statement formed by linking two or more simple statements.

Concave polygon A polygon in which at least one diagonal contains a point in the exterior of the polygon.

Conclusion In a conditional statement, the part that follows *then*. Also called *consequent*.

Conditional probability The probability of an event occurring given that some other event has already occurred.

Conditional statement A statement formed by connecting two statements with the words *if* and *then*.

Cone A three-dimensional figure that consists of a face bounded by a circle, called its *base*; a point called the *vertex* that is outside the plane of the base; and a *lateral surface* that connects the vertex to each point on the boundary of the base. The *height* of a cone is the length of a perpendicular segment drawn from the vertex to the plane of the base.

Congruent angles Angles that are equal in measure.

Congruent figures Figures that have the same shape and the same size.

Congruent polygons Polygons whose sides and angles can be placed in a correspondence so that corresponding sides are congruent and corresponding angles are congruent.

Congruent segments Segments that are equal in length.

Conjunction A compound statement that is formed by linking simple statements with the word *and*.

GLOSSARY

Consecutive angles of a polygon Two angles whose vertices are consecutive vertices of the polygon.

Consecutive integers Integers that differ by 1.

Consecutive sides of a polygon Two sides that have a common endpoint.

Consecutive vertices of a polygon Two vertices that are endpoints of the same side.

Consequent See *conclusion*.

Constant term A term that has no variable part. Also called a *constant*.

Constant of variation See *direct variation*.

Continued ratio A ratio that relates more than two numbers. Also called *extended ratio*.

Continuous data set A set of data that involves measurements such as length, weight, or temperature in which there is always another data value between any two given data values. The graph of a continuous data set is a line or a smooth curve with no holes or breaks.

Contrapositive of a conditional statement The statement that results when the hypothesis and conclusion are interchanged, then both negated.

Converse of a conditional statement The statement that results when the hypothesis and conclusion are interchanged.

Conversion factor A ratio of two measurements that is equal to one.

Convex polygon A polygon in which no diagonal contains a point in the exterior of the polygon.

Coordinate plane A number plane formed by a horizontal number line and a vertical number line that intersect at their origins.

Coordinate(s) of a point The real number or numbers that correspond to the point. On a number line, the coordinate of each point is a single number. On a coordinate plane, each point has an ordered pair (x, y) of coordinates. The first number of the ordered pair is called the *x-coordinate* of the point, and the second is called the *y-coordinate*. See also *Ruler Postulate*.

Coplanar figures Figures that lie on the same plane. Figures that do not lie on the same plane are called *noncoplanar figures*.

Corollary A theorem that follows directly from a previously proved theorem.

Correlation A measure of the relationship between two sets of numerical data. If both sets of data generally increase or decrease together, there is a *positive correlation*. If one set generally increases as the other decreases, there is a *negative correlation*. If there is no apparent relationship, there is *no correlation*.

Corresponding angles A pair of nonadjacent angles, one interior and one exterior, that are on the same side of a transversal.

Corresponding Angles Postulate If two parallel lines are cut by a transversal, then corresponding angles are congruent.

Corresponding Parts of Congruent Triangles Are Congruent Postulate If two triangles are congruent, then the corresponding sides and angles of the two triangles must also be congruent.

Cosine of an angle The cosine of an acute angle of a right triangle is the ratio of the length of the leg adjacent to the angle to the length of the hypotenuse. The symbol for the cosine of an angle A is cos A.

Counterexample A particular instance that shows a general statement is not true for all values in the replacement set.

Counting number See *natural number*.

Cross products property of proportions For real numbers a, b, c and d, where $b \neq 0$ and $d \neq 0$, if $\frac{a}{b} = \frac{c}{d}$, then $ad = bc$. Also stated as *In a proportion, the product of the means equals the product of the extremes*.

Cube A prism whose faces are bounded by six congruent squares.

Cubic polynomial A polynomial of degree three.

Cumulative frequency histogram A histogram that displays the data from a cumulative frequency table.

Cumulative frequency table A summary of a data set in which each data value is paired with the sum of the frequencies of all values less than or equal to it.

Cylinder A three-dimensional figure that consists of two parallel *bases* bounded by congruent circles and a *lateral surface* that connects the circles. The *height* of a cylinder is the length of any perpendicular segment drawn from a point on one base to the plane containing the other base.

Data A collection of information, usually numerical.

Decagon A polygon that has exactly ten sides.

Definition A statement of the meaning of a word or phrase.

Degree measure of an angle A unique real number from 0 to 180 that is paired with the angle.

Degree of a polynomial The greatest degree of any of its terms after it has been simplified.

Degree of a term of a polynomial The sum of the exponents of all the variables in the term. For a polynomial in one variable, the degree of each term is the exponent of the variable in that term. The degree of a constant term is 0.

Degree of a vertex The number of edges that meet at a vertex in a vertex–edge graph.

Denominator In the fraction $\frac{a}{b}$, the number b is the denominator.

Dependent events Two events are dependent if the occurrence of one affects the occurrence of the other.

Dependent system of equations A system that has infinitely many solutions.

Dependent variable A variable whose value is affected by the value of another variable.

Diagonal of a polygon A segment whose endpoints are nonconsecutive vertices of the polygon.

Diameter of a circle A segment, or the length of the segment, whose endpoints are points of the circle and that contains the center of the circle.

Difference The result of a subtraction.

Difference of two squares The product that results from multiplying two binomials that are the sum and difference of the same two terms. Algebraically, $(a + b)(a - b) = a^2 - b^2$.

Dihedral tiling A tessellation made up of two different congruent figures.

Dilation A dilation with center O and *scale factor n*, where $n > 0$, is a transformation in which the image of a point A is a point A' such that point A' is on $\overrightarrow{OA}$ and $OA' = n \cdot OA$. The image of point O is point O. If $n > 1$, the dilation is an *enlargement*. If $0 < n < 1$, it is a *reduction*. A dilation is also called a *similarity transformation*.

Dimensional analysis A method for converting a measurement from one unit of measure to another by multiplying by a ratio representing the relationship between the units. The ratio is called a *conversion factor*.

Direct measurement See *indirect measurement*.

Direct variation A relationship described by an equation of the form $y = kx$, where k is a constant nonzero real number. The number k is called the *constant of variation*.

Discrete data set A set of data that involves a count, such as numbers of people or objects. The graph of a discrete data set consists of points that are not connected.

Discriminant of a quadratic equation For a quadratic equation of the form $ax^2 + bx + c = 0$, the discriminant is the expression $b^2 - 4ac$.

Disjunction A compound statement that is formed by linking simple statements with the word *or*.

Distance between a line and a point not on the line The length of the perpendicular segment from the line to the point.

Distance between two parallel lines The distance between one line and a point on the other line.

Distance between two points (number line) The absolute value of the difference of the coordinates of the points. See also *Ruler Postulate*.

Distance formula (coordinate plane) The distance PQ between $P(x_1, y_1)$ and $Q(x_2, y_2)$ is given by the formula $PQ = \sqrt{(x_2 - x_1)^2 + (y_2 - y_1)^2}$.

Distributive property For all real numbers a, b, and c, $a \cdot (b + c) = a \cdot b + a \cdot c$ and $(b + c) \cdot a = b \cdot a + c \cdot a$.

Dividend In a division, the number that is being divided. In the expression $a \div b$, a is the dividend.

Divisible One number is divisible by another if the second number divides the first with remainder 0.

Division property of equality For all real numbers a and b and all nonzero real numbers c, if $a = b$, then $\frac{a}{c} = \frac{b}{c}$.

Division property of inequality For all real numbers a, b, and c,

1. If $a < b$ and $c > 0$, then $\frac{a}{c} < \frac{b}{c}$;
   If $a < b$ and $c < 0$, then $\frac{a}{c} > \frac{b}{c}$; and

2. If $a > b$ and $c > 0$, then $\frac{a}{c} > \frac{b}{c}$;
   If $a > b$ and $c < 0$, then $\frac{a}{c} < \frac{b}{c}$.

Divisor In a division, the number by which you divide. In the expression $a \div b$, b is the divisor.

Dodecagon A polygon with exactly twelve sides.

Domain of a function See *function*.

Domain of a relation See *relation*.

Domain of a variable See *replacement set*.

Dot product The sum of the products of the corresponding elements of a row matrix and a column matrix.

Edge A line segment that joins two vertices.

Edge of a polyhedron A segment that is the intersection of two faces.

Element of a set See *member of a set*.

Elimination method See *addition-multiplication method*.

Empirical probability See *experimental probability*.

Endpoint See *segment* and *ray*.

Endpoint of a kite The common endpoint of a pair of congruent sides.

Enlargement See *dilation*.

Equally likely outcomes In a sample space, those outcomes that have the same probability.

Equation A statement that two mathematical expressions are equal.

Equiangular polygon A polygon whose angles are all congruent.

Equiangular triangle A triangle that has three congruent angles.

Equilateral polygon A polygon whose sides are all congruent.

Equilateral triangle A triangle that has three congruent sides.

Equivalent equations Equations that have the same solution set.

GLOSSARY

Equivalent expressions Expressions that name the same number.

Equivalent inequalities Inequalities that have the same solution set.

Equivalent systems Systems that have the same solution set.

Euler circuit An Euler path that begins and ends at the same vertex.

Euler path A path that traverses each edge of a vertex–edge graph exactly once.

Evaluate a variable expression To replace each variable in the expression with a value from its replacement set, then simplify the resulting numerical expression.

Even number A member of the set $\{\ldots, -4, -2, 0, 2, 4, \ldots\}$.

Event In probability, any set of outcomes that are in the sample space.

Excluded value Any value excluded from the domain of a variable because that value would result in a denominator of zero. The excluded values are said to be *restricted from the domain* of the variable.

Expected value The average of the possible outcomes in a sample space.

Experimental probability A probability determined by collecting data from an experiment. Also called *empirical probability*.

Explicit sequence A sequence of terms in which subsequent terms are defined in relation to the number of the term without regard to the value of the preceding term or terms.

Exponent When a number is written in the exponential form x^n, the number n is the exponent.

Exponential form The expression x^n is the exponential form of the nth power of x. When n is a natural number, $x^n = x \cdot x \cdot x \cdot \ldots \cdot x$, with n factors of x.

Exponential function A function in the form $y = b^x$ where the variable is an exponent.

Extended ratio See *continued ratio*.

Exterior angle of a convex polygon An angle that forms a linear pair with one of the polygon's interior angles.

Extremes of a proportion In the proportion $\frac{a}{b} = \frac{c}{d}$, a and d are the extremes.

Face of a polyhedron One of its flat surfaces.

Factor of a multiplication One of a set of numbers to be multiplied. In the expression ab, a and b are the factors.

Factor a polynomial completely To express the polynomial as a product of one or more polynomials that cannot be factored further.

Factor of a whole number A natural number that divides the number with a remainder of 0.

Factorial notation The notation $n!$, which is read as "n factorial" and which represents the product $n \times (n - 1) \times (n - 2) \times \ldots \times 2 \times 1$. The value of $0!$ is defined to be 1.

Figure In geometry, any set of points.

First quartile In a numerical data set, the median of the data values that are less than the median of the entire set.

Fixed point A point that is its own image under a transformation.

FOIL method A procedure for multiplying two binomials: The product of two binomials is the sum of the product of the First terms within the parentheses, plus the product of the Outer terms, plus the product of the Inner terms, plus the product of the Last terms. Algebraically, $(a + b)(c + d) = ac + ad + bc + bd$.

Formula A literal equation in which each variable represents a quantity.

Foundation or base drawing A drawing which shows the base of a structure and the height of each part.

Frequency of a data value The number of times the value occurs in the data set.

Frequency table A summary of a set of data in which each data value is matched with its frequency.

Function A relationship in which every member of one set, called the *domain*, is assigned exactly one member of a second set, called the *range*.

Geometric construction A drawing that is made using only an unmarked *straightedge* and a *compass*. The straightedge is used to draw segments, rays, and lines. The compass is used to draw arcs and circles.

Geometric sequence When each term of the sequence varies by a constant quotient.

Graph of an equation or inequality in two variables The set of all points in the coordinate plane that correspond to solutions to the equation or inequality.

Graph of an inequality (number line) The set of the graphs of all solutions to the inequality.

Graph of a number The point that corresponds to the number on a number line.

Graph of an ordered pair The point that corresponds to the ordered pair on a coordinate plane.

Great circle Any circle in the plane that contains the center of the sphere.

Greatest common factor (GCF) of monomials The product of the greatest common factor of their numerical coefficients and the greatest common factor of their variable parts.

Greatest common factor (GCF) of natural numbers The greatest number that is a factor of each number in a set of two or more natural numbers.

Greatest integer function A step function that assigns to each real number the greatest integer that is less than or equal to that number.

Greatest possible error In a measurement, half the smallest unit on the measuring instrument.

Grouping symbol In a numerical or variable expression, a device that indicates certain operations are to be done before others. Common grouping symbols are parentheses, brackets, braces, fraction bars, radical signs, and absolute-value bars.

Half-turn A rotation of exactly 180°.

Height of a plane figure See *triangle, trapezoid, parallelogram.*

Height of a three-dimensional figure See *prism, cylinder, pyramid, cone.*

Hexagon A polygon that has exactly six sides.

Histogram A vertical bar graph of a frequency distribution. The bars represent equal intervals of the data, and there is no space between the bars.

Hypotenuse The side of a right triangle that is opposite the right angle.

Hypotenuse-Leg (HL) Congruence Theorem If the hypotenuse and one leg of a right triangle are congruent to the hypotenuse and one leg of another right triangle, then the triangles are congruent.

Hypothesis In a conditional statement, the part that follows *if*. Also called the *antecedent.*

Identity An equation that is true for all values of the variable(s).

Identity matrix A square matrix with the elements of the main diagonal equal to 1 and all other elements equal to 0.

Identity property of addition For all real numbers a, $a + 0 = a$ and $0 + a = a$. See also *additive identity.*

Identity property of multiplication For all real numbers a, $a \cdot 1 = a$ and $1 \cdot a = a$. See also *multiplicative identity.*

Image See *transformation.*

Inconsistent system of equations A system that has no solution.

Independent events Two events are independent if the occurrence of one does not affect the occurrence of the other.

Independent system of equations A system that has exactly one solution.

Independent variable A variable whose value is not affected by the value of another variable.

Indirect measurement Determining an unknown measurement by using mathematical relationships among known measurements rather than using a *direct measurement* tool such as a ruler or protractor.

Inequality A statement that consists of two expressions joined by an inequality symbol. Commonly used inequality symbols are $<$, $\le$, $>$, $\ge$, and $\ne$.

Inscribed angle An angle inside a circle that is formed by three points that lie on the circle.

Integer A member of the set $\{\ldots, -3, -2, -1, 0, 1, 2, 3, \ldots\}$.

Intercepted arc The section of a circle that is between the endpoints of an inscribed angle.

Interior angle of a convex polygon An angle determined by two consecutive sides of the polygon. Also called an *angle of the polygon.*

Interquartile range The difference when the first quartile of a data set is subtracted from the third quartile.

Intersection of figures The set of all points common to two or more figures. The figures are said to *intersect* in these points.

Inverse of a conditional statement The statement that results when the hypothesis and conclusion are both negated.

Inverse matrix The matrix multiplied by a given, the product of which is an identity matrix.

Inverse property of addition For every real number a, there is a unique real number $-a$ such that $a + (-a) = 0$ and $-a + a = 0$; $-a$ is the *additive inverse* of a, or the *opposite* of a.

Inverse property of multiplication For every nonzero real number a, there is a unique real number $\frac{1}{a}$ such that $a \cdot \frac{1}{a} = 1$ and $\frac{1}{a} \cdot a = 1$; $\frac{1}{a}$ is the *multiplicative inverse* of a, or the *reciprocal* of a.

Inverse variation When two quantities are related such that a change in one produces the opposite type of change in the other.

Irrational number A number represented by a decimal that does not terminate and does not repeat.

Isometry A transformation in which a figure and its image are congruent.

Isosceles trapezoid A trapezoid whose legs are congruent.

Isosceles triangle A triangle that has at least two congruent sides, called the *legs*. The third side is the *base*. The angles opposite the congruent sides are called the *base angles*. The third angle is the *vertex angle.*

Isosceles Triangle Bisectors Theorem The bisector of the vertex angle of an isosceles triangle is the perpendicular bisector of the base.

Isosceles Triangle Theorem If two sides of a triangle are congruent, then the angles opposite those sides are congruent. Also stated as: *Base angles of an isosceles triangle are congruent.*

GLOSSARY

Kite A convex quadrilateral in which two distinct pairs of consecutive sides are congruent.

Lateral area of a prism or pyramid The sum of the areas of the lateral faces.

Lateral face See *prism*, *pyramid*.

Lateral surface See *cylinder*, *cone*.

Law of large numbers When an experiment is repeated many times, the proportion of each possible outcome will be close to its theoretical probability.

Leading coefficient of a polynomial The coefficient of the leading term.

Leading term of a polynomial In a polynomial in one variable, the term with the greatest degree.

Least common denominator (LCD) The least common multiple of the denominators of a set of fractions.

Least common multiple (LCM) of numbers The least number that is a multiple of each number in a set of two or more numbers.

Legs of an isosceles triangle See *isosceles triangle*.

Legs of a right triangle The sides opposite the acute angles.

Legs of a trapezoid The nonparallel sides.

Length of a segment The distance between the endpoints of the segment.

Like radicals Radical expressions with exactly the same radicand.

Like terms Terms that have exactly the same variable parts.

Line A set of points that extends in two opposite directions without end. This is one of the basic *undefined terms* of geometry.

Line graph A statistical display in which paired data are represented by points, the position of the points being determined by two axes labeled with numerical scales; the points are then connected in order with segments. Also called a *broken-line graph*.

Line Intersection Postulate If two lines intersect, then they intersect in exactly one point.

Line segment See *segment*.

Line symmetry A plane figure that has line symmetry is its own image after reflection across some line in the plane. The line is called a *line of symmetry* for the figure.

Linear equation in two variables For the variables x and y, any equation that can be written in the form $ax + by = c$, where a, b, and c are real numbers and a and b are not both 0. The equation $ax + by = c$ is called the *standard form* of a linear equation in two variables.

Linear inequality in two variables For the variables x and y, any inequality that can be written in the form $ax + by \geq c$, $ax + by > c$, $ax + by \leq c$, or $ax + by < c$, where a, b, and c are real numbers and a and b are not both 0.

Linear pair Adjacent angles whose noncommon sides are opposite rays.

Linear Pair Postulate If two angles form a linear pair, then they are supplementary.

Linear polynomial A polynomial of degree one.

Literal equation An equation that contains two or more variables.

Locus The set of all points that satisfy specified conditions. The plural of locus is *loci*.

Logically equivalent statements Statements that have the same truth values.

Lowest terms A fraction is in lowest terms if the GCF of its numerator and denominator is 1.

Matrix A rectangular array of numbers.

Maximum data value The greatest data value in a set of numerical data.

Maximum value of a quadratic function The y-coordinate of the vertex of the graph of a quadratic function described by $y = ax^2 + bx + c$, where $a < 0$.

Mean The sum of the data values in a numerical set of data, divided by the number of data values in the set. Also called *average*.

Means of a proportion In the proportion $\frac{a}{b} = \frac{c}{d}$, b and c are the means.

Measure of an angle See *degree measure of an angle*.

Measure of central tendency A statistic that is in some way representative or typical of a set of data. Commonly used measures of central tendency are the *mean*, the *median*, and the *mode*.

Median of a data set The middle data value in a set of data that has been arranged in numerical order. If the number of data values in the set is even, then the median is the average of the *two* middle data values.

Median of a triangle A segment whose endpoints are a vertex of the triangle and the midpoint of the opposite side.

Member of a set Any object in the set. Also called *element of a set*.

Midpoint of a segment The point that divides the segment into two congruent segments.

Midpoint formula The coordinates of the midpoint of the segment with endpoints $P(x_1, y_1)$ and $Q(x_2, y_2)$ are $\left(\frac{x_1 + x_2}{2}, \frac{y_1 + y_2}{2} \right)$.

Minimum data value The least data value in a set of numerical data.

Minimum value of a quadratic function The y-coordinate of the vertex of the graph of a quadratic function described by $y = ax^2 + bx + c$, where $a > 0$.

Mode In a data set, the data value(s) with the greatest frequency.

Monohedral tiling A tessellation made up of congruent copies of one figure.

Monomial A number, a variable, or a product of a number and one or more variables with nonnegative exponents.

Multiple of a number The result when the number is multiplied by a whole number.

Multiplication counting principle If there are m ways to make a selection and n ways to make a second selection, then there are mn ways to make the pair of selections. If there are p ways to make a third selection, then there are mnp ways to make the three selections.

Multiplication property of equality For all real numbers a, b, and c, if $a = b$, then $ac = bc$.

Multiplication property of inequality For all real numbers a, b, and c,

1. If $a < b$ and $c > 0$, then $ac < bc$;
   If $a < b$ and $c < 0$, then $ac > bc$; and
2. If $a > b$ and $c > 0$, then $ac > bc$;
   If $a > b$ and $c < 0$, then $ac < bc$.

Multiplicative identity One. When any given number is multiplied by 1, the product is identical to the given number. See also *identity property of multiplication*.

Multiplicative inverse See *inverse property of multiplication*.

Mutually exclusive events Events that have no outcomes in common.

Natural number A member of the set $\{1, 2, 3, 4, 5, 6, \ldots\}$. Also called *counting number*.

Negation of a statement The statement formed when the word *not* is inserted into or removed from a statement. The negation of a true statement is always false. The negation of a false statement is always true.

Negative correlation See *correlation*.

Negative number On a number line, a number that corresponds to a point on the negative side of zero. If the numbers increase in order from left to right, the negative side is to the left of zero.

Net A 2-dimensional model of a 3-dimensional figure.

Network See *Vertex-edge graph*.

n-gon A polygon that has exactly n sides.

Nonagon A polygon that has exactly nine sides.

Number line A line whose points have been placed in one-to-one correspondence with the set of real numbers.

Numerator In the fraction $\frac{a}{b}$, the number a is the numerator.

Numerical coefficient See *coefficient of a term*.

Numerical expression A name for a number.

Obtuse angle An angle whose measure is greater than $90°$ and less than $180°$.

Obtuse triangle A triangle that has one obtuse angle.

Octagon A polygon that has exactly eight sides.

Odd number A member of the set $\{\ldots, -5, -3, -1, 1, 3, 5, \ldots\}$.

Open half-plane Either of two regions into which a line separates a coordinate plane. The line is called the *boundary* of each half-plane.

Open statement A statement that contains one or more variables.

Opposite(s) Numbers that are the same distance from zero on a number line, but on opposite sides of zero. The symbol for the opposite of a number n is $-n$. See also *inverse property of addition*.

Opposite angles of a quadrilateral Two angles that are not consecutive.

Opposite rays On a line, if point B is between points A and C, then $\overrightarrow{BA}$ and $\overrightarrow{BC}$ are opposite rays.

Opposite sides of a quadrilateral Two sides that are not consecutive.

Ordered pair In a coordinate plane, the pair of real numbers (x, y) that corresponds to a point.

Ordinate The value of the y-coordinate in an ordered pair.

Origin of a coordinate plane The point where the axes intersect.

Origin of a number line The point that corresponds to the number zero.

Orthographic drawing A drawing that shows a top view, a front view, and a right view.

Overlapping figures Figures that have interior points in common.

Parabola The U-shaped curve that is the graph of a quadratic function.

Parallel lines Coplanar lines that do not intersect. The symbol for parallel is $\parallel$.

Parallel Postulate Through a point not on a line, there is exactly one line parallel to the given line.

Parallelogram A quadrilateral that has two pairs of parallel sides. To calculate area, any of the sides may be considered the *base*, and the length of that side is also called the base. The *height* is then the length of any perpendicular segment drawn from a point on the side opposite the base to the line containing the base.

GLOSSARY

Pascal's triangle An array of numbers arranged in rows beginning with 1 such that the terms in each subsequent row are the sum of the two terms in the previous row.

Path The sequence of connections between vertices.

Pentagon A polygon that has exactly five sides.

Percent Percent means "per 100," "out of 100," or "divided by 100". The symbol for percent is %.

Percent of change The percent an amount changes from an original amount. The change may be a *percent of increase* or a *percent of decrease*.

Percentile rank If n percent of the data values in a set are less than or equal to a given data value, then n is the percentile rank of that data value.

Perfect square A number whose square roots are rational numbers.

Perfect square trinomial A trinomial that results from squaring a binomial. The form of the square of a binomial sum is $(a + b)^2 = a^2 + 2ab + b^2$. For a binomial difference, $(a - b)^2 = a^2 - 2ab + b^2$.

Perimeter of a plane figure The distance around the figure. The perimeter of a polygon is the sum of the lengths of its sides.

Period The interval over which a periodic function repeats itself.

Periodic function A function whose graph repeats itself over and over on an interval of a fixed length.

Permutation An arrangement of some or all objects from a set in a specific order.

Perpendicular bisector of a segment Any line, ray, or segment that is perpendicular to the segment at its midpoint.

Perpendicular lines Lines that intersect to form right angles. The symbol for perpendicular is $\perp$.

Perpendicular Transversal Theorem If a transversal is perpendicular to one of two parallel lines, then it is perpendicular to the other.

Plane A set of points that extends along a flat surface in every direction without end. This is one of the basic *undefined terms* of geometry.

Plane figure A figure whose points all lie in the same plane.

Plane Intersection Postulate If two planes intersect, then they intersect in a line.

Point A location. This one of the basic *undefined terms* of geometry.

Point-slope form of an equation of a line For an equation in the variables x and y, the point-slope form is $y - y_1 = m(x - x_1)$, where $P(x_1, y_1)$ is a point on the line and m is the slope of the line.

Point symmetry A plane figure that has point symmetry is its own image after a half-turn in the plane.

Polygon A plane figure formed by three or more segments such that each segment intersects exactly two others, one at each endpoint, and no two segments with a common endpoint are collinear. Each segment is a *side* of the polygon. The common endpoint of two sides is a *vertex* of the polygon. A polygon completely encloses a region of the plane, called its *interior*.

Polygon Exterior Angle-Sum Theorem The sum of the measures of the exterior angles of a convex polygon, one at each vertex, is 360°.

Polygon Interior Angle-Sum Theorem The sum of the measures of the interior angles of a convex polygon that has n sides is $(n - 2)180°$.

Polyhedron A three-dimensional figure formed by flat surfaces that are bounded by polygons joined in pairs along their sides.

Polynomial A monomial or a sum of monomials.

Population In a statistical study, the set of all individuals or objects being studied.

Positive correlation See *correlation*.

Positive number On a number line, a number that corresponds to a point on the positive side of zero. If the numbers increase in order from left to right, the positive side is to the right of zero.

Postulate A statement whose truth is accepted without proof.

Power The simplified form of x^n. For example, since $2^5 = 32$, 32 is the fifth power of 2.

Power of a power property of exponents For all integers m and n and all nonzero real numbers a, $(a^m)^n = a^{mn}$.

Power of a product property of exponents For all integers m and all nonzero real numbers a and b, $(ab)^m = a^m b^m$.

Power of a quotient property of exponents For all integers m and all nonzero real numbers a and b, $\left(\frac{a}{b}\right)^m = \frac{a^m}{b^m}$.

Precision The level of accuracy of a measurement.

Preimage See *transformation*.

Prime factorization An expression that shows a natural number as a product of prime numbers.

Prime number A natural number greater than 1 that has exactly two factors, 1 and the number itself.

Principal square root The positive square root of a number.

Prism A polyhedron with two parallel faces, called its *bases*, that are bounded by congruent polygons; and with *lateral faces* that are bounded by parallelograms connecting corresponding sides of the bases. The *height* of a prism is the length of any perpendicular segment drawn from a point on one base to the plane containing the other base.

Probability A number from 0 to 1, inclusive, that represents the likelihood an event will occur. If an event is *impossible*, its probability is 0. If an event is *certain*, its probability is 1. Events that are *possible but not certain* are assigned probabilities between 0 and 1.

Probability distribution For a given sample space, a table that pairs each value of the random variable with its probability.

Product The result of a multiplication.

Product of powers property of exponents For all integers m and n and all nonzero real numbers a, $a^m \cdot a^n = a^{m+n}$.

Product property of square roots If a and b are real numbers with $a \geq 0$ and $b \geq 0$, then $\sqrt{ab} = \sqrt{a} \cdot \sqrt{b}$.

Proportion A statement that two ratios are equal. The proportion that equates the ratios "a to b" and "c to d" can be written in three ways:

$$a \text{ is to } b \text{ as } c \text{ is to } d \qquad a:b = c:d \qquad \frac{a}{b} = \frac{c}{d}$$

Protractor Postulate Let $\overrightarrow{OA}$ and $\overrightarrow{OB}$ be opposite rays. Consider $\overrightarrow{OA}$, $\overrightarrow{OB}$, and all the rays with endpoint O that can be drawn in a plane on one side of $\overleftrightarrow{AB}$. These rays can be paired with the real numbers from 0 to 180, one-to-one, in such a way that:

- $\overrightarrow{OA}$ is paired with 0 and $\overrightarrow{OB}$ is paired with 180.
- If $\overrightarrow{OP}$ is paired with x and $\overrightarrow{OQ}$ is paired with y, then the number paired with $\angle POQ$ is $|x - y|$. This is called the *measure*, or the *degree measure*, of $\angle POQ$.

Pyramid A polyhedron that consists of a face bounded by a polygon, called its *base*; a point called the *vertex* that is outside the plane of the base; and triangular *lateral faces* that connect the vertex to each side of the base. The *height* of a pyramid is the length of the perpendicular segment drawn from the vertex to the plane of the base.

Pythagorean Theorem If a triangle is a right triangle with legs of lengths a and b and hypotenuse of length c, then $a^2 + b^2 = c^2$.

Pythagorean triple Any set of three positive integers that satisfy the relationship $a^2 + b^2 = c^2$.

Quadrant One of the four regions into which a coordinate plane is divided by the x- and y-axes.

Quadratic equation An equation that can be written in the form $ax^2 + bx + c = 0$, where a, b, and c are real numbers and $a \neq 0$. The equation $ax^2 + bx + c = 0$ is called the *standard form* of a quadratic equation in x.

Quadratic formula A method for determining the solution set of a quadratic equation in one variable. If $ax^2 + bx + c = 0$, and a, b, and c are real numbers with $a \neq 0$, then $x = \frac{-b \pm \sqrt{b^2 - 4ac}}{2a}$.

Quadratic function A function that can be represented by an equation of the form $y = ax^2 + bx + c$, where a, b, and c are real numbers and $a \neq 0$.

Quadratic polynomial A polynomial of degree two.

Quadrilateral A polygon that has exactly four sides.

Quadrilateral Angle-Sum Theorem The sum of the measures of the interior angles of a quadrilateral is 360°.

Quartile See *first quartile, third quartile*.

Quotient The result of dividing one number by another.

Quotient of powers property of exponents For all integers m and n and all nonzero real numbers a, $\frac{a^m}{a^n} = a^{m-n}$.

Quotient property of square roots If a and b are real numbers with $a \geq 0$ and $b > 0$, then $\sqrt{\frac{a}{b}} = \frac{\sqrt{a}}{\sqrt{b}}$.

Radical equation An equation that contains one or more radical expressions with variables in the radicand.

Radical expression An expression that contains a radical sign. The square root symbol, $\sqrt{}$, is an example of a radical sign.

Radicand An expression under a radical sign.

Radius of a circle A segment, or the length of the segment, whose endpoints are the center of the circle and a point of the circle. See also *circle*.

Radius of a sphere See *sphere*.

Random variable In probability, a variable that represents the outcomes in a sample space.

Range of a data set In a set of numerical data, the difference when the minimum data value is subtracted from the maximum data value.

Range of a function See *function*.

Range of a relation See *relation*.

Rate A ratio that compares two different types of measures.

Ratio A comparison of two numbers by division. *The ratio of a to b can be written in three ways:*

$$a \text{ to } b \qquad a:b \qquad \frac{a}{b}$$

Rational equation An equation that contains one or more rational expressions.

Rational expression An expression that can be written in the form $\frac{P}{Q}$, where P and Q are polynomials and the value of Q is not zero.

Rational number A number that can be expressed in the form $\frac{a}{b}$, where a and b are integers and $b \neq 0$.

Ray Part of a line that begins at one point and extends without end in one direction. The point is called the *endpoint of the ray*.

Real number A number that is either a rational number or an irrational number.

Reciprocal Two numbers are reciprocals if their product is 1. See also *inverse property of multiplication*.

GLOSSARY

Rectangle A quadrilateral that has four right angles.

Recursive formula An algorithm used to identify terms in a recursive sequence.

Recursive sequence A sequence of terms in which subsequent terms are defined in relation to the preceding term or terms in the sequence.

Reduction See *dilation*.

Reflection in a line A reflection in line m is a transformation such that, if point A is on line m, then the image of point A is point A; and if point B is not on line m, then its image B' is the point such that line m is the perpendicular bisector of $\overline{BB'}$. Line m is called the *line of reflection*.

Reflection in a point A reflection in point P is a transformation such that the image of point P is point P; and the image of any other point Q is the point Q' such that point P is the midpoint of $\overline{QQ'}$. Point P is called the *point of reflection*.

Reflexive property of equality For all real numbers a, $a = a$.

Regular polygon A polygon that is both equilateral and equiangular.

Regular polyhedron All of the faces of a polyhedron are regular polygons that are congruent to each other.

Regular pyramid A pyramid whose base is bounded by a regular polygon and in which the segment joining the center of the base to the vertex is perpendicular to the plane of the base. The lateral faces of a regular pyramid are congruent isosceles triangles.

Relation Any correspondence between two sets, called the *domain* and *range* of the relation.

Relatively prime Two natural numbers are relatively prime if their greatest common factor is 1.

Remote interior angles For each exterior angle of a triangle, the two nonadjacent interior angles are called remote interior angles.

Repeating decimal A decimal in which a digit or a block of digits repeats without end. The symbol for a repeating decimal is a bar over the repeating digit(s).

Replacement set The set of numbers that a variable may represent. Also called the *domain of a variable*.

Rhombus A quadrilateral that has four congruent sides.

Right angle An angle whose measure is 90°.

Right cone A cone in which the segment joining the center of the base to the vertex is perpendicular to the plane of the base. If a cone is not a right cone, then it is called *oblique*.

Right cylinder A cylinder in which the segment joining the centers of the bases is perpendicular to the planes of the bases. If a cylinder is not a right cylinder, then it is called *oblique*.

Right prism A prism in which the segments that connect corresponding vertices of the bases are perpendicular to the planes of the bases. The lateral faces of a right prism are bounded by rectangles. If a prism is not a right prism, then it is called *oblique*.

Right triangle A triangle with one right angle.

Root A solution to a quadratic equation.

Rotation A rotation of $x°$ about point O is a transformation such that the image of point O is point O; and for any other point P, its image is the point P' such that $\overline{OP} = \overline{OP'}$ and $m\angle POP' = x°$. Point O is called the *center of rotation*. The direction of rotation is specified as *clockwise* or *counterclockwise*.

Rotational symmetry A plane figure that has rotational symmetry is its own image after a rotation of 180° or less around some point in the plane. The point is called the *center of symmetry* for the figure.

Row matrix A $1 \times n$ matrix, meaning there is only one row with n number of elements.

Ruler Postulate The points of a line can be paired with the real numbers, one-to-one, so that any point corresponds to 0 and any other point corresponds to 1. The real number that corresponds to a point is the *coordinate* of that point. The *distance* between two points is equal to the absolute value of the difference of their coordinates.

Same-Side Interior Angles Theorem If two parallel lines are cut by a transversal, then interior angles on the same side of the transversal are supplementary.

Sample In a statistical study, a subset of the population being studied.

Sample space The set of all possible outcomes in a given situation.

Scalar A number by which a matrix is multiplied.

Scale drawing A two-dimensional drawing that is similar to the object it represents. The ratio of the size of the drawing to the actual size of the object is the *scale* of the drawing.

Scale factor See *similarity ratio*, *dilation*.

Scalene triangle A triangle that has no congruent sides.

Scatter plot A statistical display of the relationship between two sets of data in which ordered pairs of the data are represented by points, the position of the points being determined by two axes labeled with numerical scales. See also *correlation*.

Scientific notation A number is written in scientific notation when it is written in the form $a \times 10^n$, where $1 \leq a < 10$ and n is an integer.

Secant A line, ray, or segment, that intersects a circle at 2 points.

GLOSSARY

Sector of a circle The part of a circle formed by two radii and the arc they intercept.

Segment Part of a line that begins at one point and ends at another. The points are called the *endpoints of the segment*. Also called *line segment*.

Segment Addition Postulate If point C is between point A and point B, then $AC + CB = AB$.

Segment bisector Any line, ray, or segment that intersects a given segment at its midpoint.

Semicircle Half of a circle.

Set A group of objects.

Side of an angle One of the two rays that form the angle.

Side of an equation One of two mathematical expressions that are joined by an equals sign.

Side of an inequality One of two mathematical expressions that are joined by an inequality symbol.

Side of a polygon See *polygon*.

Side-Angle-Side (SAS) Congruence Postulate If two sides and the included angle of one triangle are congruent to two sides and the included angle of another triangle, then the triangles are congruent.

Side-Angle-Side (SAS) Similarity Theorem If an angle of one triangle is congruent to an angle of another triangle, and the lengths of the sides including these angles are in proportion, then the triangles are similar.

Side-Side-Side (SSS) Congruence Postulate If three sides of one triangle are congruent to three sides of another triangle, then the triangles are congruent.

Side-Side-Side (SSS) Similarity Theorem If corresponding sides of two triangles are in proportion, then the triangles are similar.

Side-Splitter Theorem If a line is parallel to one side of a triangle and intersects the other two sides at distinct points, then it divides those two sides proportionally.

Signed numbers Positive and negative numbers.

Significant digits Numbers that make a contribution to a value.

Similar figures Figures that have the same shape, but not necessarily the same size.

Similar polygons Polygons whose sides and angles can be placed in a correspondence so that corresponding angles are congruent and corresponding sides are in proportion.

Similarity ratio The ratio of the lengths of corresponding sides of similar polygons. Also called the *scale factor*.

Similarity transformation See *dilation*.

Simplest form of a radical expression The form of the expression in which the radicand contains no perfect-square factors other than 1; the radicand contains no fractions; and no denominator contains a radical.

Simplify a numerical expression To give the most common name for the number the expression represents.

Simplify a variable expression To perform as many of the indicated operations as possible.

Sine of an angle The sine of an acute angle of a right triangle is the ratio of the length of the leg opposite the angle to the length of the hypotenuse. The symbol for the sine of an angle A is sin A.

Skew lines Lines that are noncoplanar.

Slant height of a regular pyramid The height of a lateral face.

Slant height of a right cone The distance between the vertex of the cone and any point on the boundary of the base.

Slope On a coordinate plane, the steepness of a nonvertical line, described informally as $\frac{\text{rise}}{\text{run}}$. Formally, if $P(x_1, y_1)$ and $Q(x_2, y_2)$ lie on $\overleftrightarrow{PQ}$, and $x_1 \neq x_2$, then the slope m of $\overleftrightarrow{PQ}$ is defined by $m = \frac{y_2 - y_1}{x_2 - x_1}$.

Slope-intercept form of an equation of a line For an equation in the variables x and y, $y = mx + b$, where m is the slope of the graph and b is the y-intercept.

Solution to an equation or inequality in two variables For an equation or inequality in the variables x and y, any ordered pair of numbers (x, y) that together make the equation or inequality a true statement.

Solution to an open statement Any value of the variable(s) that makes the statement true.

Solution set of an open statement The set of all solutions to the open statement.

Solution to a system of equations or inequalities in two variables For a system in the variables x and y, any ordered pair (x, y) that is a solution to each equation or inequality in the system.

Solve an equation or inequality To find the solution set of the equation or inequality.

Space In geometry, the set of all points.

Space figure A figure whose points extend beyond a single plane into space. Also called a *three-dimensional figure*.

Sphere The set of all points in space that are a fixed distance from a fixed point. The fixed point is called the *center of the sphere*. The fixed distance is called the *radius of the sphere*.

Square A quadrilateral that has four congruent sides and four right angles.

Square of a number The second power of the number.

Square root If $a^2 = b$, then a is a square root of b. The positive square root is denoted $\sqrt{b}$. The negative square root is denoted $-\sqrt{b}$.

Standard form of an equation of a circle For a circle with center $P(h, k)$ and radius r, the equation is $(x - h)^2 + (y - k)^2 = r^2$. If P is the origin, the equation becomes $x^2 + y^2 = r^2$.

Standard form of a linear equation in two variables See *linear equation in two variables*.

GLOSSARY

Standard form of a polynomial A polynomial in one variable is in standard form when it has no like terms and the terms are written in descending order.

Standard form of a quadratic equation See *quadratic equation*.

Statement Any mathematical sentence.

Statistics The branch of mathematics that deals with the gathering, organization, analysis, representation, and interpretation of data.

Stem-and-leaf plot A display of data in which digits with higher place values are listed in a column as *stems*; digits with lower place values are listed in rows as *leaves* extending from the corresponding stems.

Step function Functions that result in graphs that are not continuous.

Straight angle An angle whose measure is 180°.

Substitution method A method used to solve a system of equations in which one equation is solved for one variable in terms of the other. Then this expression is substituted for that variable in the other equation.

Substitution principle If $a = b$, then a may be replaced by b in any expression.

Subtraction property of equality For all real numbers a, b, and c, if $a = b$, then $a - c = b - c$.

Subtraction property of inequality For all real numbers a, b, and c,

- If $a < b$, then $a - c < b - c$; and
- If $a > b$, then $a - c > b - c$.

Sum The result of an addition.

Supplementary angles Two angles whose measures have a sum of 180°. Each angle is the *supplement* of the other.

Surface area The total area of all surfaces of a three-dimensional figure.

Symmetric property of equality For all real numbers a and b, if $a = b$, then $b = a$.

System of equations or inequalities in two variables A set of equations or inequalities in the same two variables.

Tangent of an angle The tangent of an acute angle of a right triangle is the ratio of the length of the leg opposite the angle to the length of the leg adjacent to it. The symbol for the tangent of an angle A is tan A.

Term of an expression A number, a variable, or a product or quotient of numbers and variables.

Terminating decimal A decimal that stops, or terminates.

Terms of a proportion The numbers that form the proportion. In $\frac{a}{b} = \frac{c}{d}$, a, b, c, and d are the terms.

Tessellation or tiling A covering of the plane with congruent copies of the same region with no holes and no overlaps.

Theorem A statement that can be proved true.

Theoretical probability If an event E contains m favorable outcomes in a sample space that consists of n outcomes, then the theoretical probability of E, denoted $P(E)$, is given by the formula $P(E) = \frac{m}{n}$.

Third quartile In a numerical data set, the median of the data values that are greater than the median of the entire set.

Three-dimensional figure See *space figure*.

Transformation A correspondence between one figure, called a *preimage*, and a second figure, called its *image*, such that each point of the image is paired with exactly one point of the preimage, and each point of the preimage is paired with exactly one point of the image.

Transitive property of equality For all real numbers a, b, and c, if $a = b$ and $b = c$, then $a = c$.

Transitive property of inequality For all real numbers a, b, and c,

1. If $a < b$ and $b < c$, then $a < c$; and
2. If $a > b$ and $b > c$, then $a > c$.

Transitivity of Parallelism Theorem If two lines are parallel to a third line, then the lines are parallel to each other.

Translation A transformation in which the image is the figure that would result if each point of the preimage were moved the same distance and in the same direction.

Transversal A line that intersects two or more coplanar lines at different points.

Trapezoid A quadrilateral that has exactly one pair of parallel sides. The parallel sides, and the lengths of the parallel sides, are called the *bases*. Two angles of the trapezoid whose vertices are the endpoints of a single base are a pair of *base angles*. The *height* is the length of any perpendicular segment drawn from a point on one base to the line containing the other base.

Traversable A graph is said to be traversable if a path can connect each vertex of the graph to at least one other vertex without traveling the same path twice.

Tree diagram A visual method of displaying all the outcomes in a sample space by using a network of "branches" that together resemble a tree.

Trend line On a scatter plot, a line around which the data points seem to cluster. The trend line can be used to analyze the correlation between the data sets.

Triangle A polygon that has exactly three sides. To calculate area, any of the sides may be considered the *base*, and the length of that side is also called the base. The *height* is then the length of the altitude drawn to the base from the opposite vertex.

Triangle Angle-Sum Theorem The sum of the measures of the angles of a triangle is 180°.

Triangle Exterior-Angle Theorem The measure of each exterior angle of a triangle is equal to the sum of the measures of the remote interior angles.

Triangle Inequality Theorem The sum of the lengths of any two sides of a triangle is greater than the length of the third side.

Trinomial A polynomial with exactly three terms.

Truth value A closed statement is either *true* or *false*. These are its possible truth values.

Turning point of a parabola See *vertex of a parabola*.

Two Perpendiculars Theorem If two coplanar lines are perpendicular to a third line, then the lines are parallel.

Two-point form of an equation of a line For an equation in the variables x and y, $y - y_1 = \frac{y_2 - y_1}{x_2 - x_1}(x - x_1)$ where $P(x_1, y_1)$ and $Q(x_2, y_2)$ lie on a nonvertical line.

Undefined term A term that is used without a specific mathematical definition. In geometry, the three undefined terms are *point*, *line*, and *plane*.

Unequal Angles Theorem If two angles of a triangle are not congruent, then the side opposite the larger of the two angles is longer than the side opposite the smaller angle.

Unequal Sides Theorem If two sides of a triangle are not congruent, then the angle opposite the longer of the two sides is larger than the angle opposite the shorter side.

Unique Line Postulate Through any two points there is exactly one line. Also stated as: *Two points determine a line*.

Unique Plane Postulate Through any three noncollinear points there is exactly one plane. Also stated as: *Three noncollinear points determine a plane*.

Unit rate A rate per one unit of a measure. An example of a familiar unit rate is *miles per hour*.

Value of a function A member of the range of the function.

Value of a variable Any number in the replacement set of the variable.

Variable A letter that represents a number.

Variable expression An expression that contains at least one variable. Also called *algebraic expression*.

Vector A quantity that has magnitude and direction.

Venn diagram A diagram in which a rectangle represents all members of a set, with circles within it showing selected subsets and relationships among them.

Vertex angle of an isosceles triangle The angle opposite the base of an isosceles triangle. See *isosceles triangle*.

Vertex of an angle The common endpoint of the sides.

Vertex of a cone See *cone*.

Vertex-edge graph A graph in which the vertices are connected by edges to form a path.

Vertex of a parabola For a parabola that opens upward, its vertex is its lowest point. For a parabola that opens downward, its vertex is its highest point. Also called the *turning point* of the parabola.

Vertex of a polygon See *polygon*.

Vertex of a polyhedron A point that is the intersection of three or more edges.

Vertex of a pyramid See *pyramid*.

Vertical angles Two angles whose sides form two pairs of opposite rays.

Vertical Angles Theorem If two angles are vertical angles, then they are congruent.

Vertical-line test If every vertical line that intersects a graph intersects that graph in exactly one point, then the graph represents a function.

Volume of a three-dimensional figure The amount of space the figure encloses, measured by the number of nonoverlapping cubic units in its interior.

Whole number A member of the set $\{0, 1, 2, 3, 4, 5, 6, \ldots\}$.

x-axis The horizontal number line in a coordinate plane.

x-coordinate See *coordinate(s) of a point*.

x-intercept of a graph The x-coordinate of any point where the graph intersects the x-axis.

y-axis The vertical number line in a coordinate plane.

y-coordinate See *coordinate(s) of a point*.

y-intercept of a graph The y-coordinate of any point where the graph intersects the y-axis.

Zero-product property If a and b are real numbers and $ab = 0$, then either $a = 0$ or $b = 0$.

Sample

HSPA 1

This sample exam has four parts with a total of 48 questions. You will need to solve the problems on a separate sheet of paper. You can use a calculator, ruler, and compass while taking this sample examination.

DIRECTIONS FOR QUESTIONS 1 THROUGH 10: For each of the questions below, select the answer choice that is best in each case.

1 Which of the following has the same value as $-(6^{-2})(4^3)$?

A. -24

B. $-1\frac{7}{9}$

C. $-\frac{1}{24^6}$

D. 2034

2 The surface area of the earth is approximately 5.096×10^8 square kilometers. The formula for surface area of a sphere is given by Surface Area = $4\pi r^2$. What is the approximate radius of the earth?

A. 1.7964×10^2 km

B. 6.368×10^3 km

C. 1.43756×10^5 km

D. 1.6445×10^8 km

3 A certain radioactive isotope has a half-life of 5 days. There are 200 milligrams of the isotope present when $t = 0$. Use the formula $f(t) = 200(2)^{-\frac{t}{5}}$ to determine the amount of radioactive isotope remaining when $t = 5$.

A. $\frac{1}{400}$ mg

B. $\frac{1}{100}$ mg

C. 100 mg

D. 400 mg

4 Sean and three friends go to dinner and the movies. Dinner for the three of them costs $35.97 plus 6.5% tax and 15% tip. Movie tickets cost $27, but Sean has a coupon for 10% off the purchase of four tickets. If Sean has $75, how much money will they have for snacks at the theater?

A. $1.60

B. $4.30

C. $7.00

D. $12.00

5 Which of the figures below has the greatest volume?

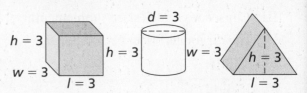

A. cube

B. cylinder

C. triangular prism

D. All the volumes are equal.

6 Which of the figures in Question 5 has the greatest surface area?

A. cube

B. cylinder

C. triangular prism

D. All the surface areas are equal.

7 Buy-Low Auto Sales and Right-Value Car Dealership are merging. The inventories of the two companies are represented in matrices below. The rows represent cars, trucks, and vans, respectively. The columns for each company represent new, used, and leased vehicles, respectively. What will the combined inventory of all new vehicles be?

$$\begin{bmatrix} 128 & 93 & 36 \\ 74 & 31 & 16 \\ 13 & 48 & 22 \end{bmatrix} \quad \begin{bmatrix} 73 & 68 & 21 \\ 24 & 55 & 7 \\ 5 & 37 & 2 \end{bmatrix}$$

A. 201   B. 317   C. 419   D. 753

8 The probability that it will rain on Friday is 40% and the probability that it will be sunny on Saturday is 60%. What is the probability that it will not rain on Friday and will be sunny on Saturday?

A. 20%   B. 24%   C. 36%   D. 40%

9 Which statements must be true of all parallelograms?

   I. All sides are congruent.

   II. All angles are congruent.

   III. Consecutive angles are supplementary.

   IV. The diagonals bisect each other.

  A. I and II

  B. III and IV

  C. I, II, and III

  D. All statements *must* be true.

10 During an end-of-season sale, all items in the store are an additional 40% off. Hoyt wants to buy a $265 coat that has already been marked down 25%. How much will Hoyt have to pay for the coat?

  A. $119.25

  B. $172.25

  C. $182.19

  D. $200.00

DIRECTIONS FOR QUESTIONS 11 AND 12: Show your work and clearly explain your answer.

11 You have 300 feet of paving stones to make a border of a rectangular garden. You want the length of the garden to be twice the width.

- What are the dimensions of the garden?

- If the garden is made directly against the house, you will only need to put the border on three sides. What are the dimensions of the largest possible garden if the three sides are the two widths and one length of the rectangle?

12 The table below shows the number of babies born in the United States since 1910.

Year	Approximate Live Births (per million)	Year	Approximate Live Births (per million)
1910	2.8	1960	4.3
1915	3.0	1965	3.8
1920	3.0	1970	3.7
1925	2.9	1975	3.1
1930	2.6	1980	3.6
1935	2.4	1985	3.8
1940	2.6	1990	4.2
1945	2.9	1995	3.9
1950	3.6	2000	4.1
1955	4.1	2005	4.1

- Make a scatter plot of the data provided. Include a title, axes labels, and a scale.

- Evaluate the scatter plot for trends. What conclusions can be drawn from the graph?

DIRECTIONS FOR QUESTIONS 13 THROUGH 22: For each of the questions below, select the answer choice that is best in each case.

13 Hannah has a collection of her favorite books. According to the table, what percent of her collection is historical fiction?

	Fiction	Non-Fiction
Animal Stories	卌 II	IIII
Adventure	卌 IIII	卌 卌 I
Historical	III	卌 II
Science	卌 III	卌

A. 3%

B. 5.6%

C. 13%

D. 16%

14 Solve the linear system.
$$\begin{cases} 3x + y = 5 \\ 2x + 3y = 8 \end{cases}$$

A. $\left(\frac{2}{3}, 3\right)$

B. $\left(\frac{35}{27}, \frac{5}{9}\right)$

C. $(1, 2)$

D. $(7, -21)$

15 During a softball game, if the height of the ball at any given time after the pitch and before the hit is graphed, the function displayed would best be described as

A. exponential.

B. linear.

C. periodic.

D. quadratic.

16 The vector diagram best illustrates which problem? Assume the origin is the starting point.

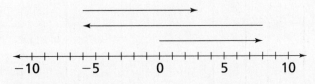

A. $8 + 6 + 8$

B. $8 + 14 - 2$

C. $8 - 6 + 2$

D. $8 - 14 + 9$

17 Twelve neighbors have decided to plan a summer block party. At the end of their first meeting everyone shook hands and agreed to meet again the following month. If each person shook everyone else's hand only once, how many handshakes were exchanged?

A. 12

B. 66

C. 72

D. 78

18 What type of function does the graph represent?

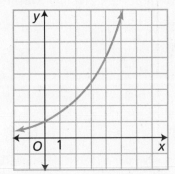

A. Exponential

B. Periodic

C. Linear

D. Quadratic

19 What is the simplified expression for the shaded region of the figure?

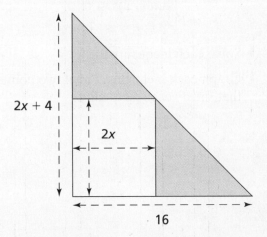

A. $4x + 2$

B. $-x^2 + 8x + 16$

C. $14x + 32$

D. $4(-x^2 + 4x + 8)$

20 The distance from the sun to Mercury is 5.791×10^7 kilometers. Earth is approximately 2.6 times farther away from the sun. What is the approximate distance from the sun to Earth?

A. 1.50566×10^7 C. 1.50566×10^8

B. 15.0566×10^6 D. 15.0566×10^8

21 Find the average rate of speed of the entire trip if a car travels 36 miles an hour for 50 minutes and 65 miles per hour for 2 hours.

A. 47.5 mph   C. $53\frac{1}{3}$ mph

B. 50.5 mph   D. 56.5 mph

22 Which of the following statements is **not** true?

A. The product of a number and its multiplicative inverse is 1.

B. The sum of a number and its additive inverse is 0.

C. Every real number has a multiplicative inverse.

D. Every real number has an additive inverse.

DIRECTIONS FOR QUESTIONS 23 AND 24: Show your work and clearly explain your answer.

23 Consider the following system of inequalities.

$$\begin{cases} 3x - 2y < 6 \\ 3x + y < 1 \end{cases}$$

- Solve each inequality for y.
- Graph each inequality. Label two points that satisfy each inequality.

24 $\triangle ABC$ lies on the coordinate plane such that $A(-7, 8)$, $B(2, 2)$, and $C(-7, 2)$.

- Sketch $\triangle ABC$.
- Translate the figure three units to the right and construct and label $\triangle A'B'C'$.
- Rotate $\triangle A'B'C'$ 90° counterclockwise around vertex B. Construct and label $\triangle A''B''C''$.

DIRECTIONS FOR QUESTIONS 25 THROUGH 34: For each of the questions below, select the answer choice that is best in each case.

25 Between which two consecutive integers does $-\sqrt{18}$ lie?

   A. 4 and 5   B. -4 and -3

   C. -5 and -4 D. -19 and -17

26 Simplify $\dfrac{4z^{-3}}{8z^{-6}}$.

   A. $\dfrac{0.5}{z^3}$ B. $0.5z^3$ C. $\dfrac{2}{z^3}$ D. $2z^3$

27 Identify the postulate or theorem which justifies the statement $\triangle ABC \cong \triangle XYZ$.

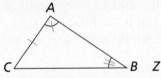

   A. SAA

   B. ASA

   C. AAS

   D. Congruence cannot be determined.

28 At what point do the lines $y = 2x - 3$ and $y = -x + 3$ intersect?

   A. $(1, 2)$ C. $(-1, 1)$

   B. $(2, 1)$ D. $(1, -2)$

29 If two fair number cubes, numbered 1 through 6, are rolled simultaneously, what is the probability that the sum of the two cubes will be at least three but less than 10?

   A. $\dfrac{29}{36}$ C. $\dfrac{31}{36}$

   B. $\dfrac{6}{7}$ D. $\dfrac{16}{21}$

30 Four students participated in a fundraising drive for the local food bank. Jamal raised $223, Kirsten raised $197, Yomani raised $314, and Cierra raised $251. If this data is displayed in a circle graph, what is the measure of the central angle that represents amount raised by Kirsten?

   A. $18°$ C. $35°$

   B. $20°$ D. $72°$

31 The first five terms of a sequence are $0, 3, 8, 15, 24$. Which expression can be used to find the nth term of the sequence?

   A. $n + (n + 1)$

   B. $n^2 - 1$

   C. $2(n + 1)$

   D. $2n - 1$

32 If the graph represents the function $f(x)$, which graph represents $f(x) + 3$.

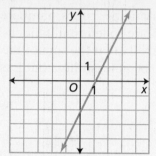

A.
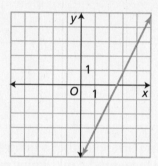

B.
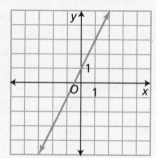

C.
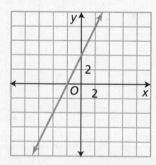

D.
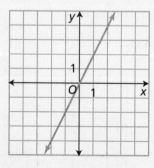

33 An arrow is shot upward from an initial height of 5 feet at a velocity of 79 feet per second. How long will it take for the arrow to hit the ground? Use the formula $-16t^2 + vt + h$ where t = time in seconds, v = velocity, and h = the initial height.

A. 1.8 seconds

B. 3 seconds

C. 5 seconds

D. 50 seconds

34 In the sequence below, each shaded triangle, after the first, is $\frac{1}{4}$ the area of the preceding shaded triangle. What is the ratio of the shaded area of the 5th figure?

1

2

3

A. $\frac{1}{16}$

B. $\frac{1}{20}$

C. $\frac{1}{256}$

D. $\frac{1}{1024}$

DIRECTIONS FOR QUESTIONS 35 AND 36: Show your work and clearly explain your answer.

35 Yonni wants to place paving stones around her garden. The total area of the garden and the walkway is 300 square feet. The dimensions of the garden are given by $w = r - 1$ and $l = 2r + 3$. The walkway is 3 feet wide all the way around the garden.

$$l = 2r + 3$$
$$w = r - 1$$

- What is the area of the garden?
- What is the area of the walkway?
- If Yonni chooses paving stones that are 6 inches square, how many paving stones does she need?

36 The total cost for admission for one adult, one senior adult, and one child to the local museum is $42. The cost of an adult admission is equal to the square of the cost of a child's admission. The cost of a senior admission is $2 more than twice the cost of a child's admission.

- Write and label an expression that represents the cost of each of the three tickets.
- What is the cost of each ticket?
- Is it more or less expensive for three children and two senior adults to visit the museum?

Sample HSPA—MATHEMATICS—PART 4

DIRECTIONS FOR QUESTIONS 37 THROUGH 46: For each of the questions below, select the answer choice that is best in each case.

37 A new alpha-numeric license plate system is adopted in your state. Each license plate will consist of four letters followed by three digits. Assuming no letter or digit is repeated on the same license plate, how many unique plates can be made?

A. 3.59304×10^5 C. 258336×10^8

B. 4.56976×10^5 D. $1.463464054 \times 10^{32}$

38 What is the vertex of the parabola $y = x^2 + 4x + 9$?

A. $(-2, 5)$ C. $(0.75, -4.25)$

B. $(0, -4)$ D. $(5, -9)$

39 Bryce earned \$2,560 working over the summer and 20% of his earnings were paid in taxes. He invests 70% of what is left after taxes. If he invests at a rate of 5% compounded quarterly, how much money will he have all together after 10 years?

Use the compound interest formula $A = P\left(1 + \frac{r}{n}\right)^{nt}$ where A = the total value of the investment after a given number of years, P = the amount of the original investment, r = the interest rate, t = the total years of investment, and n = the number of times the interest is compounded each year.

A. \$2073.60   C. \$3366.13

B. \$2356.29   D. \$4207.67

40 Solve for x, given the following lengths: $\overline{PT} = 8, \overline{TS} = 2, \overline{QR} = 2.5$.

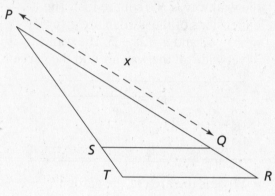

A. 7.5   C. 8.5

B. 8   D. 10

41 Simplify $\left(\frac{2a^2bc^{-3}}{ab^{-2}4c^{-5}}\right)^3$.

A. $\frac{2a^9b^9}{c^8}$ C. $2a^3b^3c^{24}$

B. $\frac{a^3b^9c^6}{8}$ D. $8a^3b^9c^8$

42 A box contains 18 colored balls. There are 2 white balls, 7 green balls, three times as many blue balls as white balls, and half as many red balls as blue balls. If two balls are drawn from the box at random, which of the following outcomes has the greatest probability?

A. 2 blue balls

B. 1 blue ball and 1 red ball

C. 1 white ball and 1 blue ball

D. 1 red ball and 1 green ball

43 In the figure below, the lines a and b are parallel, $m\angle E = 2x^2 + 10$, and $m\angle C = 2(m\angle E)$. Find $m\angle C$.

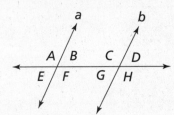

A. 100°   C. 120°

B. 115°   D. 125°

44 Which equation has an x-intercept at $x = 6$ and a y-intercept at $y = -10$?

A. $5x + 3y = -30$ C. $5x - 3y = 30$

B. $-5x - 3y = -30$ D. $-5x + 3y = 30$

45 The local video store offers a free video rental to every customer who receives a white gumball from the giant gumball machine. The gumball machine holds 1,000 pieces of gum when it is full. The machine is currently 75% full. If the original ratio of white gumballs to all other colors of gumballs is 1 to 20, approximately how many white gumballs should be in the machine?

A. 15   C. 67

B. 36   D. 150

46 The lengths of the sides of a 30°-60°-90° triangle are 5, x, and 13, respectively. What is the value of x?

A. 10   C. 13

B. 12   D. 14

Directions for Questions 47–48: Show you work and clearly explain your answer.

47 Marcie is moving out of state and wants to rent a moving van. Company A offers a van for a flat fee of $150 plus $25 per day for unlimited miles. Company B does not charge a flat fee but does charge $10 per day plus 10¢ per mile. Marcie plans to rent the van for six days.

- Write an expression to represent the cost of renting from each company.

- How many miles does Marcie drive if the cost is exactly the same from either company?

- Which company should Marcie choose if she drives 2000 miles?

48 A Petri dish contains a colony of bacteria and is 3 inches in diameter. There are about 10^5 bacteria per square inch living in the dish.

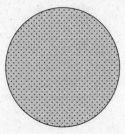

- What is the surface area of the Petri dish?

- Approximately how many bacteria are in the Petri dish?

- Another larger dish contains about 4.93×10^5 bacteria with the same density. What is the approximate radius of this Petri dish?

Sample
HSPA 2

This sample exam has four parts with a total of 48 questions. You will need to solve the problems on a separate sheet of paper. You can use a calculator, ruler, and compass while taking this sample examination.

DIRECTIONS FOR QUESTIONS 1 THROUGH 10: For each of the questions below, select the answer choice that is best in each case.

1 Ms. Deetz creates a circle graph to display the grade distribution in her Math classes. Of the 72 students in her classes, 9 have earned an A. How many degrees of the circle graph should Ms. Deetz use to represent the A students in her classes?

A. 45°   B. 37°   C. 20°   D. 12.5°

2 A teacher posed this puzzle to a class.

There is a prime number between 3 and 40 about which I will answer three "yes" or "no" questions. After I answer your questions, you should be able to determine the number.

The class asked:

- Is it one less than a multiple of 4?
- Is it greater than 10?
- Is it one more than a multiple of 5?

The answer is *yes* to all three questions. What is the number?

A. 37   B. 31   C. 19   D. 23

3 What is the vertex of the parabola $y = x^2 + 2x - 4$?

A. $(-6, 0)$ C. $(-1, -5)$

B. $(-6, 4)$ D. $(4, 0)$

4 Which of the following statements is **not** always true?

A. If a and b are positive real numbers, then $\sqrt{\frac{a}{b}} = \frac{\sqrt{a}}{\sqrt{b}}$.

B. If $a < b$ then $|a - b| = a - b$.

C. If $a > b$ and $c > 0$, then $ac > bc$.

D. If $m, n,$ and p are integers, then $(x^m \cdot y^n)^p = x^{mp} \cdot y^{np}$.

5 Which of the following is **NOT** a postulate or theorem for congruence of triangles?

A. AAA   C. SSS

B. ASA   D. SAS

6 Evaluate the following.

$$\begin{bmatrix} 8 & 6 \\ 3 & 9 \end{bmatrix} - \begin{bmatrix} 3 & 0 \\ 7 & 6 \end{bmatrix} =$$

A. $\begin{bmatrix} 8 & 3 \\ -3 & 2 \end{bmatrix}$ C. $\begin{bmatrix} 11 & 6 \\ 10 & 15 \end{bmatrix}$

B. $\begin{bmatrix} 5 & 6 \\ -4 & 3 \end{bmatrix}$ D. $\begin{bmatrix} 1 & 0 \\ 0 & 9 \end{bmatrix}$

7 A high school softball team scored the following number of runs in their first six games: 3, 5, 2, 4, 1, and 5. In their seventh game the team scored 10 runs. Which statistical measure is most affected by the number of runs scored in the seventh game?

A. mode

B. median

C. mean

D. range

8 Which equation has an x-intercept at $x = -6$ and a y-intercept at $y = 9$?

A. $-6x - 4y = 36$

B. $6x + 4y = 36$

C. $-6x + 4y = -36$

D. $6x - 4y = -36$

9 Certain bacteria grow at a rate at which the number of bacteria in the colony doubles every 24 hours. Assume there are 1,500 bacteria when $t = 0$. How many bacteria are present after 10 days? Use the formula for the population P given by $P = 1,500(2^t)$, where $t = $ time.

A. 3.0×10^4 C. 1.536×10^6

B. 3.0×10^5 D. 5.9049×10^{34}

10 Which of the following expressions has the same value as $3 - |5 - 9|$?

A. $|4 - 5|$

B. $|3 - 5| - 9$

C. $-|4 - 5|$

D. $|9 - 5| - 3$

DIRECTIONS FOR QUESTIONS 11 AND 12: Show your work and clearly explain your answer.

11 Two fair number cubes, numbered 1 through 6, are tossed.

- What two sums are least likely to occur? Explain your answer.

- Next, three 8-sided number generators that are numbered 1 through 8 are tossed. What two sums are least likely to occur? Explain your reasoning.

12 The table shows the median income of a family of four for the years 1993 through 2003.

Year	Median Income for a Four-Person Family
1993	$45,161
1994	$47,012
1995	$49,687
1996	$51,518
1997	$53,350
1998	$56,061
1999	$59,981
2000	$62,228
2001	$63,278
2002	$62,732
2003	$65,093

- Make a scatter plot of the data provided. Include a title, axes labels, and a scale.

- Evaluate the scatter plot for trends. What conclusions can be drawn from the graph?

DIRECTIONS FOR QUESTIONS 13 THROUGH 22: For each of the questions below, select the answer choice that is best in each case.

13 A human hair is measured to be 0.0033858000 inches in diameter. How many significant digits are there in this number?

    A. 11   C. 8

    B. 10   D. 5

14 A new alpha-numeric license plate system is adopted in your state. Each license plate will consist of 3 letters followed by 4 digits. Assuming it is possible for letters or digits to repeat on the same license plate, how many unique plates can be made?

    A. 2.7576×10^4 C. 1.15316136×10^8

    B. 7.8624×10^7 D. 1.7576×10^8

15 The first five terms of a sequence are $-1, 2, 5, 8, 11$. Which expression can be used to find the nth term?

    A. $n + 3$ C. $3(n - 1)$

    B. $2n + 2$ D. $3n - 4$

16 Which equation can be used to find the value of y?

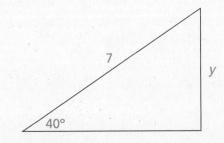

    A. $\cos 40° = \frac{7}{y}$ C. $\cos 40° = \frac{y}{7}$

    B. $\sin 40° = \frac{7}{y}$ D. $\sin 40° = \frac{y}{7}$

17 A friend asks you to draw two cards from a standard deck of playing cards. What is the probability of drawing two kings, assuming you do not replace the cards?

    A. 0.08   C. 0.005   B. 0.01   D. 0.002

18 Solve the linear system.
$$\begin{cases} 8x + 5y = -9 \\ 3x - 5y = -2 \end{cases}$$

    A. $(11, -1)$ C. $\left(-\frac{1}{8}, 2\right)$

    B. $\left(-1, \frac{1}{5}\right)$ D. $\left(2, -\frac{5}{8}\right)$

19 Solve for x.
$$7 - 2x > 11$$

    A. $x < 9$ C. $x > -2$

    B. $x > -9$ D. $x < -2$

20 David is learning about investing money in his 5th grade math class. He has $240 in his savings account that pays an interest rate of 4.5% compounded quarterly. He decides to invest half of his savings in a savings bond at a rate of 6% compounded annually. How much money will David have in each account at the end of 7 years? Use the compound interest formula

$$A = P\left(1 + \frac{r}{n}\right)^{nt}$$

where A = the total value of the investment after a given number of years, P = the amount of the original investment, r = the interest rate, t = the total years of investment, and n = the number of times the interest is compounded each year.

    A. Savings: $164.14; Bond; $127.39

    B. Savings: $164.14; Bond; $180.44

    C. Savings: $571.20; Bond; $127.39

    D. Savings: $571.20; Bond; $180.44

21 The circumference of a bicycle tire is 26 inches. Approximately how many rotations will the tire make in a 1 mile (5,280 feet) trip?

A. 230

B. 2,437

C. 137,280

D. 1,647,360

22 Which of the following is an irrational number?

A. $0.\overline{3}$

B. $\sqrt{\dfrac{4}{11}}$

C. $-\dfrac{1}{\sqrt{196}}$

D. 4^{-3}

DIRECTIONS FOR QUESTIONS 23 AND 24: Show your work and clearly explain your answer.

23 Giva needs to refinish 520 square feet of hardwood flooring. A local refinishing company will do the work for $1.20 per square foot plus $115 for supplies. A friend has offered to do the work for free if Giva rents the equipment and provides all supplies needed. The local tool company rents a floor sander for $65 per day plus a $50 fee. The sandpaper and other supplies needed cost $135.

• Write and solve an equation expressing the total cost to have the professional floor refinisher do the work.

• Giva's friend estimates that it will take him 7 days to complete the job. Is it less expensive for Giva to hire the professional or have her friend complete the work? Justify your answer.

24 Consider figure **A** in the graph below.

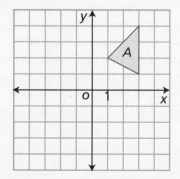

• What are the coordinates of figure **B** obtained by reflecting **A** over the y-axis?

• What are the coordinates of figure **C** obtained by reflecting **B** over the x-axis?

• Graph the figure **D** that has vertices $(-x, -y)$ for each vertex (x, y) of figure **A**. How does figure **D** compare to figure **C**?

DIRECTIONS FOR QUESTIONS 25 THROUGH 34: For each of the questions below, select the answer choice that is best in each case.

25 Amari wants to purchase a snowboard. The snowboard he wants costs $369.95. Last month the board was marked down 10%. The store is having a one-day clearance sale and is taking an additional 25% off all merchandise. How much will Amari pay for the snowboard if he buys it today?

A. $120.24   C. $249.71

B. $240.47   D. $270. 71

26 The circumference of an official size basketball is approximately half that of a standard wire basketball hoop. If the diameter of the hoop is 18 inches, what is the circumference of an official size basketball?

A. 28.27 in.   C. 63.62 in.

B. 56.55 in.   D. 254.47 in.

27 In the given figure, the lines a and b are parallel, $m\angle A = x^2 - 1$ and $m\angle D = \dfrac{m\angle A}{2}$. Find $m\angle F$.

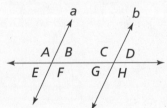

A. 59°   C. 120°

B. 60°   D. 121°

28 The vector diagram best illustrates which problem? Assume the origin is the starting point.

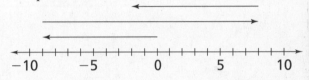

A. $-9 + 8 + (-2)$ C. $-9 + 17 + (-2)$

B. $-9 + 8 + (-10)$ D. $-9 + 17 + (-10)$

29 Jeremy organizes his music collection by type and format. According to the table, what percent of his collection is country on cassette?

Music Type	CD	Cassette
Classical	13	8
Rock	26	10
Jazz	37	25
Country	19	12

A. 20%   C. 8%

B. 12%   D. 5%

30 East Fairfield Video and North Fairfield Video are merging. The inventories of the two video stores are represented by matrices A and B below. The columns represent video cassettes and DVDs respectively. The rows represent Drama, Action, and Comedy movies respectively. What is the combined inventory of all DVDs?

$$A = \begin{bmatrix} 126 & 231 \\ 110 & 194 \\ 86 & 146 \end{bmatrix} \quad B = \begin{bmatrix} 167 & 316 \\ 153 & 458 \\ 112 & 479 \end{bmatrix}$$

A. 1,824   C. 840

B. 1,468   D. 754

31 Between which two numbers does $-\sqrt{7}$ fall on the number line?

A. -4 and -3 C. 2 and 3

B. -3 and -2 D. 3 and 4

32 The distance from Atlantic City, New Jersey to Long Beach, California is approximately 2.8×10^3 miles. If an ant walks from Atlantic City to Long Beach, it would take approximately 4.508×10^9 steps all together. Approximately how many steps does an ant take per mile?

A. 1.26224×10^3 C. 1.708×10^6

B. 1.61×10^6 D. 7.308×10^6

33 Which statements must be true of all regular polygons?
I. All interior angles are congruent.
II. All exterior angles are congruent.
III. The sum of all exterior angles is $360°$.
IV. The sum of all interior angles is $360°$.

A. I

B. I and II

C. I, II, and III

D. All statements must be true.

34 Tyus is having a cookout. At the grocery store, he purchases 6 pounds of steak, 2 bags of chips, 4 pounds of potato salad, 4 pounds of fruit salad, 6 bottles of drink, a bag of charcoal, and a stack of paper plates. The food items are not taxed, but the drinks, charcoal, and paper plates are taxed at 7.5%. What is his total bill at the grocery store?

Item	Cost
Steak	$4.29/lb
Chips	$2.99 each
Potato salad	$2.39/lb
Fruit salad	$3.58/lb
Drink	$1.29 each
Charcoal	$5.89 each
Paper plates	$2.19 each

A. $24.31 C. $76.68

B. $72.60 D. $83.20

DIRECTIONS FOR QUESTIONS 35 AND 36: Show your work and clearly explain your answer.

35 Tickets to the dinner theater for two adults and two children cost $158. An adult ticket costs $2 less than twice the amount of a child's ticket. If three adult tickets are purchased, the fourth ticket is free. Groups of 10 or more can purchase adult tickets for $5 off the regular price of each ticket.

- Write and label an expression to represent the cost of an adult ticket, a child ticket, and a group ticket.

- What is the cost of each type of ticket?

- Which would be less expensive; six adult and six children's tickets or tickets for a group of 10 adults. Explain your answer.

36 The fee for renting a boat at a lake is given by the formula $C = 2(H - 3) + 20$, where C is the fee in dollars and H is the number of hours the boat is rented.

- What is the cost of the rental if you rent the boat for 5 hours?

- Why is it unreasonable to expect that the rental cost could be $15?

- Construct a graph of the cost of the rental for each hour between 1 and 10 hours.

DIRECTIONS FOR QUESTIONS 37 THROUGH 46: For each of the questions below, select the answer choice that is best in each case.

37 What is the difference between the values of the surface area and volume of the figure?

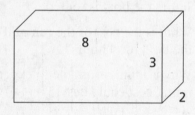

A. 44

B. 4

C. 2

D. −44

38 Which of the following is equivalent to $\left[(4^3)(-2^{-5})\right]^{-2}$?

A. −0.03125

B. $-\dfrac{1}{960}$

C. 0.25

D. 4096

39 Find BD if $AC = 11.1$, $BC = 7.4$, $DE = 2.8$, and $AE = 4.2$.

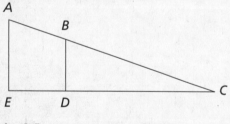

A. 0.5

B. 2.8

C. 3.7

D. 6.3

40 The following sets of numbers represent the lengths of the sides of four separate triangles. Which set cannot represent a right triangle?

A. 3, 4, 5

B. 8, 6, 10

C. 13, 5, 12

D. 25, 24, 8

41 A golf ball is hit with an initial velocity of 217 feet per second from an initial height of 0. How long will it take the ball to hit the ground the first time? Use the formula $-16t^2 + vt + h$, where t = time in seconds, v = the initial velocity, and h = the initial height.

A. 6.78 seconds

B. 7.77 seconds

C. 8.46 seconds

D. 13.56 seconds

42 The probability that Fernando passes science is 80% and the probability that he passes history is 65%. What is the probability that he passes science, but not history?

A. 15%

B. 28%

C. 52%

D. 65%

43 The distance of an arrow shot from a bow from a target at a given time is best described by which type of function?

A. Exponential

B. Linear

C. Periodic

D. Quadratic

44 Juan builds a deck where the length is three times the width. If the perimeter of the deck is 64 feet, what is the length of the deck?

A. 24 feet

B. 16 feet

C. 8 feet

D. 4 feet

45 The students in the senior class at Kennedy High School completed a survey about what they planned to declare as a major in college. The results are displayed in the circle graph below. Which statement **CANNOT** be inferred based on the circle graph?

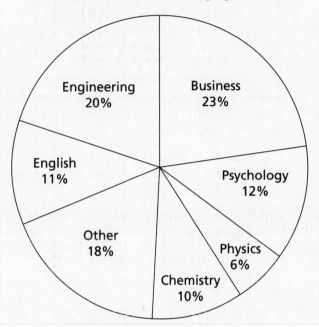

A. Business is the most common major.

B. Physics is the least common major.

C. More students plan to study English than chemistry.

D. Fewer students plan to study physics than psychology.

46 What is the simplified expression for the area of the shaded region of the figure?

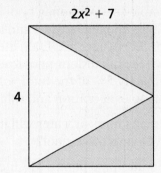

A. $8x^2 + 56$

B. $4x^2 + 28$

C. $4x^2 + 14$

D. $8x^2 + 14$

DIRECTIONS FOR QUESTIONS 47 AND 48: Show your work and clearly explain your answer.

47 An Olympic-size swimming pool is 50 meters long, 25 meters wide, and at least 2 meters deep. There are 1,000 liters in 1 cubic meter. An outdoor pool loses approximately 5% of the total volume every week due to evaporation and splash-out.

- How many liters of water will it take to fill an Olympic-size pool?
- If the water pipe pumps 318 liters per minute into the empty pool, approximately how many hours will it take fill the pool to 90% of its capacity?
- How much water will have to be replaced every week to keep the pool full?

48 Assume that the pattern of dots shown below continues infinitely, with more dots being added at each step.

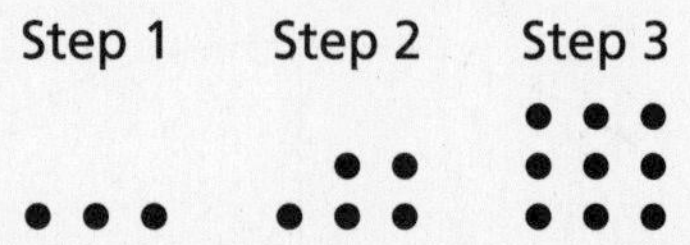

Step 1
Step 2
Step 3

Rene wants to determine the number of dots in the seventh step, but she does not want to actually draw all 7 steps and then count the dots.

- Explain how Rene could find the number of dots in Step 7 without actually drawing them.
- What would be the number of dots in the seventh step?
- Write an algebraic expression for the number of dots in Step *n*.

SAMPLE REFERENCE SHEET

Pythagorean Theorem $c^2 = a^2 + b^2$	**Trapezoid** 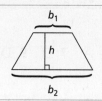 Area $= \frac{1}{2}h(b_1 + b_2)$
Rectangle 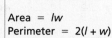 Area $= lw$ Perimeter $= 2(l + w)$	**Triangle** Area $= \frac{1}{2}bh$
Parallelogram Area $= bh$	**Circle** 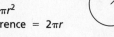 Area $= \pi r^2$ Circumference $= 2\pi r$
Rectangular Prism Volume $= lwh$ Surface Area $= 2lw + 2wh + 2lh$	**Cylinder** Volume $= \pi r^2 h$ Surface Area $= 2\pi rh + 2\pi r^2$
Sphere Volume $= \frac{4}{3}\pi r^3$ Surface Area $= 4\pi r^2$ 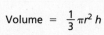	**Cone** Volume $= \frac{1}{3}\pi r^2 h$

The sum of the measures of the interior angles of a triangle = 180°

The measure of a circle is 360° or 2π radians

   Given a right triangle:

$$\sin \theta = \frac{\text{opposite side}}{\text{hypotenuse}} \qquad \cos \theta = \frac{\text{adjacent side}}{\text{hypotenuse}} \qquad \tan \theta = \frac{\text{opposite side}}{\text{adjacent side}}$$

Interest = principal $\times$ rate $\times$ time

Simple Interest Formula: $= A = p + prt$ **Compound Interest Formula:** $A = p\left(1 + \frac{r}{n}\right)^{nt}$

A = amount after t years; p = principal; r = annual interest rate; t = number of years;
n = number of times compounded per year

The number of **combinations** of n elements taken r at a time is given by $\dfrac{n!}{(n-r)!r!}$

The number of **permutations** of n elements taken r at a time is given by $\dfrac{n!}{(n-r)!}$

Given the points (x_1, y_1), (x_2, y_2),

Distance between two points: **Slope Formula:**   **Slope-intercept form of a line:**

$$d = \sqrt{(x_2 - x_1)^2 + (y_2 - y_1)^2} \qquad m = \frac{\text{rise}}{\text{run}} = \frac{y_2 - y_1}{x_2 - x_1} \qquad y = mx + b$$

425

SELECTED ANSWERS

Diagnostic Test

Chapter 1

1 A **3** C **5** A **7** D **9** D **11** C

Chapter 2

1 B **3** D **5** B **7** C **9** A

Chapter 3

1 B **3** D **5** A **7** B **9** A **11** C

Chapter 4

1 B **3** A **5** C **7** B **9** C

Chapter 5

1 D **3** C **5** B **7** A **9** D

Chapter 6

1 C **3** B **5** C **7** D **9** B

Chapter 7

1 B **3** A **5** D **7** A **9** D

Chapter 8

1 C **3** D **5** C **7** B **9** B

Chapter 9

1 B **3** B **5** A **7** C **9** C

Chapter 10

1 B **3** C **5** B **7** B **9** B

Chapter 11

1 C **3** A **5** B **7** D **9** B

Chapter 12

1 B **3** A **5** A **7** A **9** B

Chapter 13

1 D **3** A **5** C **7** A **9** B

Chapter 1

Lesson 1.1

1 C **3** D **5** B **7** C **9** D **11** B
13 A **15** A **17** 1, 31 **19** Yes **21** Yes
23 $2 \cdot 2 \cdot 2 \cdot 2 \cdot 2$ **25** 4 **27** 1 **29** 48 **31** 56
33 1 **35** Answers may vary. Sample answers:
$\frac{6}{10}, \frac{9}{15}, \frac{12}{20}$ **37** 0.94 **39** $0.\overline{3}$ **41** $\frac{18}{25}$ **43** $\frac{13}{30}$

45 $4\frac{1}{8} = \frac{33}{8}$ **47** $0.\overline{2} = \frac{2}{9}$ **49** 0; 0 is the only whole number that is not a natural number.
51 Answers may vary. Sample answer: $\frac{1}{2}$
53 Answers may vary. Sample answer: 4 and 9

Lesson 1.2

1 A **3** C **5** C **7** > **9** < **11** >
13 > **15** < **17** $-\frac{8}{9}, -\frac{13}{15}, -\frac{5}{6}$ **19** $-1.101,$
$-1.1, -1.01, -0.1001$ **21** $-\frac{9}{2}, \quad -4\frac{1}{3}, -4.3,$
$-4\frac{13}{100}, 4.\overline{3}$ **23** 0.85 **25** 0.1875 **27** $\frac{18}{25}$
29 92% **31** 56.25% **33** $\frac{27}{2500}, 0.0108$

Lesson 1.3

1 C **3** C **5** B **7** 0.6 **9** -7
11 $-\frac{3}{2}$ or $-1\frac{1}{2}$ **13** -7.28 **15** -2 **17** $\frac{49}{60}$
19 Commutative Property of Multiplication
21 Distributive Property **23** Commutative
Property of Addition **25** 9 **27** 2 **29** <
31 0 **33** Yes, since you can add odd numbers in any order and the sum is the same.

Lesson 1.4

1 C **3** C **5** 2253 mi **7** 9100 ft^2 **9** 10.6
11 33 **13** 0.1 **15** 753 yd

Lesson 1.5

1 B **3** B **5** D **7** C **9** 121 **11** 1
13 8,000 **15** 0.000031 **17** 4×10^6
19 3.409×10^1 **21** 6.5×10^7 **23** 8 **25** -1.2
27 5 and 6 **29** 3 and 4 **31** 1.73 **33** -2.2
35 0.97 **37** -17 **39** 8 **41** 2 **43** $3^3 \cdot 5^2$
45 $(4 \times 3 + 12) \div 3$ because $(4 \times 3 + 12) \div 3 = (12 + 12) \div 3 = 24 \div 3 = 8$.

Lesson 1.6

1 B **3** A **5** arithmetic **7** geometric
9 20; 29 **11** $-27; -45$ **13** 45; 405 **15** 45; 405
17 $-5; -20, -25$ **19** $-4; -4, -8$
21 0.5; 2.25, 1.125 **23** $-4; -576, 2304$
25 $a_n = 7 + (n-1)7$ **27** $a_n = -252\left(\frac{1}{6}\right)^{n-1}$
29 $a_n = 4 + (n-1)(5)$ **31** $a_n = -8\left(\frac{1}{2}\right)^{n-1}$

Lesson 1.7

1 D **3** D **5** C **7** C **9** −20 **11** $\frac{11}{2}$, or $5\frac{1}{2}$ **13** 12 **15** $-5r + 5s$ **17** $-3x - 36$ **19** $-11v + 77$ **21** $18t$ **23** $c - 17$ **25** $2(y + 9)$ **27** $\frac{a + b}{ab}$ **29** the square root of the quotient of $3a$ squared and $5b$ to the 4th **31** $-2n - 6$ **33** $m + 30$

Chapter 1: Preparing for the New Jersey HSPA

1 A **3** C **5** D **7** B **9** C **11** C **13** A **15** B **17** C **19** B **21** D **23** D **25** C **27** A **29** $\frac{2d}{c}$; $187.16 **31** 93,000,000; 140,000,000; ≈47,000,000

Chapter 2

Lesson 2.1

1 B **3** D **5** D **7** 37 **9** 21 **11** −100 **13** −21 **15** $-\frac{45}{4}$ or $-11\frac{1}{4}$ **17** 40 **19** −1 **21** $\frac{30}{11}$ or $2\frac{8}{11}$ **23** 10 **25** $p = \frac{q + r}{2}$ **27** $y = \frac{z}{x}$ **29** $t = \frac{d}{r}$ **31** $\frac{24}{5}, -\frac{24}{5}$ **33** $\frac{2}{3}, \frac{10}{3}$

35 No, Daneesha's statement is incorrect. If $3t = -3t$, it follows from the Addition Property of Equality that $6t = 0$; so $t = 0$. Therefore, the equation does have a solution, $t = 0$.

Lesson 2.2

1 C **3** C **5** C **7** 38° **9** −1

Lesson 2.3

1 B **3** C **5** C **7** B

Lesson 2.4

1 C **3** C **5** B **7** 72% **9** 12 **11** 28%; decrease **13** 150%; increase **15** 17 **17** $13.26 **19** 19.2 minutes **21** 1440

Lesson 2.5

1 A **3** D **5** B **7** $x < -1$ **9** $x < -2$ or $x \geq 4$

11

13

15

17

19 $n > -8$

21 $a \leq -18$

23 $w \geq 3$

25 $z > -9$

27 $c \leq 4$

29 $1 < x \leq 4$

31 10, 11, 12, ...

33 −4, −3, −2, −1, 0, 1, 2

35 $h < -2$ or $h > 2$

37 $-2 < t < 1$

39 *true*; Explanations may vary. Sample explanation: $2q + 5 \leq 3$ is equivalent to $q \leq -1$. There are no real numbers satisfying $q \leq -1$ and $q > 0$.

Lesson 2.6

1 B **3** B **5** D **7** 0, 1, and 2 **9** 4 **11** at least $2500 **13** no more than 20

SELECTED ANSWERS

15 any whole number of meters from 1 through 14, inclusive.   **17** The lesser partner receives at least $800 but no more than $1600. The greater partner receives at least $1000 but no more than $2000.

Chapter 2: Preparing for the New Jersey HSPA

1 A   **3** C   **5** B   **7** B   **9** D   **11** A   **13** D
15 A   **17** A   **19** B   **21** D   **23** 30 miles; 1:50 pm; 45 miles; $1\frac{1}{3}$ hours or 80 minutes
25 $510; $51; No, because the current sale price of the sofa is $459, and the cost of the sofa at 25% off is $450.

Chapter 3

Lesson 3.1

1 B   **3** C   **5** triangle   **7** $\frac{5}{3}$ **9** $-\frac{5}{3}$
11 no slope   **13** $-\frac{2}{5}$ **15** $B(-3,-4)$
17 $P(6,12)$ **19** $F(9,6.5)$ **21** 54 miles per hour

Lesson 3.2

1 C   **3** B   **5** C   **7** B   **9** A   **11** Answers may vary. Sample answer: No, because it does not pass the vertical line test.   **13** $G(T) = 9T$ (domain: $0 \le T \le 3200$; range: $0 \le G \le 28800$ and G and T are integers)   **15** $p(f) = 2f$ (domain: $f \ge 0$; range: $p \ge 0$ and f and p are integers)

17

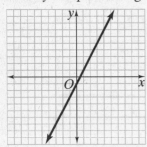

domain and range: {all real numbers}

19

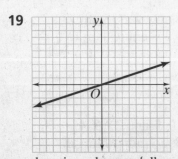

domain and range: {all real numbers}

21

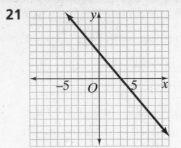

domain and range: {all real numbers}

23

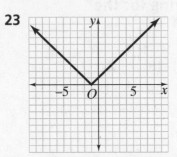

domain: {all real numbers}, range: {$f(x) \ge 0$}

25

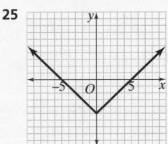

domain: {all real numbers}, range: {$f(x) \ge -5$}

Lesson 3.3

1 C   **3** D   **5** 48.2°F   **7** −17.8°C   **9** 5
11 −4.5   **13** domain: all real numbers; range: all real numbers   **15** domain: all real numbers; range: all real numbers greater than or equal to −1

17

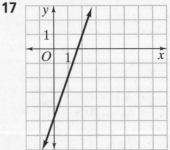

19
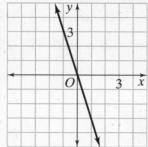

21
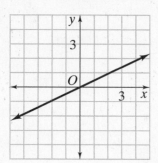

23
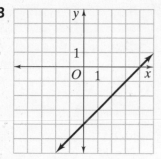

25
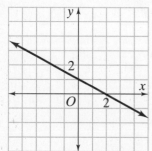

27
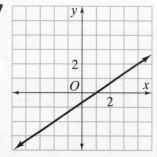

29 $0.05n + 0.1d = 1.20$ **31** $0.05n + 0.1d = 2.45$ **33** $r + b + 35 = 185; r = 70, b = 80; r = 90, b = 60; r = 75, b = 75$

Lesson 3.4

1 B **3** A **5** C **7** B **9** $y = -2x - 1$

11 $y = -\frac{3}{5}x + \frac{2}{5}$ **13** $x = -11$ **15** $y = 2x + 2$

17 $\left(0, \frac{13}{8}\right)$ **19** $3x + 5y = 15$

21 Yes; An equation for the line containing P and Q is $y = \frac{7}{8}(x + 3) - 1; \frac{7}{8}(93 + 3) - 1 = 7(12) - 1 = 83$. So, $(93, 83)$ is on the line.

Lesson 3.5

1 B

3
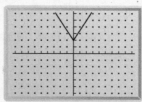

$(0, 2)$

5
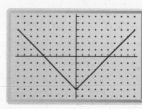

$(0, -5)$

7 $y = |x| + 9$
9 $y = |x - 9|$ **11** $y = |x - 2|$

Lesson 3.6

1 C **3** C **5** B **7** The data does represent inverse variation because the product of each pair of values is 36. Therefore the equation is $xy = 36$.

9
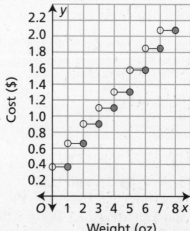

SELECTED ANSWERS

Lesson 3.7

1 C **3** A **5** D **7** $\begin{bmatrix} 4 & 0 \\ 2 & 10 \end{bmatrix}$

9 Undefined, unlike dimension

11 $\begin{bmatrix} 6 & -4 \\ 8 & 20 \end{bmatrix}$

13 $\begin{bmatrix} \frac{3}{2} & \frac{9}{4} & 3 \\ \frac{3}{4} & \frac{9}{4} & \frac{15}{4} \\ \frac{3}{2} & \frac{3}{4} & \frac{9}{4} \end{bmatrix}$

15 $L = \begin{bmatrix} 72 & 80 \\ 40 & 52 \\ 80 & 84 \end{bmatrix}$ $M = \begin{bmatrix} 20 & 12 \\ 20 & 12 \\ 35 & 25 \end{bmatrix}$ $T = \begin{bmatrix} 7 & 10 \\ 10 & 12 \\ 5 & 9 \end{bmatrix}$

17 $R = \begin{bmatrix} 160 & 160 \\ 120 & 120 \\ 200 & 200 \end{bmatrix}$

19 This change would result in a scalar multiple of the transportation matrix of 1.25. Therefore, the new transportation matrix would be

$$T_{new} = 1.25 T_{old} = \begin{bmatrix} 8.75 & 12.50 \\ 12.50 & 15 \\ 6.25 & 11.25 \end{bmatrix}$$

Lesson 3.8

1 D **3** A **5** $(-2, 1)$ **7** $(-5, -5)$ **9** Let m represent the number of months a person is a member and c represent the cost of membership.; $\begin{cases} c = 20m + 50 \\ c = 15m + 80 \end{cases}$

11 $\begin{cases} y = 2x \\ y + x = 21 \end{cases}$ **13** $(4, 3)$

15 The given system can be written $\begin{cases} y = 3x + 5 \\ y = 3x + 5 \end{cases}$. The graphs coincide. The system is dependent.

Lesson 3.9

1 D **3** D **5** $(-1, 1)$ **7** $\left(-\frac{8}{5}, -\frac{11}{5}\right)$

9 $(2, -1)$ **11** $(3, -6)$ **13** 55° and 125° **15** 47 and 23 **17** 90 boys and 160 girls **19** 11 nickels, 6 dimes, and 7 quarters **21** If $k = 2$ then the lines are parallel and have no solution.

23 Solve $\begin{cases} 3x - 5y = 4 \\ 4x + 7y = 19 \end{cases}$ The solution is $(3, 1)$. Thus, the graphs intersect at the point $(3, 1)$. **25** 3

Lesson 3.10

1 D **3** A **5** A **7** D

9
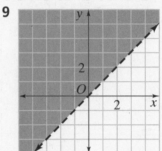

11
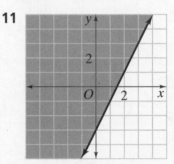

13
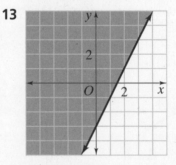

15
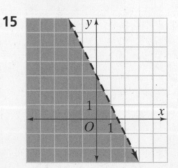

17

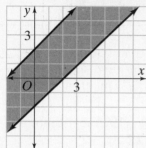

19

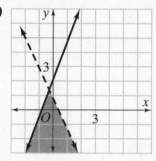

21 Jessica: 9, 10, 11, 12, 13, 14; Melissa: 11, 12, 13, 14, 15, 16, respectively
23 A triangle and its interior.

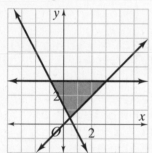

Chapter 3: Preparing for the New Jersey HSPA

1 B **3** A **5** B **7** B **9** D **11** B
13 C **15** D **17** A **19** A
21 $y = 4x - 1; y = -\frac{1}{4}x + \frac{13}{4};$

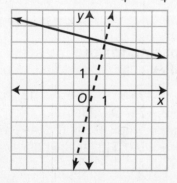

23 $x + y \leq 50, 7 \leq 0.1x + 0.25y \leq 9;$

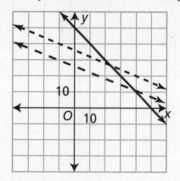

Chapter 4

Lesson 4.1

1 C **3** A **5** C **7** D **9** B **11** D
13 243 **15** $-\frac{1}{8}$ **17** $-96x^7yz$ **19** $x^{10}y^{16}$
21 $\frac{vw}{3}$ **23** $\frac{x^6}{y^{14}}$ **25** $-\frac{8y^{15}}{27x^9}$ **27** $5ab^4$
29 $-4n^4$ **31** 4 **33** -2 **35** -4
37 No; Explanations may vary. Sample: -5^2 is negative but $(-5)^2$ is positive.

Lesson 4.2

1 C **3** A **5** D **7** C **9** A **11** 5.15×10^{14} square meters **13** about 2.8×10^4 dollars = $28,000 **15** k^3 **17** $2^{10}a^5$ **19** $\frac{1}{a}$
21 c^4d^{12} **23** -6 **25** $\frac{1}{8}$ **27** $\frac{n^6}{m^4}$ **29** $\frac{3j^2}{2k^2}$
31 7.8×10^{-7} **33** 9×10^{-8} **35** 6.4×10^5
37 3.01×10^{27} **39** 259 pounds

Lesson 4.3

1 C **3** 3, 9, 27, 81, 243; $f(n) = 3^n$

Lesson 4.4

1 B **3** A **5** fall; When $0 < b < 1$, the value of the power is a fraction or decimal value. This value multiplied by the original number will cause a decrease in values over time.
7 {0.16, 0.4, 1, 2.5, 6.25, 15.625} increase
9 $\{\frac{9}{4}, \frac{3}{2}, 1, \frac{2}{3}, \frac{4}{9}, \frac{8}{27}\}$ decrease **11** A **13** D

SELECTED ANSWERS

15 $y = 0.5^x$

x	0.5^x
−2	4
−1	2
0	1
1	0.5
2	0.25

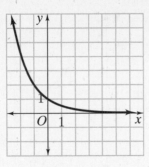

17 $y = \left(\frac{1}{3}\right)^x$

x	$\left(\frac{1}{3}\right)^x$
−2	9
−1	3
0	1
1	$\frac{1}{3}$
2	$\frac{1}{9}$

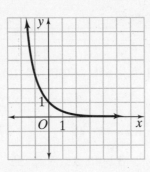

19 $y = -\frac{3}{4}^x$

x	$-\left(\frac{3}{4}\right)^x$
−2	$-\frac{16}{9}$
−1	$-\frac{4}{3}$
0	−1
1	$-\frac{3}{4}$
2	$-\frac{9}{16}$

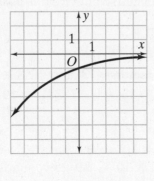

Lesson 4.5

1 C   **3** 1.025   **5** $y = 75{,}000(1.025)^x$
7 8,000,000   **9** $y = 8{,}000{,}000(0.9825)^x$
11 $10,648.93   **13** Neither   **15** Linear
17 Neither   **19** Exponential, because there is a common ratio between the values.
21 12.5 grams   **23** 2,187   **25** $y = 21{,}000(0.815)^t$

Chapter 4: Preparing for the New Jersey HSPA

1 C   **3** D   **5** B   **7** B   **9** A   **11** B   **13** A
15 C   **17** C   **19** C   **21** 6.2×10^7; 5.9×10^7; 5.1×10^{-1}; 4.9×10^{-1} **23** 8, 12, 16, 20, 24; $a_1 = 8$, $a_n = a_{n-1} + 4$

Chapter 5

Lesson 5.1

1 B   **3** C   **5** C   **7** $5m^2n^2 + 3mn^2 - 9m^2n$
9 $c^4 + 2c^2d + 3cd^2 - 13d$ **11** $4b^3 + 9b^2 - b + 1$
13 $-3v^3 + v$ **15** $6w^3 - 3w^2 + 4w - 7$
17 quadratic trinomial   **19** linear binomial
21 linear monomial   **23** $8s - 7$
25 $4a^3 + a^2 + 5a - 15$ **27** $-2r^3 - 3r^2 - 3r + 2$
29 $-9x^3 + 3z - 4$ **31** $-2a^3 - a^2 + 14a - 3$
33 $-2w^4 - 8w^3 + 11w^2 + 8w - 9$
35 $6j^2 + 5j + 7$ **37** $4z^2 + 2$ **39** No; the expression contains a negative power of x.
41 $3t - 16$

Lesson 5.2

1 D   **3** B   **5** C   **7** $24a - 12$ **9** $2y^2 - y - 6$
11 $6w^2 - w - 35$ **13** $9q^2 + 24q + 16$
15 $2k + 5$ **17** $-5p^4 - 10p^3 - 5p^2$
19 $2n^3 - 9n^2 + 13n - 21$ **21** $3z^2 - 5z - 4$
23 $-\frac{13}{2}$

Lesson 5.3

1 C   **3** C   **5** A   **7** 3   **9** rs **11** $8(n - 9)$
13 $6r(2r + 3)$ **15** $v(v^5 + v^2 + 1)$
17 $8jk(2jk - 5)$ **19** $(c + 5)(c + 9)$
21 $(x - 6)(x + 5)$ **23** $(y - 4)(y - 12)$
25 $(h + 7)(h - 6)$ **27** $(d + 1)(3d + 5)$
29 $(t - 3)(3t + 2)$ **31** $(2x - 3)(3x - 5)$
33 $(b + 2)^2$ **35** $(w - 5)^2$ **37** $(3z + 5)^2$
39 $(2p + 11)^2$ **41** $(u + 10)(u - 10)$
43 $(6a + 1)(6a - 1)$ **45** $4(n + 2)(n - 2)$
47 $5(z + 3)(z + 2)$ **49** $2t(5t - 4)(5t + 4)$
51 $k^4(k + 3)(k - 3)$ **53** $(3c - 10d)(3c + 10d)$
55 −9, −3, 3, and 9   **57** −18 and 18
59 Agree. Explanation:
$(a - b)^2 = a^2 - ab - ab + b^2 = a^2 - 2ab + b^2$
$(b - a)^2 = b^2 - ab - ab + a^2 = a^2 - 2ab + b^2$

Chapter 5: Preparing for the New Jersey HSPA

1 C   **3** D   **5** D   **7** C   **9** A   **11** A   **13** A
15 C   **17** C   **19** B   **21** D   **23** C
25 D   **27** $4x^2$ ft²; $4x^2 + 60x + 144$ ft²; 1440 ft²
29 $1200r^2 + 2400r + 1200$; $1273.08; $1285.47; $2142.45

Chapter 6

Lesson 6.1

1 C **3** C **5** 7 and −7 **7** 4 and −4 **9** 4 and −4 **11** 1 and −1 **13** 3 and −3 **15** 3.16 and −3.16 **17** 1.41 and −1.41 **19** −1.32 and 11.32 **21** 60 or −60 **23** 19.2 feet **25** $7m^2$; 5

Lesson 6.2

1 C **3** D **5** −8 and 1 **7** −8 and 8 **9** −3 and $\frac{7}{2}$ **11** −2, 0, and 9 **13** 10 **15** 4 and 9
17 8 feet and 11 feet **19** 5 **21** −1.6 and 0.6
23 1.0 and −0.5 **25** −1.2 and 3.2

Lesson 6.3

1 D **3** A **5** D **7** vertex $(0, 0)$, down, maximum **9** vertex $(0, 5)$, down, maximum
11 vertex: $\left(\frac{3}{5}, -\frac{9}{10}\right)$, up, minimum
13 vertex: $\left(\frac{1}{3}, \frac{1}{18}\right)$, down, maximum
15 vertex $(3, 8)$, down, maximum **17** 2

19
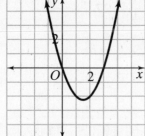

21
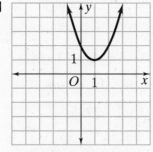

23
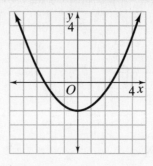

25 $4,843.75 **27** 1.8 units **29** 2 **31** 124 feet

Lesson 6.4

1 C **3** D **5** C **7** $(−1, 1)$ and $(3, 9)$
9 no solution **11** $(−1, −6)$ and $(6, 8)$ **13** no solution **15** The parabola opens up and the line is below the vertex of the parabola, so these two figures will not intersect.

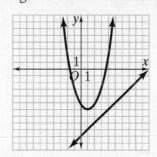

17 one point of intersection
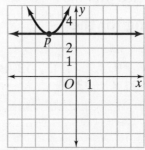

19 two points of intersection
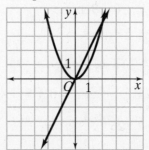

SELECTED ANSWERS

Lesson 6.5

1 B   **3** D

5

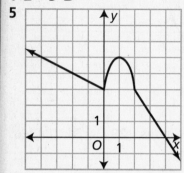

7

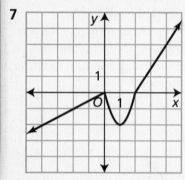

9 The graph of $f(x)$ is shifted 2 units left and reflected over the x-axis.
11 The graph of $f(x)$ is shifted 1 unit left, reflected over the x-axis, and then 4 units down.
13 The graph of $f(x)$ is shifted 3 units right, 7 units down, and reflected over the x-axis.

Chapter 6: Preparing for the New Jersey HSPA

1 B   **3** A   **5** A   **7** C   **9** A   **11** D   **13** B
15 C   **17** C   **19** A   **21** C   **23** C
25 $x^2; x^2;$ 9 feet

Chapter 7

Lesson 7.1

1 C   **3** B   **5** A   **7** $h \neq 0$ **9** none
11 $a \neq 0, a \neq b$ **13** $\frac{u}{u + 2}, u \neq -2$
15 $\frac{1}{2t - 1}, t \neq 0, t \neq \frac{1}{2}$ **17** $\frac{1}{c}, c \neq 0, c \neq -3$
19 $\frac{3 - 6w}{2w^2}, w \neq 0$ **21** $\frac{x - y}{x + y}, x \neq 0, x \neq -y$
23 $\frac{1}{v - 7}, v \neq 7, v \neq -7$ **25** $\frac{r + 2}{r + 4}, r \neq -4, r \neq 3$
27 $\frac{z + 1}{2}, z \neq \frac{1}{4}$ **29** $-g - 3, g \neq \frac{3}{2}$

31 $-\frac{m}{n}, n \neq 0, n \neq m$ **33** No; When $p = 3$ and $q = -1, p^2 - 9q^2 = (3)^2 - 9(-1)^2 = 0.$

Lesson 7.2

1 B   **3** B   **5** $\frac{27}{j^2}$ **7** $\frac{1}{2c}$ **9** $\frac{2m^6}{27}$ **11** $16y^3$
13 $\frac{15}{2x^2 y^2}$ **15** $\frac{4(2 - t)}{t(4 + t)},$ or $\frac{8 - 4t}{4t + t^2}$ **17** $\frac{8}{3}$
19 $\frac{2(y + 4)}{y},$ or $\frac{2y + 8}{y}$
21 $\frac{1}{g(g - 1)},$ or $\frac{1}{g^2 - g}$ **23** $\frac{b + 2}{b - 2}$
25 $\frac{n + 4}{n - 2}$ **27** $6(h - 3),$ or $6h - 18$
29 $\frac{y - 5}{(y + 5)(y - 2)},$ or $\frac{y - 5}{y^2 + 3y - 10}$

Lesson 7.3

1 C   **3** B   **5** $\frac{10}{g}$ **7** $-\frac{2}{r}$ **9** $\frac{9}{v}$ **11** $\frac{c + 10}{5c}$
13 $-\frac{b}{b + 3}$ **15** $\frac{1}{5}$ **17** $\frac{8a}{a - 4}$ **19** $\frac{2q - 9}{q + 1}$
21 $\frac{2z - 8}{z - 3}$ **23** $\frac{5}{2(k + 1)},$ or $\frac{5}{2k + 2}$
25 $\frac{3y - 8}{4(y - 4)},$ or $\frac{3y - 8}{4y - 16}$ **27** $\frac{2}{x - 2}$
29 $\frac{2a}{(a - b)(a + b)},$ or $\frac{2a}{a^2 - b^2}$
31 $\frac{-5a + 28}{a - 4}$

Lesson 7.4

1 B   **3** D   **5** 5   **7** -60 **9** 0.8   **11** $\frac{18}{65}$
13 1 and 2   **15** 2   **17** ± 8 **19** -7
21 6 and 7   **23** -9 or 9   **25** 18 minutes

Lesson 7.5

1 B   **3** C   **5** 18   **7** 200   **9** $\frac{13}{5}$ **11** $\frac{\sqrt{10}}{3}$
13 $\frac{5\sqrt{2}}{9}$ **15** $7w^3$ **17** xy^3 **19** $c\sqrt{ab}$
21 $\frac{4v\sqrt{v}}{5}$ **23** 16   **25** $2\sqrt{2}$ **27** $5t\sqrt{7}$
29 $2d\sqrt{d}$ **31** $4\sqrt{11}$ **33** $5\sqrt{2}$ **35** $\sqrt{3}$
37 $2 + \sqrt{6}$ **39** $15 - 2\sqrt{10}$ **41** $-1 - 2\sqrt{2}$
43 3   **45** $7\sqrt{3} - 5\sqrt{6}$ **47** $\sqrt{16(n + 2)} + \sqrt{4(n + 2)} = 4\sqrt{n + 2} + 2\sqrt{n + 2} = 6\sqrt{n + 2}$ **49** $x = 18$ **51** $v = 12$
53 $y = 1$

Chapter 7: Preparing for the New Jersey HSPA

1 C **3** B **5** D **7** D **9** A **11** C **13** B
15 A **17** D **19** D **21** B
23 $\frac{1}{40} + \frac{1}{60} = \frac{1}{x}$; 24 minutes

Chapter 8

Lesson 8.1

1 B **3** B **5** A **7** The event with
probability 0.6. **9** 55% **11** $\frac{5}{36}$ **13** $\frac{1}{18}$

15

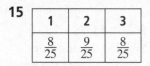

1	2	3
$\frac{8}{25}$	$\frac{9}{25}$	$\frac{8}{25}$

Lesson 8.2

1 D **3** C **5** $\frac{4}{13}$ **7** $\frac{7}{26}$ **9** $\frac{1}{3}$ **11** $\frac{2}{3}$ **13** $\frac{2}{9}$
15 $\frac{1}{3}$

Lesson 8.3

1 A **3** C **5** A **7** $\frac{5}{36}$ **9** $\frac{1}{11}$ **11** $\frac{7}{22}$
13 $\frac{3}{8}$ **15** $\frac{1}{2}$ **17** $\frac{28}{65}$ **19** 1 **21** $\frac{1}{30}$ **23** $\frac{1}{20}$

Lesson 8.4

1 D **3** B **5** 27,600; 13,680

Lesson 8.5

1 C **3** D **5** C **7** 720 **9** 30 **11** 240
13 720 **15** 120 **17** 120 **19** 0.01 **21** 0.05

Lesson 8.6

1 C **3** A
5 5.5; No, because you cannot move 0.5 spaces
on a typical game board.; 3

Chapter 8: Preparing for the New Jersey HSPA

1 A **3** D **5** C **7** A **9** A **11** D **13** D
15 B **17** B **19** C **21** D **23** B **25** A

27 The 10th row of Pascal's Triangle is:
1 10 45 120 210 252 210 120 45 10 1
The third diagonal in the 10th row corresponds
to the entry 120. Therefore, there are 120
possible combinations.; 1140; 300

Chapter 9

Lesson 9.1

1 B **3** A **5** D **7** 8.2 **9** 20–22
11 $\frac{4n + 6}{4}$ **13** 12.75 **15** 6

Lesson 9.2

1 D **3** 54% **5** $1 less

Lesson 9.3

1 a. Population − NFL players   b. Sample −
25% that responded   c. The variable of
interest − Use of steroids in training
d. Potential for bias − Nonresponse. Difficult to
generalize because who responds is related to
the question asked. Users of steroids probably
will not respond to the survey.   **3** a. Population
− Air in the school   b. Sample − 20 air samples
c. The variable of interest − quality of aid,
d. Potential for bias − Where were the samples
taken? Were the locations randomly selected?
Were all sections of the school represented in
the sample?   **5** Yes. Telephone subscribers
are probably different from nonsubscribers.
For example some people only have a cell
phone and do not subscribe to regular phone
service. Others, screen their calls and may not
answer survey calls.   **7** No, the process may
go bad after the first 30 items. Sampling
randomly throughout the day would be
preferred.   **9** Qualitative   **11** Qualitative
13 Quantitative, continuous   **15** Bivariate
17 Bivariate   **19** Voluntary response sample −
unbiased   **21** Convenience and voluntary
response sample − biased

SELECTED ANSWERS

Lesson 9.4

1 C **3** D **5** 50%

7

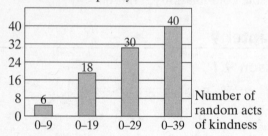

Random Acts of Kindness on Television
Cumulative frequency

9 3.4 pounds

Lesson 9.5

1 D **3** B

5

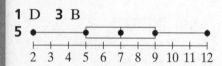

7

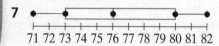

9 B **11** B **13** True **15** 30 **17** 42.5
19 47.5

Lesson 9.6

1 A **3** A

5

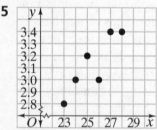

7

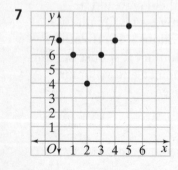

9

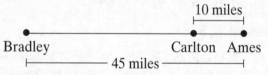

Approximately 14 miles per gallon; about
4250 lbs. **11** 24.5°F

Chapter 9: Preparing for the New Jersey HSPA

1 B **3** D **5** B **7** D **9** B **11** C **13** B
15 D **17** A **19** mean: $43,754.17; median:
$45,050; The mean and the median increase by
$1000.

Chapter 10

Lesson 10.1

1 A **3** B **5** *No* **7** *No* **9** *Yes* **11** *No*
13 plane *DFE*, plane *DFB*, plane *BFE*
15 points *J* and *H* **17** point *H*
19 line *p*, or $\overleftrightarrow{JH}$ **21** 5 **23** 2 **25** *R* **27** *X*
29 $c = 4.5$
31 Carlton is between Bradley and Ames.

Lesson 10.2

1 D **3** C **5** C **7** C **9** C **11** 34°
13 $(90 - x)°$ **15** 138.5° **17** 68° **19** 29°
21 false **23** false **25** The measure of each
angle is 45°. **27** 120°

Lesson 10.3

1 A **3** D **5** 147° **7** 105° **9** 75° **11** 75°
13 49° **15** 90° **17** 131° **19** 96° **21** 96°
23 128° **25** Converse of the Same-Side
Interior Angles Theorem

Lesson 10.4

1 B **3** B **5** False **7** False **9** False
11 $m\angle X = 43°$, $m\angle Y = 47°$, and $m\angle Z = 90°$
13 118° **15** 152° **17** longest: $\overline{RS}$; shortest: $\overline{RT}$
19 largest: $\angle Q$; smallest: $\angle P$ **21** Yes **23** 90°
25 76°

Lesson 10.5

1 B **3** D **5** A **7** $m\angle P = 80°$, $m\angle Q = 112°$, and $m\angle R = 50°$ **9** 143° **11** seven **13** three
15 twenty **17** decagon; 144

Lesson 10.6

1 C **3** A **5** $\triangle RST \cong \triangle HJG$; AAS
Congruence Theorem **7** $\triangle ABD \cong \triangle CBD$;
SSS Congruence Postulate
9 $\triangle EJF \sim \triangle GJH$; SSS Similarity Theorem;
similarity ratio: $\dfrac{\text{sides of } \triangle EJH}{\text{sides of } \triangle GJH} = \dfrac{5}{6}$
11 $\overline{JK}$ **13** $\overline{LN}$ **15** $\angle KMJ$
17 104°; Since the sum of the measures of the
angles in a triangle is 180°, $m\angle WZX = 52°$. Since
$\triangle WXZ \cong \triangle YZX$ by the ASA Congruence
Postulate, $m\angle WZY = 52° + 52° = 104°$.

Lesson 10.7

1 A
3

Statements	Reasons
$\angle PSR \cong \angle TRS$	Given
$\angle PRS \cong \angle TSR$	Given
$\overline{RS} \cong \overline{RS}$	Reflexive Property
$\triangle PRS \cong \triangle TSR$	ASA Congruence Theorem

5

Statements	Reasons
$\triangle XYZ$ is an equilateral triangle.	Given
A is the midpoint of $\overline{YZ}$.	Given
$\overline{XY} \cong \overline{XZ}$	Definition of equilateral triangle
$\overline{YA} \cong \overline{ZA}$	Definition of midpoint
$\overline{XA} \cong \overline{XA}$	Reflexive Property
$\triangle XYA \cong \triangle XZA$	SSS Congruence Theorem
$\angle XYA \cong \angle XZA$	CPCTC

Lesson 10.8

1 C **3** B **5** 4; Each vertex of an Euler circuit
must be even. Therefore, the minimum degree of
each vertex is 2.

Chapter 10: Preparing for the New Jersey HSPA

1 A **3** C **5** D **7** C **9** A **11** A
13 C **15** A **17** A **19** A **21** A
23 $m\angle JLK = 90°$; $m\angle M = 71°$; $m\angle KJM = 38°$

Chapter 11

Lesson 11.1

1 B **3** B **5** B **7** B **9** A **11** 5.75 gal
13 5,000 m **15** 0.355 L **17** 35 mL **19** 100 mm
21 9.4 yd **23** 81.7 yd **25** 1.4 mi **27** 14,340 ft

Lesson 11.2

1 C **3** B **5** 26 cm **7** 40 cm **9** $16\pi \approx$
50.27 cm **11** $0.9\pi \approx 2.83$ m **13** 32 units
15 radius: 13; diameter: 26 **17** 18π in.
19 36 m^2 **21** 10.8 units

Lesson 11.3

1 B **3** C **5** B **7** 49π in.^{2} **9** 6,480 in.^{2}
11 198 in.^{2} **13** 16.8 cm^2 **15** 273.0 square
units **17** 21.5 ft^2

Lesson 11.4

1 B **3** C **5** C **7** $2\sqrt{61} \approx 15.6$ **9** 15
11 $5\sqrt{2}$ **13** diagonals: 14 in. and $14\sqrt{3}$ in.;
area: $98\sqrt{3}$ in.^{2} **15** $12\sqrt{2}$ **17** $a = 4\sqrt{3}$,
$b = 4$, and $c = 8$

Lesson 11.5

1 B **3** D **5** A **7** midpoint: (1.5, 6.5);
length: $\sqrt{514}$ **9** midpoint: (5.5, 1); length: $5\sqrt{5}$
11 $\sqrt{113} \approx 10.63$ **13** 7 **15** $\sqrt{34} \approx 5.83$

SELECTED ANSWERS

Lesson 11.6

1 B   **3** C   **5** 3.5 in.   **7** The 5′ 11″ pitcher in 1967   **9** It increases; 37.1 ft; Sample answer: No, just because one leg of the Pythagorean triangle is doubled doesn't mean the other (non-hypotenuse) leg doubles. To figure out the missing length one must use the converse of the Pythagorean Theorem.

Lesson 11.7

1 B   **3** C   **5** $x = 2$

Lesson 11.8

1 D   **3** D   **5** 33.7°   **7** $a \approx 24.6$; $b \approx 17.3$ **9** 1,710 ft   **11** $m\angle P \approx 22°$; $m\angle R \approx 68°$; $m\angle Q = 90°$

Lesson 11.9

1 D   **3** C   **5** 20° North of East

Lesson 11.10

1 C   **3** No, because $7^2 + (3.75)^2 \neq 8^2$

Lesson 11.11

1 D   **3** C   **5** A   **7** $m\angle DCE = 50°$ **9** $m\angle A = 105°$; $m\angle D = 82°$; $m\overset{\frown}{BCD} = 210°$

Chapter 11: Preparing for the New Jersey HSPA

1 B   **3** A   **5** D   **7** B   **9** A   **11** C   **13** B   **15** D   **17** C   **19** B   **21** B   **23** 48.2 ft; 103.5 ft; 0.5%

Chapter 12

Lesson 12.1

1 A   **3** 136 in.^{2} **5** 80 m^2 **7** L.A. = 60 m^2 ; S.A. = 96 m^2

Lesson 12.2

1 C   **3** B   **5** A   **7** 108π yd^2 **9** 1.25 gallons   **11** 300π cm^2 **13** 200π in.^{2} **15** L.A. = 3.75π in.^{2}; S.A. = 6π in.^{2} **17** L.A. = 37π m^2; S.A. = 64.38π m^2 **19** 646.4π cm^2

Lesson 12.3

1 B   **3** A   **5** one family-size can   **7** 6739.2 pounds

Lesson 12.4

1 A   **3** surface area: 314 in.^{2}; volume $= 523\frac{1}{3}$ in.^{3} **5** surface area: 576π, about 1809.6 units^2; volume: 2304π, about 7238.2 units^3 **7** 2304π cm^3

Lesson 12.5

1 C   **3** B   **5** B   **7** D   **9** $P = x + \dfrac{60}{x}$, or $P = 2x + \dfrac{30}{x}$; 15.5 m   **11** 64 ft; 8 seconds

Lesson 12.6

1 B   **3** A   **5** C   **7** D

9   **11**

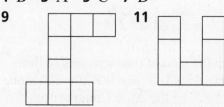

Chapter 12: Preparing for the New Jersey HSPA

1 D   **3** B   **5** A   **7** C   **9** B   **11** D   **13** B   **15** A   **17** C   **19** 188.4 ft^2; $2,072.40; 207.26 ft^3 **21** 95.38 cm^3; 286.13 cm^3; 190.75 cm^3

Chapter 13

Lesson 13.1

1 B   **3** B   **5** B

7

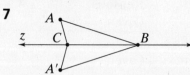

9 $R'(1, -1)$, $S'(5, -1)$, and $T'(5, -3)$ **11** $E'(-3, -3)$, $U'(-5, -3)$, $D'(-1, 1)$, and $P'(1, 1)$ **13** $B(-3, 2)$, $C(3, -2)$, and $D(3, 2)$

15 The image is shown as a dashed curve.

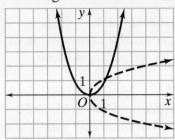

Lesson 13.2

1 B **3** A **5** B **7** $A'(-4, -1)$ **9** $C'(-7, 8)$
11 $E'(3, -4)$
13

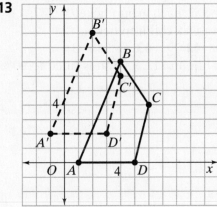

15

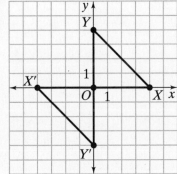

17

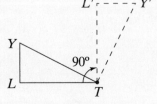

Lesson 13.3

1 A **3** C **5** A **7** C
9

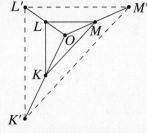

11 $A'(-3, 1.5)$, $B'(4.5, 1.5)$, and $C'(-3, 7.5)$
13 $X''(3, -3)$ and $Y''(21, 6)$

Lesson 13.4

1 D **3** A **5** C

Lesson 13.5

1 D **3** A **5** $V = 10,048$ in.^{3}, $L.A. = 1004.8$ in.^{2},
$S.A. = 3516.8$ in.^{2} **7** 157 in.^{3}
9 An isosceles triangle with height 7 cm and base 4 cm is rotated about its altitude to form the cone shown.

Lesson 13.6

1 B **3** C **5** C **7** An interior angle of a dodecagon = 150° and the interior angles of an equilateral triangle = 60°; therefore, 2(150) + 60 = 360. Each vertex in the tiling would contain two dodecagons and one triangle.

Chapter 13: Preparing for the New Jersey HSPA

1 A **3** C **5** B **7** C **9** B **11** C
13 B **15** D **17** C
19

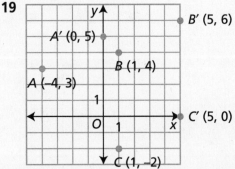

The transformation is a slide. The houses at points A', B', C', are about 4.7 miles farther (as the bird flies) from the library as the houses at A, B, and C.

SELECTED ANSWERS

21

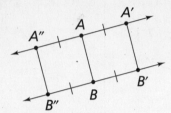

Sample HSPA 1

1 B   **3** C   **5** A   **7** B   **9** B
11 width = 50 ft, length = 100 ft; width = 75 ft, length = 150 ft
13 B   **15** B   **17** B   **19** D   **21** D
23 46. $y > \frac{3}{2}x - 3$, $y < -3x + 1$;

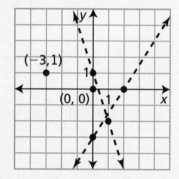

25 C   **27** A   **29** A   **31** B   **33** C
35 117 ft^2; 183 ft^2; 732   **37** C
39 B   **41** B   **43** C   **45** B
47 Company A costs = 150 + 6(25) = $300, Company B costs = 60 + 0.10x, where x is the number of miles; 2400 miles; Company B

Sample HSPA 2

1 A   **3** C   **5** A   **7** D   **9** C
11 2, 12 as there is only one combination of numbers that can be rolled to get these sums; 3, 24
13 C   **15** D   **17** C   **19** D   **21** B
23 $C = 115 + 1.2(520) = \$739$; $7(65) + 50 + 135 = \$640$. The cost of the friend with seven days rental plus the fee and supplies is cheaper than the professional.
25 C   **27** C   **29** C   **31** B   **33** C
35 child ticket = x; adult ticket = $2x - 2$; each group ticket = $2x - 7$; child ticket = $27, adult ticket = $52, each group ticket = $47; the six adult and six children tickets
37 A   **39** B   **41** D   **43** B   **45** B
47 2,500,000; 118 hr; 112,500 if it is filled to 90% capacity

INDEX

441

INDEX

INDEX

INDEX

INDEX

Staff Credits:

The people who made up the *High School Brief Review* team—representing design, editorial, education technology, manufacturing and inventory planning, market research, marketing services, planning and budgeting, product planning, production services, project office, publishing processes, the business office, and rights and permissions—are listed below. Bold type denotes the core team members.

Stacey Clark, Meredith Glassman, Rebecca Higgins, Rosamond Kane, **Chris Langley, Cheryl Mahan, Michael O'Donnell,** Heidi Wilson

Additional Credits:

The Mazer Corporation: Dayton, OH;
Victoria MacKeown, Sue Tauer, Grace Ninneman, Fran Hoover, Dustin Anderson

GGS Book Services: York, PA

Cover Image:

Panoramic Image, Getty Images; bridge and shore, Kord.com/agefotostock